The Soviet Union

y T. M. Oberlander

yracuse University / Department of Geography

Scale

200 400 600 800 1000

Miles

Geography of the U.S.S.R.

Geography of

The Moscow Kremlin

Paul E. Lydolph

the U.S.S.R.

Courtesy of the Foreign Languages Publishing House, Moscow

Professor of Geography, University of Wisconsin—Milwaukee

John Wiley and Sons, Inc., New York • London • Sydney

Library of Congress Catalog Card Number: 64-11501
Printed in the United States of America

To Ed, Don, Paul, Tom, and Andy

and to Georgia, Sunshine of the Southland

Preface

The Union of Soviet Socialist Republics looms so large in all considerations of world affairs that one can ill afford ignorance of its history, polity, ideology, and present-day geography and economy. This book on the geography of the U.S.S.R. draws on a wide range of literature in an attempt to tie together the many-faceted physical, cultural, and economic landscapes in a complete geographical analysis of the country.

A regional analysis is taken up first, after an introductory chapter briefly sets the framework. The chapters on regions are followed by chapters that consider individual topics of cultural and economic geography—population, agriculture, industry, transportation, trade, and international relations. These topical chapters cut across regional boundaries and treat the Soviet Union as a whole.

The arrangement of regional discussions first and topical discussions second is a reversal of general practice in geography textbook writing that has been prompted by experience from 10 years of teaching the geography of the U.S.S.R. It has been clearly demonstrated to me that the sooner the course gets into regional discussions the quicker the interests of the students pick up. Analyses of interworkings of complexes of phenomena in specific localities attached to place names are more real and meaningful to the beginning student than are discussions of social and economic abstractions. The regional discussion acquaints the student with

the country. Once he learns where things are, he naturally begins to wonder how the parts fit together. At this stage of intellectual curiosity the student is then ready for detailed topical analyses of individual phenomena.

A word about source materials and supplemental readings. For most topics on the geography of the U.S.S.R. abundant literature now exists, the most in Russian, some in English. Selected readings have been listed at the ends of individual chapters. These are not the sole sources of information for these chapters, or even the main sources. They are readings that are specifically oriented toward the material in the respective chapters, and they are largely English language sources for the convenience of the bulk of students and teachers who will use this text. Materials for all chapters have been drawn from a wide variety of general readings.

For the student or teacher who is not versed in the available sources of information, the following briefly annotated lists of general sources are offered.

Bibliographies

1. For a list of the basic books, serials, atlases, and bibliographic references published in Russian in the Soviet Union about the geography of the U.S.S.R. see Harris, Chauncy D., "The Land," chapter II, in *Basic Russian Publica-*

tions, a Selected and Annotated Bibliography on Russia and the Soviet Union, edited by Paul L. Horecky, University of Chicago Press, Chicago, 1962, 25–48. Other chapters cover the people and economic and social structure, among other topics.

2. For an extensive list of American doctoral research on all aspects of the Soviet Union see Dossick, Jesse J., *Doctoral Research on Russia and the Soviet Union,* New York University Press, New York, 1960.

3. The *Referativnyy Zhurnal* (published in the U.S.S.R. in Russian) section on geography is one of the most complete abstract journals in the world. It lists titles and summaries of periodical articles and monographs published all over the world.

4. The Library of Congress *Monthly Index of Russian Accessions* has been a major bibliographic source for American researchers.

5. *The American Bibliography of Russian and East European Studies,* published yearly by Indiana University.

Serials

Among English language periodicals the following are the most useful for geographic information on the U.S.S.R.

1. *Soviet Geography: Review and Translation,* published by the American Geographical Society, an indispensable publication of translated articles from professional geographical journals in the Soviet Union. Materials from this journal have been used extensively throughout the book.

2. *Soviet Studies,* published by the University of Glasgow, Scotland. A scholarly journal with occasional articles pertinent to geography.

3. *The Annals of the Association of American Geographers.* A few articles pertaining to the Soviet Union.

4. *The Geographical Review.* A few articles pertaining to the Soviet Union.

5. *The Geographical Journal.* A few articles pertaining to the Soviet Union.

Books of Direct Geographical Interest

1. Baransky, N. N., *Economic Geography of the U.S.S.R.,* Foreign Languages Publishing House, Moscow, 1956, 413 pp. (in English).

2. Berg, L. S., *Natural Regions of the U.S.S.R.,* translated into English and published by The Macmillan Company, New York, 1950, 436 pp.

3. Cherdantsev, G. N., Nikitin, N. N., and Tutykhin, B. A., *Ekonomicheskaya Geografiya SSSR;* three volumes: *obshchiy obzor,* 1958, 280 pp., *RSFSR,* 1956, 490 pp., and *SSSR,* 1957, 371 pp. (in Russian).

4. Cole, J. P., and German, F. C., *A Geography of the U.S.S.R.,* 1961, 290 pp.

5. Davydova, M. I., Kamenskii, A. I., Nekliukova, N. P., and Tushinskii, G. Z., *Fizicheskaya geografiya SSSR,* Moscow, 1960, 679 pp. (in Russian).

6. Fitzsimmons, Thomas, Malof, Peter, and Fiske, John C., *U.S.S.R., Its People, Its Society, Its Culture,* HRAF Press, New Haven, 1960, 590 pp.

7. Lyalikov, N. I., *Ekonomicheskaya Geografiya SSSR,* 1960, 343 pp. (in Russian).

8. Maslov, Yevgeny, *The Russian Federation,* Foreign Languages Publishing House, Moscow, 1960, 215 pp.

9. Mikhailov, Nicholas, *Soviet Russia: The Land and its People,* Sheridan House, 1948, 370 pp.

10. Mikhailov, Nicholas, *Glimpses of the U.S.S.R., its Economy and Geography,* Foreign Languages Publishing House, Moscow, 1960, 199 pp.

11. Suslov, S. P., *Physical Geography of Asiatic Russia,* translated into English, published by Freeman and Co., San Francisco, 1961, 594 pp.

12. *The U.S.S.R. and Eastern Europe,* Regional Economic Atlas, Oxford University Press, London, 1956, 134 pp.

Regional Monographs and Statistical Handbooks Published in the U.S.S.R.

1. The Institute of Geography of the U.S.S.R. Academy of Sciences has published thirteen volumes of a series of regional physical and economic geographies of the U.S.S.R. More are in press.

2. The Academy of Sciences has also published eleven regional monographs, and ten more are under way.

3. *Narodnoe khozyaystvo* (statistical abstracts), series of U.S.S.R. and regions. Listed in the January issues of Soviet Studies beginning in 1959.

General Reference Materials for International Comparisons

1. *United Nations Yearbook* and *Monthly Bulletin of Statistics.*
2. *Commodity Yearbook.*
3. *The Economic Survey of Europe,* United Nations, Geneva, published yearly. Contains summary chapters on the economy of the Soviet Union.

Books for Background on the Economy of the U.S.S.R.

1. Campbell, Robert Wellington, *Soviet Economic Power: Its Organization, Growth, and Challenge,* Houghton Mifflin, Boston, 1960, 209 pp.
2. Clark, Colin, *The Real Productivity of Soviet Russia,* United States Government Printing Office, Washington, 1961, 61 pp.
3. Dobb, Maurice H., *Soviet Economic Development Since 1917,* International Publishers, New York, 1948, 475 pp.
4. Grossman, Gregory, ed., *Value and Plan,* University of California Press, Berkeley, 1960, 370 pp.
5. Holzman, Franklyn D., *Readings on the Soviet Economy,* Rand McNally, New York, 1962, 763 pp.
6. Katkoff, Vladimir, *Soviet Economy, 1940–1965,* Dangary Publishing Co., Baltimore, 1961, 559 pp.
7. Lyashchenko, Peter I., *History of the National Economy of Russia to 1917,* translated by L. M. Herman, The Macmillan Company, New York, 1949, 880 pp.
8. Nove, Alec, *The Soviet Economy,* Praeger, New York, 1961, 328 pp.
9. Schwartz, Harry, *Russia's Soviet Economy,* Prentice-Hall, Englewood Cliffs, N.J., 1950, 592 pp.
10. Schwartz, Harry, *The Soviet Economy: 1956–1958,* The National Industrial Conference Board, New York, 1958, 20 pp.

Quantities in the tables and illustrations have been expressed in some cases in English units, in some cases in metric or other units commonly used in the U.S.S.R., usually depending on the source of information. There has been no particular attempt to standardize, and indeed I believe that students should be exposed to the various units of measure used. To facilitate conversion from one system to another, a table of equivalent measures is given at the end of the book.

Unless otherwise stated, all quantities in tables expressed in tons are in metric tons, and all population figures are as of the all-Union Census on January 15, 1959. Accent marks are shown on place names in the index so that the index may double as a pronouncing gazetteer. In general, place names have been transliterated according to the system proposed by the United States Board on Geographic Names, except that the hard and soft signs have been ignored. Names have been transliterated literally except for those familiar to non-Russians in Angelicized form, such as Moscow, Archangel, the Caspian Sea, the Dnieper River, etc. Names from Central Asia and the Far East have been transliterated from Russian, rather than from Chinese or some other language in the area. Thus, Tyan Shans, rather than Tien Shans. So far as possible, standard Russian map symbols have been used on illustrations to acquaint students with the Russian symbols and thereby to facilitate use of Russian wall maps and atlases.

I wish to express my thanks to Professor Chauncy D. Harris for his critical advice and constant encouragement throughout the writing of the text and to Randall Sale and his assistants, Rodney Helgeland and Jeanne Tsou, who worked so diligently on the maps and diagrams. My colleague, Barbara Zakrzewska, read and commented on the chapters dealing with Kazakhstan and Middle Asia. It was largely through her persuasion that I split Kazakhstan. Also, my heartfelt appreciation goes to Nyla Albrecht, Judy Jens, Barbara Bartz, Maryann Felss, Bonnie Held, Gigi Gabert, Linda Mammano, and Margot Murray for compiling data, sketching maps, and patiently typing manuscripts over and over again from my inaudible dictation, illegible scrawl, and multi-inked, dissected copy. They also reminded me when I had classes to teach!

PAUL E. LYDOLPH

Milwaukee, Wisconsin
October, 1963

Contents

Introduction to the U.S.S.R.

The geography of the U.S.S.R. is the geography of one sixth of the earth's land surface. Part East, part West, the country sprawls across two continents. Progeny of the old Russian Empire, the U.S.S.R. is the result of more than a thousand years of acquisition and consolidation of lands on all sides. Its expansion at times has been explosive across vast empty areas, at times painfully slow and faltering against major adversaries in Europe and eastern Asia. Occasionally submerged by strong neighbors or internal strife, it sometimes appeared on the verge of breaking up and dissolving altogether as one of the world's great powers. But like the phoenix, each time it rose from seeming extinction to size and strength never attained before.

Gradually it has taken on somewhat stable form. International boundaries have been established where its power has been matched by some other strong country; generally the international boundaries between the major contenders have been set in intermediate zones, in which weak buffer countries have been maintained. Boundaries in the fracture zones have been subject to wide oscillations as major power blocks have shifted in the backgrounds.

The U.S.S.R. presently bounds on Finland and the satellite countries in eastern Europe, on Turkey, Iran, and Afghanistan in the Middle East, and on Pakistan, China, the Mongolian Peoples Republic, Korea, and Japan in the Far East. There is no territorial contact with other major military powers of the world. But it is the major power blocks that have established these boundaries and that now maintain the identities and status quo of the states that border directly on the U.S.S.R.

World War I and subsequent revolutions and civil wars appeared for a while to have torn the Russian Empire asunder. But once again the area was resurrected into a stronger state than before. The most important net result of World War I was the establishment of the Soviet Union. And World War II was the catalyst that coagulated its diverse units into a consolidated country. The Soviet Union now is larger, more integrated, and more powerful than the Russian Empire ever was.

The U.S.S.R. is not a homogeneous state. In its growth by accretion of peripheral territories, the Russian Empire acquired many diversified pieces of land peopled by widely varying nationalities. The old Russian Empire has been referred to as "a prison of nations." The Soviet Union today is, therefore, a multinational state with many non-Russian peoples living in non-Russian ways. And in spite of the fact that the Soviet system has been imposed on everyone, individual

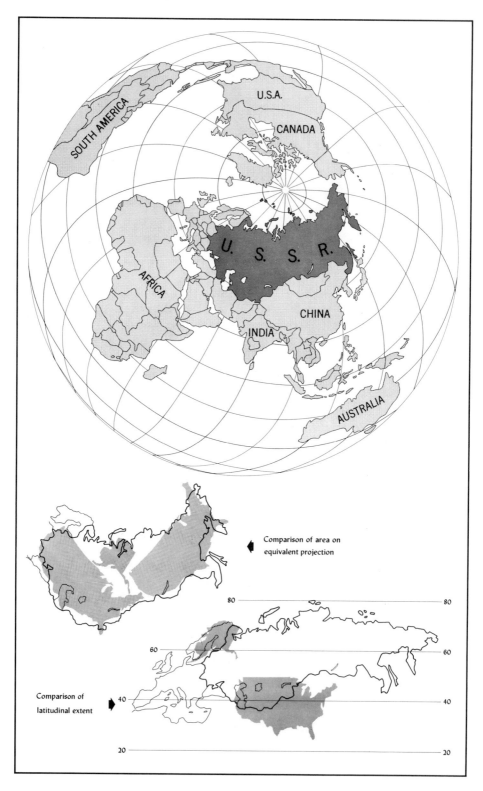

Figure 1-1   The U.S.S.R. in its world setting.   The U.S.S.R. occupies an area nearly $2\frac{1}{2}$ times that of the United States, most of which lies at a latitude north of the Canadian border.

responses to this system reflect the indigenous cultures.

Thus the U.S.S.R. is a very large country that contains widely varying landscapes, both cultural and physical. For discussion purposes it will be divided into its various regions and each region will be dealt with in its entirety. Then the regions will be welded together by considerations of separate items of culture and economy that transcend regional boundaries. But first, a brief look at the history of territorial growth of the country and at its broad zones of natural environment and cultural development is necessary to set the perspectives for regional discussions.

Emergence of the Russian State and Subsequent Territorial Acquisition

The Russian State emerged on the east European plain after centuries of invasion, conquest, and sporadic settlement. Wave after wave of nomadic peoples, presumably from somewhere in Central Asia, swept across the Black Sea steppes and into Central Europe long before the Christian era. Scythians, Goths, Huns, Avars, and many other tribal groups crisscrossed the area during the period from 1000 B.C. to A.D. 800. Some settled for brief periods in what was to become the Russian plain, only to be assimilated by indigenous peoples or driven on by succeeding movements.

The origin of the Slavs is not clear, but they emerged in the area that is now the Ukraine in the eighth and ninth centuries as a sedentary peasant people engaged in agriculture. The first Slavic state was organized in 862 under a Scandinavian prince named Rurik. This governmental control under the Scandinavians, or the Varangians, as they were called, was established to secure the trade route from the Baltic Sea to Constantinople. Two cities that became focal points on this trade route were Kiev along the Dnieper River in the south and Novgorod on the shores of Lake Ilmen in the north.

Kiev quickly became established as the primary center of the Slavic area, and Kievan Rus flourished until the Tatar invasion in A.D. 1240 under Batu, the grandson of Genghis Khan. At the same time, Novgorod became a great trading city, one of the Hanseatic League cities in the north with connections westward along the Baltic. But Novgorod was peopled by a cosmopolitan group of central and west Europeans, as well as Russians and was always looked upon as an alien city, not a center of Slavic culture. During the period of Kievan Rus, A.D. 862–1240, the middle portion of the Russian plain, which was to become so important later, was primeval forest.

With the fall of Kiev to the Tatars, the Slavic peoples in the southern part of the plain either fled into the forest or perished. There is no agreement on the fate of these peoples. Although Novgorod was never captured by the Tatars, and flourished commercially for 200 years more, it did not serve as a center of the Slavic peoples as Kiev had. It appeared for a time after the Tatar invasion that the Slavic state might be doomed forever. The record becomes quite obscure here; apparently the area in the central European plain was broken up into a great number of small feudal-type states with the Tatars exacting tribute from everyone. The Tatars established themselves first in the town of Sarai, near the present site of Volgograd (Stalingrad) on the lower Volga, and controlled much of what is now European Russia from this strongpoint. Later, with the breakup of the Tatar tribes into separate groups, centers were established at Kazan at the great bend of the Volga, at Astrakhan on the north coast of the Caspian, and in the Crimea.

While the Tatars were in control and were exacting tribute from the Russian area, several major Russian princely states were beginning to emerge from the many smaller states that had existed immediately after the Tatar invasion. By a series of clever maneuvers by unscrupulous rulers over a period of 100 years or more, Moscow emerged as the

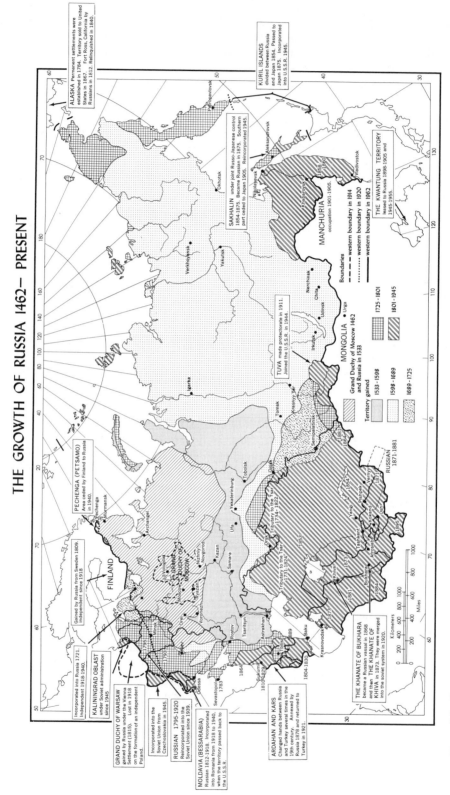

Figure 1-2 Expansion of the Russian Empire. Part of the information on this map was derived from the Oxford Regional Economic Atlas of the U.S.S.R. and Eastern Europe, pp. 98–99, by permission of the Clarendon Press, Oxford, England.

Figure 1-3   The walled city of Novgorod on the shore of Lake Ilmen.   Novosti Press.

predominant princely state, and the Moscow prince was named the Grand Prince of all the Russias by the Tatars more often than were any of the other Russian princes.

It was during the reign of Ivan III, or Ivan the Great, from 1462–1505, that the Muscovy state finally emerged supreme over all the other Russian states. During his reign, Novgorod, with all its lands to the north, fell to Muscovy. Also, it was during his reign that the Muscovy state became strong enough to tackle the Tatars themselves, and a major stalemate was reached with the Tatars on a battleground near the Ugra River south of Moscow in 1480. This date often is given as the end of the so-called "Tatar Yoke," because no more tribute was paid from then on, but the Tatars continued to harass the Russian area for another century. Kazan was not captured until 1552 during the reign of Ivan IV, or Ivan the Terrible, and as late as 1571 much of Moscow was burned to the ground by an expedition of Tatars from Crimea.

All during this period when the Russian princely states were fighting amongst themselves for supremacy and were resisting the Tatar horde, various Russian princes also

were gathering armies to repulse the Swedes, the Germans, the Poles, and the Lithuanians in the north and west, and later the Ottoman Turks in the south, who had taken over the Byzantine Empire with the fall of Constantinople in 1453. The struggle along the Baltic dates back to Alexander Nevsky's battle with the Swedes on the Neva River in 1240, the very same year that Kiev in the south was falling to the Tatars, and to the

Figure 1-4   Statue of Vladimir-the-Saint on the high west bluff at Kiev facing down the Dnieper toward Constantinople (Istanbul). Vladimir is credited with introducing Greek Orthodox Christianity to Kievan Rus around A.D. 1000. Photograph by the author.

defeat of the Germans on Lake Peipus (Chudskoe) in 1242. In 1410, at the Battle of Tannenburg, a great Pan-Slav army under a Polish-Lithuanian prince defeated the so-called Livonian Knights and thereby set the eastern limits of German penetration for centuries to follow. During the sixteenth century, Poland, which had joined with the Lithuanian provinces, was the largest state in Europe and stretched from the Baltic to the Black Sea. It controlled all of what is now western Russia, White Russia, and the Ukraine and even succeeded in placing a king on the Russian throne in Moscow from 1610–1613.

While all this was going on in the west, during the reign of Ivan IV an expedition under the leadership of a Cossack named Yermak to open up Siberia was sponsored by the fur trading family of Stroganov. His little band of Cossacks crossed the Urals and conquered the town of Sibir, a Tatar stronghold in western Siberia. Within half a century the quest for furs took the Russian explorers across Siberia to the shores of the Pacific, where in 1649 Okhotsk became the first Russian settlement on the eastern coast. The movement through Siberia met with little resistance, for the area was practically devoid of population. Only a few tribes of Paleo-Asiatic nomads occupied the area at the time. Since the climate of the area was so harsh, there was little inducement for settlement; the Russians did not stop to take up land, but continued across the continent in their race to the sea. In 1652 a fort was established on the Amur River on the site of the modern city of Khabarovsk. Here the Russian pioneers came into conflict with the northernmost Chinese, and in 1689 the Far Eastern territories were partitioned between the two countries by the Treaty of Nerchinsk.

Russian fur traders continued on across the Bering Straits into Alaska, where in 1784 permanent settlements were established, and they continued on down the coast of North America until in 1812 they founded their southernmost fort, Fort Ross, only a few miles north of present-day San Francisco.

Later, pressures on the central government in Moscow from the Crimean War and from the opposition of British fur trading companies in Canada forced the Muscovy government in 1867 to sell Alaska to the United States and to relinquish all claims to the south along the west coast of North America.

Also during the reign of Ivan the Terrible the movement southward to reoccupy the steppes of southern Russia and the Ukraine was begun under the impetus of the oppression of Ivan's government in Moscow. People escaped from the central area and moved southward into the "no man's" land of the steppes to either settle and become farmers or to join in seminomadic bands to become so-called "Cossacks." It is this Russian movement southward into the steppes, and not the movement eastward through Siberia, that corresponds so closely in character to the movement westward into the Great Plains of North America. The movement southward occupied a semiarid region of open grasslands and good soils with great farming possibilities. The economy of the time was a mixture of sedentary agriculture and a seminomadic cowboy-like existence.

The roving Cossacks consisted of diverse nationalities, mainly Russian, who had escaped the jurisdiction of the central government to establish a law of their own in the "wild field." Usually they joined in bands and either preyed on the settlers, robbing and looting, or hired themselves out to the central government to carry on some military campaign in the outlying provinces. It was such a group of men, banded together under Yermak, who were commissioned to open up Siberia.

Although the Cossacks were scattered widely over the southern plains, they were concentrated in two or three localities. The so-called Don Cossacks occupied the lower Don River area and established a center at Aksay only a few miles northeast of the present large city of Rostov. The other concentrations of Cossacks were in the Ukraine around Kiev and farther south on some islands of the Dnieper River near the present site of Zaporozhye. It was the Cossacks in the Ukraine who during the seventeenth century rebelled against the Polish-Lithuanian state and finally established their independence of the power and brought on the weakening of Poland. But the independence of the Ukraine was short-lived; in 1667 Kiev bowed to the control of Moscow. During the same year, the old city of Smolensk, in the western part of European Russia, was ceded to Moscow by Poland.

Consolidation of these gains in the south under an organized governmental control was begun by Peter I, or Peter the Great, during his reign from 1682–1725. After a few skirmishes along the Sea of Azov with the Ottoman Turks, however, his attention was diverted to the north by the Swedes in the Baltic, where he first suffered a major defeat from Charles XII near the city of Narva. But in 1709 he recuperated his armies to defeat Charles decisively in the Ukraine at the town of Poltava, a battle which the Russians consider one of the decisive battles of history. Even though this was a major victory for the Russians, the Swedes harassed them in the Baltic area throughout Peter's reign. The opening up of the South remained undone for another half century until the accession to the throne of Catherine the Great. Nevertheless, Peter's war with Sweden established a Russian hold on the Baltic and weakened Swedish power from then on. In 1703 Peter the Great began building St. Petersburg on the Baltic Sea, and in 1713 he moved the national government from Moscow to his new city where it remained until 1918. This move shifted the center of influence of the Russian government and assured a stronghold on the Baltic and a western position on the European Plain.

During the reign of Catherine the Great (1762–1796) the offensive to the south was reopened, and many battles were fought with and against the Austrians, the Prussians, and the Turks until by the end of the reign the entire north shore of the Black Sea was secured to Russia. The Crimea was occu-

Figure 1-5   River station at Aksay, the old Don Cossack stronghold on the high west bluff near the mouth of the Don River just upstream from the present large city of Rostov. Most river stations in the Soviet Union are old river boats that have been permanently lashed to the shore.   Photograph by the author.

pied in 1783. The ancient city of Odessa which had been captured from the Greeks by the Turks was captured by the Russians in 1774, was lost again, and was recaptured in 1789. Bukovina, west of the Dniester, which had been occupied by the Austrians in 1773, and Bessarabia, which was still in Turkish hands, both were ceded to Russia in 1812. It was also during the reign of Catherine that the three partitions of Poland took place, the latter of which in 1795 brought almost all of the territory of Poland, including Warsaw, under the Russian throne, where it remained with varying degrees of autonomy until 1915. Thus by the end of Catherine's reign the boundaries of the Russian empire extended from their most western extent in Poland eastward to the Pacific. Expansion to the northwest was completed in 1809 when Finland was acquired from Sweden.

Two more great advances remained to be carried out in the nineteenth century to round out the Russian Empire as it existed in its greatest extent in 1904. The first of these was the advance into the Caucasus, a movement that began by the founding of towns along the northern foothills of the Great Caucasus during the latter part of Catherine's reign. The movement continued across the Caucasus during the reign of

Alexander I in the early part of the nineteenth century. Tbilisi, the capital of Georgia, fell to Russia in 1801. Baku, later to become the capital of the Azerbaydzhan Republic, came under Russian control in 1806, and the Black Sea coast south to Sukhumi was secured by 1810. The advance was completed in 1828 when, after the capture of Yerevan, Russia met the growing British influence in Persia.

The second advance proceeded into the deserts of Middle Asia from such established bases as Orenburg along the southern fringe of the Ural Mountains. Tashkent was captured in 1865 and Bukhara and Samarkand (Afrosiab) in 1868. The last remaining khanates of Khiva and Kokand were subjugated in 1873 and 1876 respectively. Although many Moslem towns remained nominally independent of the Russian "protectorate" until after the Revolution in 1920, the Russians controlled the area to the high mountains in the south. The Russians occupied this area primarily to subjugate the nomadic tribes that periodically foraged northward into southwestern Siberia and the southeastern part of the European Plain to harass the Russian settlers. In Central Asia British influence was met again, and in 1883 the frontier between Russia and India was agreed on with Afghanistan established as a buffer state.

In 1860 Russian expansion was revived in the Far East after the weakening of the Chinese influence and in response to the expansionist tendencies of Japan. Vladivostok was founded in 1860 after the annexation of the Amur Provinces from China. Three decades later, in 1892, construction was begun on the Trans-Siberian Railway, and great pressure was brought to bear on China to allow the extension of the railway through northern Manchuria to Vladivostok. Finally, in 1904, after the Boxer Rebellion in China, Russia occupied the whole of northern Manchuria. This action brought on the Russo-Japanese War in 1905 in which Russia was defeated decisively, and thus ended Russian expansion in the Far East. The loss of southern Sakhalin to Japan in 1905 was the first diminution in Russia's frontiers since the fifteenth century, and the year 1904 marks the greatest expanse of the territory controlled by the tsars. The total area of the country at that time was approximately 8,550,000 square miles, about 50,000 square miles less than the present area of the Soviet Union.

The ultimate result of defeat in World War I, followed by revolution, civil war, and intervention by the Allies, was the loss of Finland, Estonia, Latvia, Lithuania, and Poland, as independent countries, and Bessarabia and Northern Bukovina in the southwest to Rumania. Immediately after the revolution in 1917, with Lenin's decree of self-determination for the various nationalities, such areas as the Ukraine, the Transcaucasian areas of Georgia, Armenia, and Azerbaydzhan, as well as some of the areas in Middle Asia east of the Caspian, declared their independence and set up so-called White Republics. The White Republics, however, were short-lived, and all these areas were brought within the boundaries of the newly constituted Soviet Union by 1923.

All the territories lost as a result of World War I, except for Finland and part of the Polish area, were regained at the end of World War II, and some territory which never had been under the Russian Empire also was acquired at this time. Poland was partitioned again in 1939 between Germany and the Soviet Union, but this partition did not stand after Germany's attack on the U.S.S.R. After the war, all of eastern Poland became part of Belorussia or the Ukraine within the Soviet Union, whereas the country of Poland was shifted bodily westward to occupy much of what had been eastern Germany. The Baltic States of Estonia, Latvia, and Lithuania were regained by the Soviet Union during the early part of the war. Bessarabia was later regained and Bukovina newly gained from Rumania to be incorporated partly into the new republic of Moldavia and partly into the western Ukraine. Small pieces of territory were taken over from Finland, particularly the Pechenga area in the far north, which contains important nickel and copper desposits, and the Karelian Isthmus in the south next to Leningrad. Two areas in the west that were taken after World War II which had never been under Russian control were the Ruthenian area of Czechoslovakia, which became the Transcarpathian Ukraine, and the northern half of East Prussia, which became Kaliningrad Oblast. In the Far East, southern Sakhalin and the Kuril Islands were regained from Japan. Also, in 1944, Tuva joined the Soviet Union, after the establishment of a protectorate which dated back to 1911. In 1946 the area of the Soviet Union was given as 8,606,300 square miles, which compares to 3,615,210 square miles in the United States.

The Physical Setting

Topography As has been seen, the Soviet Union is a huge country, nearly three times the area of the United States. We would expect to find within such an expanse of territory much variety of landforms, climate, soils, and natural vegetation, and we do. But there are some generalizations that can be made. Very simply, the landforms of the Soviet Union can be described as an extensive plain, only a few hundred feet above sea level in the central and western portions, surrounded by high mountains and rugged plateaus on the south and east. This arrangement of landforms, as will be seen later, has a great effect on the climate and the zonations of soil and natural vegetation.

Geologically, the European Plain, from the western borders of the country to the Urals, is an old stable block of the earth's crust underlain by ancient crystalline rocks of igneous and metamorphic origin that over millions of centuries have been planed down by stream erosion to a rough, rolling surface. This crystalline basement rock outcrops at the surface in the northwestern part of the country in the so-called Karelian and Kola

Peninsula areas. It also outcrops at the surface in a few places in the southern part of the plain where the major streams have eroded channels deep enough to expose it. But over most of the plain the crystalline rock is covered to a depth of several hundred feet by younger sedimentary rocks lying in nearly horizontal positions. Dating from Paleozoic times, these sediments compare in age, type, and present attitudes to the rock layers in the Middle West of the United States.

Here and there the European Plain has been warped gently into broad swells and shallow swales which inject some variety into the landscape; the higher portions of the Plain have undergone more severe stream dissection, and differential erosion on the dipping sedimentary layers has produced a system of low-lying cuestas that have exercised considerable control on the development of the major stream pattern. The broadest upwarps have resulted in the Central Russian Uplands, which run northwest to southeast through the center of the Plain, and the Volga Heights, which lie to the west of the Volga River in its central portion. There also has been a broad upwarp in the south through the Ukraine and Moldavia, which runs essentially west-east across the major south-flowing rivers and forces an abrupt eastward bend of the rivers as they cross the axis of uplift. This upwarp is known in the west as the Podolian Plateau and in the east as the Donets Ridge.

At what is usually considered to be the boundary between Europe and Asia, the Plain is interrupted by the low range of the Ural Mountains. These old, worn-down mountains of Paleozoic age correspond in elevations to the Appalachian Range in the United States. No doubt they have been much higher in the past, but erosion has worn them down to the bare stumps and has exposed old Paleozoic sedimentary rocks on the western slopes and even older crystalline rocks on the eastern slopes. The greatest heights in the Urals are now little above 6000 feet and general elevations are no more

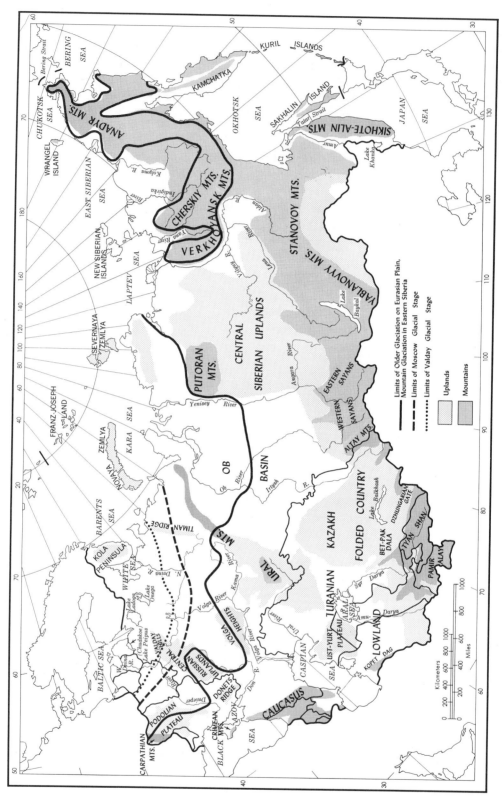

Figure 1-6 General landform features of the U.S.S.R.

than 2000 feet. In the middle, most heavily populated section, the range splits into numerous individual ridges which here and there become discontinuous and are very low in altitude so that sections of the area are not mountainous at all. The range therefore is no barrier to transportation or other cultural endeavors or to physical phenomena such as climate and soils.

East of the Urals, the Plain continues until it reaches the River Yenisey where it stops abruptly against the Central Siberian Upland. This plain between the Urals and the Yenisey River, drained by the mighty Ob, is as flat as a floor. It represents a recently uplifted part of the Continental Shelf which has been covered by the Arctic Sea since the Glacial Period. The surface materials are young marine sediments, in many cases very poorly consolidated, with no outcrops of older rock, and everywhere the drainage is exceedingly poor.

Surrounding the east European and west Siberian plains on the south and east are rugged, young, folded mountains and associated plateaus. In the very southwestern part of the country, in the area that was acquired from Czechoslovakia after World War II, the Carpathian Mountains reach heights above 6000 feet. Farther east, on the Crimean Peninsula, the Crimean Mountains reach elevations above 5000 feet and plunge abruptly to the sea on the southeast along a fault system that continues into the Caucasus between the Black and Caspian Seas. The Great Caucasus with elevations over 18,000 feet have no low passes and are a definite barrier for climate and other phenomena.

The high mountains continue eastward around the southern and of the Caspian Sea where the Elburz Mountains in northern Iran reach an elevation of more than 19,000 feet. Without a break, these ranges continue eastward along the border of Iran and the Soviet Union as the Kopet Dag, or "Dry Mountains," which reach elevations of about 10,000 feet in the Soviet Union and are extremely arid. Farther east, in Afghanistan,

the Hindu Kush range leads up to the "Roof of the World," the Pamirs.

The Pamir-Alay Mountains and the Tyan Shan to the north are the highest mountains in the Soviet Union. In the southeastern corner of Soviet Middle Asia they reach elevations well above 20,000 feet. These high mountains form a complete barrier to climate and to communication between the Soviet Union and adjacent countries. Their snow-capped peaks provide abundant irrigation water to the cotton-growing areas of Soviet Middle Asia. Their west-to-east-oriented ranges here and there are broken by rather broad synclinal valleys, the broadest of which, the so-called Dzhungarian Gate, lies east of Lake Balkhash.

The extensive lowland lying to the north of the broad arc of Central Asian mountains is a desert of low plateaus, eroded hills, expansive sand dunes, and basins of interior drainage, the chief ones of which contain the three large bodies of water: the Caspian Sea, the Aral Sea, and Lake Balkhash. This lowland opens northward onto the Ob Basin in western Siberia from which it is distinguished more by climate than by topography.

The high mountains continue northeast of the Dzhungarian Gate in ranges oriented roughly northwest-southeast. The westernmost ranges, on the border between Kazakhstan and Siberia, are the Altay Mountains. These mountains are considerably older geologically than those to the southwest and have been eroded down somewhat more and are not quite as high or rugged as are the Tyan Shans and Pamirs. They still reach elevations of more than 16,000 feet, however, and their importance will become obvious under the discussion of mineral resources. These high mountains and intervening basins continue eastward along the border of the Soviet Union and Mongolia and further east between the Soviet Union and China.

To the north, stretching all the way to the Arctic Sea between the Yenisey and Lena Rivers, is a broad roughly dissected upland known as the Central Siberian Uplands or the East Siberian Plateaus. Different sections are known by different names that correspond to the major river systems. The general elevation of the upland is only about 2000 feet above sea level, but locally it rises to 6000 feet. It has been deeply dissected everywhere by streams, which in some cases lie in true canyons. Much of the upland is underlain by an old crystalline rock platform, a stable block that has resisted tectonic movement as younger mountains have been folded up along its flanks. In places the crystalline rocks outcrop at the surface, but more likely they are covered by younger sedimentary rocks, many of which are coal bearing, or by recent outflows of lava. The southern fringe has been splintered by recent faults that have divided the area into a series of horsts and grabens. Lake Baykal lies in one of the deep grabens.

Beyond the Lena River, high mountains and intervening river basins continue eastward to the Bering Sea. These ranges are part of the arcuate mountain ranges that run the full length of the east coast of Asia and continue offshore in a series of islands and peninsulas. The island of Sakhalin, and particularly the peninsula of Kamchatka, are part of this arcuate mountain system which is a zone of contemporary intensive disastrophism and vulcanism. Kamchatka has approximately 100 active volcanoes, the highest of which, Mt. Klyuchevskaya, reaches an elevation of more than 16,000 feet. It is one of the world's great volcanoes, rising nearly from sea level to its lofty peak, which is perpetually snow capped.

Climate   The climate of the Soviet Union reflects the high latitude of the country, the enormous land area, and the rim of high mountains along the south and east. Everywhere it shows strong influences of continentality; precipitation in most cases is only moderate or deficient, and temperatures are extreme. Most of the moisture that comes to the Soviet Union comes from the Atlantic Ocean. By the time the air reaches European Russia it has lost much of its capacity for precipitation.

Cyclonic storms follow northeasterly tracks across the European plain, and usually dissipate along the Arctic Coast of Western Siberia. This is particularly true during winter when storms are squeezed off the continent by the strong and persistant Siberian high-pressure cell. The precipitation is most adequate in the northwestern part of Russia and diminishes southeastward into Middle Asia. Yearly totals in northwestern Russia amount to approximately 25 inches, but along the northern shore of the Black Sea this total has dropped to less than 16 inches, and it continues to diminish eastward until around the northern end of the Caspian Sea it is only 8 inches. Farther east, in the area around the Aral Sea, an extensive area of desert receives less than 4 inches of precipitation per year. Much of Siberia, except for parts of the southern fringe, can be classified as humid, but this classification stems not so much from abundant precipitation as it does from cool temperatures and low evaporation rates. In the Far East, particularly in the south, precipitation increases again as a result of monsoonal influences from the Pacific. Precipitation in the Far East is heavily concentrated in middle and late summer when monsoon winds blow into the land from the Pacific Ocean. This rainfall regime is not very favorable for crop growth since the heaviest rain often falls during the harvest time.

The high mountains along the southern fringes of the country may catch as much as 40 inches of precipitation on their windward slopes, much of it coming in the form of snow during the wintertime. Parts of Transcaucasia and Middle Asia are in latitudes that are affected by cyclonic storms during the winter that follow a southern track through the Mediterranean Sea and eastward across southwestern Asia along the southern fringes of the Siberian High. The heavy fall of snow in the wintertime in the southern mountains is of great significance to irrigation agriculture in the adjoining plains since the precipitation is held over

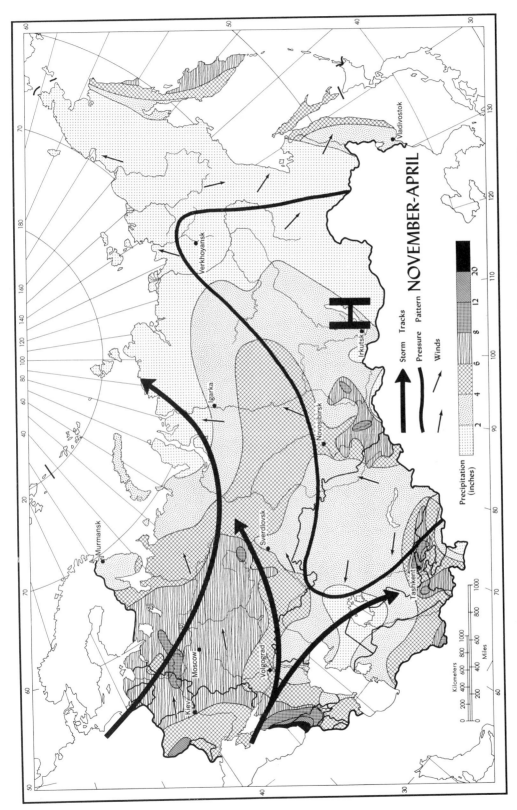

Figure 1-7   Storm tracks and precipitation in the U.S.S.R., November–April.   Adapted from Davydova and Alisov.

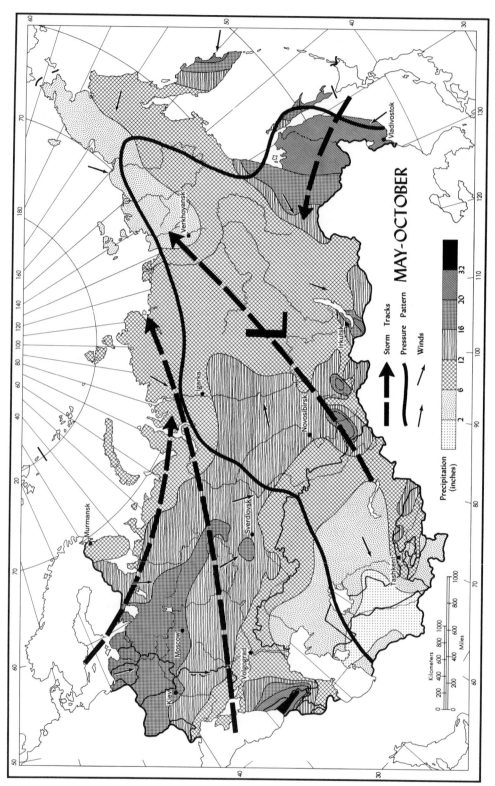

Figure 1-8   Storm tracks and precipitation in the U.S.S.R., May–October.   Adapted from Davydova and Alisov.   The summer storm tracks are shown by dashed arrows to indicate that they are less frequented by cyclones than the winter tracks are.

in the form of snow until midsummer when it reaches its maximum melting at the time of greatest need.

Only two small spots in the Soviet Union receive what might be called excessive precipitation. These are at either end of Transcaucasia, bordering on the eastern end of the Black Sea and on the southwestern side of the Caspian. The Colchis Lowland at the eastern end of the Black Sea receives 60 inches or more of rain per year and totals as high as 90 inches are received in the mountain foothills around Batumi. Summers here are hot and humid and the precipitation comes mainly in the form of thundershowers, whereas winter precipitation is due primarily to cyclonic storms that move in from the Mediterranean across the Black Sea. On the Caspian side of Transcaucasia, a much smaller area known as the Lenkoran Lowland receives around 60 inches of rainfall. Both the Colchis Lowland and the Lenkoran Lowland have mild winters and hot, humid summers and thereby classify as having humid subtropical climates.

The climate of nearly all the Soviet Union is either humid continental and subarctic or dry. The winters are always severe. Even in Middle Asia the plain is wide open to cold blasts of air during the winter. Much of European Russia classifies as a humid continental, cool summer type of climate, similar to the Great Lakes and adjacent parts of the United States and Canada. Moscow sits approximately in the center of this belt of climate in a latitude corresponding roughly to the southern part of Hudson Bay. In southeastern European Russia the summers become longer and warmer, but they also become drier. Before the summers become long and warm enough for a wide variety of crops, the precipitation has diminished to the point where the climate no longer classifies as humid. The Soviet Union does not have the combination of long, hot, moist summers that prevail in the North American Corn Belt. Traveling from Moscow to the southern Ukraine climatically corresponds to traveling from Minnesota to

eastern Montana. Hence corn has not been a major crop in the Soviet Union, although now it is being introduced under governmental decree.

The northern part of European Russia has a subarctic climate and lies beyond the limits of most agriculture. This type of climate extends eastward across the Urals and expands latitudinally until it engulfs much of Siberia. Most of this subarctic region still is covered by virgin coniferous forests. The northern fringe along the Arctic seas and some of the mountainous areas east of the Lena River in eastern Siberia have a tundra climate in which no month averages above 50°F. These areas are largely devoid of trees and contain only sparse tundra vegetation of mosses and lichens.

Only the southern fringes of Siberia are warm enough to be classified as other than subarctic. This particularly pertains to southwestern Siberia, but it also applies to mountain basins along the southern fringes of Siberia all the way to the Pacific. In Maritime Kray and along the lower Amur River the climate once again is of a humid continental, cool summer type, but here the precipitation is more concentrated in summer owing to the monsoonal flow of air from the Pacific at that season. During the winter, much of eastern Asia is covered by a very intensive high-pressure cell usually centered somewhere south of Lake Baykal, and the winds, circulating clockwise about the high, blow from the northwest across Maritime Kray to the Pacific and strictly limit precipitation. In addition they bring severe temperatures even to the coastal areas of the Pacific.

South of a line running from the western Ukraine to southwestern Siberia, the Eurasian plain is an area of dry climates. The fringes generally are steppe or semiarid, but an extensive region from the eastern shore of the Caspian Sea to the eastern end of Lake Balkhash classifies as true desert. The more humid fringes of the steppe regions contain the best soils in the country, and hence an

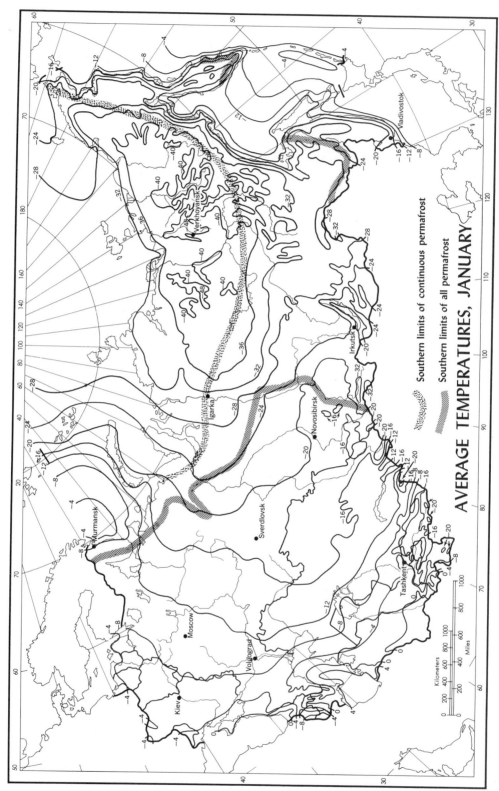

Figure 1-9   Average temperatures in degrees centigrade, January.   From Atlas selskogo khozyaystva SSSR, p. 10.

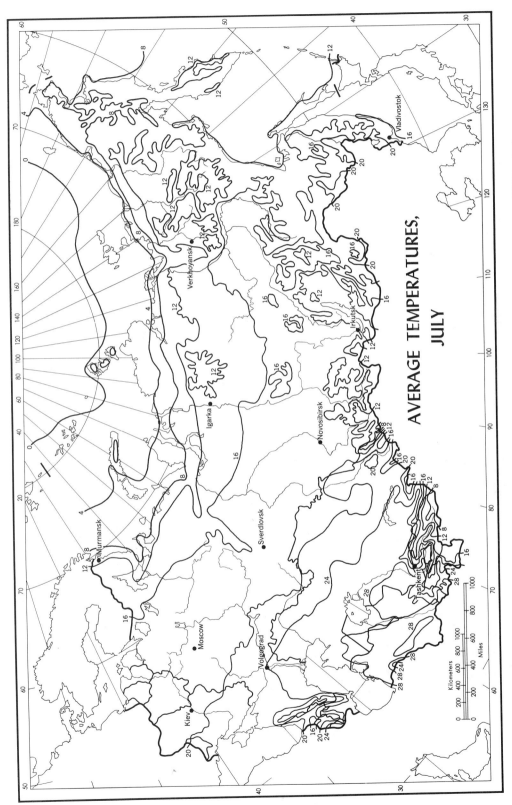

Figure 1-10 *Average temperatures in degrees centigrade, July. From Atlas selskogo khozyaystva SSSR, p. 11.*

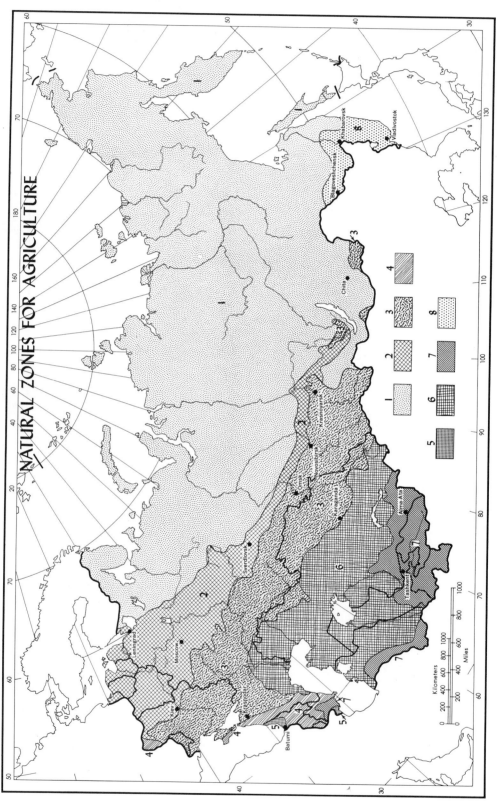

Figure 1-11   *For descriptive legend see opposite page.*

intensive grain-growing agricultural economy is practiced in spite of the drought climate.

Only three small spots in the south classify as humid mesothermal climates. These are the two limited areas of humid subtropical climate at either end of Transcaucasia and the southern side of the Crimean Peninsula. In each spot mountains to the north protect these areas from cold winter winds, so that winter temperatures average above freezing. The climate along the southeast shore of Crimea classifies as a Mediterranean type which receives all its rain in the wintertime from cyclonic storms.

Natural Vegetation, Soils, and Land Use

The natural vegetation and soils are distributed in zones oriented roughly west-east, which closely correspond to the zones of climate. The northern fringe of the country is covered by tundra vegetation and infertile tundra soils. Further south, a broad expanse of coniferous forest, the taiga, occupies much of European Russia north of 56° latitude and widens east of the Ural Mountains until it engulfs much of Siberia. Associated with the coniferous forests are heavily leached, gray, infertile podzol soils. The drainage throughout much of the tundra and the northern coniferous forest is very poor. Much of the area in Siberia is underlain by permafrost, which makes drainage even poorer, since downward percolation of water during the warm season largely is prevented by the frozen subsoil. Possibilities of agriculture throughout the entire region are very limited.

South of the coniferous forest lies a belt of mixed forest dominated by broad-leaf deciduous trees. Along the western border of the Soviet Union this forest occupies a wide band from the shores of the Baltic nearly to the Black Sea. The belt narrows rapidly eastward in a triangular shape until at the Urals it has been largely pinched out between the taiga to the north and the steppes to the south. The soils throughout this region are gray-brown podzolic, which are somewhat leached of plant minerals but which can be made quite productive through proper management and generous additions of fertilizers. General farming has developed here based on crops that are adapted to cool, moist, acidic soil conditions such as potatoes, flax, rye, barley, oats, hay, and a variety of hardy vegetables, particularly cabbage and beets. Dairying and livestock raising are very important.

South and east of the mixed forest lies a rather narrow zone of so-called "wooded steppe" in which the natural vegetation is tall grasses interspersed by clumps of trees, particularly along streams. Further south lies the true steppe, a rolling, open grassland devoid of trees. It is within the zone of wooded steppe and the northern parts of the steppe that the famous black earth or chernozem soils of Russia exist. The black earth belt of Russia begins in the west-central Ukraine and extends east-northeast across the middle Volga and southern Urals into southwestern Siberia and northern Kazakhstan, where it narrows to a belt approximately 150 miles wide, straddling the 55th parallel of latitude. The black soils are encountered here and there farther east along similar latitudes in the steppe basins that lie between the mountains of southern

Figure 1-11 Natural zones for agriculture. Adapted from Atlas selskogo khozyaystva SSSR, *p. 8.*

1. Northern forests and tundra, podzol and tundra soils, little agriculture. 2. Mixed forests, podzolic soils, general farming (flax, potatoes, oats, rye, barley, hay, livestock). 3. Wooded steppe and steppe zones, Chernozem and chestnut soils, cash farming (wheat, sugar beets, sunflowers, corn, livestock). 4. Mountain forests and soils of the Carpathians, Crimea, and Caucasia; little agriculture. 5. Humid subtropical climate and soils of the Colchis and Lenkoran Lowlands; citrus, tea, tobacco, grapes, other fruits and vegetables, corn, rice, livestock. 6. Desert vegetation and soils; extensive grazing, scattered irrigation agriculture. 7. Mountains and mountain forelands with semidesert climates and serozem soils; dry farming of wheat and intensive irrigation of cotton, alfalfa, and other crops; transhumance of livestock. 8. Low mountains and basins of the Far East; cool monsoon climate, mixed forests, forest and steppe soils; wheat, sugar beets, soy beans, rice, grain sorghums, livestock.

Siberia. These are the best soils of Russia, and indeed, some of the best soils in the world. The area is hampered by its droughty climate, so that it is not as productive as some areas of the world that have less fertile soils. Nevertheless, this is the heart of the farming country in the Soviet Union. The main crops here are wheat, corn, sugar beets, and sunflowers, but a great variety of other crops are grown, and livestock raising is very important. Farming here is done on a more commercial level than it is further north.

The steppes extend south to the northern coast of the Black Sea, southeast into the North Caucasian Foreland, and east across northern Kazakhstan. The soils continue to be good, but the climate becomes drier further south, and agriculture becomes more commercial and more specialized. Wheat and sunflowers are grown on extensive scales. Only in the Kuban District in Krasnodar Kray along the northwestern slopes of the Caucasus does the climate once again become humid enough for such crops as sugar beets and corn. The Kuban District rivals the better parts of the Ukraine in agricultural potentialities and production.

South of the Caucasus, the humid subtropical Colchis and Lenkoran Lowlands are utilized for specialty crops such as citrus fruits, tea, and tobacco, which are exotic to the rest of the Soviet Union and enjoy monopolies on nationwide markets. The drier Kura Lowland is important for its irrigated cotton and alfalfa.

The large area of Middle Asia between the Caspian Sea and Lake Balkhash has a desert climate, and, hence, desert vegetation and desert soils. The vegetation here is a sparse cover of saxaul trees, brush, and certain types of cactus. Much of the surface is not covered by vegetation; hence, the soils are largely lacking in humus. The mineral content is high, however, and wherever irrigation water can be applied, the soils prove to be quite productive. In border areas on the southeast sides of the deserts the great cotton-growing areas of the Soviet Union have developed on a discontinuous belt of thick loess deposits, utilizing irrigation waters from northwestward-flowing streams which come down from the Tyan Shans and the Pamir-Alay ranges.

In the Far East, Amur Oblast and Maritime Kray are areas of mixed forests and gray-brown podzolic soils similar to those in central European Russia and the northern Ukraine. Here the general farming of the Ukraine and western Russia has mingled with the rice paddies, soy beans, and grain sorghums of Manchuria and North Korea.

The effectively occupied territory of the Soviet Union is limited primarily to the wedge of agriculturally productive land, in the contiguous zones of the mixed forest, the wooded steppe, and the steppe, which stretch from the Baltic to the Black Sea in the west and taper to a narrow belt in western Siberia. Three major outliers of settlement are the basins of Transcaucasia, the oases of Middle Asia, and the southern valleys of the Far East. The total area of these cultivated lands is approximately equal to the area under cultivation in the United States, and in general the cultivated land in the United States lies in warmer and moister climates. Thus, although the U.S.S.R. contains nearly three times the area of the United States, the agricultural potentialities of the two countries are approximately equal. The United States might even be slightly better endowed. So far, the United States certainly has produced much more than the U.S.S.R. has; the reason for this is largely that agriculture in the United States has been much better organized and more efficient; 110 million farmers, wives, and children in the U.S.S.R. produce somewhat less agricultural produce than do approximately 30 million farm people in the United States. With a total population of approximately 30 million more people than are in the United States, the U.S.S.R. obviously has a considerably lower per capita consumption of farm products than does the United States.

Political and Economic Subdivisions

The Soviet Union is divided into sub-regions on the bases of nationality and administrative convenience. Marxian ideology on the one hand calls for national self determination, and on the other it says that the political structure should reflect the economic structure. In practice this duality of ideology has led to conflict on several occasions; adherence to the principal of political recognition of nationality groups tends to stabilize internal boundaries, whereas economic determination of political boundaries in such a rapidly developing country calls for almost constant change. Although boundary and name changes have occurred frequently enough in the Soviet Union to excite comment, in general traditionalism has induced an element of ultraconservatism in the laying out of political subregions, even where nationality is not a question. The political subdivisions of European Russia look very much the same as they did when they were first formed by the government of Catherine the Great in the latter part of the eighteenth century.

At present, the U.S.S.R. is divided into fifteen Soviet Socialist Republics (S.S.R.), sometimes called "Union Republics," on the basis of nationalities. These fifteen Republics represent the fifteen most populous and most culturally advanced groups of peoples in the U.S.S.R. Administratively, they would correspond somewhat to the fifty states of the United States. Actually, according to the constitution of the U.S.S.R., the Union Republics have a wider latitude of jurisdiction than do the states of the United States. The constitution of the U.S.S.R. really is a confederate one, reserving the rights to the individual member republics to coin money, enter into foreign agreements, and secede from the Union at any time. In actuality, the constitution is paid little attention to in the Soviet Union, and the individual republics have very little latitude of operation outside the surveillance of Moscow. The

Russian Republic is much bigger and much more populous than any of the other republics and it definitely is the "first among equals." The provisions of the constitution are adhered to only when it is expedient to do so. A good illustration of this is the fact that three seats are occupied in the United Nations by the Soviet Union; one for the U.S.S.R., one for the Ukrainian Republic, and one for the Belorussian Republic, on the contention that these republics really are independent countries.

The Union Republics, except for some of the smaller ones, are divided into oblasts, krays, and Autonomous Soviet Socialist Republics (A.S.S.R.), all of which are on a commensurate level of jurisdiction, and all

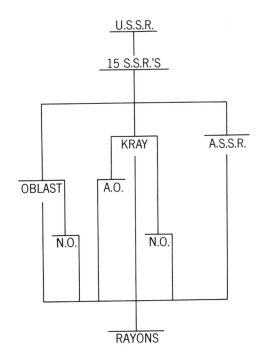

Figure 1-12   Organizational structure of political administrative units in the U.S.S.R. Exceptions to the general scheme depicted above are: (1) the newly formed Krays in the Kazakh S.S.R. contain oblasts, (2) Maritime Kray in the Far East has no subdivision, (3) Tuva A.O. is directly responsible to the R.S.F.S.R., (4) small S.S.R.'s are divided directly into rayons; they have no oblasts, and (5) some of the larger cities have been placed under the direct jurisdiction of their respective S.S.R.'s.

of which are directly responsible to their respective Union Republics. The oblast is purely an administrative subdivision that contains no significant nationality group other than the titular nationality of the Union Republic within which it is located. The A.S.S.R. administratively serves the same function as the oblast, but its boundaries have been drawn to give political recognition to an important minority nationality group. The kray is sort of a combination of the other two. Its boundaries have been laid out rather arbitrarily, primarily for administrative facility, but it contains within it lesser political subdivisions that are based on nationality groups—autonomous oblasts (A.O.) or national okrugs (N.O.) or both. Theoretically, any administrative unit can contain within it nationality-based political units on any of the lower echelons. For instance, several oblasts encompass national okrugs. But an oblast cannot contain an autonomous oblast. An administrative unit containing an autonomous oblast would become a kray. In a sense, then, the kray is a higher unit than is the oblast, but they are both directly responsible to the Union Republic.

A nationality group is given political recognition in one of the following four administrative units ranked in decreasing order of importance: (1) S.S.R., (2) A.S.S.R., (3) A.O., and (4) N.O. The national okrug is usually assigned to large remote areas of sparse population, such as areas in northern Siberia occupied by semi-nomadic reindeer herders. In cultural development these areas might be likened to Indian reservations in the United States. However, the national okrugs in the Soviet Union do have some representation in the national government. There are many small nationality groups in the U.S.S.R. that have no political identities because of their limited numbers.

At the lowest level of administration, all areas are divided into "rayons." There are rural rayons and city rayons. Most Soviet production statistics and other information are not broken down for individual rayons; rarely are they reported for units smaller than oblasts, if that. In this book, discussion will be based on oblasts, krays, and A.S.S.R.'s. These units administratively might be likened to counties in the United States, but generally their areas are much larger. The rural and city rayons might be likened to townships and city wards. Outside this hierarchy of administrative regions, a number of cities have been given a special status which excludes them from the governmental jurisdiction of the regions within which they are located and makes them responsible directly to their Union Republics.

The political administrative organization of the U.S.S.R. is rather complex. It embodies elements of administrative convenience, nationality recognition, and traditionalism. It also contains some inconsistencies. Tuva came into the Soviet Union in 1944 and was made an autonomous oblast directly responsible to the Russian Republic (R.S.F.S.R.). Primorskiy (Maritime) Kray in the Far East has no nationality-based political unit within it. It once included a politically recognized minority nationality when it extended farther northward. Since then its boundaries have been changed, but its name has not.

Complicating the administrative picture still further are two systems of economic regions that involve groupings of political regions. Since 1940 economic planning and production has been based largely on thirteen gross economic regions. In 1957, when the administration of industry was reorganized, the country was divided into 105 economic administrative regions. Since then, the boundaries and numbers of these administrative regions have changed, and now the thirteen planning and reporting regions are being altered. Under communist policy that administrative regions should reflect economic conditions, we can expect constant changes to take place in regional boundaries. As time progresses, perhaps political administrative regions will be altered to more closely match economic administrative regions, par-

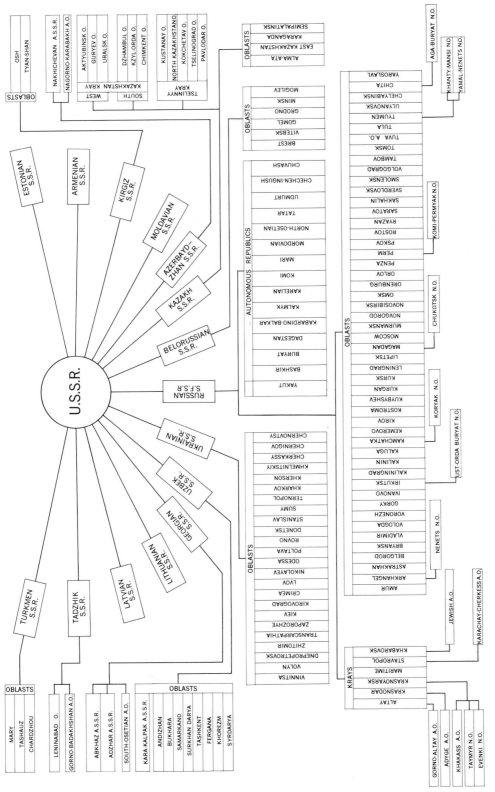

Figure 1-13   Political subdivisions of the U.S.S.R. as of July 1, 1963.

ticularly if the Soviet social system eventually erases the influences of nationality and tradition.

Each nationality-based political unit has representation in the House of Nationalities in the legislative branch of the national government. There is a given number of representatives for each S.S.R., A.S.S.R., A.O., and N.O. In the House of the Union, on the other hand, one representative is chosen for every 300,000 people. Thus, the U.S.S.R. has a bicameral legislature with a House of Nationalities corresponding roughly to the United States Senate and a House of the Union corresponding to the United States House of Representatives. There the analogy ends, however, for the houses in the U.S.S.R. always meet in joint session as the "Supreme Soviet" and act only as a rubber stamp body to approve legislation initiated by the Communist Party. The executive and judicial branches of the government grow out of the Supreme Soviet and are dependent on it. A Council of Ministers, stemming from the economic administrative setup, is the real political administrative body.

Reading List

Henderson, Daniel MacIntyre, *From the Volga to the Yukon,* Hastings House, New York, 1944, 256 pp.

PART ONE

The Regions of the U.S.S.R.

SPLITTING THEIR COUNTRY INTO "NATURAL" REGIONS has become almost a national pastime for Soviet geographers and economists. Since they are all apparently committed to the principle that natural divisions do exist to be discovered, they search for them and they argue vehemently in print about them. Many maps have been drawn, and each has been offered as the final word on regionalization of the country. On each, purportedly, boundaries have been set according to objective criteria. But as much as the Soviets would like to believe that the Revolution released them from the fetters of the past, their thinking is still beclouded much more than they realize by traditional premises that have become ingrained in their minds. And, often as not, a scheme of regionalization, which was conceived on the bases of objective criteria, in the final presentation degenerates into a reinteration of traditional boundaries.

A good case in point is the resultant regionalization of the 1957 reorganization of industry. The movement started with a sweeping abolishment of most of the ministries in Moscow and a revolutionary reform to regional control based on a relatively small number of rather larger regions. But in the demarcation of regions the movement bogged down and finally stagnated within boundaries of oblasts and autonomous areas that have existed almost in their original forms since the time of Catherine the Great. The so-called economic regions set up in 1957 corresponded generally to political regions and bore little relation to economic phenomena.

To some degree political regions affect the regional schemes that have been discussed by economic geographers in articles and textbooks. Although general economic regions have been devised in various fashions, combining several political administrative units into one geographical region, the boundaries of the larger regions follow along administrative boundaries and do not cut across oblasts. Hence the traditional oblast is held inviolate and the entire oblast is either included or excluded from a geographical region as a unit. Thus it is that sections of oblasts of very primitive nature with absolutely no industrial development are included in such a highly developed area as the Central Industrial Region.

In devising the regionalization scheme used in this book, three things have been taken into account. First, there are reasonably well-

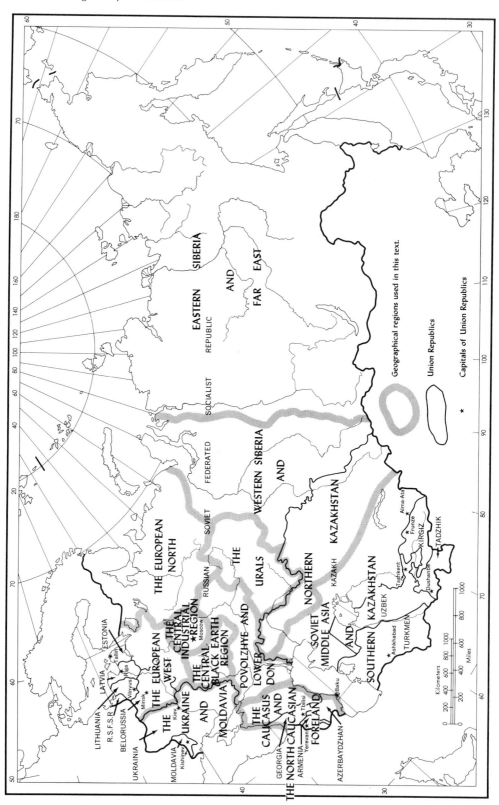

Figure 1-14   Geographical regions used in this book.

defined zones of agricultural production which are closely related to the natural environment; second, there are recognizable industrial nodal areas which lie within and transgress the boundaries of the agricultural regions; and third, there are traditional areas whose names have a real but unclearly defined significance in the minds of the Russian people. Just as the regional terms "New England," "the South," "the Middle West" have meaning to an American, so the terms "Central Chernozem Region," "the Ukraine," "the North Caucasian Foreland," and "the Povolzhye" have meaning to a Russian. These regional concepts are part of the life and the thinking of the Russian people. Although no layman has stopped to draw boundaries around these regional concepts, the whereabouts of the core areas are tacitly understood and need no definition. The geographer who is attempting to catch the content and spirit of the Soviet Union cannot deny the existence of such conceptual regions. Therefore these concepts must be weighed against economic phenomena and other criteria for regionalization.

The author of this book, like many of the Russian authors, has often found these traditional regions to have more real significance than regions based purely on economic criteria. Thus the regionalization used here is primarily the traditional one. But tradition has been tempered, or more precisely, focused, by a consideration of present economic conditions in drawing boundaries of the traditional regions. The individual oblast has not been held inviolate, nor has the Union Republic, in some instances. Only where the Union Republic has some significance in the regional thinking of the people, as in the Ukraine, has the Union Republic been treated as a unit. (The very word "Ukraine" stems from regional concepts; it means "extremity" or "borderland" and originated during the growth of Muscovy when the area of the Ukraine was one of the frontiers of the Empire.) The sprawling Kazakh Republic, however, a political unit newly conceived under the Soviet regime, has been divided and its parts included with adjacent areas.

The regions within the R.S.F.S.R. have also not been dealt with in their entirety before areas in other Union Republics were taken up, as seems to be the rule in Soviet texts. Contiguous and adjacent areas are discussed in succession, regardless of political boundaries, beginning in the heart of the country and spiralling outward in a clockwise fashion to include the most highly developed and interconnected regions of the U.S.S.R. before moving out into remote border areas. Figure 1-14 shows the eleven regions that will be used as the basis for discussion in this text.

The Central Industrial Region

Circumscribed by a circle centered at Sobinka 15 miles southwest of Vladimir with a radius of approximately 150 miles. Contains all or most urbanized parts of following oblasts:

Oblast	Area (sq mi)	Population	People (sq mile)[a]	% Urban[a]
Moscow	18,400[b]	10,949,000[b]	603.2	78
Yaroslavl	14,200[b]	1,396,000[b]	99.4	58
Vladimir	11,300	1,402,000	125.6	57
Ivanovo	9,400	1,322,000	142.5	66
Kostroma	6,000[c]	420,000[c]	39.6	39
Gorky	11,400[c]	2,250,000[c]	127.2	52
Ryazan	15,500[c]	1,445,000[b]	94.9	30
Tula	4,000[c]	980,000[c]	193.5	60
Kaluga	2,400[c]	294,000[c]	81.3	37
Kalinin	6,500[c]	647,000[c]	55.4	44
Total	99,100[d]	21,105,000[d]		

[a] All figures are for entire oblasts.

[b] Populations and areas of entire oblasts, although small portions lie outside Central Industrial Region.

[c] Estimated populations and areas of portions of oblasts lying within Central Industrial Region.

[d] Does not include northwestern corner of Mordovian A.S.S.R., which falls within circle.

2

The Central Industrial Region

Definition of the Region

Let us start the regional discussion of the Soviet Union with the very heart of the country at the central position on the European Plain around Moscow. This region emerged as an area of relatively dense population some time after the fall of Kiev in the thirteenth century, and two centuries later the Russian State began to expand and to take form from this center. The cultural and economic focus of the country today, it is known universally as the Central Industrial Region.

Definition of the Region

Although the Central Industrial Region has become a traditional area in the minds of the Russian people, and although everyone is agreed that the core of the area consists of a region of closely spaced cities, its boundaries have been defined in various ways.

Russian geographers, in their reluctance to violate political boundaries, always include entire oblasts, in spite of the fact that large sections of some of the outlying oblasts are not urbanized at all. For instance, the city of Kalinin is definitely part of the Central Industrial Region, but the city lies near the eastern border of Kalinin Oblast. The rest of the oblast is a poor agricultural area at

best, and the northern part is sparsely inhabited forest land. The same is true of Kostroma Oblast to the northeast. In the southeast, the cities along the Oka should be included within the Central Industrial Region, but the southern and eastern portions of the oblasts within which these cities lie, and of which they often are the political centers, are largely rich agricultural lands. They contain good-sized towns, but the towns are simply regional centers for the rural population, and in most are not industrialized. Likewise, in the south, the city of Tula and its satellite cities are heavily industrialized and belong very definitely to the Central Industrial Region, but the southern part of Tula Oblast is a rural agricultural area.

We might fairly well define the boundaries of the Central Industrial Region by drawing straight lines between four corner cities, Kalinin in the northwest, Vologda in the north, Gorky in the east, and Tula in the south. Such a quadrilateral would well demonstrate the eccentric position of Moscow within this industrial complex, for Moscow is not in the center of the area but is on the western edge of the concentration of cities, and the urban growth has taken place primarily to the northeast, to the east, and to the south of Moscow. However, this four-sided figure leaves out some of the

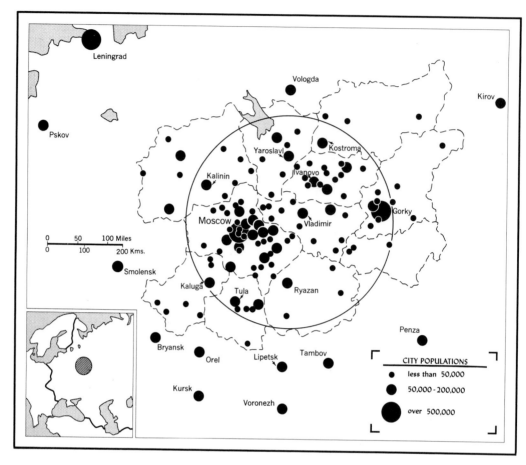

Figure 2-1   The Central Industrial Region.   A circle centered southwest of Vladimir with a radius of approximately 150 miles separates an enclosed area with dense urban concentration from a surrounding area containing only scattered cities.

important cities in the southeast along the Oka River. It also eliminates Kaluga and some other important towns in the southwest, and it includes some territory in the north which is very sparsely populated.

The region of urban concentration can best be circumscribed by a circle with a radius of approximately 150 miles centered near the town of Sobinka, just southwest of the old city of Vladimir. Thus will the Central Industrial Region be defined here. Such a circle passes through Gorky in the east, Tula in the south, Kalinin in the west, and a few miles north of the concentration of cities along the Volga in the northeast. It includes all or most of Moscow, Yaroslavl,

Vladimir, Ivanovo and Ryazan Oblasts and parts of the surrounding oblasts of Kalinin, Kostroma, Gorky, Tula, and Kaluga. The area thus encompassed contains around 21 million people, almost 70 per cent of which now are classified as urban. More than half of these people live in heavily urbanized Moscow Oblast.

The Physical Setting

The natural resources of this region are limited. The area is comprised of a rather flat plain underlain by sedimentary materials that is gently upwarped to the west of

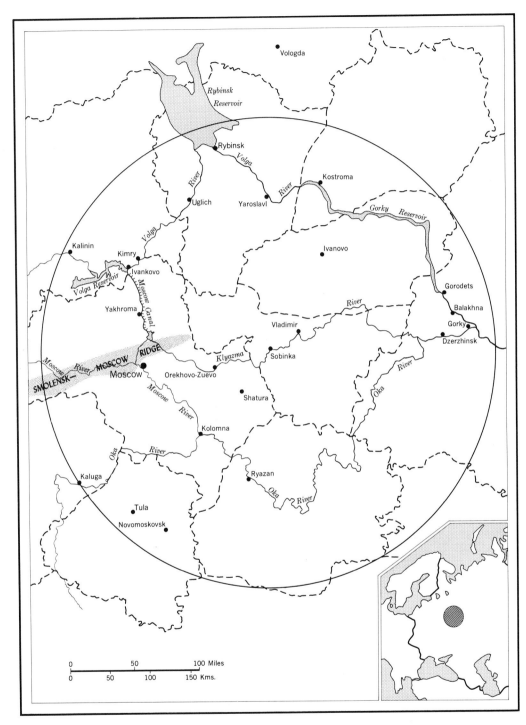

Figure 2-2 The Central Industrial Region.

Moscow along the eastern flanks of the Central Russian Uplands. The entire area has been glaciated, but only the northern half has been affected by the most recent glacial advance and today displays the features of continental glaciation. The so-called Smolensk-Moscow Ridge, running from west-southwest to east-northeast just north of the city of Moscow, is the terminal moraine that marks the southern limits of the most recent glaciation. North of this line the drainage is universally poor, and lakes and swamps abound. The drainage is poor in the southeast, also, along the very flat floodplains of the Oka River and its tributaries. The area is best drained in its southwestern portion where the bulge of the Central Russian Uplands has elevated the surface slightly and induced enough stream erosion to produce a rolling topography.

The Central Industrial Region lies in a cool, humid climate similar to that of southern Canada with relatively short summers and long, cold winters. The precipitation is modest, being somewhere between 20 and 25 inches per year, but the cool temperatures limit evaporation and make for effective dampening of the soil. Such conditions have been conducive to the growth of a forest vegetation. This is largely an area of mixed forest, with coniferous trees predominating in the north and deciduous trees predominating in the south. The forest vegetation and abundant soil moisture have led to a podzolization of the soil which has leached away much of the mineral content and has added only a minimum of organic matter. The resultant gray-brown forest soils are rather low in fertility, although they can be made to be quite productive under the correct adaptations of crops and farming methods and generous applications of fertilizers.

Agriculture A general farming has developed that in the past has been more subsistence than commercial, although this is gradually changing. Flax, being well adapted to cool, moist conditions and acidic soils, is the chief cash crop, and this region,

together with the European West, is the main area of flax growing in the country. Potatoes occupy more acreage, however, and serve both as a staple food and as a base for ethyl alcohol for the chemical industry. The Russians use the potato for everything from drinking to riding! Vodka is made from potatoes, and synthetic tires are made from potato alcohol.

The small hardy grains, rye, barley, and oats, and a variety of hay crops, take up most of the rest of the cultivated land. Dairying and grazing of livestock for meat are important, utilizing fairly good pastures during most of the summer and hay in the winter. Dairying is particularly developed in the cooler, moister areas in the north and around the larger cities. The meat supply of the area has recently been increased by a great expansion in hog and poultry raising, utilizing garbage and waste produce from canneries, potato alcohol distilleries, and the like. A variety of fruits and vegetables are raised, particularly around the larger cities to serve the urban markets. In general, farming improves from north to south in the region as the climate becomes a little milder and the soil improves.

Minerals Mineral resources as a basis for industrialization in the Central Industrial Region largely are lacking. The most important mineral resource in the area is the brown coal of the so-called Moscow Coal Basin, which provides fuel for heating and electrical generation, but which is not of coking quality and cannot be used in metallurgical industries. In spite of its low grade, local demand for the coal is so great that the Moscow Basin ranks fourth among producing basins in the U.S.S.R., annually producing between 9 and 10 per cent of the country's coal.

Next in importance are the iron ore deposits in the south around the city of Tula, that, however small, were the basis for the development of the first iron industry in the Russian Empire in the eighteenth century and which still support some iron and steel industries in the cities of Tula and Lipetsk. The vast iron ore deposits outside of this region to the south in the oblasts of Kursk and Belgorod may revive this steel industry in the near future and raise it to heights never known before, but this iron ore lies in another region and will have to be shipped into the Central Industrial Region.

Other than low-grade coal and minor deposits of iron ore, about the only mineral resources are various type of building stones and clays and scattered deposits of phosphate rock, which are becoming important in the agricultural fertilizer industry and in certain chemical industries. Such resources cannot explain the growth of this area into the most urbanized and industrialized region of the Soviet Union which contains approximately 10 per cent of the population of the country and produces approximately 20 per cent of the country's industrial output. We must turn to economic considerations of market, labor, early start, central position, and the like for an explanation of this industrialization.

Urban Growth and Industrialization

Located in the forest zone among the headwaters of the great Volga River system, the Central Industrial Region enjoyed a somewhat strategic position with regard to water routes and to defense from the Tatar hordes to the south. It thereby got an early start as a center of relatively dense population, which in the seventeenth and eighteenth centuries provided the basis for the beginning of industrialization in the form of home industry. Thus the emergence of this region as the most important industrial area in the country was prompted by an early concentration of people that provided both labor and market and that accumulated capital for the basis of a growing economy.

Larger towns grew up early on the main river routes along the headwaters of the Volga. Northwest of Moscow, at a strategic point of navigation on the Volga, the old city of Tver, now named Kalinin, during the thirteenth and fourteenth centuries challenged the position of Moscow for supremacy over the central part of the Russian Plain. About 150 miles northeast of Moscow a string of cities along the Volga River early grew into a major manufacturing district. Here lie the old cities of Yaroslavl, Kostroma, Ivanovo, and many lesser towns. Farther down the river to the southeast the large industrial city of Gorky, the old city of Nizhny Novgorod, grew up at the junction of the Volga and its main right-bank tributary, the Oka.

A string of lesser cities has grown up along the Oka. Cities such as Ryazan and Kolomna date back to medieval times. Today they perform important functions in industry, commerce, and government, but none of them has reached the size or preeminence of the cities along the Volga.

It is between the Volga River and its tributary, the Oka, however, that the greatest urban development has taken place. Cities grouped around Moscow extend in two lines eastward along two minor streams, the Moscow River, which flows through the city of Moscow and joins the Oka at Kolomna, and the Klyazma River, which flows eastward north of the city of Moscow.

A smaller concentration of urban settlements has developed in the iron and phosphate ore district about 100 miles south of Moscow around the city of Tula.

Thus the urbanization of the area proceeded from several positions: from the city of Kalinin in the northwest, from the concentration of cities along the Volga to the northeast, from the port and industrial center of Gorky at the most important river junction, from a central position along the minor streams around Moscow, and from Tula in the south. Gradually the area between these centers has filled in with urban settlements until today there is a close concentration of cities throughout the region that distinguishes it from its surroundings.

Industrialization began with the textile industries, primarily in Moscow and in the cities to the northeast along the Volga. Very early the city of Ivanovo became known as the "Manchester of Russia" because of its concentration on cheap cotton textiles. At first the cotton textile industry in Russia was largely dependent on imports of raw cotton. As late as 1928, over half the raw cotton used in the Soviet Union was supplied by imports from Egypt, India, and the United States. Since then cotton growing in Soviet Middle Asia and Transcaucasia has been expanded to almost entirely meet the needs of the country. Although textile plants have been built in the cotton-growing areas, the Central Industrial Region still produces almost 80 per cent of the cotton textiles in the U.S.S.R.

The manufacture of linen, based on locally grown flax, also became important in this region, particularly in the city of Kostroma. Russia has always led the world in flax production, and Kalinin Oblast northwest of Moscow raises more flax than any other political unit in the Soviet Union.

Later, with the development of the iron and steel industry around Tula, then in the Urals, and finally in the eastern Ukraine, the machine-building industries got started in the Central Industrial Region. Moscow became the primary center for this industry, but many other cities shared in it and some of them came to concentrate heavily on one particular item. Kolomna became known for its manufacture of railroad locomotives, and Kalinin for the manufacture of railroad rolling stock. Gorky, the most important port on the Volga, became the center of the ship-building industry and then later of the automobile industry. Yaroslavl, upstream from Gorky, in the 1930's became the center of the new synthetic rubber industry.

At the same time that the textile and machine-building industries were developing, of course, the whole range of food-processing industries were growing to serve the large urban markets. These are dispersed throughout most of the cities, but are concentrated somewhat in intermediate-sized cities in the better farming regions of the south.

At present the fastest growing group of industries in the Central Industrial Region are the chemical industries, which until recently have been based primarily on potato and grain alcohol and on local phosphate deposits. In the last few years a rapid shift to the utilization of natural gas and by-product gases of oil refining, which are being piped into this area from the south and east in ever-increasing quantities, has greatly speeded their development.

So far, among industries of the Central Industrial Region the textile industries still occupy first place, in terms of workers employed. The textile industries employ 28 per cent of all factory workers, and machine construction and metalworking employ 21 per cent. In Moscow Oblast in 1956 workers were employed as is shown in Table 2–1.

Table 2–1   Workers Employed by Industry in Moscow Oblast in 1956, in Per Cents of Total

Industry	Per Cent of All Workers
Textiles	30.2
Machine construction and metalworking	29.8
Construction materials	6.6
Chemicals	5.7
Woodworking	2.2
Food	2.2
Peat	2.1
Electric generation and heat	0.9
Heavy metallurgy	0.8
Leather working, furs, and shoes	0.7
Other	18.8

Source: Voprosy geografii, Vol. 49, 1960, p. 21.

Textiles are most dominant in some of the intermediate and smaller sized cities. In Moscow itself they occupy a much less significant position, although Moscow produces more textiles than does any other city. The industrial structure of Moscow is approximately one-third machine construction and metalworking and one-sixth each of heavy metallurgy, chemicals, textiles, and food processing. Chemical and metallurgical industries usually require far fewer workers for a given value added by manufacture than do such industries as textiles and food processing. Thus, when the industries are ranked according to numbers of workers, the role of heavy industries is minimized in comparison to light industries.

The Central Industrial Region is credited with almost one-fourth of all the industrial output of the U.S.S.R. and the city of Moscow alone with approximately 8 per cent.

Transportation

Since both the industry and the concentrated population of the Central Industrial Region depend on large imports of raw materials and foodstuffs from other parts of the country, the transportation system is all impor-

tant to the area. It focuses on Moscow in a radial pattern from all other parts of the Union. Many of the finished products of manufacturing likewise are shipped out of this area to all parts of the country, and these, too, have fostered a close network of transportation lines. Although the rivers were the primary means of transport when this area was emerging in the Middle Ages, today the railroads have greatly superseded the streams in total traffic. As in most parts of the Soviet Union, the railroads in the Central Industrial Region handle over 80 per cent of incoming and outgoing freight. True, the Volga River is the most heavily traversed river in the Soviet Union, but we must remember that in the Moscow area it is closed by ice at least 5 months of the year. Also, river traffic is slow and is economical only with regard to the handling of bulky, low-cost goods. Lumber, coal, petroleum, and grain make up the bulk of

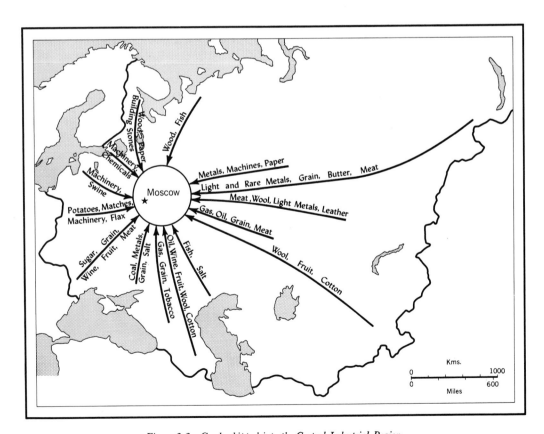

Figure 2-3 Goods shipped into the Central Industrial Region.

water shipments, and much of these commodities is brought in by rail.

The railways must bring in cotton and wool from the southeast; grain, meat, butter, and milk from the east; timber and fish from the north; machine tools and finished products from the Baltic Republics to the northwest; and sugar, grain, meat, coal, and steel from the south in the Ukraine. They must carry out a great variety of finished products in all directions.

Highways serve simply to supplement the role of the railroads; intercity truck traffic is not well developed in the Soviet Union. The average length of truck hauls is about eight miles, indicating that trucks serve only in distributing produce once it is brought into the city by rail.

To supplement the railroads, pipelines to carry oil and gas from the Caucasus, from the Ukraine, and from the Volga regions are being constructed into the Central Industrial Region. As the fuel balance shifts during the next 15 years from one predominantly of coal to one predominantly of oil and gas, pipelines will become of increasing importance.

Water Construction Projects Although river traffic's share of total traffic has been decreasing, river traffic has been increasing

Figure 2-4 Boats on the Moscow River outside the Ukraine Hotel in Moscow. The river has been canalized for traffic and lined with granite blocks within the city of Moscow. Many wide bridges span its meander loops. Photograph by the author.

through the years, and during the Soviet period improvements to navigation, which also serve other functions, have been made on the Volga and its tributary streams. The main obstacle to navigation on the Volga, other than ice, was its large seasonal fluctuation in flow, with floods in spring and shoals in late summer and fall. The small Moscow River was not navigable for boats of appreciable size.

To provide Moscow with a navigable waterway, the Moscow Canal was completed in 1937. It joins the Moscow River in Moscow, through a system of eight locks, with the Volga 128 kilometers to the north. A dam with a hydroelectric power plant of 30,000 kilowatts capacity was constructed on the Volga River near Ivankovo, which raised the water level on the Volga as far as 100 kilometers above the city of Kalinin to form the Volga Reservoir. One third of the water collected in the reservoir is used to feed the Moscow Canal, and the rest goes down the Volga into the Uglich Reservoir. The Uglich dam and power plant, with a capacity of 110,000 kilowatts, was put in operation in 1940. In 1941 the Rybinsk Reservoir was formed by two dams on the Volga and its tributary, the Sheksna. With a surface area of 4550 square kilometers, it was the largest man-made body of water in the world at the time. The power plant at Rybinsk (Shcherbakov), with a capacity of 330,000 kilowatts, provides electricity to Moscow, Yaroslavl, and Kalinin Oblasts.

These reservoirs have regulated the flow of the upper Volga and have supplied additional water to the Moscow River via the Moscow Canal to provide a deep-water route for navigation from the city of Moscow to the Volga River. The reservoirs and the canal also have assured recreational facilities and a domestic water supply for the city of Moscow, which before the digging of the canal drank about half of the Moscow River. The deepened channel of the Moscow River meanders through Moscow between granite-lined embankments and landscaped parks. Pleasure craft make regular runs between river stations which in most cases consist of old double-decked river boats that have been lashed securely to the river bank and converted into combination restaurants and dance halls. If one desires, he can spend a weekend making a round trip up the Moscow Canal to Kimry. The locks along the way have been constructed to blend esthetically with the landscape.

In 1955 the Gorky Sea, 420 kilometers long, was formed by the dam at Gorodets 55 kilometers upstream from Gorky. Its power plant, with a capacity of 400,000 kilowatts, supplies electricity to the cities of Gorky and Moscow as well as to Gorky and Ivanovo Oblasts. The construction of larger dams downstream from Gorky has enhanced navigation all along the Volga. With the opening of the Volga-Don Canal near Volgograd in 1952, the waters of the Volga were united with the traffic of the open sea, so the Volga River system no longer ends in a dead end in the Caspian. Moscow is now connected to the Azov, Black, and Caspian Seas in the south and, through older canal systems, lakes, and rivers, to the Baltic and the White Seas in the north. Hence, the Russians' references to Moscow as the "Port of Five Seas."

Cities

Moscow   Moscow is the metropolis of the Soviet Union. Besides serving as the governmental and cultural center of the U.S.S.R. and the R.S.F.S.R., it is the country's largest industrial producer. The census of January 15, 1959 showed that it had a population of 5,046,000. Since that date the population has increased, through normal growth and through the annexation of suburban territory, to 7,200,000. Since Moscow is the nerve center of the entire country, it will be described in considerable detail. The city will be discussed as an example of both the prototype and the ultimate in city planning and development in the Soviet Union.

The city of Moscow is roughly circular with streets and railways radiating outward in all directions from the center and crossing circular boulevards and railways in an ever-widening pattern. Its form reflects the historical process of city building throughout much of old Russia. The kremlin, or citadel, erected in 1147, was a construction of high walls along the bank of the Moscow River surrounding an area of perhaps three or four blocks which contained all the important governmental and religious buildings as well as most of the individual dwellings at the time (see frontispiece). As the city grew, new walls were constructed around successive peripheries of the expanding city to defend it from marauding nomads from the south and east.

The present Moscow Kremlin walls of weathered red brick date back to the fifteenth century. Early in the sixteenth century the so-called White Wall was constructed, delineating the boundaries of the city, and later in the sixteenth century, after Tatar attacks, another rampart of wood and earth was built around the periphery of the city. Since then the city has far outgrown the area enclosed within these walls and has outgrown the function that the walls served, but the imprint of the walls remains in the present street pattern. In 1943, a Ten-Year Plan was launched to revamp the city of Moscow, and all the old walls, except for the Kremlin walls, were pulled down, and the areas they occupied were used for the construction of wide, circular boulevards. The outermost of these boulevards, which lies a little more than a mile from the Kremlin, is called "Sadovaya Ulitsa," or "Garden Street," after the old earthen wall that preceded it. The squares that are formed where the radiating streets cross the circular streets still are known by the names of gates; reminders that previously these streets passed through gates in the walls of the city.

Between this simple lattice of intersecting radial and circular main streets lies a maze of narrow, crooked, discontinuous secondary streets reminiscent of the old cities of western Europe. They stand in great contrast to boulevards such as Sadovaya Ulitsa, whose

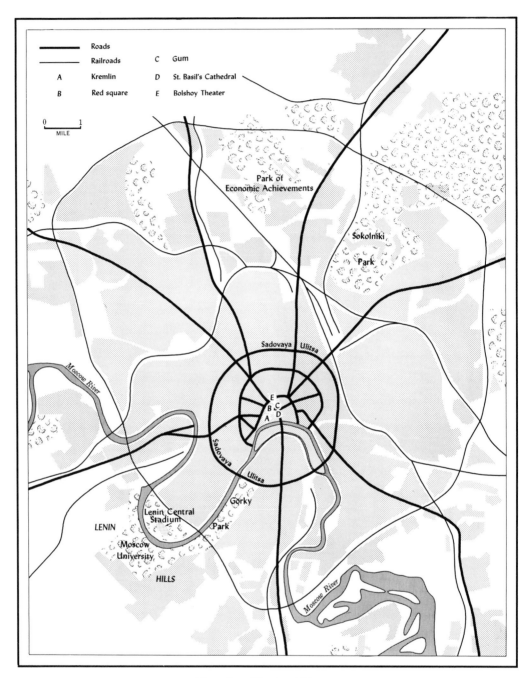

Figure 2-5   The city of Moscow.

broad expanse of unmarked lanes is bewildering in its immenseness to the few buses, trucks, and taxis that wander upon it, not to mention the poor pedestrian who must plan his crossing well to seek islands of refuge from wildly careening occasional vehicles. To add to the confusion, small and large streets alike typically change names every block or so!

Farther from the center of the city, beyond

Sadovaya Ulitsa, is a circular railway that completely encircles Moscow and eliminates train traffic from the heart of the city. Several train stations are located along the circular railway at the ends of major rail lines coming into the area from various parts of the country. Train traffic terminates at these stations, and communication with the central part of the city is made by subway, which now is a well-developed system of three branching lines diametrically crossing under the city and intersecting with a line that encircles the city.

A belt highway 109 kilometers long, now under construction around Moscow, approximately marks the new city limits. Beyond this a so-called "green belt" approximately 6 miles wide has been preserved from agricultural and industrial use. Primarily wooded with pines and birch trees, this green belt contains residential suburbs and dachas, or summer homes, of people living in Moscow. Almost 1 million people live within its confines. This belt is under the jurisdiction of Moscow Oblast, but two main airports lying beyond it, as well as various water supply and sewage disposal systems, have been placed under the jurisdiction of the city of Moscow. The city of Moscow is under the direct jurisdiction of the Russian Republic, of which it is the capital, and not under Moscow Oblast.

In the center of Moscow, the 64 acres of land within the triangular-shaped Kremlin are covered with governmental palaces, onion-domed cathedrals, and museums. Many of the streets around Red Square outside the Kremlin also are lined with government buildings, historical museums, and hotels. Across Red Square to the east of the Kremlin the block-long state department store, GUM, with its high-arched glass ceiling, houses two floors of individual bazaar-like stalls.

Down the hill toward the river from Red Square stands conspicuously the brightly painted baroque onion-domed spires of St. Basil's Cathedral. A short distance to the north of the Kremlin is the Bolshoy Theater, or large theater, the Malyy Theater, or small theater, and the Hall of Columns, which is now used for important court trials. Not far away is the Lenin Library, which is perhaps the largest library in the world, containing some 18 million volumes. Several art museums round out the major buildings in the civic center.

Figure 2-6   Traffic on the unmarked lanes along a broad section of Sadovaya Ulitsa in Moscow.   Courtesy of Robert H. Dawson.

Figure 2-7   Red Square.   Saint Basil's Cathedral in the background.   The block-long building on the left is GUM department store, and on the right is the Kremlin.   Notice the line of people waiting to enter the Lenin Mausoleum outside the Kremlin wall.   Photograph by the author.

Figure 2-8   The interior of GUM (State Department Store).   Two floors of bazaar stalls are enclosed by a high arched glass roof.   Courtesy of Lois Barland.

In the southwestern portion of the city, where the Moscow River cuts through the so-called Lenin Hills, stands the University of Moscow with its magnificent central building rising to a height of 32 stories. Across the river from the University is the new Central Lenin Stadium and other facilities forming a complete sports area within one of the loops of the Moscow River. This southwestern portion of the city is the newer, more sought-after residential area, known as

Figure 2-9   The main building of the University of Moscow.   Photograph by the author.

Figure 2-10   The main auditorium in the University of Moscow.   Photograph by Lois Barland.

the Lenin Hills, although it is indeed about as flat as the rest of the city. About the only topographic feature of any note is the high bank along the western side of the Moscow River which rises perhaps 200 feet above the level of the water. Eventually many of the embassies of foreign countries will be relocated in new buildings in this area from the ancient structures that they now occupy, which are scattered about the central portion of the city.

Beginning about a mile and a half south of the Kremlin and stretching for another mile and a half along the river is Gorky Park, which at present is the most highly developed park within the city. Here there are all sorts of sports facilities, theaters, outdoor bandshells, areas for chess and other games, a huge ferris wheel, and many other items. And, as in all the parks of the Soviet Union, there are many billboards and banners proclaiming the goals and ideals of the Soviet system and loudspeakers adding to the din, exhorting people to produce to their utmost. In the north-northeast part of the city lies Sokolniki Park, site of the American Exhibition in 1959, and, to the northwest of that, the Park of Economic Achievements.

The Park of Economic Achievements is a large area that has been set aside for the permanent display of agricultural and industrial products of the various republics in the Soviet Union. Each Union Republic has a large pavilion that houses the major products produced in that republic. In addition, such organizations as the Academy of Sciences have pavilions, and a large building serves for the Soviet Union as a whole.

All the parks are minutely landscaped

Figure 2-11   View from the top of Moscow University. Formal gardens in foreground and Central Lenin Stadium across Moscow River in background. Photograph by the author.

Figure 2-12   In the Park of Economic Achievements on the north side of Moscow.   The ice cream vendor is a common sight on Soviet streets.   The elaborate fountain in the background spews water from fifteen statues representing the fifteen Union Republics.   Photograph by the author.

Figure 2-13   The pavilion of the Uzbek S.S.R. in the Park of Economic Achievements.   Cotton-picking machines in the foreground signify the main product of the Republic. Photograph by the author.

and neatly kept. Formal gardens seem to be a fetish with the Russians. They are found not only in parks but about many public buildings. The formal gardens surrounding the University of Moscow are outstanding. Perhaps part of the painstaking care of these gardens is explained by the fact that many old or unskilled people are kept busy by digging at the flowers in these parks. Thus the Soviets are able to boast that there is no unemployment.

The Moscow subways also are something at which to marvel. They are truly outstanding among the subways of the world, in regard both to splendor and cleanliness and to service. The Soviets seem to have put their hearts and souls into the construction of a monumental showpiece in the form of a 40-mile labyrinth of passages and 70 stations deep beneath the city. Extensive use has been made of statuary, chandeliers, mosaics, marble, porcelain, bronze, and stain-

Figure 2-14   An open-air restaurant in the Uzbek pavilion in the Park of Economic Achievements, Moscow.   Photograph by the author.

Figure 2-15   The Kremlin at Gorky on the confluence of the Oka and the Volga.   Novosti Press.

less steel to express the motif of each station. The escalators leading down to the subways themselves are awe inspiring. Plunging at inclines of 45 degrees, they are so long that one cannot see one end from the other. Hundreds of thousands of people are moved by subway and bus in the city every day, for there is very little privately owned vehicular traffic. Nearly any time of day the public transportation facilities are jammed to capacity by commuters. A surprising number of taxis augment the mass transportation facilities.

Gorky Next in size of population is the city of Gorky at the important river confluence of the Oka and the Volga. Gorky, on January 15, 1959, was listed as having 942,000 people. This, together with population of several important industrial suburbs, brings the Gorky metropolitan area to third place in total population in the Soviet Union, after Moscow and Leningrad. However, the population of 942,000 people for the city of Gorky alone falls behind that of Kiev and Baku.

Gorky is the automotive center of the

Soviet Union and has been dubbed the "Detroit of the Soviet Union." Approximately 50 per cent of the industrial production in Gorky is in the machine-building industries, which besides automobiles include ship building, aircraft industries, and many other machine-building industries. The other 50 per cent of Gorky's industry is made up of food and diversified industries. Southwest of Gorky, the suburban city of Dzerzhinsk, with a 1959 population of 163,000, is a new city concentrating on chemical industries, particularly on the production of synthetic rubber and synthetic and artificial fibers. Northwest of Gorky is the suburban city of Balakhna, a paper-processing city, which, among other things, produces all the newsprint for *Pravda,* the leading newspaper in the Soviet Union.

During Russian Empire days, Nizhny Novgorod was known for its annual fairs that attracted business people from all over Russia. Since the death of the writer Maxim Gorky, the city has been renamed after him. His life was linked to the city along the Volga much as Mark Twain's life was linked to Hannibal, Missouri, along the Mississippi.

Yaroslavl The third most populous city in the Central Industrial Region is Yaroslavl, with a 1959 population of 407,000. This is the major city within the group of cities that were established very early along the Volga, northeast of Moscow. It has maintained its supremacy among this group of cities concentrated on the textile industries, and in recent years has grown steadily under the impetus of the synthetic rubber industry. Yaroslavl has been dubbed the "Akron of the Soviet Union" because it is the leading tire-producing city in the country. It is surpassed in its per cent of population working in industry only by cities that are highly concentrated on the mining of some important mineral, such as Baku in Transcaucasia. In other words, it is the most intensively industrialized of cities in the Soviet Union whose industrialization depend on manu-

facturing. Approximately 60 per cent of the gainfully employed in Yaroslavl actually work in factories. Such percentages are much higher than anything experienced in the United States because the tertiary activities, the service industries, so important in the United States, are very little developed in the Soviet Union.

Tula Fourth in population within the Central Industrial Region is the city of Tula, which in 1959 had a population of 316,000. Tula is the old city to the south of Moscow, bordering on the rich agricultural area of the Central Black Earth Region, which is located among some minor iron ore deposits and which first developed iron and steel industries. Today it still is an important center for heavy metallurgy, but it is not of first-rank importance in that respect. About 65 per cent of its production is in machine-building industries of various sorts, and much of the rest is in heavy metallurgy. A large iron and steel plant is now under construction to utilize iron ore from the Kursk Magnetic Anomaly to the south. Just to the southeast of Tula is the relatively new important chemical city of Novomoskovsk, which until 1961 was named Stalinogorsk. It is located near phosphate rock deposits, and has developed these as the raw materials for a superphosphate industry for agricultural fertilizers and various other products.

Ivanovo Fifth in size of population is the city of Ivanovo northeast of Moscow in the same general region with Yaroslavl, which in 1959 had a population of 335,000. As has been mentioned, Ivanovo early became a center of the cotton-textile industry and was dubbed the "Manchester of the Soviet Union." It still is the city whose industry is most highly concentrated on cotton textiles; however, its total production of cotton textiles is not as great as that of Moscow.

Kalinin Sixth in size is Kalinin, on the upper Volga northwest of Moscow, which in 1959 had a population of 261,000. As has been mentioned before, Kalinin is the old city of Tver, which during the thirteenth to fifteenth centuries vied with Moscow for supremacy over the central Russian plain. It early became an important center for textile industries, and more recently an important center for the manufacture of railroad rolling stock.

Ryazan   To the southeast of Moscow lies the city of Ryazan, one of the old centers on the Oka River, which was the frontier of settlement during the time of the Tatar hordes. Many times it withstood the first onslaught of the Tatars in their punitive expeditions from Sarai to Moscow. Today, with a population of 214,000, Ryazan is a city of diversified industries, with some emphasis on forging equipment, heavy machine tools, and calculating machines. At present it seems to be experiencing a spurt in industrialization with the construction of an electric steel furnace, a rayon plant using the viscose process, and an oil refinery to process crude oil from the Tatar A.S.S.R. to the east.

Rybinsk and Kostroma   Northeast of Moscow are two more important old cities on the Volga, Rybinsk and Kostroma. Rybinsk, with a population of 182,000, sits at the site of the dam that forms the Rybinsk Reservoir. It is especially known as a ship building and woodworking center. Known alternately as Shcherbakov, the city reverted to its previous name, Rybinsk, in 1957. Kostroma, the most concentrated center in the Soviet Union of the linen textile industry, in 1959 had a population of 172,000.

Other Cities   In the vicinity of Moscow, particularly to the east, are many industrial cities with populations between 50,000 and 150,000 which concentrate on textile industries, machine-building industries, and chemicals. Largest among these is the medieval city of Vladimir. Three newer cities that are approaching Vladimir in size and that are heavily concentrated on chemicals are Shatura, Orekhovo-Zuevo, and Yakhroma. Cities of this class also are concentrated in the important textile region along the Volga northeast of Moscow and along the Oka River between Moscow and Gorky.

Kolomna, at the confluence of the Moscow and Oka Rivers, already has been mentioned for its railroad locomotive industry. This industry was established by French capital in the latter half of the nineteenth century, and for a long time Kolomna was the only city in Russia producing locomotives.

Reading List

Saushkin, Yu. G., *Moskva*, 1955, 191 pp. (in Russian).

Moskva i podmoskovnye rayony, *Voprosy geografii*, No. 51, Moscow, 1961, 220 pp. (in Russian).

Tsentralno-promyshlennyy rayon, *Voprosy geografii*, No. 49, Moscow, 1960, 157 pp. (in Russian).

The Central Black Earth Region

Region	Area (sq mile)	Population	People (sq mile)[a]	% Urban[a]
Orel Oblast	9,700	929,000	97	24
Kursk Oblast	11,600	1,483,000	129	20
Belgorod Oblast	10,600	1,226,000	117	18
Lipetsk Oblast	9,400	1,141,000	122	30
Voronezh Oblast	20,400	2,369,000	117	35
Tambov Oblast	13,400	1,549,000	117	26
Penza Oblast	16,800	1,510,000	90	33
Mordovian A.S.S.R.	10,200	1,000,000[b]	99	18
Tula Oblast	6,000[c]	940,000[c]	193	60
Total	108,100[d]	12,147,000[d]		

[a] All figures are for entire regions.

[b] Population of entire region, although northwest corner lies within circle defining Central Industrial Region.

[c] Estimated population and area of portion of oblast lying within the Central Black Earth Region.

[d] Does not include southern fringe of Ryazan Oblast, which lies within the Central Black Earth Region.

3

The Central Black Earth Region

Southward, beyond the circle delimiting the Central Industrial Region, a rapid change takes place from a northern area that is predominantly urban to a southern one that is predominantly rural. The rural region to the south, known as the Central Black Earth Region, is in many ways analogous to the Middle West in the United States. It is one of the better farming regions in the country; on one side it borders on the main industrial belt of the country, and on all other sides it merges imperceptibly with adjoining regions. Although it is a traditional region in the minds of the Russian people, they would be hard put to define its boundaries precisely. As defined by Russian geographers it lies wholly within the Russian Republic, its southwestern boundary being the political boundary of the Ukraine. But as far as climate, soil, natural vegetation, and land use are concerned, the area continues westward into the Ukraine. On the east the region merges imperceptibly with the middle Volga Valley.

In deference to tradition, the boundary on the south will be taken as the republic boundary, and the whole Ukraine will be considered later. On the east, again traditional Russian boundaries will be accepted between the Central Black Earth and Volga regions. This puts Penza Oblast in the Central Black Earth Region, which is quite in keeping with its agricultural character but ignores the fact that the industries of Penza Oblast are more directly tied to the economy of the Volga Region. In the north, traditional Russian boundaries have been ignored in the definition of the Central Industrial Region, and a line has been drawn to separate a predominantly urban area from a predominantly rural one. The Central Black Earth Region thus contains the southern half of Tula Oblast and the southern fringe of Ryazan Oblast. As is shown on the summary sheet at the beginning of this chapter, the region here defined contains an area of approximately 108,000 square miles with a population of around 12 million people who are predominantly Russian. Its outstanding characteristic is its relatively dense population, more than 100 people per square mile, 70 per cent or more of whom are rural. A prime agricultural area that has not undergone extensive industrialization, the rural-urban ratio has not changed significantly since the Revolution.

Agricultural Resources and Development

Topographically the Central Black Earth Region lies in much the same position as does the Central Industrial Region. The western half of the area, on the Central

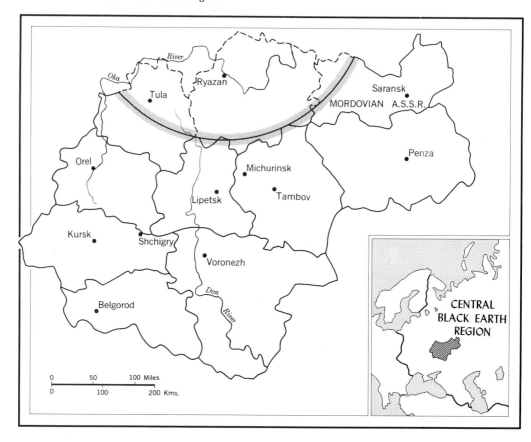

Figure 3-1   The Central Black Earth Region.

Russian Uplands, is a stream-dissected roll-ing plain, whereas the eastern half is the flatter Oka-Don lowland, sometimes known as the Tambov Plain.   The Oka River drains this plain to the northeast and the Don River drains it to the south.

Climatically the Central Black Earth Re-gion is a little warmer and a little drier than the Central Industrial Region.   The seem-ingly small gradient in moisture toward the southeast induces an all-significant change in natural vegetation and soil development. Much of the region lies in the belt of wooded steppe with its chernozem soils, hence its name.   The northwestern fringe, in Orel and Tula Oblasts, originally was covered by deciduous trees which were conducive to the development of a gray-brown forest soil.   The southeastern fringe, in Voronezh and Tam-bov Oblasts, was vegetated by steppe grasses

and contains the best chernozem soil.   In general, the drainage throughout the area is adequate.

During the Tartar dominance on the Russian plain much of the Central Black Earth Region was a no man's land between the Russian-dominated area around Moscow and the Tatar stronghold at Sarai on the lower Volga.   As the Tatar hold began to break, patricularly in the fifteenth to seven-teenth centuries, some of the bolder Russians escaped from the oppression of the Russian princes and migrated southward into what was then known as the "wild field" to either settle and cultivate the land or to band into seminomadic groups of horsemen to carry on forays against the Tatars, against Moscow, against the Turks to the south, and against the settlers in the area.   Hence in the fif-teenth to seventeenth centuries the Central

Black Earth Region served as a frontier land that was being reopened by settlers from the north, much as the Great Plains of the United States were opened by settlers from the east two centuries later. The physical environment and the mode of settlement in both was much the same.

The Don Cossacks, as the horsemen of the plains were known, worked hard, fought hard, and were game for any adventure. In attitudes and actions they much resembled the cowboys of the early days of the American West. Often they derived their livelihood by serving as a military arm to the Tsar in Moscow, from whose rule they had previously escaped, to bring some order to outlying regions where men lived by their own laws. During the eighteenth century the wild field disappeared; the Central Black Earth Region became a completely settled integral part of the Russian Empire, and the frontier moved southward, and the Cossacks with it, to the steppes of the Black Sea and the lower Don.

During the eighteenth and nineteenth centuries the Central Black Earth Region, being nearer to the populous center around Moscow than was the Ukraine to the southwest, became one of the most productive agricultural areas in the country with one of the densest rural populations. The peasants, as was the case throughout the Russian Empire, were serfs in a feudal system of land holding, a system which led to the neglect of the fertile soils, excessive erosion, and the ultimate near collapse of the rural economy. Thus, owing to overpopulation and a feudal land tenure system, one of the richest naturally endowed agricultural regions of the country remained an area of underdevelopment and rural poverty. Collectivization of the land under the Soviets thus far has shown little gain either in agricultural production or mode of life. Although the land is now held in large collective farms, most of the people have not been consolidated into larger villages or cities; they still live in their haphazardly scattered villages along muddy stream valleys. The typical rural dwelling

in the forests of the north is the log cabin *izba,* and in the steppes of the south the adobe *khata.* About the only change in dwelling type that has taken place thus far has been a gradual substitution of corrigated sheet metal roofs for the thatched roofs of yesteryear. Only since the accession of Khrushchev, with his interest in agriculture, has much official attention been paid to conservation methods in farming and the heavy use of fertilizers to increase yields per acre.

The Central Black Earth Region is an area of general farming, transitional between the potato, small grain, flax-growing area of the Central Industrial Region and the commercial wheat fields and sunflower fields of the steppes to the southeast. Wheat always has been produced in some quantity, but only in Voronezh Oblast does it occupy the largest portion of the cultivated land. The other small grains—oats, barley, and rye— are important throughout the region, particularly in the north. Potatoes are important in the northeast. The sunflower belt begins in the drier southeast and culminates in the steppes of the lower Don and North Caucasus. Sugar beets are the main cash crop in Kursk and Belgorod Oblasts in the southwest. In 1957 Belgorod Oblast provided a fifth of the sugar beets of the Russian Republic, and cash from sugar beets provided 37 per cent of the monetary income of collective farmers in the area. The sugar beet belt continues southwestward into the west-central Ukraine. Much of the hemp raised in the Soviet Union is raised in the Central Black Earth Region. Tambov Oblast is the principal producer of millet in the Soviet Union. Recently corn has been introduced, both for grain and for silage. The raising of dairy cattle, beef cattle, and hogs is very important. Until shortly after World War II, the experimental raising of kok-sagyz and tau-sagyz, two dandelion-like rubber-bearing plants, was being pushed very strongly in this region, but during the last decade little mention has been made of them.

The expansion of sugar beet and corn

growing is the most important trend in the agriculture of the region at the present time. Sugar beets are being extended to oblasts other than Kursk and Belgorod and are rapidly becoming the chief industrial crop. So far, much of the expansion of sugar beet growing has been at the expense of the growing of sunflowers or other technical crops, such as the makhorka, a low grade tobacco, even in the traditional makhorka growing region of Lipetsk Oblast, whereas the acreage in grain has remained much the same. The Seven-Year Plan calls for some reversal of this trend with a considerable increase in the growing and yield of oil crops for vegetable oils and the expansion of sugar beet growing at the expense of grain, which, since the initiation of the virgin lands program, is being grown over vast areas in western Siberia, northern Kazakhstan, and the Trans-Volga region. The Central Black Earth Region now plays only a secondary role in grain production. It is hoped that by means of heavy fertilization and better farming methods grain production in this area can be maintained at its present level and the acreage reduced. Corn, which yields more heavily than do the small grains, is being substituted more and more for the small grains.

Industrial Resources and Development

Thus far, the Central Black Earth Region has had little basis or little reason for industrial development. No rich coal basins underlie the area and no great rivers exist for harnessing. The development of local mineral resources so far has been limited primarily to the small deposits of iron ore in the Tula and Lipetsk areas. But these minor resources have long since been largely exhausted, and even the small steel plants at Tula and Lipetsk for a number of years have been securing the bulk of their iron ore from Krivoy Rog in the Ukraine. For future development the primary mineral resources will be the large iron ore deposit of the Kursk Magnetic Anomaly and the

sedimentary rocks themselves, which will provide an abundance of agricultural lime and phosphate and a variety of building materials, including cement.

The Kursk Magnetic Anomaly is a large body of iron-rich quartzites lying mainly in Belgorod and Kursk Oblasts. Reserves are now estimated at approximately 50 billion tons. About two thirds of the ore consists of magnetite quartzite which has an iron content of between 25 and 45 per cent; the other third has an iron content somewhere between 50 and 65 per cent. Much of the richer ore lies at depths of more than 500 meters and is covered by thick water-bearing strata. These conditions largely explain why the deposit has not been exploited thus far in spite of its strategic location between the Central Industrial Region and the heavy industry area in the eastern Ukraine. Toward the edges of the basin the ore is nearer the surface, and a few open-pit mines have been developed. The deeper ores are to be exploited during the seven-year plan by large-scale shaft mining which is to raise production by 1965 to about 20 million tons per year, an amount equal to nearly one fifth of the total iron ore production of the U.S.S.R. in 1960. In 1956 this region, together with small-scale mining around Tula and Lipetsk, produced only 1.8 million tons of iron ore. The "KMA" ore eventually will serve not only the needs of the Tula and Lipetsk plants, but also to the Donbass plants, to some extent. This will make rational use of railroad equipment by utilizing returning cars which have brought coal from the Donbass to the Tula and Lipetsk steel plants. Coal will be shipped northward and iron ore southward.

Both the Kursk and Belgorod regional economic councils have put forward plans for the development of iron and steel plants in their respective regions at strategic points where the movements of iron ore and coal cross. Water supply seems to be the critical item in these locations. Some planners have pointed out that construction of large iron and steel plants in these areas would leave important cities without an adequate water supply.

Other than the iron ore, about the only significant mineral deposit is the Belgorod chalk, which forms a prominent escarpment in Belgorod Oblast and provides the basis for an important cement industry. Belgorod Oblast, along with the city of Novorossiisk on the Caucasian coast of the Black Sea, provides much of the high-grade cement for distribution throughout the Soviet Union. Widespread deposits of limestone, which in some places contain a significant amount of phosphorus, also can be used for agricultural fertilizers and other chemicals.

Undoubtedly the greatest future resources for industrial development in the Central Black Earth Region are, first, its intermediate location on the dense network of railroads that run between the Central Industrial Region to the north and the heavy industries area of the Ukraine to the south, and second, its large rural population which represents a rich potential source of industrial labor supply. The greatest single drawback is the power shortage. At present no integrated electrical grid system exists; adequate electrification is limited to the oblast capitals where thermal plants fueled by Donets coal generate the power. This condition largely may be corrected by the completion of gas pipelines running through the area from the gas fields of the North Caucasus and the eastern Ukraine to the Central Industrial Region and the northwest. The Central Black Earth Region again benefits by its intermediate location between main suppliers and main consumers, and can tap these gas lines for part of the gas to fuel new thermal electric stations. Also, the gas provides the basis for the conversion of synthetic rubber and other chemical industries from their present vegetable bases and provides for the establishment of new chemical plants.

Compounding the fact that thus far the Central Black Earth Region has not industrialized to any great extent is the fact that much of the industrialization that has taken place has developed rather irrationally in light of the local resources and market. The manufacture of farm machinery, which would appear to be needed in the Central Black Earth Region more than any other kind of industry, is poorly developed. Lipetsk has a tractor plant, but it is still turning out clumsy caterpillar-type tractors although the need is primarily for wheel-type lighter tractors. The building-materials industry, in spite of its entirely adequate and well-distributed supply of raw materials, is inadequately developed and does not provide for all the region's requirements. The cement industry, for example, is too concentrated in Belgorod and Voronezh Oblasts, and should be more dispersed throughout the area. A rather large proportion of the industries that have been established in the largest oblast capitals depend entirely on materials from the outside and to a large extent export their products to regions outside the Central Black Earth Region. There is no industrial economic unity in the Central Black Earth Region.

With the development of the Kursk Magnetic Anomaly and its attendant establishment of large iron and steel plants at Tula and Lipetsk, the coming of natural gas to the region, and the utilization of the region's advantageous location and potential labor supply, the Central Black Earth Region may develop industrially very rapidly during the next couple of decades, and a continuous industrial belt may finally be established from the Central Industrial Region to the eastern Ukraine. So far there has been no announcement of a grand scheme to accomplish this, but the economic and cultural conditions appear to be ripe for such a development.

Cities

In general, the largest cities of the Central Black Earth Region are the capitals of the respective oblasts, and they serve the function primarily as regional centers providing governmental and commercial services. Although industrialization in general has not been great, at least one of the cities has become an industrial city, and other cities have developed particular types of industry. A consideration of the largest cities and their industries follows.

Voronezh Voronezh is the metropolis of the region with a population of 448,000. It has transcended its original role of governmental center and has become an industrial city in its own right. Half of its industry is concerned with the production of many types of machines, such as ore-concentration equipment, excavators, forge and press equipment, machine tools, grain-cleaning machines, small electric motors, radio and television sets, and machines and equipment for the food industry and the production of building materials. The city is probably better known, however, for its chemical industries, particularly the synthetic rubber industry and automobile tire industry. Voronezh early became established, along with Yaroslavl in the Central Industrial Region, as one of the main centers for the synthetic rubber industry. In Yaroslavl the industry was based on potato alcohol; in Voronezh it was based on grain alcohol. The rubber industry in Voronezh is now being converted to the use of natural gas as pipelines are being built through the area. The highly developed food industries are based on local raw materials: grain, sunflower seeds, and sugar beets. The processing of sugar is becoming more important as the growing of sugar beets is extended. Industries producing building materials also are important.

Penza Penza, with a population of 255,-000, is second in importance to Voronezh, both in population and in industrialization. Although Penza Oblast is included within the Central Black Earth Region, the industries of Penza are more oriented toward the needs of the Volga Valley. Approximately half of the industries of the city of Penza are concerned with the production of machines such as equipment for shipbuilding and the extraction and refining of petroleum,

chemical equipment, textile equipment, compressors, diesels, and various instruments. Paper manufacturing and food industries also are important.

Kursk Third in size is Kursk with a population of 205,000. It is primarily the governmental and commercial center of Kursk Oblast. The industries of Kursk are concentrated on machine building, chemicals, and food. Just to the east of Kursk is the smaller city of Shchigry whose industries are concentrated totally on chemicals, particularly superphosphate fertilizers, derived from phosphorite deposits in the vicinity.

Tambov Fourth in size is Tambov with a population of 172,000. Like Kursk, its industries are divided among machine building, chemicals, and food. The machine industries turn out equipment for sugar and alcohol plants and auto and tractor spare parts. The chemical industries furnish some rubber and asbestos materials for the lining of tractor and automobile engines and aniline dyes for textile factories. The food industries process local products such as sugar, alcohol, fruit, and tobacco.

Lipetsk Lipetsk has already been mentioned for its rejuvenated steel industry and the present construction of a super iron and steel plant, which will be one of the largest in the country. With a population of 157,000, Lipetsk is the most rapidly growing city in the Central Black Earth Region. It appears to be in the process of transformation from merely a regional center to a truly industrial city. Its industries are classified as about half heavy metallurgy and half machine building. Chemical and building material industries also are important. Among its machine industries, the caterpillar tractor plant is outstanding.

Orel In the northwestern part of the region, Orel, with a population of 150,000, is the governmental and commercial center for Orel Oblast. Its industries are rather diversified with about one third concentrating on machine building and one third on food.

Saransk In the northeast, Saransk, with a population of 91,000, is the capital of the Mordovian A.S.S.R. Its role as capital of the Autonomous Republic is its chief function. Its industries are concentrated on machine building, woodworking, and food. The Mordovians are a Finno-Ugrian group of people who now are somewhat outnumbered by Russians in their own Republic.

Michurinsk Lying just north of the midway point between Lipetsk and Tambov is the smaller city of Michurinsk, with a population of 81,000. It is primarily known as the home of Michurin, the "Soviet Luther Burbank." His experimental nurseries have developed special strains of plums, peaches, apples, and other fruits and vegetables. The diversified industries of Michurinsk include machine building, textiles, and food.

Belgorod In the south, Belgorod, with a population of 72,000, is the remaining oblast center. Two thirds of its industries are concerned with the building construction materials derived from the chalk escarpment in the vicinity. As has been pointed out, it is one of the main cement producing centers of the Soviet Union. Its other industries are primarily food processing.

The Povolzhye and Lower Don

Region	Area (sq mile)	Population	People (sq mile)[a]	% Urban[a]
Gorky Oblast (Eastern three-fifths)	17,200[b]	1,341,000[b]	127.2	52
Kirov Oblast (Southern half, including Kirov City)	23,900[b]	1,076,000[b]	40.4	37
Mari A.S.S.R.	9,100	648,000	72.3	28
Chuvash A.S.S.R.	7,100	1,098,000	156.4	24
Tatar A.S.S.R.	26,600	2,850,000	108.5	42
Ulyanovsk Oblast	14,600	1,117,000	77.7	36
Kuybyshev Oblast	21,000	2,258,000	109.0	62
Saratov Oblast	39,200	2,163,000	56.1	54
Volgograd Oblast	44,600	1,854,000	41.9	54
Astrakhan Oblast	17,200	702,000	41.3	52
Kalmyk A.S.S.R.	29,600	185,000	6.2	21
Rostov Oblast[c]	39,300	3,312,000	85.2	57
Total	289,400	18,604,000		

[a] All figures are for entire regions.

[b] Estimated population and area of portion of region lying within the Povolzhye.

[c] Rostov City and the coal-bearing area to the north of the city are included here for convenience, although economically they are closely tied to the Donets Basin in the eastern Ukraine.

4

The Povolzhye and the Lower Don

East of the Central Industrial Region and the Central Black Earth Region is an elongated area that stretches from the city of Gorky east and then south to the mouth of the Volga on the Caspian Sea, generally known as the Povolzhye, or "Along the Volga." Extending from the cool, humid forestland of the north to the hot, dry deserts of the Caspian, this region shows much variety in natural and cultural landscapes. But the region is held together by the great Volga River itself, the major navigational waterway in the Soviet Union, which exchanges the products of the different parts up and down the river. To the Povolzhye now must be added the lower Don, because the Volga-Don Canal, opened in 1952, links the lower Volga southwestward with the Sea of Azov. Thus the lower Don is now a vital part of the Volga waterway system.

Nationalities and Political Units

Politically this region includes the following oblasts and autonomous republics: Gorky Oblast east of the city of Gorky, Kirov Oblast south of and including the city of Kirov, the Mari A.S.S.R., the Chuvash A.S.S.R., the Tatar A.S.S.R., Ulyanovsk Oblast, Kuybyshev Oblast, Saratov Oblast, Volgograd Oblast, Astrakhan Oblast, the Kalmyk A.S.S.R., and Rostov Oblast.

The "ethnological museum" of the Middle Volga presents a political checker board of Russian oblasts and non-Russian autonomous republics. During the ninth to twelfth centuries, the Volga Bend area was settled by Bulgars, farmers and traders, Turkish in language and Moslem in religion. They had subdued earlier Finnish-speaking settlers, and all in turn were overwhelmed in the early thirteenth century by the Tatars. Finally, during the second half of the sixteenth century, the Russians gained control of the entire Volga, established scattered farming colonies and towns such as Samara and Saratov, and attempted to Russify their subject peoples. In the seventeenth century, the Mongol Kalmyks established themselves in the semidesert west of the Volga delta, and later German colonists centered on the Middle Volga around Saratov.

After the Revolution most of these non-Russian peoples were given political recognition as autonomous oblasts or autonomous republics within the Middle Volga Kray or Gorky Kray and eventually were elevated to the status of A.S.S.R. The Tatar A.S.S.R., formed in 1920, was one of the first autonomous republics in the country.

During World War II the Volga German and Kalmyk A.S.S.R.'s were abrogated, al-

Figure 4-1   The Povolzhye.

legedly for collaborating with the Germans, and their peoples were scattered throughout the Russian and Middle Asian Republics. In 1956 the Kalmyks were reinstated as an autonomous oblast within Stavropol Kray and very soon thereafter as an A.S.S.R.

Russians constantly have been moving into the non-Russian autonomous republics of the Volga region as well as into the Russian-dominated oblasts. This is particularly true in the larger cities where most of the industrialization is taking place. In the Tatar and Chuvash A.S.S.R.'s, the titular Turkic groups constitute about 50 and 80 per cent of the populations respectively. In the Mari A.S.S.R., the Mari, a Finno-Ugrian group, make up about 50 per cent of the total population. Much of the remaining population in these three republics is Russian.

Two other non-Russian autonomous republics lie just to the east of the region under consideration. The Bashkir A.S.S.R., peopled by a Turkic group, and the Udmurt A.S.S.R., peopled by a Finno-Ugrian group, traditionally are included in the region of the Urals. They might just as well be included with the other non-Russian republics in the Povolzhye, particularly now that the Volga-Urals oil fields, which overlap these regions, have somewhat united their economies. The Bashkir and Udmurt Republics still have strong economic ties with the Urals, however, and they do not touch on the Volga River, so until more justification is forthcoming for their inclusion in the Povolzhye, they shall continue to be grouped with the Urals.

Physical Landscape

Topographically the Povolzhye is divided into two parts, east and west, along the Volga River itself. Along the right bank, the west side, lie the so-called Volga Heights, which geologically are a counterpart of the Central Russian Uplands farther west, an old upwarp with some faulting. The Volga in its process of erosion has exposed different strata of sedimentary rocks, all dipping southwestward, and has adjusted its valley to follow along the strike of one of the hardrock layers. A cuesta of hard sandstone underlain by weaker limestone has been etched along the western bank of the river. In places the top of the escarpment stands as much as 500 feet above the river. The highest part of the cuesta lies within the Samara Bend near Kuybyshev where it is known as the Zhiguli Mountains. This spot has long been a haunt of people seeking recreation in the hilly wooded area surrounded on three sides by water. Although this is not a mountainous area, the topography is truly rugged, the edge of the cuesta being deeply dissected by steep, short tributaries which run down into the Volga. The sandstone uplands are forested primarily by coniferous trees whereas the ravines are clothed in a lighter green of deciduous trees. Before the construction of the Kuybyshev Dam, the short Usa River flowed northward through this narrow band of hills into the Volga. A favorite trip of young people was to leave Kuybyshev by rowboat, float downstream on the Volga to the point opposite the headwater of the Usa, carry their small boat up over the hills for a distance of approximately one mile, and then embark down the Usa back to the Volga and down the Volga again to Kuybyshev. This jaunt they called the "Round the World Cruise." The entire trip took about a fortnight. Now the Usa Valley is flooded by the great Kuybyshev Sea.

The left bank, or east side of the Volga, is almost the antithesis of the right bank. The left bank is a very flat marshy lowland, which represents the "slip-off slope" that the Volga River has leveled out in its process of shifting westward with the dip of the rocks. The contrast between the two sides of the river is greatest from Kazan to Volgograd and disappears both to the north and to the south. Between Volgograd and the Caspian the river flows through a flat desert plain, a part of the previous bed of the Caspian. To a lesser degree, the relation of topography to river and rock strata along the lower Don is a replica of the middle Volga.

Not only is the topography markedly different on the two sides of the Volga, but also the river seems to be something of a climatic divide. Apparently the extra elevation along the west side of the stream alters the air flow enough to produce additional precipitation and to reduce temperatures slightly, so that the upland on the west appears to be considerably more humid than

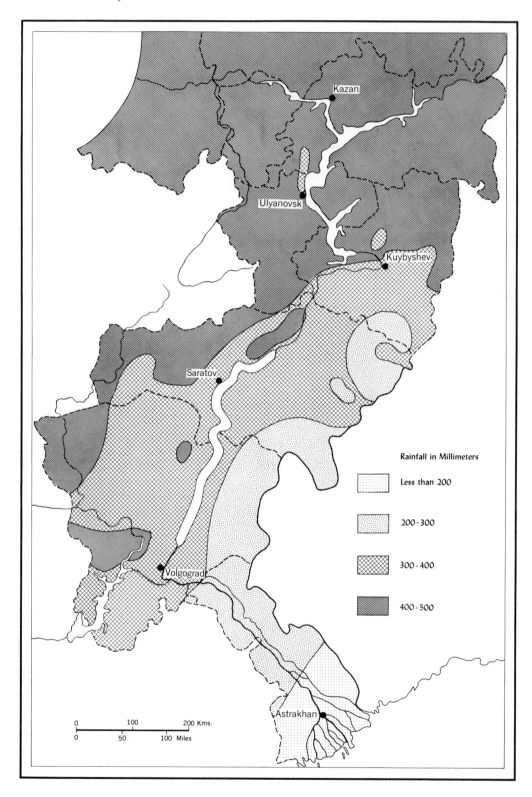

Rainfall in Millimeters

Less than 200

200 - 300

300 - 400

400 - 500

Figure 4-2   Annual precipitation in the Povolzhye.   After Lyalikov.

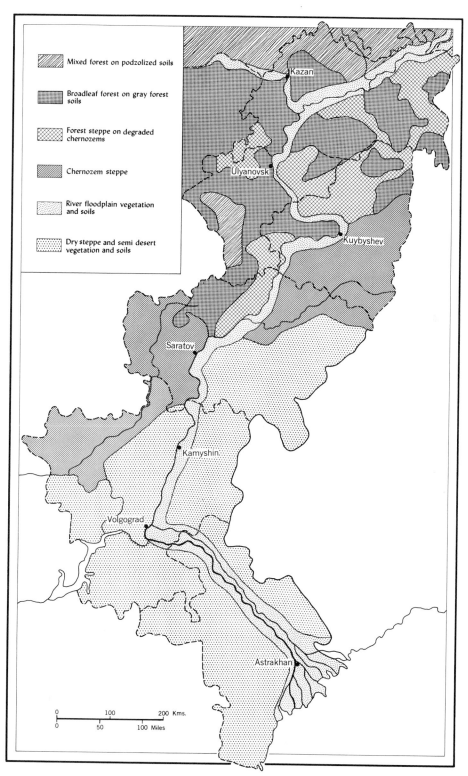

Figure 4-3 Natural vegetation and soil zones of the Povolzhye. After Cherdantsev.

Figure 4-4   Steppe lands and river breaks at a small river station along the lower Don.   Photograph by the author.

the lowland to the east. The forests, which in the north cover the entire width of the area under consideration, extend southward much farther along the west side of the river on the Volga Heights than they do on the east in the so-called Transvolga Meadows. East of the river and from Kuybyshev south, the forests have almost entirely disappeared and open steppeland is at hand. Thus the climate changes significantly in two directions in this region, from north to south and from west to east.

Cool, humid conditions in the north have been conducive to the growth of coniferous trees and the development of podzol soils in Kirov Oblast and in the Mari A.S.S.R. Southward the forest changes to one of mixed deciduous trees which continue southward on the western bank to the vicinity of Saratov. East of the river the deciduous forest ends in the center of the Tatar Republic. Within the area of deciduous forests, the soils are of a gray-brown forest variety similar to those around Moscow. Southward, in the vicinity of Kuybyshev on the east bank and Saratov on the west bank, the forest rapidly gives way to the wooded steppe and then to the true steppe, and the soils become rich chernozems and chestnut-browns. These conditions gradually give way to the semidesert and desert downstream from Volgograd.

Between Volgograd and Astrakhan the Volga becomes an exotic stream and divides into a series of intertwining distributary channels that make their way through the sands eventually to empty their waters into the Caspian Sea. Between the Volga on the west and its main distributary, the Akhtuba, on the east, a floodplain 10 to 20 miles wide is available for irrigation agriculture. The delta itself is poorly drained and is overgrown by a tangled mass of water-loving reeds. A myriad of wild animals and water fowl occupy this delta region. The Soviets have been trying to put the wealth of reeds to some use; such things as walls for prefabricated houses and mats of all varieties have been tried, but so far none of these ideas seem to have been very practical.

Southwest of Volgograd, along the route of the Volga-Don Canal and the lower Don River, lies an extensive area of open steppe. Here the climate is semiarid, the natural vegetation is grass, and the soils are a deep, rich chestnut-brown with occasional patches of sand. In places between the lower Don and the lower Volga the soils become too saline for use.

Agriculture

The Volga Region is not as good an agricultural area as is the Central Black Earth Region. In the north the soils are infertile, the drainage is poor, and the summers are cool and short; in the south the area is desert. Only in the middle portion, between Kazan and Saratov, particularly west of the Volga, is a commendable amount of agriculture carried on.

In the north, Kirov Oblast and Mari A.S.S.R. correspond agriculturally to the northern fringe of the Central Industrial Region. The fields are interspersed among the forests, and the chief crops are flax for cash, potatoes, hay, and small grains. Dairying is very important.

Southward more general farming is practiced on the dissected western upland where wheat, hay, and other small grains now are being interspersed with significant acreages

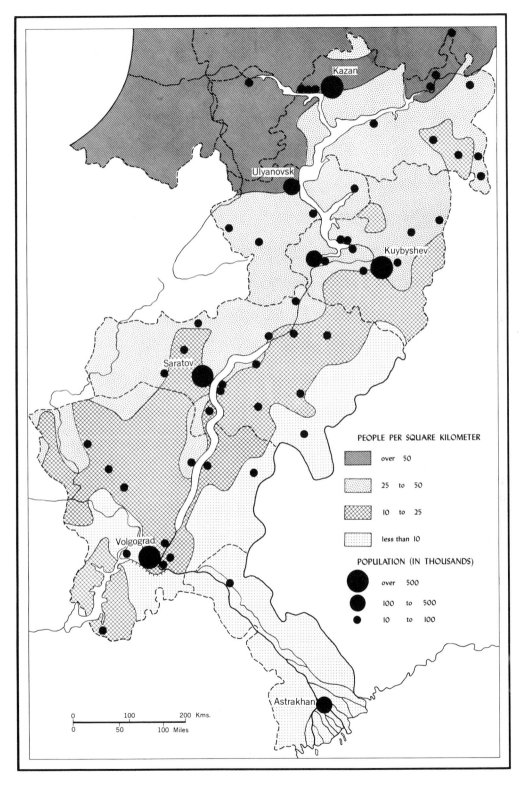

Figure 4-5 Population in the Povolzhye. After Lyalikov.

of corn and sugar beets. Since 1954 much of the drier Transvolga Meadows east of Kuybyshev has been plowed up under the "Virgin Lands Project" and seeded to spring wheat. Winters here are too severe for the survival of winter wheat. Scattered fields of sunflowers are found on both sides of the river all the way from Kazan to Volgograd, but this is not part of the major sunflower belt. Millet is grown in some of the drier parts of the region. Beef cattle, sheep, and pigs are being raised in ever increasing numbers.

On the floodplain between the Volga and the Akhtuba from Volgograd to Astrakhan a strip of intensively irrigated agriculture cuts through the dry desert. Melons, fruit, vegetables, rice, and a little cotton are grown in the irrigated strip. Otherwise the lower Volga is a dry grazing land.

The steppes of the lower Don are used for the extensive growing of such drought-resistant crops as wheat, sunflowers, and millet and for the grazing of cattle and sheep. This is the midsection of the main crescent-shaped belt of sunflower growing which has two nodes of more intense cultivation, one on either side of the lower Don, in the eastern Ukraine and in the North Caucasus. On the delta of the Don near the head of the Sea of Azov overhead irrigation is now being used to grow some alfalfa, vegetables, and fruit.

Industrial Resources and Development

History of Development The industrial revolution, which came belatedly to the Moscow region and the eastern Ukraine during the latter part of the nineteenth century, passed the Volga Region by. At the turn of the century only 5 per cent of the population in the area were employed in industry, and cottage or craft industries were much more important than factories. What factories existed were engaged primarily in the processing of local agricultural produce; flour milling, distilling, soap mak-

ing, tanning, and leather working were outstanding. Other industries were ship-building, cement, and timber. Lime kilns still dot the west side of the Volga where limestone outcrops at the base of the escarpment. The processed lime and cement are loaded directly into river boats for distribution.

In 1917 a cursory report on the prospects for the development of the Volga basin concluded that since it was mainly an agricultural district the question of the provision of power was not important. It was stated that the use of the river for water-power was precluded, not only by the weakness of the current because of the slight gradient, but also by ice in winter and drought in summer. Apart from some asphalt and oil shale near Syzran, no minerals, metals, or industrial fuel of any kind were obtainable from the Middle Volga.

During the first twenty years following the Revolution the Volga Region remained a Cinderella among the rapidly developing industrial regions of the Moscow area, the eastern Ukraine, the Urals, and western Siberia. In 1937 the Volga region still had virtually no power supply of its own. Although the Volga-Ural oil-bearing region had been discovered, its great extent was not yet known, and it was being exploited only at scattered points. Only in the mid 1930's were the foundations laid for the metal-using industries, and even then the emphasis was primarily on the production of agricultural machinery.

World War II, with its attendant movement of industries eastward was the catalyst that triggered the development of the Middle Volga region that has continued since the war at an undiminished pace. For a time during the war when Moscow was under heavy siege, even the central government largely was relocated in Kuybyshev. Since 1940, the Middle Volga and adjacent "pre-Ural" region has been the most rapidly developing region in the country in terms of growth of industrial production, trade, and major cities. Only Novosibirsk Oblast in western Siberia even approaches the growth rates of the Middle Volga and pre-Ural regions. The much-vaunted growth of production in the rest of Siberia, the Far East, and Middle Asia is in no way comparable to that in the Middle Volga. This fact often is obscured by Soviet statements stressing the importance of the eastern regions and by methods of reporting production statistics which split the Middle Volga—pre-Ural region down the middle and include the eastern half with the Urals, whose production statistics in turn are included in "the eastern regions," a catchall that includes Middle Asia and extends to the Pacific.

In 1956, the industrial production of the U.S.S.R. was 254 per cent of what it had been in 1940. By comparison, the industrial output in Kuybyshev Oblast in 1956 was 1014 per cent of what it had been in 1940; in the Bashkir A.S.S.R., 919 per cent; and in the Tatar A.S.S.R., 788 per cent. Other indices of growth similarly reveal the preeminence of the Middle Volga. Employed manpower in the U.S.S.R. in 1956 was 152 per cent of what it had been in 1940; in Kuybyshev Oblast it was 232 per cent. Railroad freight traffic also has increased the most rapidly in the Middle Volga—pre-Ural area. Such indications of sustained growth have given rise to predictions that the Middle Volga is an emerging focal region of the Soviet Union.*

Petroleum Production and Natural Gas
There is little doubt now that the Volga Region is the greatest powerhouse in the Soviet Union. The Volga-Urals oil fields, stretching from Volgograd northeastward to Perm, are now credited with containing more than 80 per cent of the total reserves of the Soviet Union and since 1956 have been producing more than 65 per cent of the country's petroleum. The Tatar A.S.S.R. is now first in the production of petroleum,

* Much of the preceding discussion of the historical development of the Volga Region derives from David J. M. Hooson, "The Middle Volga—An Emerging Focal Region in the Soviet Union," *The Geographical Journal,* vol. CXXVI, Part 2, June 1960, pp. 180–190.

Kuybyshev Oblast is third, after the Bashkir A.S.S.R., to the east, and Volgograd Oblast is scheduled to take over fifth place by 1965. The Tatar A.S.S.R. and Kuybyshev Oblast each considerably outproduce the famous old area of production in Transcaucasia around Baku.

Production costs in the Volga-Urals oil fields are several times lower than they are in other oil fields in the Soviet Union. The oil in the Volga-Urals fields is found in a number of essentially flat-lying strata which are particularly adaptable to contour flooding. As oil wells are drilled into the tops of oil-bearing structures, holes are driven downslope on the rock structure in all directions, and water is pumped in at approximately the same rate as oil is extracted. Natural pressure thereby is maintained, ultimate recovery is greatly increased, and production costs are reduced.

Kuybyshev and Syzran have become important centers for oil refining, and other cities in the region are getting new refineries. Oil pipelines are being built to the west and to the east to distribute Volga-Urals oil to a region stretching from Leningrad in the west to Irkutsk in the east.

A major gas deposit near Saratov was developed during World War II, and in 1946 a gas pipeline was laid from Saratov to Moscow. Lesser gas fields are now in production northwest of Volgograd.

The high development of the oil and gas industries in the Volga Region have allowed for a reduction of long, expensive coal hauls into the region from the Donets, Kuznetsk, and Karaganda basins. Also, natural gas and gaseous by-products of oil refining have provided a new broad base for the development of a variety of chemical industries in the Volga Region, particularly those producing synthetic rubber, artificial fibers, fertilizers, and alcohol.

Other Resources and Industries Extensive deposits of oil shale exist in Ulyanovsk and Kuybyshev Oblasts, and a significant production of oil from shale has been carried

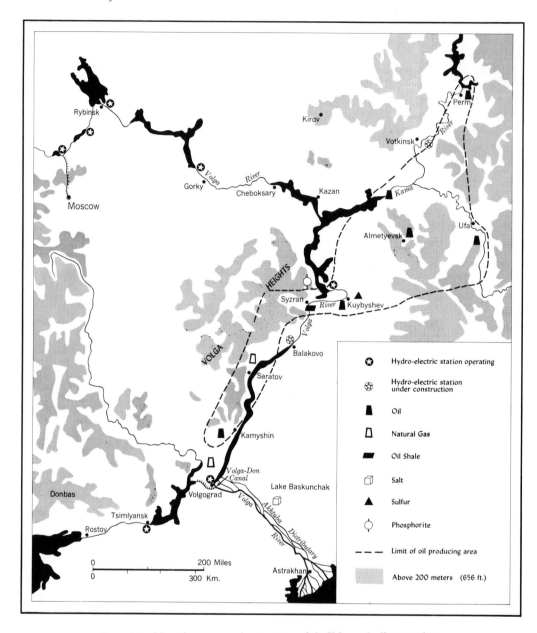

Figure 4-6   Mineral resources and water power of the Volga and adjacent regions.

on for a number of years, particularly in the vicinity of Syzran. Some oil is still being produced from shale in this area in spite of the growth of the petroleum industry.

In the same general areas as the oil shales are important deposits of phosphorites and limestone for the agricultural fertilizer industries. In addition, in the Samara Bend area there are some deposits of sulfur and pyrites, important to fertilizer and other chemical industries.

Along the lower Volga, southeast of Volgograd in the Caspian Lowland, lie several salt lakes which are remnants of the once more extensive Caspian Sea. These lakes supply a large portion of the Soviet Union's salt.

The chief producing lake beds are Baskunchak and Elton. The salt produced here is important to the fishing industry in the northern Caspian, which for many years was the richest fishing ground of the Soviet Union and still is of major importance. Much of the world's black caviar is produced from sturgeon caught in the shallow northern end of the Caspian.

Other than the mineral resources and the fish of the Caspian, the chief natural resource are the forests of the north in Kirov Oblast and in the Mari A.S.S.R. This is a significant lumbering area, and logs are floated down the tributary streams into the Volga to go to the treeless Caspian Plain in the south or through the Volga-Don Canal and down the Don River to the Ukraine.

The Factor of Location Equally important with the petroleum boom to the development of industry and urban growth in the Volga Region is its intermediate position on major transport routes between the three great industrial nodes of the Soviet Union—the Central Industrial Region to the west, the Urals to the east, and the Donets Basin to the southwest.

With the building of the Volga-Don Canal, the Moscow Canal, and the large reservoirs on the Volga and Kama rivers, a navigable all-water route in the shape of a large Y now exists between the three industrial nodes, and the Middle Volga occupies the strategic point at the fork of the Y.

Major rail lines connecting west and east have been constructed across the Volga at Kazan, Ulyanovsk, Kuybyshev, and Saratov, and during World War II a line was laid along the western bluffs parallel to the river. This line crosses the river at Volgograd and continues along the eastern side to Astrakhan. With the growth in exchange of products between the three industrial nodes across the Middle Volga via the rail and water transport systems, the Middle Volga hardly could have escaped economic development eventually had it been completely devoid of local resources. The opening up of the huge petroleum deposits, has, of course, greatly speeded this development.

The greater rate of industrial development of the Middle Volga Valley than at either end, plus the fact that the rapid industrialization and the oil fields continue eastward into the Bashkir A.S.S.R. and Perm and Orenburg oblasts, eventually may warrant the consideration of this area as a separate region, cutting across and breaking down the traditional regional divisions of the Volga and the Urals. So far, industrialization in this area has not progressed so far as to induce a change in the thinking of these regions by Russian geographers. For the sake of convenience, traditional boundaries will be adhered to now.

The Volga Waterway

Trade The unity of the Povolzhye depends on the Volga River, for it is the river and the traffic on it that historically has bound together the ends of the region and induced the establishment of towns along its banks. Now the towns have transcended their original functions and grown into great industrial cities, and the river traffic has been eclipsed by rail traffic. Although the trade function of the cities and the water transport of the total freight have been relegated to minor roles, absolutely, both have increased greatly during the Soviet period.

Figure 4-7 Traffic on the Volga River as seen from the high western bluff in the city of Volgograd. Photograph by the author.

Figure 4-8   Log rafts floating down the Volga near Volgo-grad. A log cabin is built on each raft to house the work-men who accompany the rafts to their destinations where both rafts and cabins are sold. This practice explains the presence of log cabin dwellings in the treeless Caspian Lowland. The raftmen return to their places of employ-ment by rail. Photograph by the author.

Wheat, coal, and pig iron from the Ukraine, fish from the Caspian, salt from the lower Volga, and, until recently, oil from Baku, go up the river in great quanti-ties to supply the population concentrations in the Central Industrial Region, the North-west, and the Urals. Timber and finished products move down the river to the lower Volga and the Ukraine. Oil is still being moved on the river in large quantities, but the direction of some of the flow has been reversed since the rapid development of the Volga-Urals fields. Refineries have not been built as fast as petroleum production has been expanded in the Volga-Urals area, so that some crude oil is actually being shipped down the river to be refined in the Caucasus, and refined products are being shipped back upstream to markets in the Central Industrial Region and the Urals. As refining capacity in the Volga-Urals area is increased, oil traffic on the Volga undoubtedly will de-crease, but the steady growth in other freight will counterbalance the decrease in oil.

The Great Volga Scheme The con-tinued growth of traffic on the Volga has prompted the grand scheme to completely control the flow of the river, by constructing

a stairway of huge reservoirs, each of which would reach upstream to the dam forming the next reservoir. This would assure com-plete navigability during the 6 or 7 months when the river is free of ice and incidentally would provide large amounts of hydroelectric power and some water for irrigation of the steppes from Kuybyshev southward. The construction projects on the upper Volga already have been discussed within the con-text of the Central Industrial Region.

The first project to be completed on the lower Volga was the Volga-Don Canal, which in 1952 connected the Volga with the Don at the point where they bend most closely toward each other and provided an outlet for the Volga traffic to the sea. The canal starts at the foot of a huge statue of Joseph Stalin along the west bank of the Volga a few miles below Volgograd and follows a looping course for 62 miles across the lowest part of the divide to the Don River. Thir-teen locks, each with a lift of about 30 feet, lift the water 145 feet above the Don and drop it 290 feet to the Volga. The Volga at Volgograd is just about at sea level. To provide water for the canal and to improve the channel on the lower Don, an earthen dam was strung for more than 7 miles across the broad, shallow valley of the Don River at the town of Tsimlyansk. The Tsimlyansk Dam raised the water 85 feet and backed it up the Don Valley 216 miles to form the Tsimlyansk Sea. With a surface area of approximately 1000 square miles, the Tsimlyansk Sea surpassed the Rybinsk Reservoir in size and was the largest man-made body of water in the world until it was eclipsed by other reservoirs on the Volga. Each succeeding project has been larger than the previous.

From the vantage point of a steamer in the middle of the reservoir, the Tsimlyansk Sea appears as vast as the Great Lakes of North America, but it is quite shallow. In most places, boats are forced to follow the submerged channel of the Don River in order to stay out of shoal water. Navigation aids in the form of large signboards along the banks enable the navigators to keep the boats in the channel. The signs consist of white-painted billboards about 10 feet high with a broad black stripe painted vertically down the middle. To keep on course the navigator must keep two of these striped boards in alignment.

The dam at Tsimlyansk has a power plant with a capacity of 160,000 kilowatts and two large locks that raise and lower boats from the Tsimlyansk Sea to the Don River. Below the dam, the boats follow the narrow, winding course of the Don River between the willows and cottonwoods lining the dissected dryish loess bluffs. At constricted bends and tributary junctions, dredges must be used continually to remove the yellow silt from the Don to maintain a navigable channel.

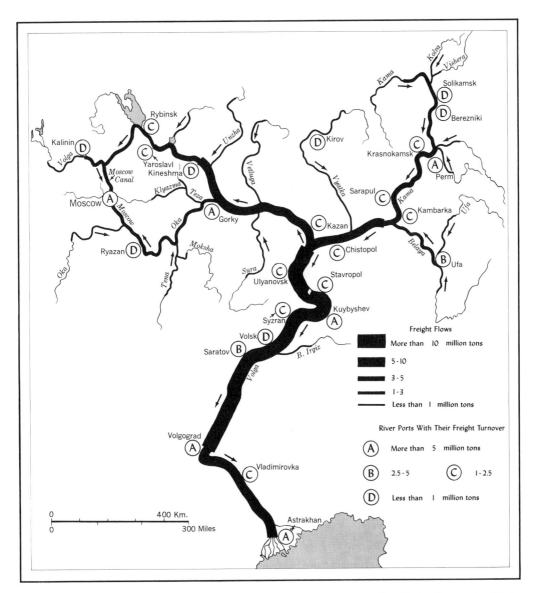

Figure 4-9   Freight traffic densities and major ports on the rivers of the Volga Basin.   From Soviet Geography: Review and Translation, *June 1961, p. 86.*

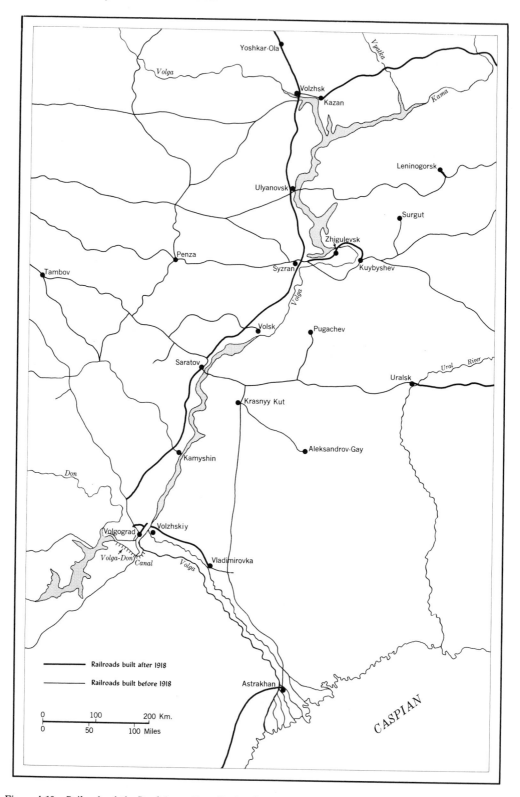

Figure 4-10   Railroads of the Povolzhye.   From Soviet Geography: Review and Translation, *June 1961, p. 80.*

Figure 4-11 The Volga entrance to the Volga-Don Canal. The statue of Stalin sits a few hundred yards to the south of the entrance. Photograph by the author.

Figure 4-12 Navigational aids along the banks of the Tsimlyansk Sea in the Volga-Don Canal System. The ship's navigator stays on the course of the submerged channel of the Don River by lining up the black stripes on two successive sign boards. Note the dry steppe nature of the countryside. Photograph by the author.

Even this far south, the Volga-Don Canal system is closed by ice 5 months of the year, from December to May. A small amount of the water in the Tsimlyansk Reservoir is led off in canals to irrigate some land to the southeast.

The Tsimlyansk Sea enjoyed the reputation as the world's largest artificial body of water for only 4 years when it was surpassed in size by the Kuybyshev Sea, which was filled in 1956. The earth and concrete spillway dam upstream from Kuybyshev raises the Volga water 80 feet and backs up a reservoir some 380 miles up the Volga and

its tributaries, the Kama River, and others. The city of Kazan, which formerly was 2 miles east of the Volga up the small Kazanka River, now sits on the shore of the Kuybyshev Sea. The dock facilities of Kazan had to be relocated, and a 20-mile earthen dike was built to protect the city. Some 280 villages containing more than 40,000 houses had to be moved to prepare for the flooding of the reservoir. With a capacity of 2,100,000 kilowatts, the hydroelectric plant is somewhat larger than that of Grand Coulee Dam in the United States. Hence, at the time of its dedication in 1957, it was the largest hydroelectric plant in the world. High-voltage transmission lines (400,000-volt) carry power west to Moscow and east through the Tatar and Bashkir oilfields to Zlatoust in the Urals. A double canal and lock system by-pass the dam and allow for simultaneous passage of boats in both directions. Also, a 3-kilometer stretch in the by-pass canal provides a winter harbor with repair docks. Eventually, 1 million hectares of land southeast of Kuybyshev will be irrigated.

Since 1957 the Kuybyshev Dam and Reser-

Figure 4-13 Passenger boats navigating the Volga-Don System stop frequently at small river stations to unload and take on passengers. Natives are on hand to sell fresh produce to the travelers. Note the thick chernozem soil profile developed on a mantle of loess. The Don here is thickly silted with yellow mud. Photograph by the author.

Figure 4-14   The Volgograd Reservoir just upstream from the Volgograd Dam.   The cranes in the far right are sitting on top of the dam while construction work is being completed.   Courtesy of Robert H. Dawson.

voir have been surpassed in size by those at Volgograd. The capacity of the hydroelectric plant at Volgograd is more than 2,500,000 kilowatts. The reservoir extends about 400 miles upstream. About 40 per cent of the power is transmitted all the way to Moscow over 500,000-volt transmission lines. It is planned to irrigate some land on both sides of the Volga downstream from Volgograd. Originally a 400-mile canal was projected to carry Volga water eastward to the Ural River and provide irrigation along the way for 60,000 square kilometers of land in the North Caspian Lowland. There is not enough surplus water in the Volga to accomplish this, however, and there is no indication that construction ever was started.

Two other dams apparently are in some stage of construction, at Cheboksary in the Chuvash A.S.S.R. at the upper reaches of the Kuybyshev Sea, and at Balakovo above Saratov at the upper limit of the Volgograd Sea. When these two dams are completed and their reservoirs are filled the Volga will be largely a stairway of connecting reservoirs all the way from the Moscow Canal to Volgograd. Even below Volgograd, initial plans have been laid to construct a dam

somewhere upstream from Astrakhan to maintain a navigable channel on the lower river. Whether or not these plans will be carried out remains to be seen.

Irrigation of land along the Volga is severely limited by the limited flow of the Volga, which if diminished will cause a damaging drop in the water level of the Caspian. In fact, the Caspian, which receives about three fourths of its water from the Volga, already has suffered an alarming drop in level, owing to a slightly warmer, drier climate since 1929 and increased evaporation of Volga River water from the extensive surfaces of the man-made reservoirs. The delta shoreline has extended out into the shallow northern end of the sea until at present Astrakhan lies about 40 miles inland, and a transfer point known as "Twelve-Foot Roads" has to be maintained near the edge of the delta to transship oil and other freight from large Caspian steamers to smaller river boats. Although new shallow-draft vessels have been devised that can negotiate both sea and river, a continued drop in the Caspian level would make navigation all the more difficult and seriously impair the rich fishing grounds of the northern banks.

The maintenance of the level of the Caspian Sea has been deemed such an important problem in the Soviet Union that an all-Union conference was called on April 11, 1960 to discuss the question. The results of this conference and a more complete description of the Caspian are included in the chapter on Middle Asia and Southern Kazakhstan (Chapter 10), after all the surrounding territories have been discussed.

Cities

The Volga region is rapidly becoming a string of great cities, each of which marks an important rail crossing of the river. As noted before, these cities, which started as defense outposts and evolved through a stage when trade was their primary function, under the Soviets have developed into full-fledged industrial centers.

Kuybyshev Gorky excluded, the largest city on the Volga is Kuybyshev, a pre-eminence only recently attained. At the time of the Revolution it was smaller than both Kazan and Saratov. With its present population of 806,000 and several good-sized suburbial towns around it, Kuybyshev is becoming the focal center of the entire Volga region. The largest of these satellite towns is Syzran about 50 miles around the Samara Bend to the west on the other side of the river. Together, Kuybyshev and Syzran are the chief refining centers of the Volga-Urals oil fields. A long railroad bridge crosses the river between Syzran and Kuybyshev and continues eastward to join with the Trans-Siberian Railroad.

Kuybyshev is the old city of Samara, located at the mouth of the small Samara River where it flows into the Volga from the southeast. Samara early distinguished itself as the financial capital of the Volga wheat trade during the days of the Russian Empire. The wheat barons constructed bank buildings along the main street facing the river, and further out in the countryside they established large estates. Many of the bank buildings and mansions still stand, but they now serve as government buildings, rest homes, childrens homes, and so forth.

Today Kuybyshev is a great industrial city concentrating on machine building, oil refining, and food processing. Now that this region is the major oil-producing area in the country, we can expect a growing importance of oil refining and the development of a whole range of chemical industries associated with the by-products of oil refining. According to the seven-year plan, the machine-building industry in Kuybyshev Oblast is to increase 2.4 times between 1958 and 1965, crude oil production is to increase 2.5 times, natural gas production is to increase 3.3 times, and the chemical industries are to grow by a factor of 14 times. It may be that in the future oil refining and oil-based chemicals will become even more important than the machine industries in this region.

Kazan The second largest city in the Volga region is Kazan, the old center of the Tatars which now serves as the capital of the Tatar A.S.S.R. In 1959 Kazan had a population of 647,000. It is growing at a rate similar to that of Kuybyshev and is being industrialized in much the same way. It also lies within the Volga-Urals oilfields, the Tatar Republic being the main producer of oil in the Soviet Union at present. So far, however, Kazan has not become the center of oil refining that Kuybyshev has. It early became a center for buying cattle hides and furs, and this trade determined its first development of industries. Tanning, shoe making, and the tallow industry for soap and candles became of first importance. These industries still occupy about a fourth of the manufactures of Kazan, but the machine-building industries and chemical industries each make up a fourth of Kazan's industry, and the other fourth is made up by food industries. Kazan is particularly known for its manufacture of a variety of business machines—typewriters, calculators, etc. We might expect that machine-build-

Figure 4-15 New suburban individual dwellings in Volgograd. Photograph by the author.

ing and chemical industries will become even more important in the future.

Volgograd Third in size is Volgograd with a population of 592,000. Volgograd is the old city of Tsaritsyn, which gained Union-wide fame during the Civil War following the Bolshevik Revolution, and then gained world-wide fame in World War II when it withstood the onslaught of the Germans and eventually proved to be the battle that signified the turning point in the war. Stalin distinguished himself here as a leader in the Red Army after the Revolution and the name "Tsaritsyn," which was derived from "Tsarina" or "Tsar's wife," was changed to Stalingrad. With the posthumous purge of Stalin in 1961, the name was changed once more to Volgograd.

Tsaritsyn started simply as a Russian fort overlooking the steppes to the southeast. In the late nineteenth century it became an important transshipping point between rail and water for oil, lumber, coal, and fish. Lying just east of the heavy industrial area in the eastern Ukraine, Volgograd has been the recipient of some heavy metallurgy and much machine building based on the iron and steel supply of the Ukraine. At present the industrial makeup of Volgograd is one fifth heavy metallurgy, one fifth machine building, one fifth chemicals, one fifth food industry, and one fifth diversified. Volgograd has been known all through the Soviet

period as one of the two great centers of tractor building. The caterpillar tractor plant and the Red October metallurgical works on the narrow floodplain on the north side of the city are still the largest industries in Volgograd. Chemical and lumber industries dominate the floodplain to the south of the city.

The city holds a strategic position on the high right bank of the Volga where the Volga makes its major bend toward the southeast. The city stretches in a crescent-shaped arc for about 35 miles along the west side of the river. A low narrow floodplain exists between the high right bank and the river, and on this floodplain much of the industry of the city is located.

The city suffered much damage during World War II and has been designated as one of the "hero cities" of the Soviet Union, along with Moscow and Leningrad. Much of the rubble has been cleared away since World War II, and most of the city has been reconstructed. But near the center of town overlooking the Volga, a large bombed-out shell of a building has been left standing as a war memorial. A tall graceful obelisk dominates the central square of the city, on the base of which are commemorated the fallen heroes of World War II. The Soviet people keep this monument smothered in flowers. The entire tone of the city of Volgograd is one of war-stricken grief from which the people have never recovered. Their remembrances are much too vivid for them to view the war with any sort of objectivity.

With the completion of the Volga-Don Canal in 1952, Volgograd occupies a much more strategic position on the river than it did previously. It now has become the point from which trade goes either on down the Volga southeast to the Caspian or through the Volga-Don Canal and down the Don River southwest into the Sea of Azov and the important industrial areas of the Ukraine. It is also on a major rail line that parallels the west bank of the river from the north, and then crosses the river in the vicinity of Volgograd and continues on southeastward to Astrakhan, passing through the important testing grounds for intercontinental ballistic missiles at Kapustin Yar. Railroads also connect Volgograd to the northwest with Moscow and to the west and southwest with the Ukraine and the Northern Caucasus.

The building of the dam about 10 miles north of the city has assured the area of an abundance of electrical power. The dam has an ultimate capacity of 2,563,000 kilowatts which makes it the largest power plant on the river. A workers' settlement of modern aspect has been established on the east end of the dam, and this town of 5000 or so people is to be maintained and to increase to a city of approximately 50,000 people that will concentrate on chemical industries using electrical power and natural and by-product gases to produce synthetic fibers and plastics. Important gas fields lie near Frolovo about 50 miles northwest of Volgograd, and a gas pipeline connecting the two centers has existed for some years. An aluminum industry is being located in Volgograd to make use of the hydroelectric power for converting alumina from the Urals to aluminum.

Saratov Nearly as large as Volgograd is Saratov, located halfway between Volgograd and Kuybyshev on the high bluff of the river, with a 1959 population of 581,000. Saratov occupies the site of one of the major rail crossings of the Volga. The rail line continues on eastward to the southern Urals and eventually connects up with the Trans-Siberian Railroad. Saratov is the center of one of the major gas fields on the Volga. A pipeline was built to Moscow in 1946. At present Saratov has about one third of its industry engaged in machine building, one third in chemicals, and one third in food industries. We can probably expect the chemical industries to grow at a more rapid rate than the others in the future.

Across the river from Saratov are the towns of Marx and Engels which lay in the Volga German A.S.S.R. before World War II. During the war, the Volga Germans were accused of collaboration with Germany and were dispersed throughout the Soviet Union, many of them being sent as far east as Soviet Middle Asia or eastern Siberia. The Volga German Republic is about the only political unit that was abolished during World War II which has not been restored to its previous status since the death of Stalin.

Astrakhan Astrakhan, at the mouth of the Volga, has been growing at a much slower rate than the four previously mentioned cities. In 1959 it had a population of 296,000. It of course lies on a dead-end branch of the waterway off the mainstream of products going between the Ukraine, the Central Industrial Region, and the Urals, and it cannot be expected to grow in the future at a rate commensurate with the rest of the cities. Its function remains primarily that of a port city handling products of the local water area: fish, oil, and salt. Its industries are about one third machine building, one third food processing, and one third diversified. With the diminishing of the flow of oil from Baku up the Volga, the role of Astrakhan may actually diminish.

Kirov The sixth city in size in the Povolzhye is Kirov, lying on the northern boundary of the region. Until 1934 Kirov was known as Vyatka, after the Vyatka River, which is a tributary of the Kama. Lying in the forest zone, it has become an important center for wood processing and fur processing. Thirty per cent of the teaching aids in the U.S.S.R. are made in Kirov. Besides these, such things as matches, prefabricated houses, and furniture are made from local wood supplies. At present the industry of Kirov is characterized as being one fourth machine building, one fourth chemical, one fourth woodworking, and one fourth food processing. In 1959 the population of Kirov was 252,000. The city sits at just about the northern limit of concentrated agriculture, with only scattered dairying, potato growing, some flax growing, and very little grain growing to the north.

Ulyanovsk Next in size is the city of Ulyanovsk located on the Volga about halfway between Kuybyshev and Kazan. This is the old city of Simbirsk which was renamed Ulyanovsk after Lenin because it was his birthplace. In 1959 Ulyanovsk had a population of 206,000; it has been sharing in the growth of all the cities along the river. Its industry is characterized as being about 65 per cent machine construction and 35 per cent food processing.

Other Cities Other than these major cities, there are numerous ones of the 50,000–150,000 class. Syzran, west of Kuybyshev, has already been mentioned as a center of the oil and gas industry. About half of its industry is machine construction. Another city of similar size is Kamyshin, located about halfway between Volgograd and Saratov, which is concentrated on the textile industries, particularly cotton textiles.

The large city of Rostov and the coal mining area to the north of it will be discussed along with the rest of the Donets Basin in the eastern Ukraine.

Reading List

Hooson, David J. M., "The Middle Volga—An Emerging Focal Region in the Soviet Union," *The Geographical Journal,* June 1960, 182–190.

Pociuk, Stephan G., "The Territorial Pattern of Industrialization in the U.S.S.R.: A Case Study in Location of Industry," *Soviet Studies,* July 1961, 69–95.

The Ukraine and Moldavia[a]

Region	Area (sq mile)	Population	People (sq mile)	% Urban
Ukrainian S.S.R.	234,000	41,869,000	180.5	46
Moldavian S.S.R.	13,200	2,885,000	221.7	22

[a] Since the industries of the city of Rostov and the coal mining area to the north are tied intimately to those of the rest of the Donets Basin, the economy of the western part of Rostov Oblast will be discussed with that of the eastern Ukraine, although the entire area and population of Rostov Oblast were included in the Povolzhye.

5

The Ukraine and Moldavia

The Ukrainian S.S.R., in the southwest corner of the Soviet Union, is in many respects a continuation of the parts of the Russian Republic that lie along its northeastern border. The Central Black Earth Region of Kursk and Belgorod Oblasts penetrates southwestward into the Ukraine and perhaps even into northern Moldavia, and the steppes of the lower Volga roll unbroken over the Ukraine's southeast. In the northwest the forests of the Pripyat Marshes spread into adjacent areas of the Russian Republic and Belorussia. Thus the character of this constituent republic of the U.S.S.R. changes from region to region as its terrain merges imperceptibly with that of neighboring republics. A discussion of the Ukraine as a separate unit can probably be justified, however, for it is known throughout the world as a political and economic entity, second in importance in the U.S.S.R. only to the Russian Republic.

The Ukraine represents 3 per cent of the area of the U.S.S.R. and 20 per cent of its population. In 1960 it accounted for 33 per cent of the coal, 56 per cent of the coking coal, about half the iron ore, half of the manganese, half of the pig iron, 40 per cent of the steel, 57 per cent of the corn, 55 per cent of the sugar beets, 42 per cent of the sunflowers, 10 per cent of the wheat, 20 per cent of the meat, 25 per cent of the butter,

and 28 per cent of the vegetable oil produced in the Soviet Union. At the time of the Revolution it had been even more significant to the total economy of the country. In 1913 the Ukraine produced 78 per cent of the coal, 69 per cent of the iron, 58 per cent of the steel, and 35 per cent of the wheat and had long been the primary source of grain for export, an item vital to the establishment of foreign exchange which paid for the initial industrialization in the 1920's and 1930's.

Outside the U.S.S.R., the Ukraine compares favorably in area, population, and primary production with the leading countries of Europe. Its 234,000 square miles make it larger than any country on that continent, with the exception of the remainder of the Soviet Union, and its 41,869,000 citizens constitute one of Europe's most populous political units.

There are 37,000,000 Ukrainians, of whom 32,000,000 speak their native language. Next to Russian, Ukrainian is the most widely spoken Slavic tongue. The Poles in 1960 numbered only 29,000,000.

The postwar republic of Moldavia is discussed with the Ukraine because it is not large enough nor is its role in the economy of the Soviet Union important enough to warrant separate study. In many ways it is similar to the Ukraine, on which it borders.

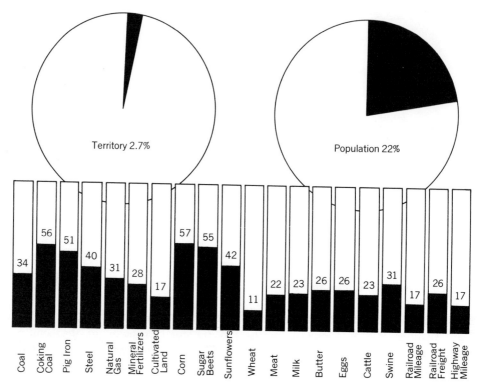

Figure 5-1   The Ukraine's share of the U.S.S.R. total Territory, Population, and Production, in per cent.

In addition, the western third of Rostov Oblast, including the city of Rostov, in the Russian Republic, is treated with the eastern Ukraine because economically and geographically it is tied to the all-important Donets Coal Basin, which overlaps the boundary between the Ukraine and the R.S.F.S.R.

Political History

The word "ukraine" means extremity or borderland.   During the rise of Moscow after the Tatar invasion, this area was the frontier, a no man's land between the Russians, the Poles, the Lithuanians, the Tatars, the Turks, and various nomadic tribes to the south. Gradually it was resettled, primarily by people from the north, and incorporated into the Polish-Lithuanian state, which in the sixteenth and seventeenth centuries stretched from the Baltic to the Black Sea.   Toward

Table 5-1   Comparison of the Ukraine and Some European Countries by Area (in Square Miles)[a]

Country	Area
Ukraine	234,000
France	216,000
Spain	197,000
Poland	122,000
Italy	118,000
Yugoslavia	100,000
West Germany	97,000
United Kingdom	95,000

[a] *Sources: Narodnoe khozyaystvo SSSR v 1960 godu* and *United Nations Demographic Yearbook*, 1960.

the middle of the seventeenth century a successful Cossack revolt under the leadership of Bogdan Khemelnitsky liberated the Ukraine from Poland, but a few years later

Table 5–2 *Comparison of the Ukraine and Some European Countries by Population, 1959[a]*

Country	Population
West Germany	52,785,000
United Kingdom	52,157,000
Italy	49,052,000
France	45,097,000
Ukraine	41,869,000
Spain	29,894,000
Poland	29,257,000
Yugoslavia	18,448,000

[a] *Sources: Narodnoe khozyaystvo SSSR v 1960 godu* and *United Nations Demographic Yearbook*, 1960.

Table 5–3 *Comparison of the Ukraine with Leading European Countries in Coal Production, 1960 (in Millions of Short Tons)[a]*

Country	Coal Production
West Germany	486
United Kingdom	228
Ukraine	189
Poland	122
France	64

[a] *Sources: Commodity Yearbook* and *Narodnoe khozyaystvo SSSR v 1960 godu.*

Table 5–4 *Comparison of the Ukraine with Leading European Countries in Pig Iron and Steel Production, 1960 (in Millions of Short Tons)[a]*

Country	Pig Iron	Steel
Ukraine[b]	27	29
West Germany	25	36
United Kingdom	16	27
France	15	19

[a] *Sources: Commodity Yearbook* and *Narodnoe khozyaystvo SSSR v 1960 godu.*
[b] The Ukraine also produces about one third of the world's manganese.

Table 5–5 *Comparison of Ukraine with Leading Producing Countries of Corn, 1960 (in Millions of Bushels)[a]*

Country	Corn Production
United States	4353
Ukraine	335
Yugoslavia	241
Argentina	200
Hungary	125

[a] *Sources: Commodity Yearbook* and *Narodnoe khozyaystvo SSSR v 1960 godu.*

Table 5–6 *Comparison of Ukraine with Leading Producing Countries of Sugar, 1960 (in Thousands of Short Tons)[a]*

Country	Sugar Production
Cuba	5800 (cane)
Ukraine	4125 (beet)
India	3595 (cane)
United States	3070 (cane and beet)

[a] *Sources: Commodity Yearbook* and *Narodnoe khozyaystvo SSSR v 1960 godu.*

it fell to the power of Moscow, under which it remained until World War I.

The war and subsequent revolution resulted in the loss of the Polish provinces to a newly organized Poland, and Moldavia and Bessarabia fell to Rumania. For a short time after the Revolution the Ukrainians, independent of Russia, governed the land that remained theirs, and several years of bitter civil war ensued before the Ukraine was finally absorbed by the Soviet Union. Civil war broke out again in 1929 and in 1930 when the farmers were forced to collectivize.

During World War II Moldavia, Bes-

sarabia, Bukovina, and the two southeastern provinces of Poland, Volhynia and Galicia, were regained by the Soviet Union and were constituted into what is now known as the Western Ukraine and the newly established

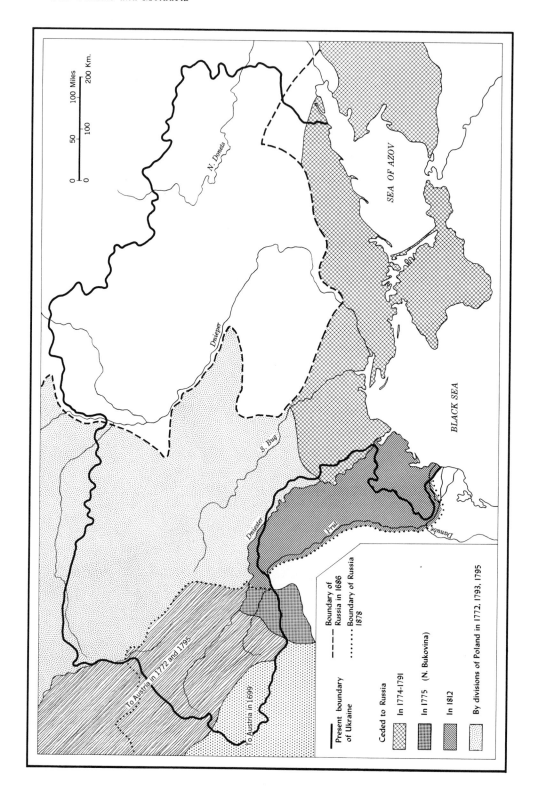

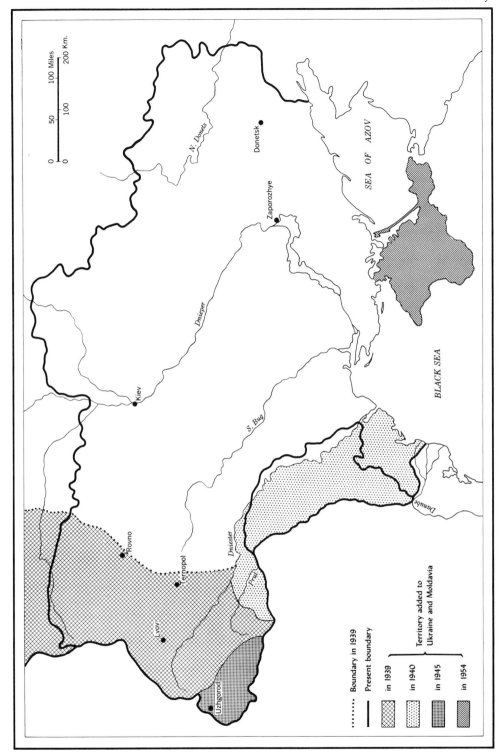

Figure 5-2 Historical exchanges of territory in the Ukraine.   Upper map: The Ukraine from 1686 to 1917 and at present.   Lower map: Acquisitions of territory during and since World War II.   After Cherdantsev.

Moldavian S.S.R. At the end of the war the Soviet Union demanded and was given the eastern end of Czechoslovakia on the basis that it was inhabited by Ukrainians (Ruthenians). This territory is distinguished from those previously mentioned in that it had never been part of the Russian Empire. The Soviet Union now extends over the Carpathians onto the floor of the Hungarian Plain in the so-called Transcarpathian Ukraine. In 1954 the Crimean Peninsula was transferred from the Russian Republic to its southern neighbor.

Thus the Ukraine is now larger and more populous than it has ever been before. About 77 per cent of its people are Ukrainians, 17 per cent are Russians, and the rest are Jews, Poles, Belorussians, Moldavians, Bulgarians, Hungarians, Greeks, and various other nationalities from adjacent areas. Forty-six per cent of the people are classified as urban dwellers, which places the Ukraine 2 per cent below the national average for urbanization. Moldavia and the Ukraine have the highest average population densities of all the union republics.

General Survey

Geology and Topography Topographically and geologically the Ukraine throughout most of its territory is a flat-lying sedimentary plain that is now undergoing some stream dissection. In the south a broad upwarp has induced more erosion, which has resulted in a rolling, broken landscape and the exposure of older rocks. The higher western part of the upwarp, known as the Podolian Plateau, covers much of the southwestern Ukraine and Moldavia along the northeastern base of the Carpathian Mountains. The eastern part of the upwarp north of the Sea of Azov is known as the Donets Ridge. Between the two, the Dnieper River has cut through the sedimentary strata to the hard crystalline basement rock below, which produces a series of rapids in the vicinity of Zaporozhye. At this point the

river makes a pronounced bend as it alters its course along the strike of the surface formations to flow directly down the dip slope of the rock into the Black Sea.

The Carpathians in the western Ukraine reach altitudes of 6000 to 7000 feet. Their steep slopes on both sides are heavily forested, and recent glaciation has given the landscape an alpine character. In Crimea the mountains rise abruptly from the Black Sea coast to an altitude of more than 5000 feet. Composed primarily of limestone rocks that have undergone considerable underground solution, these mountains exhibit a rugged outline. The south slopes dropping off to the sea are especially steep because of recent movement along a major fault zone that borders the north edge of the Black Sea.

Climate, Vegetation, and Soils Climatically, the Russians look upon the Ukraine as a mild region, but actually it has severe winters and relatively cool summers, except along portions of the Black Sea coast. And everywhere but in the northwest it is plagued by drought. January temperatures in Kiev average 21°F, and annual precipitation averages 21 inches. These conditions closely approximate those of central Nebraska, but the July average temperature of 67°F is more like that of northern North Dakota. In the northwest there are 24 or more inches of precipitation each year, an amount that diminishes steadily southeastward until along the coast of the Black Sea annual precipitation varies between 8 and 16 inches. In the warmer summers of the southern fringe this amount of rainfall is insufficient for many crops.

The natural vegetation of the Ukraine reflects the transition in moisture from northwest to southeast. Vegetation and soil zones are oriented generally in a southwest to northeast direction, perpendicular to the moisture gradient. In the northwest, extending southeastward to the city of Kiev, is an area of mixed deciduous forest, similar to that in adjacent parts of the Russian Republic and Belorussia. In this region the soils

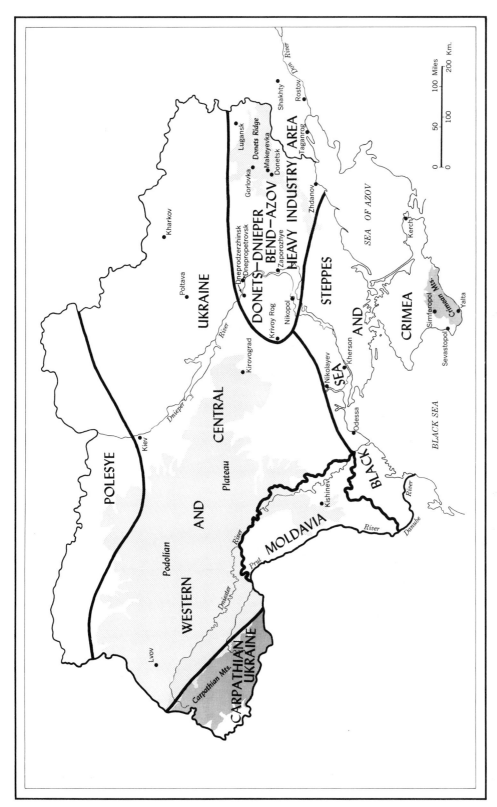

Figure 5-3 Subdivisions and landform regions of the Ukraine and Moldavia.

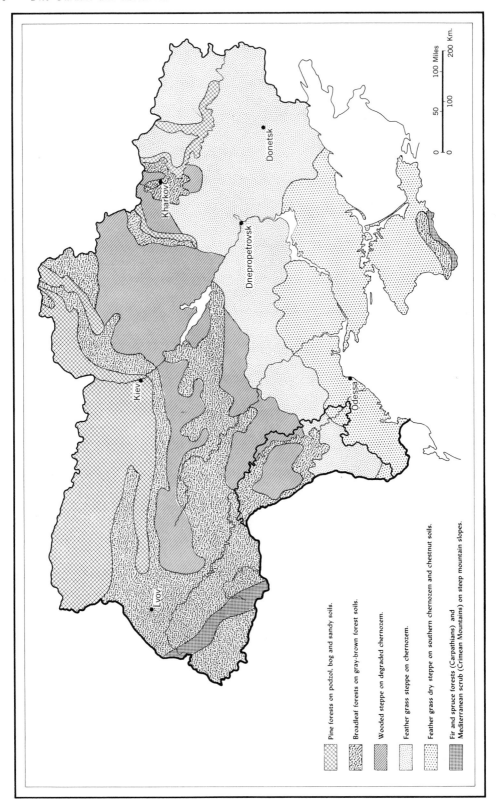

Kharkov
Donetsk
Dnepropetrovsk
Kiev
Lvov
Odessa

100 Miles
200 Km.
50
100
100
0
0

Pine forests on podzol, bog and sandy soils.

Broadleaf forests on gray-brown forest soils.

Wooded steppe on degraded chernozem.

Feather grass steppe on chernozem.

Feather grass dry steppe on southern chernozem and chestnut soils.

Fir and spruce forests (Carpathians) and
Mediterranean scrub (Crimean Mountains) on steep mountain slopes.

Figure 5-4   Soil and natural vegetation zones of the Ukraine and Moldavia.   After Cherdantsev.

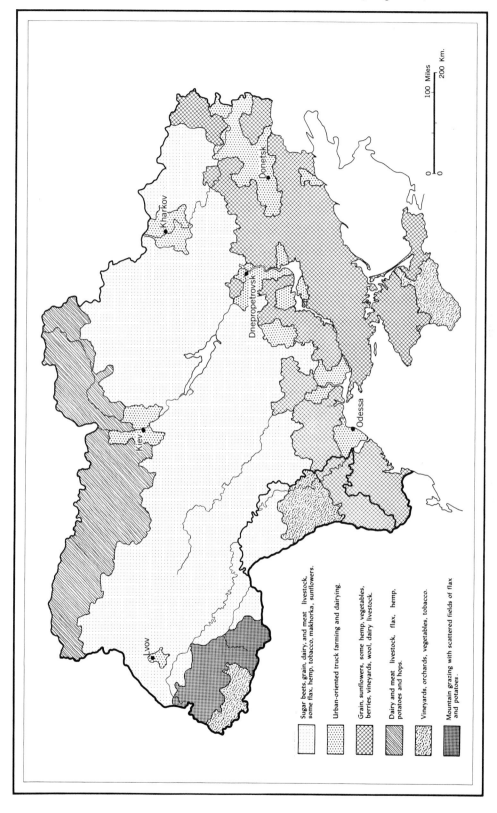

Figure 5-5   Agricultural regions of the Ukraine and Moldavia.   From Atlas selskogo khozyaystva SSSR, pp. 238, 239, 243.

Sugar beets, grain, dairy, and meat livestock, some flax, hemp, tobacco, makhorka, sunflowers.

Urban-oriented truck farming and dairying.

Grain, sunflowers, some hemp, vegetables, berries, vineyards, wool, dairy livestock.

Dairy and meat livestock, flax, hemp, potatoes and hops.

Vineyards, orchards, vegetables, tobacco.

Mountain grazing with scattered fields of flax and potatoes.

are gray-brown podzolic, and in the poorly drained area of the "Polesye" the soils are ground-water podzol and bog. Just south of Kiev is the "wooded steppe," characterized by extensive areas of open grassland interspersed with clumps of trees, particularly along the stream valleys. This region, which is the beginning of fertile chernozem soils, continues to Zaporozhye, beyond which lie the chernozem and chestnut soils of the open steppes.

The soils of the Ukraine are in general quite good as is to be expected in an area of subhumid and semiarid climates. In addition, over much of the land a mantle of loess has greatly increased their mineral constituents. The chief drawback to agriculture is the cool and droughty climate. Agriculture as a rule is commercial; specialty crops raised on an extensive cash basis are distributed according to the climate of each region.

The Dnieper River The Dnieper River, much as the Volga, is being harnessed by dams that will remake the stream into a large stairway of reservoirs. The chief function of most of these structures is to produce hydroelectric power, but navigation will also be improved. Irrigation is the primary purpose of the southernmost dam and is to be an auxiliary function of a proposed dam across the middle portion of the river.

The first dam built before World War II

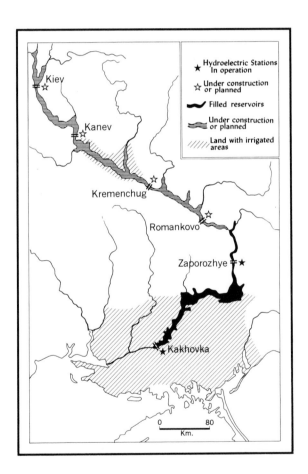

Figure 5-6 Construction projects on the Dnieper River. From Soviet Geography: Review and Translation, *January 1961, p. 78.*

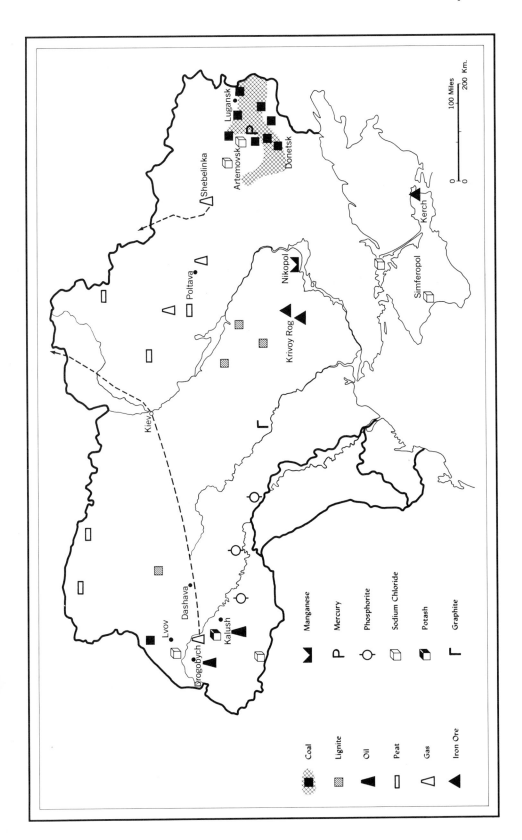

Figure 5-7   Mineral resources of the Ukraine.

was the Dnieper, just north of the city of Zaporozhye where the river cuts into the old crystalline basement rock and flows through a constricted channel over a series of nine large rapids. The name Zaporozhye means "across the rapids." This dam raised the water level more than 100 feet, thereby drowning the rapids and connecting the upper portion of the river with the lower, both of which are navigable. With a generating capacity of 650,000 kilowatts, the power station was the largest in Europe at that time. Early in World War II, in the face of the advancing Germans the Russians dismantled the power plant and carried away all movable equipment. Later, as they retreated, the Germans blew up the dam; at the end of the war there was nothing left but a pile of concrete rubble and twisted steel in the river bed. This was more than just a mortal blow to a power station; it was a blow to the young ego of the Soviet Union, for the Dnieper Dam, as the first major construction project in the new country, had become a symbol of Soviet strength, even though the work had been directed by American engineers.

Since the war the old dam has been completely reconstructed, and a second dam has been built downstream at the town of Kakhovka, not far from the mouth of the Dnieper, to produce electric power and to provide irrigation for the Black Sea steppes. The capacity of the Kakhovka Station has been placed at 312,000 kilowatts. In 1954 a third hydroelectric station was started on the Dnieper near Kremenchug, about halfway between Zaporozhye and Kiev. This dam was completed and all generating units with a total capacity of 625,000 kilowatts were installed by November 1960. A fourth station is under construction at Romankovo just above Dneprodzerzhinsk, and two other stations are planned upstream from Kremenchug, near Kanev and at Kiev. When all these projects are completed the area will be well supplied with electricity, and navigation will be much improved, both for river craft

and for floating timber from the north to the treeless south.

Mineral Resources In addition to the enormous agricultural potential of the Ukraine, there are rich mineral resources as the basis for industry. Most valuable are the coal fields of the Donets Basin, the nearby iron depoists at Krivoy Rog and Kerch, and the manganese at Nikopol. There are also substantial supplies of oil, natural gas, salt, mercury, antimony, and several other minerals.

Railroads Another important resource, which must not be overlooked, is the Ukraine's excellent transport network. Railway construction began around 1870 and proceeded rapidly as industrialization took place in the Donets Basin. Rail lines were needed also to ship grain and other food products to the central regions of Russia for domestic consumption and to Black Sea ports for export. The heaviest rail traffic in the Soviet Union moves between the eastern Ukraine and the Central Industrial Region, and, in spite of the fact that a good all-water route, via the Volga-Don Canal, now exists between the two areas, rail shipment is much more direct, much faster, and much the preferred method of transport among Soviet shippers.

Regional Division Industries based on the mineral, waterpower, and transport strength of the country have given it an aspect other than agricultural; hence the subregions of the Ukraine are complicated by two unrelated economies, urban industrial and rural agricultural. Crop complexes correspond closely to the climate and soils; they cut across the area in broad zones oriented southwest-northeast perpendicular to the moisture gradient. The belt of heavy industry in the eastern Ukraine ignores the agricultural zones. For convenience of discussion, the Donets-Dnieper Bend-Azov industrial area has been lifted from its agricultural context and discussed separately, and

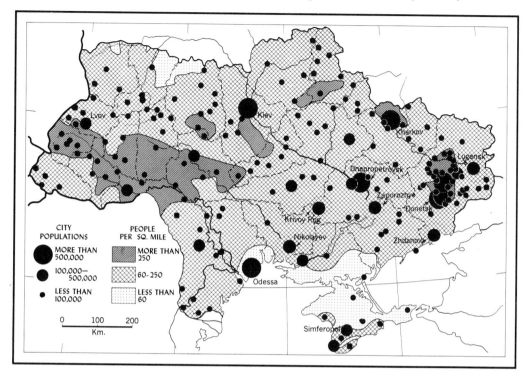

Figure 5-8 Population densities and cities of the Ukraine and Moldavia.   After Cherdantsev.

the rest of the Ukraine is divided into four somewhat traditional regions: (1) the Central and Western Ukraine, (2) the Carpathian Ukraine, (3) the Polesye, and (4) the Black Sea Steppes and Crimea. (See Fig. 5-3.) Moldavia is treated as a separate region.

The Donets-Dnieper Bend-Azov Heavy Industry Area

Rich deposits of coal, iron, and manganese, the main raw materials for heavy industry, as well as rock salt, limestone for fluxing, and lesser amounts of a variety of minerals lying in proximity in the eastern third of the Ukraine have induced the development of a broad industrial area within which lie three nodes of more intensive concentration.

The Donets Coal Basin in Donetsk and Lugansk Oblasts in the eastern Ukraine and the western fringe of Rostov Oblast in the Russian Republic, by no means contains the richest coal fields in the Soviet Union, but it is the most highly developed mining area. Mining began here in the 1840's, and the basin quickly became Russia's major coal producer. In 1913 it was responsible for 87 per cent of the country's supply. Although under the present regime its share of the total production has diminished, owing to the development of other coal basins, its absolute production has continued to increase until today the basin is mining more coal than ever before. In 1960 the Donbas still led the country with one third of the coal and more than half of the coking coal.

Coal in the Donets lies in a series of rather thin seams interbedded among the essentially flat-lying sedimentary rocks of Carboniferous age along the lower portion of the "little Don," or Donets River, in the eastern Ukraine. Actually, the seams extend northwestward into Kharkov Oblast, but only the southeastern part of the basin has been developed. Here and there the rocks are more steeply tilted along the flanks of the Donets Ridge, where tectonic movement has been severer and metamorphosis has been more extreme. The beds in Donetsk Oblast and adjacent areas supply most of the coking coal and yield a high-grade bituminous product; those of more highly metamorphosed tipping beds in the vicinity of Lugansk contain higher grade anthracite, which is required for purposes other than the metallurgical industries. Hence the iron and steel industry has concentrated in Donetsk Oblast. Everywhere the seams lie deep below the surface, so that shaft mining is the only practical method. The average depth of the mines is about 1000 feet, but some reach more than half a mile into the ground. During World War II the mines were largely disabled by the Soviet Army in the wake of the German invasion, and, when in retreat, the Germans flooded the shafts with millions of gallons of water. Nevertheless, by 1948 the mines had been rehabilitated and the prewar production level regained.

Two locations in the eastern Ukraine are credited with containing 42 per cent of the country's iron ore. Within the bend of the Dnieper River, the Krivoy Rog deposits consist of more than 2 billion tons of rich ore containing 53 to 64 per cent iron and more than 18 billion tons of iron quartzites containing 30 to 36 per cent iron. This is about double the reserves of the Kursk Magnetic Anomaly. On the eastern tip of the Crimean Peninsula, the low-grade Kerch deposit is estimated at around 2 billion tons. Just east of Krivoy Rog, at the town of Nikopol on the west bank of the Dnieper River, lies the world's greatest reserve of manganese.

Krivoy Rog iron and Nikopol manganese were exploited in the last two decades of the nineteenth century with the rapid development of the iron and steel industry in the Donets Basin. Major plants were established in the coal area of what is now Donetsk and Lugansk Oblasts, and later in the 1930's others were built in the Dnieper Bend area. Iron and manganese are now moved eastward into the Donets Basin, and coal is transported westward into the Dnieper Bend to serve steel industries at both ends. Krivoy Rog iron ore is also shipped westward to Poland and East Germany. The Soviets hope to supplant this consumption in the satellites by ore from the Kursk Magnetic Anomaly as mining is developed in that area.

Although the primary centers of the steel industry continue to operate in the Donets Basin, both this nodal region and the one around the Dnieper Bend have been expanding at a rapid rate until at present they have become almost one continuous belt of heavy industry. The building of the Dnieper Dam at Zaporozhye increased the industrial growth of that area by adding to its resources an abundant supply of hydroelectricity and also by improving navigation on the river.

In the last decade or two a third nodal area of heavy industry, in the form of a short string of cities along the northwest coast of the Sea of Azov, has reached the point of merging on the north with the industrial belt just described. The cities along the Azov coast, such as Zhdanov and Taganrog, lie between the iron ore of the Kerch Peninsula to the south and the Donets Coal Field to the north. Iron ore is transported from Kerch by water directly to these cities and coal is carried the short distance from the Donets Basin by rail. A small iron and steel works has been built at Kerch to utilize returning empty ore boats from Zhdanov. Some of the Donets coal that is brought to Zhdanov by rail is transferred to boats and sent on to Kerch. Likewise, some of the iron ore shipped from Kerch to Zhdanov is transferred to the empty coal cars returning to the Donets Basin. Hence some Kerch ore is mixed with the Krivoy Rog ore in the Donbas.

High amounts of sulfur and phosphorus delayed use of the Kerch iron ore until smelting processes were perfected to extract these elements in usable forms. They have now become important by-products of the iron industry as the bases for mineral fertilizer and other chemicals.

Cities and Industries in the Donets Basin
The major cities in the Donets Basin are Donetsk, with a population of 669,000, Makeyevka, with a population of 358,000, and Gorlovka, with a population of 293,000. These three cities lie close together in Donetsk Oblast and are the major producers of coal, pig iron, and steel. They also support other industrial activity, chief among which is the production of chemicals based on coal tars and gases derived from coke. To the north-

east, Lugansk, a less highly industrialized city of 275,000, is situated in the heart of the anthracite coal-mining area. It is noted for the manufacture of railroad locomotives and other heavy machinery. Until 1957 Lugansk was named Voroshilovgrad in honor of Voroshilov, who for many years held the figurehead position of president of the Soviet Union, and until 1961 Donetsk was named Stalino. Both Stalin and Voroshilov distinguished themselves in the Red Army on the lower Volga after the Revolution. Now both have been purged, and cities named after them have been renamed. Among the coal-mining towns of the Donets Basin is Shakhty which is across the Ukrainian border

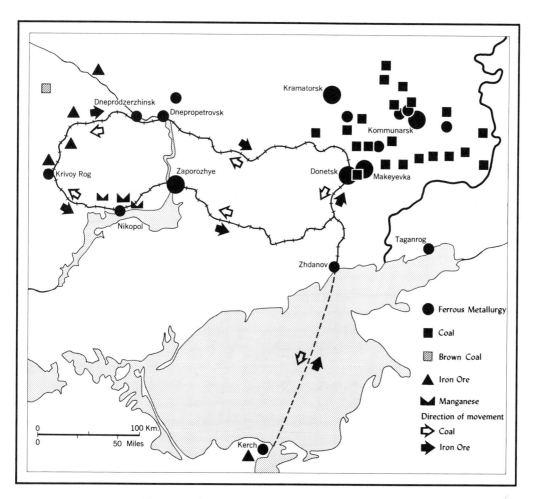

Figure 5-9 Donets-Dnieper Bend-Azov metallurgical area.

in the western part of Rostov Oblast in the Russian Republic. Rostov Oblast normally produces about one fourth of the Donbas coal. A number of smaller cities in the vicinity of Donetsk also maintain heavy metallurgical and chemical industries.

Cities and Industries of the Dnieper Bend

Several cities have been built in the Dnieper Bend area, the largest of which is Dnepropetrovsk, with a population of 60,000. Next in size is Zaporozhye, downstream from Dnepropetrovsk, with a population of 435,000, and the third is Dneprodzerzhinsk, with a population of 194,000. These cities utilize the hydroelectric power generated by the river and carry on considerable trade by water. All are becoming highly industrialized in heavy and light metallurgy, machine building, and chemicals. The abundance of hydroelectric power has attracted the location of aluminum plants to convert alumina shipped in from the Urals.

To the west of these cities, within the bend of the river and in the heart of rich iron-ore deposits, is the city of Krivoy Rog, which now has a population of 388,000 and is rapidly undergoing heavy industrialization. A large new steel furnace, which has been dubbed the "Magnitogorsk of the Ukraine," is under construction, and it has been speculated that steel from this plant may be utilized to satisfy the needs of satellite countries in eastern Europe. Nikopol, on the Dnieper downstream from Zaporozhye, with a population of 83,000, has been mentioned before as the site of the world's largest manganese deposit.

Cities and Industries of the Azov Coast

Along the north shore of the Sea of Azov two important iron and steel cities get their iron ore from Kerch in Crimea and their coal from the Donets Basin. The first of these is Zhdanov, in the Ukraine, which until 1948 was named Mariupol. Zhdanov is the principal port for the Donbas and now has the Azovstal metallurgical works, which is one of the largest in the vicinity of the Donets Basin. In 1959 Zhdanov had a pop-

ulation of 284,000. The other steel city is Taganrog, across the border in Rostov Oblast. Taganrog has a population of 202,000. Like Zhdanov, it is an important seaport and has recently added important heavy industries.

Characterizations and Analogues of Cities

The cities within this belt of heavy industry might be characterized as follows. Donetsk, Makeyevka, and Gorlovka have heavy concentrations of fuel-oriented metallurgical and chemical industries and might be compared to Pittsburgh in the United States, to the Ruhr in Germany, or to metallurgical centers of northeastern England. Krivoy Rog in the Dnieper Bend and Kerch in Crimea are secondary metallurgical centers dependent on iron ore and correspond closely to Duluth in the United States. Zaporozhye, Dnepropetrovsk, and Dneprodzerzhinsk in the Dnieper Bend and Taganrog and Zhdanov on the north shore of the Sea of Azov are metalworking and machine-building cities located between iron and coal much as are the Great Lakes centers of Chicago, Gary, and Cleveland in the United States. The three cities on the Dnieper, like Buffalo, New York, have hydroelectric power to supplement their industrial complexes. These ten cities make up the largest urban areas of the three core regions within the belt of heavy industry, and all are concentrated on primary metalworking.

Ringing these cities are others that utilize the products of heavy industry to turn out machinery of all types. Nikolayev to the west, at the mouth of the Southern Bug River, specializes in ship building, Kirovograd to the northwest, builds agricultural machinery, Kharkov, in the north, is the greatest general manufacturer of machinery in the Soviet Union, Lugansk to the northeast, has already been mentioned as an important producer of railroad locomotives, and far to the east, Volgograd is known for its autotractors.

Beyond this ring, cities more diversified in function, some of them even larger in population than those in the heavy-industry belt, take from it many of their raw materials.

Among them are Kiev in the northwest, Odessa in the southwest, Simferopol in Crimea, and Rostov at the mouth of the Don River. These peripheral and outlying cities are discussed in their respective regions.

Rostov-on-Don Rostov is fairly close to the Donets Basin and might well be discussed as part of it, but it stands somewhat alone as a major city in its own right, and its industries are not concentrated on any one item. Heavy metallurgy occupies only a small portion of its economic activity. Its principal factory is "Rosselmash," which is the largest agricultural machine plant in the U.S.S.R. Besides its function in industry, Rostov is a busy seaport controlling the mouth of the Don River whose traffic now has been greatly increased by the Volga-Don Canal. In 1959 Rostov had a population of 600,000 which can be expected to increase at a rapid rate. It is a surprisingly pleasant city, situated on the delta of the Don. In the evenings soft breezes from the Sea of Azov cool the streets, and an air of lightness, so often lacking in Soviet cities, is evident among the pedestrians. The main boulevards, divided by grassy strips, are wide and are bordered by broad, tree-lined sidewalks.

Agriculture The fact that the Donets-Dnieper area is heavily industrialized should not obscure the fact that it is agriculturally important. The long hot summers and fertile steppe soils are conducive to the production of crops that can withstand the drought conditions. Wheat and sunflowers, which are grown extensively, are most adaptable to this environment. This is the western half of the sunflower belt, which wraps around the head of the Sea of Azov and continues southeastward into the northern Caucasus. Other small grains and grain-sorghums are harvested in significant amounts, and dairying and livestock raising around centers of dense urban population are developing rapidly. In the last few years corn has been introduced into the region; in 1960 it occupied more than 30 per cent of the cultivated area.

Central and Western Ukraine

The second region to be considered is the general farming area in the central and western Ukraine, which covers much of the rest of the republic outside the industrial belt. This broad section has rich soils and a good agricultural climate, long summers, and in most cases sufficient moisture for a great variety of crops. It might be subdivided on the basis of crop complexes or on historical development, for there are variations in these elements from one part of the Ukraine to another. But suffice it to say that physically it becomes moister toward the northwest; natural vegetation changes gradually from steppe grasses in the southeast to mixed forests in the north, and soils and crops differ accordingly. Also, there is a general transition in land form from east to west, from an exceedingly flat plain with little stream dissection to a rather rough, rolling stream-dissected plain in the foothills of the Carpathian Mountains.

This region is not traditional in the Soviet Union; rather it incorporates three areas, all of which have been given some local designation by the Ukrainians and Russians. The area lying to the east of the Dnieper is usually referred to as the "Left Bank Ukraine" and that lying to the west as the "Right Bank Ukraine." The newly acquired area farther west is known as the "Western Ukraine." There is some topographic break along the Dnieper, since the river occupies a position along the base of a cuesta escarpment similar to those of the Volga and Don rivers. The area to the east is lower and generally flat, but to the west it is a rolling, stream-dissected upland. Perhaps there is a noticeably abrupt change in soil moisture conditions and natural vegetation along the river, the east having a drier aspect than the west. But zones of soil types and crop complexes are continuous across the river and extend on into the western Ukraine. Thus the area is somewhat of a unit agriculturally; the differences in crop complexes that do exist form zones cutting across the traditional regions from west-southwest to east-northeast to form indistinct subdivisions along a north-south line.

Agriculture   In the middle, in the very heart of the Ukraine where soils are best and moisture still sufficient, the dominant crops are sugar beets and wheat. Sugar beets usually account for at least one quarter of the cash income of farms. This is the sugar-beet belt of the Soviet Union which extends from Kursk and Belgorod Oblasts in the Central Black Earth Region southwestward and then westward south of Kiev and on to the western Ukraine. The concentration of sugar beets increases westward as the zone widens from Rovno south to the Carpathians and into northern Moldavia. Since 1953 corn has, in general, replaced wheat. Many other crops are grown including grains, sunflowers, potatoes, vegetables, and fruit.

To the northwest lies a somewhat narrower belt in which a transition takes place from the strong concentration on cash crops to a more general type of farming in which sugar beets and wheat are no more important than other grains, potatoes, and flax. This belt is the beginning of the mixed forest where there is greater moisture and somewhat podzolized soils. To the southeast is a region of drier climate more adapted to growing sunflowers than sugar beets. This zone, which begins just north of Kirovograd, extends southward to the region along the Black Sea and continues eastward into the belt of heavy industry. Wheat and sunflowers are the dominant crops here, and farming is done on a more extensive scale than it is to the northwest. Some other crops are raised, and corn has recently been introduced.

Interspersed within this great agricultural region around the major cities are numerous urban-oriented truck farms.

Rural population, which is heavy throughout the central and western Ukraine, increases westward where greater moisture permits more intensive and varied cultivation. In the western Ukraine the population density is between 350 and 400 persons per square mile. The farmers live in large villages, sometimes reaching populations of several thousands, strung helter-skelter in the stream valleys near sources of water. The typical rural dwelling is a one-room hut of whitewashed adobe walls and thatched or corrugated sheet and metal roof. The adobe "khata" of the south reflects the chief local building material (clay) as the log cabin "izba" of the north reflects the forests.

Minerals   In addition to the favorable conditions for agriculture in this large region, there are several sources of minerals, particularly of the mineral fuels. In the western Ukraine along the foothills of the Carpathians are significant deposits of coal, oil, and natural gas. The coal fields are exploited to satisfy local needs, but reserves are in no way comparable to those of the Donets Basin; supplies are limited and the quality is insufficient for coking. The oil fields in Drogobych Oblast, also of secondary importance, supply local needs; a refinery is located in Lvov. The natural gas deposits are of more significance to the country as a whole than are either coal or oil. The Dashava gas fields have been producing since before World War II, and a pipeline has been constructed to Kiev and Moscow. Other gas pipelines are under construction to supply Leningrad and the principal cities of Belorussia and the Baltic Republics. Until 1955 the Dashava gas fields were the only ones in the Ukraine and were one of the major producing areas in the Soviet Union. Since then new gas deposits have been discovered at Shebelinka, south of Kharkov, in the northeastern Ukraine, which appear to be larger than those at Dashava. The production at Shebelinka is expected to approximate that of Dashava by 1965. Lying on the main lines of gas transport between the northern Caucasus and the Central Industrial Region, the Shebelinka fields are more profitably located than are the fields in western Ukraine.

Also in the western Ukraine are significant deposits of potash salts, second in value in the Soviet Union only to those of the Urals. Chemical industries are being established in the western Ukraine and Belorussia to utilize these potash salts.

Cities Kiev, with a population of 1,102,- 000, Kharkov, with a population of 934,000, and Lvov, with a population of 411,000 are the major cities in this region and all are focal points for the railroads of the Ukraine. Kiev and Kharkov are the largest cities in the Ukraine and rank third and sixth in the Soviet Union, respectively. Kharkov already has been mentioned as a machine-building center.

Kiev, of course, is the historical center of the Ukraine, which flourished during the ninth to thirteenth centuries as the capital of Kievan Rus. Damaged severely during World War II, Kiev has been rebuilt into perhaps the most beautiful city of the Soviet Union. The opportunity has been taken during the reconstruction to lay out modern sewage, gas, and water lines and to build the first subway in the city.

The natural setting is magnificent. Situated on the high loess-covered western bluff of the Dnieper, at the confluence of its main left-bank tributary, the Desna, the city overlooks the blue water and white sandbars of the many-channeled river to the east. Beautiful beaches abound along the banks of the river, for great quantities of white sand have been carried down from the Polesye in the north. The wind has whipped some of this sand out of the immediate floodplain of the river and has created extensive areas of sand dunes on the flat, low-lying meadowland to the east. A surprising number of boats ply the river, and considerable quantities of timber are floated down from the northern forests. With the completion of all the proposed reservoirs, navigation will be greatly improved, but many of the sandy beaches will be submerged.

Tree-lined double boulevards with broad sidewalks are modern innovations; but the gilded domes of St. Sophia's Cathedral and the catacombs of the monastery in the loess

Figure 5-10 Traffic on the blue Dnieper viewed from the high west bluff at Kiev. Unlike the muddy Volga and Don rivers, the Dnieper contains beautiful clear water interspersed by bars of white glacial sands washed down from the Polesye to the north. Photograph by the author.

bluffs are reminders of the old Kiev. A tall, graceful obelisk commemorating the heroes of World War II stands in a park along the rim of the high western bluff, overlooking the huge gray statue of Saint Vladimir facing down the Dnieper.

Lvov is a medieval city with narrow cobbled streets and picturesque houses. It was acquired from Poland during World War II.

Other cities in the central Ukraine are Poltava, with a population of 143,000, Kirovograd, with a population of 128,000, and a number of smaller oblast centers which serve primarily as governmental and trading centers for rich agricultural regions. Poltava, west of Kharkov, is the site of the decisive victory of Peter the Great over Charles XII of Sweden in 1709.

Carpathian Ukraine

The third region to be considered is that in the western part of the republic, which includes the Carpathian Mountains and the Transcarpathian Ukraine. This region was taken over from Czechoslovakia in 1944 and includes a small portion of the Hungarian Plain southwest of the Carpathians. It is inhabited by Ruthenians, who are Ukrainian in origin.

The Carpathians in this section rise to elevations of more than 6000 feet; they are heavily forested by coniferous growth on the higher slopes and have been strongly dissected by the headwaters of the Dniester and the Danube. The higher portions of the mountains underwent strong mountain glaciation during the Pleistocene, which left their slopes exceedingly steep.

Lumbering and cattle and sheep grazing are carried on in the highlands. The small area of the Hungarian Plain southwest of the mountains is occupied by vineyards, truck gardens, and orchards and a mixture of wheat fields, sunflowers, sugar beets, and tobacco. Half of Transcarpathia is still covered by forests.

Polesye

In the northwest, bordering on the Belorussian Republic, lies the fourth region of the Ukraine, the so-called "Polesye," or "woodland." This is the southern limit of an area that lies primarily in Belorussia in the basin of the Pripyat River, which flows from west to east into the Dnieper. It is a proglacial lake bed that is almost as flat as a floor and is everywhere poorly drained. More than 30 per cent of the area is still forested. In many places vegetation has failed to gain a permanent foothold because of active wind deflation in loose glacial sands. Agriculture at best is meager; the cultivated land is on poor podzolic soils. The chief crops are flax, potatoes, and small grains, including buckwheat, which is a stable food crop throughout much of the western part of the Soviet Union. Considerable timber cut in the Polesye is floated down the Dnieper to southern markets.

Black Sea Steppes and Crimea

The fifth and last region of the Ukraine is comprised of the Black Sea Steppes and the Crimean Peninsula. This area extends from the mouth of the Danube on the border of Rumania eastward along the Black Sea in a strip of land 50 to 100 miles wide across the mouths of the Dniester River, the Southern Bug, and the Dnieper to the northwestern shores of the Sea of Azov. It includes the entire peninsula of Crimea. The western extremity of this region, the so-called Izmail District, was taken from Rumania during World War II and was incorporated into the Ukraine rather than into the Moldavian Republic; the reason given was that the region contained a majority of Ukrainians.

The Black Sea Steppes The strip of land along the northern shore of the Black Sea is a flat coastal plain with a semidesert climate. The mineral-rich steppe soils are conducive to extensive crop growing, but drought conditions make agriculture hazardous. These climatic and soil conditions extend across the narrow Perekop Isthmus onto the northern plains of the Crimea, which occupy about two thirds of the peninsula. The crops here are almost exclusively wheat and sunflowers, grown on an extensive scale. Some experimentation with dry-farmed cotton has been carried out but has proved unsuccessful. With the construction of the dam at Kakhovka on the lower Dnieper, irrigation has become possible over several hundred thousand acres of the plain and across the Perekop Isthmus into Crimea.

In many places along the Black Sea the land descends to the water in a series of low, sandy terraces fronting on shallow, salty, stagnant lagoons, or limans, which are hemmed in from the sea by elongated offshore sand bars. Many of the sandy terraces in this mild climatic region are planted in vineyards. Some of the most stagnant water lies in the area between the Crimean Peninsula and the mainland coast of the Ukraine on both sides of the Perekop Isthmus. The most completely surrounded body of water, known as the Sivash Sea, or putrid sea, is east of the Perekop Isthmus and adjacent to the Sea of Azov. Some salt is taken from it. Fishing is also important in these semien-closed bodies of water. The shallow water of the Sea of Azov and adjacent parts of the Black Sea abounds in fish.

The major cities in the Black Sea Steppes are Odessa in the west, Nikolayev on the estuary of the Southern Bug, and Kherson near the mouth of the Dnieper. All three serve as ports, although Odessa is much more active than the other two in this respect. Odessa is the primary wheat-exporting port of the Soviet Union and also handles considerable quantities of lumber. It is the chief entrepot for Caucasian oil products which are shipped across the Black Sea for distribution in the Ukraine. In 1959 Odessa had a population of 667,000, fourth in size in the Ukraine. Nikolayev is noted for shipbuilding. Kherson, although the smallest of the three, has the longest history. It was a thriving city in the fifteenth century when it was transferred to Muscovy by the Byzantine emperor at Constantinople on the occasion of the marriage of his niece to Ivan the Great.

The Crimean Mountains The southeastern third of the Crimean Peninsula is made up of the Crimean Mountains, which rise abruptly from a fault system along the northern shore of the Black Sea to elevations of more than 5000 feet. This western extremity of the young folded belt of mountains that extends eastward into the Caucasus, displays the features of recent faulting and mild volcanism. The mass of the Crimean Mountains is made up of limestone, which comprises three belts and forms three separate ridges. The highest of these ridges is the southernmost, where the limestone is not so crumbly as in the others. The middle slopes of the Crimean Mountains are covered with a rather sparse forest, but the summits are alpine meadows. These upland grassy areas are known as "Yaila," a term which is sometimes applied to the entire mountain range. Along the eastern end of the mountains and

extending eastward into the Kerch Peninsula are mud volcanoes and fumaroles which indicate recent volcanic activity.

The Crimean Mountains are not high, but their altitude is sufficient to protect the southeast coast of Crimea from the cold blasts of northern winds, so that the strip of coast from Yalta to Alushta has a Mediterranean-type climate. Its winters average above freezing temperatures and its summers are long, warm, and dry. This section of the Black Sea Coast has become one of the most popular resort areas in the Soviet Union. Its principal city, Yalta, received world attention during World War II as the site of a conference between Premier Stalin, President Roosevelt, and Prime Minister Churchill. Many impressive white buildings stand out in bold relief against the backdrop of shrubs and trees among the steep hills overlooking the sea far below. Some of these buildings date back to the Tsarist times when they served as summer palaces for the imperial court, but many have been built under the Soviet regime. Apparently the new rulers know no other grandeur to aspire to than that effected by the nobles of fifty or more years ago, for the new buildings have been constructed in the prerevolutionary style, and it is impossible to distinguish the new from the old. Both now serve as resort hotels and sanatoria for Soviet citizens who are lucky enough to be sent there for recreational or health purposes.

Two other cities, considerably larger in size, lie on the Crimean Peninsula. The first is Simferopol, with a population of 186,000, on the northern slopes of the Crimean Mountains, which is the seat of government for Crimea Oblast. It serves as the governmental, transport, and cultural center for Crimea, but its industries are only of local importance. To the southwest of Simferopol, on the southwest tip of the peninsula, is the important port and naval base of Sevastopol. Twice during the last century Sevastopol has gained world renown as a stronghold that stood up under long siege; first in the Crimean War, when it became the subject of Tennyson's famous poem, "The Charge of the Light Brigade," and again during World War II when it was attacked by the Germans.

One other Crimean city, Kerch, at the extreme eastern end of the peninsula has already been mentioned in conjunction with the industrial belt. In addition to being the center of the iron-mining district, Kerch is a seaport and a fish-processing center.

The Moldavian S.S.R.

The Moldavian Republic lies in the extreme southwestern corner of the Soviet Union in the Podolian Upland between the Dniester and Prut rivers. It was formed in 1940 largely from parts of the regions known as Bessarabia and Bukovina, which had just been annexed from Rumania, and from a small portion of the southwestern Ukraine, which had been part of the Moldavian A.S.S.R. It is interesting to note that although the Moldavian A.S.S.R. had existed for a number of years within the Ukrainian Republic, much of the territory that had been in the A.S.S.R. was left in the Ukraine when the Moldavian S.S.R. was established. This seems to indicate that the Moldavian A.S.S.R. had never had a majority of Moldavians in its population, which is supposedly the basis for the formation of such a political unit. Apparently the Moldavian A.S.S.R. had been created along the boundary of Rumania to induce the Moldavians in eastern Rumania to agitate for incorporation in the Soviet Union. (This technique has been used again and again along the borders of the Soviet Union and may be demonstrated in the north in the now defunct Karelo-Finnish Republic and in Soviet Middle Asia in the Tadzhik Republic bordering on Iran.) Sixty-five per cent of the people in this area are Moldavians who speak a Rumanian dialect and use the cyrillic alphabet. Approximately 14 per cent are Ukrainians, 10 per cent are Russians, mainly in the cities, and the remainder are Jews, Bulgars, Gypsies, Greeks, and Armenians.

Moldavia is the most densely populated (222 persons per square mile) republic in the Soviet Union. Large rural villages, with populations of more than 5000 people, line the river valleys and crowd the landscape in a dense pattern; only 22 per cent of the population is classified as urban. Kishinev, the capital, is its only city of any size; in 1959 it had a population of 216,000. Although this is nearly double the 1939 population, the growth of Kishinev has been more the result of its function as a capital than of its industrialization.

Moldavia has few natural resources other than the fertile soils and favorable climate for agriculture, so we might expect the region to remain predominantly rural. Climatically, it is one of the mildest parts of the Soviet Union.

Agriculturally, the Moldavian republic may be divided into three parts; the central zone is considerably higher and more rolling than either the north or the south. Elevations of slightly more than 1400 feet are reached where the loess-covered limestone upland has been deeply dissected from both sides by the tributaries of the Dniester and the Prut. The rougher portions of this upland are still covered by forest, whence comes the name "Kodry" (forest). The trees are oak, ash, maple, and other deciduous varieties, and the soils are gray-brown podzols. To the north of the Kodry lies the level Beltsy Steppe, which has good black soils and a fairly abundant supply of moisture. To the south lies the drier Budzhak Steppe, which also has black soils but is severely hampered by drought.

Grain and livestock raising predominate, but viticulture, the raising of fruits, nuts, and vegetables are most characteristic of the region. More than one fourth of all the vineyards of the U.S.S.R. are located in Moldavia. One might say that Moldavia is the Champagne of the Soviet Union. The principal wine-producing districts are in the

Kodry, in the picturesque hills around Kishinev.

Grain occupies 75 per cent of the sown area in Moldavia, principally in the northern and southern steppes, and corn is the chief grain crop, occupying at least one third of the grain fields. The entire corn plant is put to use; corn porridge is a staple food, and the stalks are used for fuel, in the building of fences, and in the thatching of roofs. Winter wheat is a valuable crop in the northern and southern portions of the republic,

Figure 5-11   Grape harvesting in Moldavia.   Novosti Press.

as are also barley and winter rye. Since this is a very mild area climatically, experimentation with a wide variety of crops has been carried on. Tobacco, sugar beets, soybeans, sunflowers, flax, hemp, opium poppies, mustard seed, kok-sagyz, castor beans, caraway seed, mint, rice in the Danube delta in the Izmail district, and cotton have been tried. Dairy cattle and hogs are raised in the north and sheep and goats in the south. In its middle and lower portions the Dniester flows entirely within the Moldavian Republic on a broad, well-watered flood plain, on which are found irrigated vegetable gardens flanked by strips of orchards. The banks of the valley are covered by vineyards, and grain, particularly corn, occupies the dry uplands away from the river.

Reading List

Atlas silskovo gospodarstva ukraynskoy RSR, Kiev, 1958. (in Ukrainian)

The European West

Region	Area (sq mile)	Population	People (sq mile)[a]	% Urban[a]
Within the R.S.R.S.R.				
Bryansk Oblast	13,600	1,550,000	115.0	35
Kaluga Oblast (Southwest four-fifths)	9,200[b]	642,000[b]	81.3	37
Smolensk Oblast	19,500	1,143,000	59.3	32
Kalinin Oblast (excluding Kalinin City and adjacent area)	26,400[b]	1,160,000[a]	55.4	44
Novgorod Oblast	21,600	736,000	34.4	38
Pskov Oblast	21,500	952,000	44.6	27
Leningrad Oblast	33,500	4,566,000	137.9	86
Kaliningrad Oblast	5,900	611,000	104.9	64
Belorussian S.S.R.	81,200	8,055,000	99.2	31
Lithuanian S.S.R.	25,500	2,711,000	107.7	39
Latvian S.S.R.	24,900	2,093,000	85.2	56
Estonian S.S.R.	17,600	1,197,000	68.6	56
Total	300,400[c]	25,416,000[c]		

[a] All figures are for entire regions.
[b] Estimated population and area of portion of region lying within the European West.
[c] Does not include western fringe of Moscow Oblast, which lies within the European West.

6

The European West

The region that here is called the European West stretches from the northern boundary of the Ukraine to the Baltic Sea and extends eastward to the boundary of the Central Industrial Region and westward to the international boundary with Poland. In the minds of the Russian people this is not a traditional region; rather, it includes within its boundaries several areas that they traditionally identify individually. Nevertheless, it is a fairly homogeneous area in terms of physical landscape and economic development, and it justifies treatment as a unit in spite of the fact that it combines several oblasts of the Russian Republic and the entire area of Belorussia and the three Baltic Republics—Lithuania, Latvia, and Estonia.

Within the Russian Republic, the area includes the following oblasts: in the southwest, Bryansk and about two thirds of Kaluga; in the west, Smolensk and the northwestern half of Kalinin Oblast, excluding the city of Kalinin which was included in the Central Industrial Region; and in the northwest, Novgorod, Pskov, and Leningrad Oblasts. In the extreme western part of the Soviet Union, bordering on Poland and the Baltic Sea west of Lithuania, is an isolated segment of the Russian Republic that was formed out of the northern part of what was East Prussia before World War II. This has been named Kaliningrad Oblast, and the old city of Koenigsberg has been renamed Kaliningrad. This oblast is part of the Russian Republic in spite of the fact that the Baltic Republics lie between it and the rest of the R.S.F.S.R. We might speculate that this region was considered too strategic to be placed under the jurisdiction of one of the adjacent Baltic Republics, and therefore it was placed under the direct jurisdiction of the Russian Republic. With the removal of most of the Germans after the war, Kaliningrad Oblast was resettled primarily by Russians so as far as nationality is concerned, the Russians can justify its inclusion in the Russian Republic.

Altogether, the European West contains approximately 25,416,000 people, who in most areas are rural dwellers. The population has not increased significantly since 1939; some areas that suffered heavily during World War II have less population now than they did before the war. This is particularly true of Belorussia and some of the newly acquired areas, such as Kaliningrad Oblast, where wholesale exchanges of nationality groups have taken place since the war. Population densities are lower here than in the areas to the south and the east, but they still are high enough to exert considerable pressure on the limited natural resources of the region. Population density and urbanization are highest in Leningrad Oblast

Figure 6-1   The European West.

because of the presence of the city of Leningrad, which is an urban anomaly sitting in an otherwise sparsely populated countryside.

The Physical Landscape

The European West is divided northwest and southeast along the southern limit of most recent glaciation by a rather prominent moraine oriented southwest-northeast through the cities of Minsk, Smolensk, and Moscow. To the northwest of the moraine lies an undulating glacial plain with many lakes and swamps and deranged streams. To the southeast the area generally is slightly hillier and somewhat better drained. Some of the southern portion also suffers from poor drainage, however. A broad swampy region, the Polesye, occupies a large section of land along the Pripyat River in southern Belorussia, and it presents a problem to the development of the republic. Some drainage has already been carried out in the Polesye, and there are plans for considerably more drainage to be done in the future. However, there still are large areas of the Polesye that are unusable, and some Soviet scientists fear that extensive drainage might upset the ground water balance so important to the drier areas to the south.

Because of the swamps in the northwest due to glaciation and in the southwest due to flatness, the Belorussian Republic is best suited for agriculture in the east, and it is here that the population densities are highest and the major cities of the republic are located. The terminal moraine running from Minsk to Moscow, the so-called "Smolensk-Moscow Ridge," is a little higher and better drained than the country on either side. On it are laid the major highway and railway from Warsaw to Moscow. It is along this route that armies from the west, including those of Napolean and Hitler, have invaded Russia to attack Moscow.

To the north of this terminal moraine the country is mainly one of glacial aspect, but in certain areas promontories induced by the structure of the underlying rock transcend the glacial features and rise above the general level of the terrain. One such area lies in eastern Latvia, in what is called Latgale. This is a region of hilly upland underlain by the eroded edge of a resistant sedimentary rock layer surmounted by irregu-

Figure 6-2 Digging drainage ditches in the swamps of the Polesye, Belorussia. Novosti Press.

lar heaps of glacial detritus. This upland extends into southern Estonia where elevations of over 1500 feet are reached.

Along the southern shore of the Gulf of Finland, in northern Estonia and Leningrad Oblast, the eroded edge of a hard layer of limestone forms an abrupt escarpment a short distance back from the seacoast, which rises as high as 450 feet above the narrow terrace that skirts the Gulf. This long cliff of flinty rock is known as the "Glint"; its eroded remnants form literally hundreds of islands in the Baltic Sea along the northern coast of Estonia. The eastern arm of the Baltic and its extension, the Gulf of Finland, lie in an inner lowland along the northern edge of this outcropping cuesta escarpment. Farther west, along the Gulf of Riga and southwestward, the coastal hills become much lower, and long offshore bars paralleling the coast for many miles provide excellent sandy beaches. One bar, over 50 miles long, has completely enclosed the outlet of the Neman River in Kaliningrad Oblast and western Lithuania to produce a stagnant lagoon and swampy delta plain.

In the Russian Republic northwest of Moscow, the Valday Hills, a dissected cuesta escarpment partially covered by moraines and other glacial debris, reach elevations slightly over 1000 feet and form the drainage divide between the headwaters of the four main river systems of the area—the Volga, the Dnieper, the Western Dvina (Daugava), and the Msta. In effect, these rivers are connected at their sources in a vast, mossy bog overgrown by forest.

Natural Resources and Economy

In spite of the fact that this western portion of the Soviet Union is one of the older civilized areas of the country with fairly advanced cultures in such areas as the Baltic Republics, it remains one of the least economically developed parts of the Soviet Union. This lack of development can be understood by a cursory glance at its natural resources.

Agriculture   Climatically the area is cool and moist. These conditions have been conducive to the growth of a mixed forest vegetation and the development of podzolic soils. The infertile soils coupled with poor drainage definitely limit agricultural possibilities. The main crops are flax, small grains other than wheat, hay, and potatoes. Sugar beets are being introduced slowly, and corn for silage is now being grown. Other than these crops, a variety of hardy vegetables and fruits are grown for local consumption. Dairying and hog and poultry raising are becoming increasingly important. Much of the agriculture is carried on in almost a subsistence manner, and the rural population is rather sparse and widely scattered. The rural villages diminish in size steadily from the Ukraine northward through Belorussia and the Baltic Republics, until we find in Estonia villages of only two or three homesteads, and indeed, even separate homesteads on individual farms. The people of this area have carried on some agriculture for centuries in spite of the shortcomings of the natural environment, but the area has never been a prime agricultural region. In general, agriculture improves southeastward as the climate becomes warmer and drier, the soils become more fertile, and the drainage improves. Bryansk Oblast contains the best agricultural land in the region.

In spite of the limited nature of the agricultural resource of this area, it is the main resource, and agricultural products are the main bases for the light industries that have developed. Such industries as food processing, particularly of dairy products, tanning and leather working, flax retting, brush making from hog bristles utilize the local products and excess labor and serve local and, in some cases, national markets.

Forestry   Other industries are based on the forest resources, which is the second most important resource in the area. Forests still cover approximately 25 per cent of the total

Figure 6-3   Flax harvesting near Minsk, Belorussia.   Novosti Press.

area, and in some places in the Baltic Republics they cover as much as 50 per cent of the land. Woodworking of all sorts is important; the manufacture of furniture, prefabricated houses, and matches is of nation-wide significance.

Fishing and Shipping Fishing is important in the Baltic as well as in the many inland lakes and streams, and the cities along the Baltic are significant to the Soviet Union as seaports. Ice covers the eastern arm of the Baltic part of the year and hampers the Gulf of Riga to a certain extent, but southwest of the Gulf of Riga lie the minor seaports of Ventspils and Liepaya, which are used the year around. Kaliningrad, the old Prussian city of Koenigsberg, at the most westerly position in the Soviet Union, might eventually become one of the major seaports of the country. So far there is no indication that this is to take place; perhaps the Russians are still wary of holding this western position permanently.

Inland waterways are limited in size. The chief one connects Leningrad eastward through the Great Lakes to the Baltic-White Sea Canal in the north and the old Mariinsk Canal system to the south. Canals skirting the southern shores of Lakes Ladoga and Onega link the Neva and Svir rivers to form a navigable waterway from Lake Onega to the Gulf of Finland. The Great Lakes themselves cannot be used because storm waves on them capsize the small canal boats. A little traffic moves on the two main rivers of the West, the Western Dvina and the Neman, but navigation is limited to very small boats. It now is planned to improve navigation on the Western Dvina and to construct a cascade of reservoirs for the production of hydroelectricity.

Minerals   Mineral resources are limited to the oil shale of eastern Estonia, the bauxite deposits at Boksitogorsk east of Tikhvin in Leningrad Oblast, and a newly opened potash deposit in south-central Belorussia near Starobin. The oil shale covers a fairly extensive area along the shores of Lake Chudskoe and north along the Narva River to the Baltic. A pipeline has been carrying gas products from this area eastward to Leningrad and westward to Tallin for a number of years, but no notable expansion of this operation can be anticipated in the light of greatly increased oil and gas production in other parts of the country. Pipelines from the Volga-Urals oil fields and the North Caucasian and Western Ukrainian gas fields are now being constructed to Leningrad, Riga, Minsk, and other major cities of the northwest. Oil refineries are being built at Kirishi 60 miles southeast of Leningrad and Polotsk in Belorussia to refine Volga-Urals crude oil.

The alumina and aluminum plant at Volkhov, opened in 1932 to utilize the bauxite ore at Boksitogorsk and electricity

of the newly constructed Volkhov hydroelectric plant, was the first plant to produce aluminum in the country, but the aluminum content in the red clay hills east of Tikhvin is not high, and already the plant at Volkhov has been switched partially to the use of nephelite from the Kola Peninsula far to the north. Newer plants in the Urals, the Ukraine, and Transcaucasia have already eclipsed the operation at Volkhov.

The potash deposit in Belorussia is auspiciously located to provide for the development of a large mineral fertilizer industry to serve the needs of this agricultural area with its mineral-poor soils. Other than these minerals, building stone, gypsum and limestone for cement, clay, sand, etc. are of local significance.

Many of the light industries of the area are those typically developed to utilize the skills of the people to produce small products of advanced design to capture national markets. In the Park of Economic Achievements in Moscow the pavilions of the Baltic Republics display wide assortments of small consumer items patterned after modern designs so characteristic of the Scandinavian area. Modern furniture, cooking utensils, dishes, and household gadgets dominate the displays.

Cities

The cities of this western region are not large, except for Leningrad and some of the capitals of the non-Russian republics. In general, the populations of the capital cities have increased rapidly while those of other cities have increased slowly or not at all.

Leningrad   By far the largest city in this area, and second largest in the Soviet Union, is Leningrad, which in 1959 had a population of 3,300,000. This is slightly smaller than it was in 1939. Leningrad suffered terribly during the war, when, for more than 900 consecutive days it was under continuous siege by the German army. Since the war, a principle has been established that population migration into the larger cities, particularly into Leningrad, will be prohibited. Therefore we might expect that the Leningrad population never again will reach its prewar level.

Nevertheless, Leningrad is a great city, having served as capital of the Russian Empire from its founding by Peter the Great in 1713 until after the Revolution in 1919. It was Peter's "window on the west" which was built in the swamps of the delta of the Neva River at the cost of the lives of many Russian peasants. In spite of the fact that it was situated in a forested wilderness of poorly drained podzol soils with meager possibilities for agriculture, its artificial auspices as the capital of the Russian Empire and as the main contact with the rest of Europe caused it to prosper and grow into the largest city of the Russian Empire at the time of the Revolution. From 1713 to 1914 it was known as St. Petersburg, but in 1914, after the beginning of World War I, it was renamed Petrograd, to eliminate the German terminology. In 1924, after Lenin's death, it was named Leningrad to commemorate the foremost leader of the Revolution.

Leningrad has the most vivid history of any of the cities in the Soviet Union, having acted as the capital during the momentous years of the growth of the Russian Empire which culminated in the Revolution and the formation of the Soviet Union. Tsarist society reached its zenith here and left its mark in the many monumental buildings and spacious grounds, and the revolutionary resistance groups formed and grew up in St. Petersburg under the very eyes of the so-called "Third Section," the secret police arm of the tsars. Although Leningrad is not looked on so much as an indigenous Russian city as Moscow is, and although it is losing out to Moscow in most aspects of economic and cultural life, it still is a showplace of the Soviet Union for tourists. It is curious to witness the Russian guides expound about the monuments left by the tsars while at the same time consciously trying to eliminate mention of the tsars from their explanations. There are some tsars, such as Peter the Great, who have been adopted by the Soviets as being revolutionaries and ahead of their times, and these are eulogized to a considerable degree. However, it is hard to reconcile present Soviet ideology with the fact that one is being guided through one of the most elaborate displays of material wealth on earth in the Hermitage Museum. And the Russian Museum in Leningrad is perhaps an even greater contradiction; it contains all of what is considered to be great of Russian painting, and practically all of the huge murals and paintings on the walls have religious themes. It is truly a startling experience to listen to the atheistic Soviet guide explain the religious theme of each painting when it is quite obvious that she has never read the Bible!

Leningrad is built on the many low, muddy islands that separate the distributaries of the delta of the Neva River. With its more than 500 bridges, it has been likened to Venice in Italy. Although it is only 50 miles long, the Neva is about a mile wide and it has a consistant flow because it drains the large glacial Lake Ladoga into the Gulf of Finland. The river does not flood, but the delta on which Leningrad sits is so flat and so low above the sea that a strong west wind can raise the water level in the Gulf of Finland enough to innundate the lower sections of the city. Such floods have occurred from time to time, and especially high floods have occurred exactly 100 years apart, in 1824 and in 1924. Placards on some of the main buildings along the Nevsky Prospect mark the water levels reached by these floods.

Nevsky Prospect, the main street of Leningrad, is lined by rows of five-story buildings that culminate at the southeast bank of the Bolshaya Neva, the main distributary of the Neva River, in a series of large squares surrounded by palaces, government buildings, and monuments reminiscent of Empire days.

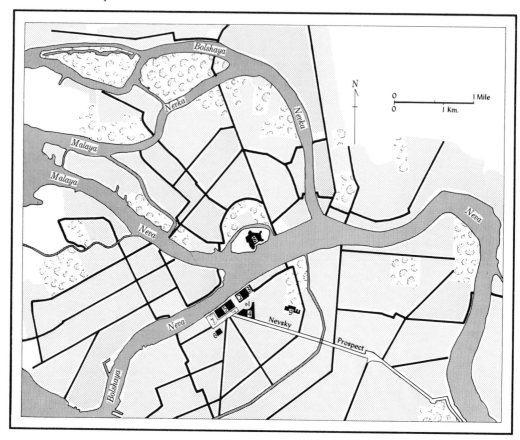

Figure 6-4 Downtown Leningrad. 1. Palace Square. 2. Winter Palace. 3. Hermitage Museum. 4. General Staff Building. 5. Admiralty Building. 6. St. Isaac's Cathedral. 7. Decembrists' Square. 8. Sts. Peter and Paul Fortress. 9. Russian Museum.

The largest of these squares is the so-called Palace Square hemmed in by the Winter Palace and the Hermitage Museum along the river, the semicircular arc of the General Staff Building, and the Admiralty Building with its gilded spire. In the center of the square a slender red granite monolith 150 feet high, with the figure of an angel at the top, commemorates the victory over Napolean. Another square is dominated by the massive St. Isaac's Cathedral, whose dome reaches an elevation of 330 feet, the highest point in the city. In front of it, Decembrists' Square, a broad formal garden, is fronted on the river by a 4000-ton, rough-hewn granite monolith surmounted by the figure of Peter the Great on a rearing horse.

Most of these monumental buildings are painted pale yellow and trimmed in pale green in classic style, although many of them look as if they have had very little paint added to them since the Revolution. The Winter Palace is perhaps the most imposing structure; a five-story green building facing on the Neva River, it served as the home of the royal family during the long winters in Petersburg. During the reign of Catherine the Great a large addition was added to the building to provide for a private art gallery for Catherine. This addition has become the Hermitage Museum, which houses one of the most elaborate collections in the world. Outside, the Hermitage and the Winter Palace appear as dull, dirty green buildings, but inside all is polished mahogany and gold leaf with crystal chandeliers dominating the rooms.

On an island across the broad channel of the River Neva sits the red brick-walled fortress of Saints Peter and Paul, which in the beginning served as the kremlin for the initial town in the area. At that time the fort was composed of crude buildings enclosed by a log and earthen wall. Later, the wall was replaced by granite and brick, and more imposing cathedrals and governmental buildings were built inside. The cathedrals eventually became the burying places for the tsars, and the casement walls became one of the most infamous prisons in the Russian Empire. During the second half of the nineteenth century, practically every person in Russia who did any thinking at all was imprisoned sooner or later in Sts. Peter and Paul Fortress.

Fringing Leningrad on the south and west are a number of old tsarist estates which in most cases served as the summer homes for the royal family. The best preserved of these is Petrodvorets, about 20 miles southwest of Leningrad, along the southern shores of the Gulf of Finland. Here again we find the pale yellow buildings with gold leaf trim, but they are in much better repair and are much shinier in appearance than are the buildings in Leningrad. The huge grounds surrounding the palace are landscaped with literally hundreds of fountains in various arrays, which are fed by a natural head of water from the limestone escarpment to the south. Farther east are other tsarist grounds, the most elaborate of which is Tsarskoye Selo, the "tsar's village," which since the Revolution has been renamed Pushkin, because Alexander Pushkin attended a lycee near there. Pushkin was occupied by the Germans for a considerable time during World War II. A good deal of damage was wrought, and many art treasures were carried off. The Russians are restoring the area and making it into a combination museum and weekend recreation park.

As has been pointed out before, Leningrad was besieged during World War II for a period of almost 3 years. During this time the German armies had the city nearly encircled, except for a narrow strip along its eastern edge, and they constantly lobbed artillery shells into the city and staged air raids to bomb the city. Throughout this long period the people of Leningrad, in the face of death from starvation, freezing, and

Figure 6-5 The Winter Palace across Palace Square, Leningrad. The granite spire commemorates the 1812 victory over Napoleon. It is surmounted by the figure of an angel with the face of Alexander I. Photograph by the author.

Figure 6-6 Peterhof (Petrodvorets). Peter the Great's summer palace is noted for its beautiful displays of fountains. Photograph by the author.

disease, as well as from artillery shells and other instruments of war, maintained a spirit of resistance that enabled them to emerge victorious. There was a saying during this period that "one could go to the front by tram." A so-called "Road of Life" was kept open to the east, through the narrow neck of land that was not held by the Germans, to Lake Ladoga and then across the Lake to what the Russians termed the "Mainland," which was unoccupied during the war. Travel across Lake Ladoga was limited primarily to winter when the lake was frozen over and a road could be established across the ice with trucks moving in long caravans carrying supplies of food and ammunition into Leningrad and women, children, and wounded out of Leningrad. The Germans continually bombed the caravans and blew big holes in the ice, but the Russian Army was able to keep a route posted across the ice with soldiers acting as traffic cops to guide the trucks around the holes. Such caravans of trucks, however, could not compensate fully for the seven railroads that normally fed the city, and many people died of famine and freezing, due to lack of food and fuel. Those in the lower age groups were particularly vulnerable; it has been reported that infant mortality rose to 75 per cent. As a result of its great resistance during World War II, Leningrad has been

designated as a hero city along with Moscow and Volgograd.

It was in St. Petersburg that the Industrial Revolution made its greatest inroads in the 1890's. Here a semiskilled labor pool, or proletariat, was developed and here the prototypes of all sorts of industrial products were manufactured. The first synthetic rubber was produced in Leningrad in the 1930's. Moscow, under the Soviets, largely has preempted these functions of industry and culture from Leningrad, but Leningrad still has a monopoly on certain industries that require special skills, such as the manufacture of very fine machine tools and giant hydroelectric turbines. The chief industries in Leningrad at present are the machine-building industries, the chemical industries, textiles, food, and printing. All raw materials for the industry of Leningrad must be brought in from other parts of the Soviet Union, and many of the finished products of the region must find markets in the rest of the country. Leningrad utilizes about 10 per cent of the steel output of the U.S.S.R. It brings in coal from Vorkuta in the far northeast corner of European Russia, iron ore from the Kola Peninsula and the Karelian A.S.S.R., oil products and natural gas from the northern Caucasus, cotton from Middle Asia, and food products of all kinds from the south. The main steel center to serve the machine industries of Leningrad has been established in Cherepovets, at the north end of the Rybinsk Reservoir, utilizing coal from Vorkuta and iron ore from the Kola Peninsula. Shipbuilding is an important industry, as might be expected in the biggest port in the country. Kronshtadt, an important naval base, was constructed during Russian Empire days on Kotlin Island offshore in the Gulf of Finland.

Riga The second city in size in the European West is Riga, the capital of Latvia, with a population of 580,000. Riga has long served as the focal city of the Latvian nationality group, and between the two world wars it served as the capital of the free republic of Latvia. Sitting on the shore of the Gulf of Riga at the mouth of the Western Dvina River, it has been one of the major ports along the Baltic from early times, and during the Middle Ages it became one of the Hanseatic League cities. Its main function, therefore, is one of commerce, with such industries as shipbuilding and fishing being of prime importance. Other than these functions, its industries are primarily those to serve the local market and to make use of some of the local products, such as the food and textile industries.

Minsk Third in size in the European West is Minsk, the capital of the Belorussian Republic, with a population of 509,000. Minsk long has served as the center of the Belorussian nationality group, although this group has not always enjoyed political identity. In fact, Minsk has never been the capital of an independent country; the area of Belorussia has always existed either within the Russian Empire or within some empire to the west, such as the Polish-Lithuanian Empire in the seventeenth and eighteenth centuries. Since World War II, the boundaries of Belorussia have been pushed westward into territory that has been eastern Poland between the World Wars, so that now Minsk occupies almost an exact central position in the Belorussian Republic. Serving simply as the capital city of this republic and as the commercial center for the region, Minsk has a variety of light industries and is an important transport center. Recently, machine-building industries, such as a truck assembly plant, have been introduced into Minsk to bolster the economy of the Republic.

Tallin Fourth in size is Tallin, the old city of Reval, which now serves as the capital for the Estonian Republic. Besides serving as a capital, Tallin is a fairly important port on the Baltic Sea, and it contains a variety of light industries to utilize the products of local agriculture and fishing and to serve the local market. In 1959 Tallin had a population of 282,000.

Vilnyus Fifth in size is Vilnyus, the capital of the Lithuanian Republic, which in 1959 had a population of 236,000. Vilnyus is located inland, and therefore does not enjoy a port function as do Riga and Tallin, and it has not grown as fast as they have. It is simply the seat of government and a center of light industries and transport within the Lithuanian Republic.

Bryansk Sixth in size is Bryansk with a population of 207,000. It is a regional center within a rich agricultural area in southwestern R.S.F.S.R.

Kaliningrad Seventh in size is Kaliningrad with a population of 204,000. Kaliningrad is the old city of Koenigsberg, which was the main seaport in the section of East Prussia that was taken over by the Russians after World War II. Kaliningrad has only about half the population of the former city of Koenigsberg, and so far it has not assumed the importance as a seaport that Koenigsberg had. However, in the future we might expect that Kaliningrad might become a more important port to the Soviet Union since it is the most western of the major ports on the Baltic and is therefore the least hampered by ice during the winter. Perhaps the slowness of the development of Kaliningrad so far has been due to a fear on the part of the Russians that this westernmost point is too exposed to risk a great buildup at present.

Other Cities Next in size are a couple of cities in the eastern part of the Belorussian Republic; Gomel, with a population of 168,000, and Vitebsk, with a population of 148,000. These cities have largely stagnated during the Soviet period; lack of growth is common throughout this western area with the exception of the capital cities.

One other city that might be mentioned in Russia is Smolensk, with a population of 147,000, which, like Vitebsk, suffered heavily during the war, and now has a population less than it had in 1939. Smolensk lies on the direct route of invasion from the west toward Moscow, about halfway between Minsk and Moscow along the so-called Smolensk-Moscow Ridge, the terminal moraine or high ground along which the major highway is laid. Founded in 882, Smolensk is one of the oldest cities in the country. It has suffered the first blows of many wars between Muscovy and western powers, and it has changed hands many times between Russia, Poland and other states. It is the seat of government for Smolensk Oblast and the commercial center for a relatively poor agricultural area.

Besides these major cities, mention might be made of some smaller seaports on the Baltic: Klaypeda in Lithuania, which is the old town of Memel, and the towns of Liepaya and Ventspils in Latvia. Another important old town lies in southeastern Estonia and is now named Tartu. This is the old university city of Dorpat.

Reading List

Atlas of Belorussia. (in Russian)

French, R. A., "Drainage and Economic Development of Polesye, U.S.S.R.," *Economic Geography,* April 1959, 172–180.

Taskin, George A., "The Soviet Northwest: Economic Regionization," *The Geographical Review,* April 1961, 213–235. Vakar, Nicholas P., *Belorussia: The Making of a Nation,* Harvard University Press, Cambridge, Mass., 1956, 297 pp.

The European North

Region	Area (sq mile)	Population	People (sq mile)[a]	% Urban[a]
Karelian A.S.S.R.	67,400	651,000	9.8	63
Murmansk Oblast	56,600	568,000	10.1	92
Archangel Oblast	229,000	1,276,000	5.7	53
Nenets National Okrug	69,000	46,000	0.8	56
Vologda Oblast	56,900	1,308,000	23.3	35
Kirov Oblast (Northern half excluding Kirov City)	23,900[b]	840,000[b]	40.4	37
Kostroma Oblast (Excluding southwest quarter and Kostroma City)	17,600[b]	500,000[b]	39.6	39
Komi A.S.S.R.	163,000	806,000	5.2	59
Total	614,400	5,949,000		

[a] All figures are for entire regions.

[b] Estimated population and area of portion of region lying within the European North.

7

The European North

The vast expanse of territory in eastern Europe lying mostly north of the 60th parallel and extending from the Finnish border on the west to the Ural Mountains in the east is variously known to the Russians as the European North, or, dividing it in two parts, as the European Northwest and the European Northeast. In the south it begins with the transition zones of the various regions previously discussed, the Volga Region in the east, the Central Industrial Region in the center, and the European West in the west, and it stretches northward through a primarily nonagricultural, forested and tundra area to the shores of the Arctic. The northern fringes of the three regions to the south already showed some of the characteristics of this area: the thinning of agriculture, the beginnings of dense stands of coniferous forest, cool moist climatic conditions, and podzol soils. These conditions are climaxed in the area now under consideration.

Politically this area includes the Karelian A.S.S.R. and Murmansk Oblast in the west and the large areas of Archangel Oblast and the Komi A.S.S.R. in the east, as well as Vologda Oblast and large northern sections of Kostroma and Kirov Oblasts in the south. Altogether the area is comprised of more than 600,000 square miles and contains almost six million people. With a population density of 10 people per square mile, this is the emptiest area considered thus far. The entire area lies within the Russian Republic, but it includes three areas of predominantly non-Russian peoples or of populations with large minority non-Russian groups. Two of these non-Russian areas make up two autonomous republics, the Karelian A.S.S.R. in the west and the Komi A.S.S.R. in the east. The third non-Russian area is the Nenets National Okrug, a sparsely populated region of primitive nomads, which lies within Archangel Oblast.

The entire area is quite homogeneous in climate, which is primarily subarctic with a tundra fringe along the north, in soils, which are everywhere podzols and tundra; and in drainage, which everywhere is exceedingly poor. Geologically, however, the west is very different from the east, and on this basis the area is often divided into two regions. The Karelian A.S.S.R. and Murmansk Oblast in the west are part of the Scandinavian Shield, an area of ancient crystalline rocks which has recently acted as the center for continental glaciation. Thus it is a region of ice-scoured bedrock, rough, rolling topography, and thousands of lakes. On the other hand, much of Archangel Oblast and the Komi A.S.S.R. to the east is an exceedingly flat, low-lying plain underlain by nearly horizontal sedimentary rocks. The eastern

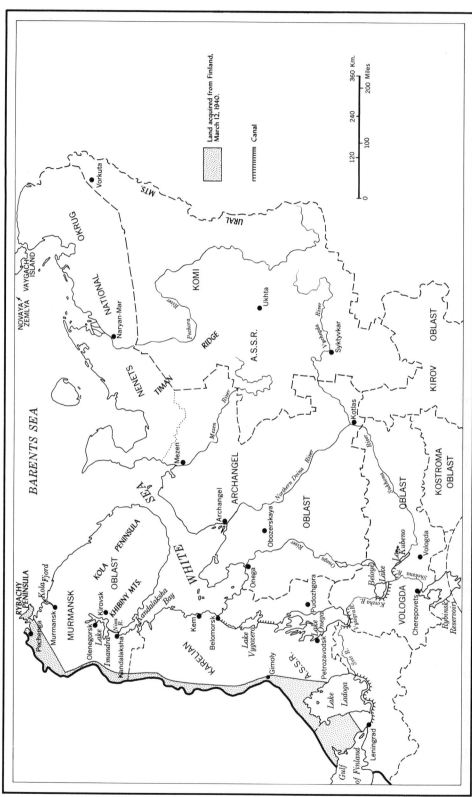

Figure 7-1 The European North.

part of this section, in the Komi A.S.S.R. and the Nenets National Okrug, is particularly flat because a postglacial inundation from the Arctic Seas rewashed what thin glacial deposits there were and produced a surface almost as flat as a floor.

Vologda, Kostroma, and Kirov Oblasts also are underlain by horizontal sedimentary rocks that have recently been covered with glacial till, but they lie in a transition area climatically, so that agricultural possibilities are considerably greater here than they are in the Archangel and Komi areas. Hence this southern region might be considered separately as a third subregion of the European North. Therefore the area will be discussed in three sections: the northwest, the northeast, and the south.

The Karelian A.S.S.R. and Murmansk Oblast

Territorial Development Parts of the Karelia-Kola Peninsula region have changed hands internationally through the centuries between Russia, Finland, and Sweden, and several boundary adjustments were made between Finland and the Soviet Union during the Russo-Finnish War early in the period of World War II. When the Soviet Union was constituted in 1923, the Karelian Area was made into the Karelian A.S.S.R. within the Russian Republic to give recognition to the Karelian nationality group. Then in 1940, with the onset of World War II, the area was reconstituted into the Karelo-Finnish S.S.R., apparently to entice the Finns to be more kindly disposed toward the Russians. It is quite obvious now that this was purely a political maneuver, since in 1956, without any forewarning or explanation, the union republic was downgraded once more to an autonomous republic and again was placed under the jurisdiction of the Russian Republic. The area never did warrant union republic status according to the constitution, which states that in order for an area to

become a union republic it must have at least one million people with a majority of those people being of the titular nationality. The Karelian A.S.S.R. in 1959 had only 649,000 people; slightly less than one-fourth of them were of Karelian and Finnish stock, and over 65 per cent were Russian.

As a result of World War II, several minor boundary changes took place along the Finno-Russian border, with the largest areas going to the Russians in the extreme north and the extreme south. The Pechenga area in the north, or Petsamo as it was known by the Finns, is an area with important nickel and copper deposits. This area, along with the Rybachy Peninsula, or "Fishermen's Peninsula," were taken over by the Russians in two different maneuvers in 1940 and in 1944. In the south, the entire Karelian Isthmus between Leningrad and Vyborg was ceded to the Soviet Union by the Finns, and this area was placed under the jurisdiction of Leningrad Oblast, probably for strategic and economic reasons. Besides the acquisition of these territories, the Russians acquired the lease of land west of Helsinki for military purposes, but this lease has since been relinquished.

Geology and Topography As has been stated before, the Karelia-Kola Peninsula area is an ancient crystalline shield that has been worn down essentially to a rough peneplain by millions of years of stream erosion and recently has been heavily ice scoured, since it acted as a center of glaciation during the Pleistocene. Thus the topography is one of a rolling plain that here and there rises into hills or even low, eroded mountains. Rough, bare bedrock outcrops at the surface in many places among the myriad of lakes, swamps, and marshes. Within the Karelian A.S.S.R. elevations do not reach much above 1500 feet, but in Murmansk Oblast the Khibiny Mountains rise to heights of slightly more than 3800 feet. This is well above the tree line at these latitudes so that the mountains have a truly alpine character with tundra vegetation and glacial features.

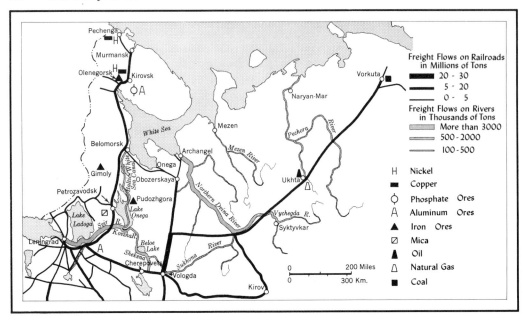

Figure 7-2   Rail and river freight traffic and mineral resources of the European North.   Adapted from Soviet Geography: Review and Translation, *June 1961, pp. 66–67.*

Climate, Vegetation, and Soils   Throughout the Karelian area the subarctic climate has been conducive to a fairly good stand of coniferous trees, chiefly pine and fir; the Karelian A.S.S.R. is second only to Archangel Oblast in lumber production in the Soviet Union.   Much of Murmansk Oblast, on the other hand, is tundra-like because of its high latitude and somewhat higher elevation; thus lumbering is relatively unimportant in this region.   The soils and drainage conditions throughout both areas are extremely poor, and agriculture is significant only in southern Karelia.

Minerals   The complex rocks that outcrop at the surface make for a wide variety of possibilities in mineral resources, and it is largely because of the opening of some mining areas that Murmansk Oblast has developed rather rapidly under the Soviets.   The fact that the population of Murmansk Oblast in 1959 was classified as being 92 per cent urban attests to the insignificance of agriculture as compared to the importance of mining, fishing, and trading.

The most significant mining area at present is in the vicinity of the new city of Kirovsk in the Khibiny Mountains in central Murmansk Oblast.   Here are found the greatest known deposits of apatite in the world, which serve as the basis for a large phosphate fertilizer industry, primarily in Leningrad, and nephelite, which recently is being utilized in the production of aluminum at Kandalaksha and at Volkhov.   Across Lake Imandra, in the region that is known as Monche Tundra, lie important ores of nickel and copper.   In the far northwestern corner of Murmansk Oblast, in the area known as Pechenga, is another important deposit of nickel and some copper.   Low-grade iron deposits are scattered throughout the area, often as residue of leaching in glacial lake beds, with significant deposits at Olenegorsk in Murmansk Oblast and at Gimoly and Pudozhgora in the Karelian A.S.S.R.   Iron concentrate is shipped by rail from Olenegorsk to Cherepovets at the northern end of the Rybinsk Reservoir for conversion into steel utilizing coal from Vorkuta.   Besides these major ores, about sixty other useful elements appear in lesser quantities, and some of them are now being utilized. Such things as titanium, radium, zirconium, and molybdenum are being used in small quantities, and the largest mica plant in the Soviet Union is located in Petrozavodsk on the western shore of Lake Onega.

Fish Other than mining and lumbering, fishing is very important throughout much of the area. Since World War II the Barents Sea has become the second most important fishing area in the Soviet Union, exceeded only by the Sea of Okhotsk in the Far East. In the mixture of waters between the warm Gulf Stream coming around the northern end of Scandinavia and the cold water of the Arctic Ocean a rich growth of plankton feeds large numbers of cod, herring, sea perch, etc. Murmansk is the main base of the fishing fleet in the Barents Sea, and serves as the most important fish canning and processing center as well. Along the western shore of the White Sea lie three other important fishing centers—Kandalaksha in the north and Kem and Belomorsk farther south. Besides these major centers, many small centers of fishing exist, either along the seacoast or along the many interior lakes and streams.

Water Power The area contains considerable water power resources, although the streams are frozen a good portion of the year. Some of these resources have been developed by the Soviets, with one of the larger hydroelectric plants being established

Figure 7-3 Part of the fishing fleet in Murmansk harbor. Note the barren, rocky cliffs of the ice-scoured, tundra shore. Novosti Press.

on the Niva River, flowing southward from the Khibiny Mountains into Kandalaksha Bay. This short river cascades swiftly down a steep rocky slope and does not freeze enough during the winter to stop hydro-electric production. The city of Kandal-aksha has acquired an aluminum industry based on hydroelectricity from the dam and the nephelite ore of the Khibiny Mountains, which originally was discarded as waste from the apatite mines.

Transportation A major waterway that has been developed by the Soviets is the Stalin White Sea–Baltic Canal, which was opened in 1933. This leads southwestward from the White Sea at Belomorsk utilizing many lakes, such as Lake Vygozero, or Crescent Lake, in its course to Lake Onega 140 miles away. From Lake Onega west-ward this system links up with the canal system that leads down the Svir River to Lake Ladoga, around the southern end of Lake Ladoga, and then down the Neva to Leningrad and the Baltic Sea. The stretch of canal from Belomorsk to Lake Onega utilizes nineteen locks. During World War II the Finns destroyed much of the system, but it was quickly reconstructed after the war.

Of course the canal is closed by ice at least half of the year so that the region still is dependent primarily on the railroad. The main line, the Kirov Railroad, was con-structed in 1916 from Leningrad northward to Murmansk. During the early part of World War II, when great quantities of lend-lease materials were being shipped into Murmansk and when Leningrad was almost surrounded by the Germans, the so-called "Obozerskaya Bypass" was built leading off from the Kirov Railroad at Belomorsk and going eastward around the southern end of the White Sea to Obozerskaya, on the rail line running from Archangel to Moscow. This provided an all-rail route from Mur-mansk to the Moscow area without going through occupied territory. In December 1960 a railroad was opened from Murmansk to Pechenga. But in winter even the rail-roads are difficult to maintain, and trans-portation remains a grave problem through-out the area.

Cities There are few cities in this western region. Murmansk is by far the largest city, with a 1959 population of 222,000. This makes it the largest polar city in the world. Founded in 1915 at the northern terminus of the Kirov Railroad, Murmansk has grown during the Soviet period from a town of 8777 persons in 1926 to its present size because of its importance as a northern sea-port in the center of a large fishing industry. The city sits in a somewhat sheltered posi-tion near the head of Kola Fjord about 40 miles from the sea. Although the climate here is cold and raw much of the year, the sea remains ice-free in the winter because of the Gulf Stream. Murmansk replaces Len-ingrad as the northern port of the Soviet Union from December to May. As the home base for the fishing fleets in the Barents Sea and the western terminus of the North-ern Sea Route, it has developed important shipbuilding and ship repair yards. Much of the apatite of the Kirovsk area moves through the port of Murmansk. During World War II it served as the port of entry for most of the lend-lease goods shipped from the United States to the U.S.S.R.

Second in size is Petrozavodsk, the capital of the Karelian A.S.S.R., with a population of 136,000. Petrozavodsk, or "Peter's Plant," owes its name to the fact that Peter the Great established a rudimentary steel plant on the west shore of Lake Onega during his reign. Petrozavodsk is simply a regional center and a governmental seat that has undergone some minor developments of industry.

The other city of importance is Kirovsk. Before the opening of the apatite and nephe-lite mines in the early 1930's the Kirovsk area was nothing but open tundra land peo-pled only by nomadic reindeer herders. Within the course of 2 or 3 years it was developed into a mining boomtown.

The major lumber port within the area is Belomorsk, but Leningrad handles more Karelian lumber than any city within Karelia itself.

Archangel Oblast and the Komi A.S.S.R.

Topography The second subregion, consisting of Archangel Oblast and the Komi A.S.S.R., as noted before, is a very flat glacial plain which in recent geological times was inundated by the Arctic seas. A low anticlinal upwarp, the Timan Ridge, forms a slightly higher, more eroded area in the central part and separates the drainage basins of the Northern Dvina and the Pechora rivers. Along the eastern border of the Komi Republic lie the Ural Mountains, but their description will be deferred until the entire chain of mountains is considered. It must be noted here, however, that the northwestward extension of a branch of the Northern Urals, the Pay-Khoy, continues as Vaygach Island and Novaya Zemlya, both of which, along with Franz Josef Land, are under the jurisdiction of Archangel Oblast. Novaya Zemlya is a steep, rocky, treeless island that culminates in an elevation of 3640 feet. Heavily glaciated, it is notched by deep fjords, one of which cuts the island in two at Matochkin Shar, which is a narrow strait connecting the Barents and Kara Seas. Glaciers still exist in some of the higher elevations on Novaya Zemlya as well as on most of Franz Josef Land to the north.

Forestry The most significant resource of this area is its forests, with Archangel Oblast being the first producer of timber in the Soviet Union, and the city of Archangel being the most important lumber port. Thirteen per cent of the nation's timber and two thirds of all the sawn lumber exported from the Soviet Union comes from the European northeast. The most common trees are spruce and Scotch Pine. From May to October logs are floated down the Vychegda and other tributaries of the Northern Dvina.

Floating fences of connecting logs across the streams at constrictions and tributary junctions temporarily catch the logs in ponds for sorting and raft formation. The logs are usually rafted together and pulled by tugs over smooth stretches of the rivers and across lakes, but the rafts are broken up and the logs are floated separately down swift stretches containing rapids. Log rafts may be lashed together and broken apart at several different points along the streams before the logs finally reach Archangel. Because of the log rafting, the Northern Dvina ranks second only to the Volga among rivers in the U.S.S.R. in total freight moved.

At Archangel the logs are piled in long rows along the many distributaries in the delta of the Northern Dvina. By fall, Archangel appears to be nothing more than a series of watery corridors between piles of logs. Over 150 sawmills operate during the winter to convert the logs into lumber, which is shipped out after the ice breaks up in the White Sea in the spring.

Most of the other rivers in the area are utilized for log floating also, but the prime timber is in the western section between the Northern Dvina and the smaller Onega River. The small town of Onega at the mouth of the Onega River is an important lumber port. The Mezen River east of the Northern Dvina also has good stands of timber along its banks, and the town of Mezen at its mouth is a little Archangel. Some timber is floated down the Pechora to Naryan-Mar, the capital of the Nenets National Okrug, but compared to the basin of the Northern Dvina the Pechora Basin is relatively insignificant in lumber production. The entire Nenets National Okrug lies within the tundra.

Several towns in the interior also are important lumber milling centers, such as Syktyvkar, the capital of the Komi Republic, on the Vychegda River, and Kotlas at the important junction of the Vychegda and the Northern Dvina rivers and the Pechora Railroad. Strings of sawmills are located in smaller towns along both the Northern and

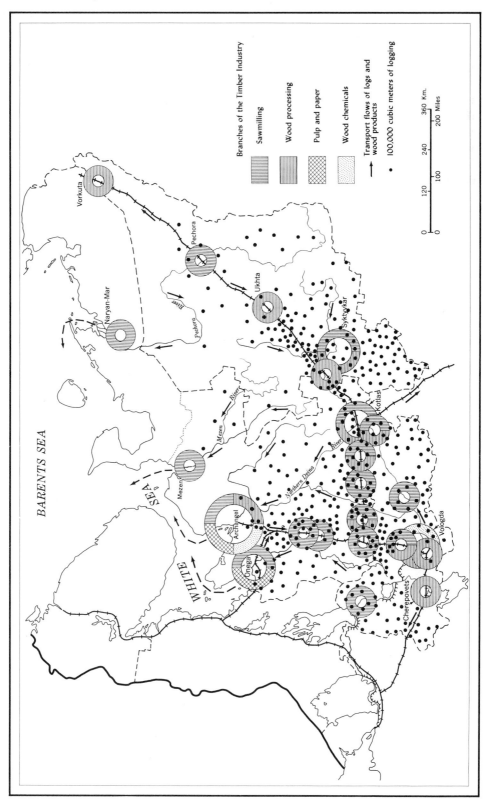

Figure 7-4 The timber industry of northeast European Russia. From Soviet Geography: Review and Translation, April 1961, p. 55.

Pechora Railroads. Much of the lumber sawed in these towns moves southward by rail to the heavily urbanized areas of the Central Industrial Region and the Povolzhye.

Minerals Other than the forest, about the only resource in the area is some of the mineral fuels. Since this is a flat sedimentary basin, we would not expect to find metallic ores, but we might find coal, oil, and natural gas. And such is the case. Coal was discovered in the far northeast corner of this area near the city of Vorkuta early in the Soviet period, and during World War II mining was developed to a considerable extent to compensate partially for the loss of the Ukraine to the Germans. In 1942 an important railroad was opened from Kotlas to Vorkuta to enable the movement of this coal into the central part of the country. During the war and for several years after, Vorkuta was run as a slave labor camp, but

Figure 7-5   Timber floating in one of the mouths of the Northern Dvina at Archangel.   Novosti Press.

since the ascension of Khrushchev it has been stated that all labor in Vorkuta is free, as it is in all other coal-mining areas of the country.

It has been stated that the Vorkuta reserves are even more abundant than those of the Donets Basin in the Ukraine and are just as high in quality. But development here cannot be expected to proceed at a consistently rapid rate because of economic reasons; Vorkuta is a long way from markets, and it has a rugged climate. All coal mined in Vorkuta today is utilized at Cherepovets to produce the steel for the Leningrad area and as fuel in the various cities of the European North. Some mention has been made of building a rail line parallel to the Ural Mountains along their western side to bring Vorkuta coal into the heavily industrialized area of the central and southern Urals, but this distance is just as long as the distance from the Donets Basin to the southern Urals, or from Karaganda in Kazakhstan to the southern Urals, so it appears unlikely that Vorkuta will be highly developed or that a railroad paralleling the Urals ever will be built.

Halfway between Vorkuta and Kotlas lies the oil and gas area of Ukhta. Some oil is now being produced and refined at Ukhta, and a gas pipeline has been scheduled to be built from the small town of Komsomolsk to Perm during the seven-year plan. These are not major reserves, however, and full development here cannot be expected as long as better reserves lie nearer to the main markets of the country.

Agriculture Agricultural possibilities throughout Archangel Oblast and the Komi Republic are universally poor. The railroad from the city of Vologda cuts straight northward through virgin forest, and very little land clearing is encountered all the way to Archangel. Some agriculture has developed in the southern part of the Komi Republic, particularly around its capital city, Syktyvkar, but it consists of only hardy grains, flax, hay, pasture, and livestock. Living conditions are almost unbelievably primitive. Syktyvkar, in spite of its status as the capital city of an autonomous republic, is still a sleepy, muddy, backwoods town, with unpainted clapboard houses and grassy streets. A road is maintained from Syktyvkar southward to Kirov during the winter when the ground is frozen, but in the summer the only connection between Syktyvkar and the outside world until 1960 was down the Vychegda River to Kotlas. In December 1960 a railroad was completed from Syktyvkar northwestward to link up with the Pechora mainline northeast of Kotlas.

Cities The only city of any size in this area is Archangel with a population of 256,-000. Archangel was established during the reign of Ivan the Terrible shortly after 1553 when an English ship under the command of Sir Hugh Willoughy was driven into the mouth of the Northern Dvina by a storm on the White Sea. The survivors of the shipwreck eventually made their way to Moscow and negotiated a trade agreement with Ivan the Terrible. Archangel then was established as the entrepot for goods from England and the export of goods from Muscovy. At the same time, Vologda to the south was established as the outpost of populated Muscovy on the border of the unbroken forests to the north. Vologda controlled an important portage on the river system between Archangel and Moscow and hence became a center for the transhipment of goods. Actually Vologda was founded in 1147, whereas Archangel was founded in 1583, but both cities got their major impetus from the Russo-English trade in the latter part of the sixteenth century. Other than Archangel, only Syktyvkar, with 64,000 people and Vorkuta, with 56,000, are cities of notable size.

Vychegda-Pechora Diversion Project One of the big construction works that may be undertaken in the near future in this area is the Vychegda-Pechora River diversion project, which would not particularly enhance the economy of the local area but which would be of major importance to the lower

Volga region. Early in the 1930's, when the first five-year plans were being developed, a great deal of talk ensued about the possibilities of constructing a huge reservoir between the headwaters of the Northern Dvina, the Pechora, and the Kama rivers that would allow for some reversal of flow in the tributaries of the Northern Dvina and the Pechora to the tributaries of the Kama River. This would transfer water from flowing uselessly to the Arctic Ocean into the Volga River system, which has a deficit of water, particularly in late summer, for all the functions of navigation, electric power, and irrigation that are possible in that region. The Pechora River reaches its greatest flow in summer when the Volga is at its lowest.

It already has been pointed out under the discussion of the Povolzhye that any diversion of irrigation water from the Volga will greatly endanger the maintenance of the level of the Caspian Sea as well as reduce

Figure 7-6   Finno-Ugrian women of the Komi nationality group.   Novosti Press.

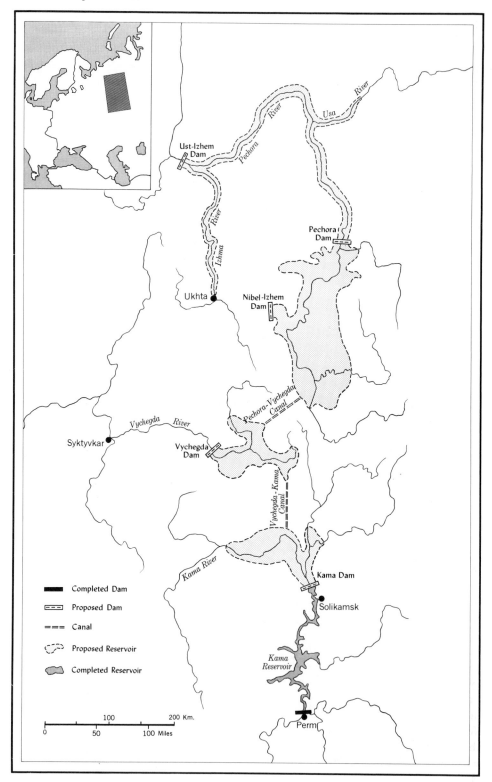

Figure 7-7   The Vychegda-Pechora Diversion Project.   Information from Soviet Geography: Review and Translation, *May 1962, p. 46.*

the possibilities of navigation of the Volga itself. Hence, it would be very helpful if somehow more water could be dumped into the Volga system. The only feasible solution appears to be this one to divert water from the Pechora and the Northern Dvina, or from its major right-bank tributary, the Vychegda. Since 1960 this project seems to have been revived in the minds of long-range planners, and it is quite possible that construction will begin sometime during the plan period immediately following 1965. The divide between these three river systems is a flat, marshy area, and an old canal exists between a portion of the Vychegda head-waters and the Kama. Thus the scheme is quite feasible. If such a reservoir and canal system were to be built, it would provide an all-water route for the transfer of Vorkuta coal to the central Urals. This might completely change the prospects for the development of coal mining in Vorkuta.

Vologda, Kostroma, and Kirov Oblasts

Economy The southern tier of three oblasts that are included in northern Euro-pean Russian—Vologda, Kostroma, and Kirov—are transitional in character be-tween the severe conditions of the north and the more moderate conditions of the Central Industrial Region and the Povolyzhe. Hence considerable agriculture is carried on in these areas as well as considerable lumber-ing. The agriculture is highly concentrated on dairying and the raising of flax, hardy grains, and potatoes. Vologda Oblast is the most noted dairy region in the country; it might be called the Wisconsin of the Soviet Union. Actually the Ukraine produces more dairy products, but dairying makes up a much larger portion of the economy in Vol-ogda Oblast than it does in the Ukraine.

No great amount of industry has been established in the area, although Cherepovets now serves as the steel center for the Lenin-grad area and to a small extent for the Cen-tral Industrial Region. In 1959 Chere-povets had a population of 92,000. The cities of Kostroma and Kirov have been ex-cluded from this region, so that the only city of any size that exists here is Vologda. In 1959 Vologda had a population of 139,000.

Mariinsk Canal System Through the western part of Vologda Oblast runs the 150-year old Mariinsk Canal system, which leads up the Sheksna River from the north-ern end of the Rybinsk Reservoir to Beloe Lake, or White Lake, then up the Kovzha River, across the Kovzha-Vytegra divide, and down the Vytegra River to Lake Onega, where connections are made to the west down the Svir River, Lake Ladoga, and the Neva River to the Gulf of Finland and to the north through the Baltic-White Sea Canal to the White Sea. The Mariinsk is the deepest of three old canal systems that connected the Center with the Northwest. But even this canal is shallow and slow and involves a system of forty locks, thirty-four of which are wooden, that require hours of waiting for boats making passage. It takes between 20 and 30 days for barge caravans to travel from Cherepovets to Leningrad, and the caravans must be broken up and reformed as many as fourteen times en route in order for barges to be tugged through smaller locks individually. Freight from the Volga traffic must be transshipped at Chere-povets from the large Volga barges to the smaller Mariinsk barges, and canals have to be maintained around the edges of Beloe, Onega, and Ladoga Lakes because storm waves on the lakes could capsize the small boats. All this makes barge freight rates about three times as high as railroad freight rates, so very little freight is moved by barge.

This old waterway is now being revamped into a modern Volga-Baltic waterway to pro-vide a channel 12 feet deep to connect the Center, the Northwest, the Urals, and the South. A dam is being built across the Sheksna where the Northern Railroad crosses the river near Cherepovets that will back up water 225 kilometers to form the Chere-povets Sea, completely inundating the valley of the Sheksna as well as Beloe Lake and raising the water level up the Kovzha clear to the divide. Six large modern locks will lower the boats down the north slope of the divide into the Vytegra River. The large Volga barges will be able to navigate all the way to Leningrad. Transport costs are to be cut to one third that of railroad freight costs, and travel time from Cherepovets to Leningrad is to be reduced to about 10 days for tug-drawn barges and 5 days for self-propelled barges.

It is hoped that these improvements will induce increased movements via water of grain, wood, petroleum, salt, cotton fiber, potash, and building materials into the Leningrad area. Also, iron ore from the Kola Peninsula and coal from Vorkuta can be brought to Cherepovets mainly by water to reduce production costs of steel there and make it an economical enterprise. Steel can be shipped from Cherepovets to Leningrad, Gorky, Yaroslavl, and Moscow entirely by water. Wood can be shipped in barges all the way from sawmills in Northern European Russia to the Center, the Volga, and the South. Grain from western Siberia, the Volga, and the Kama areas is expected to move westward along the water route, and apatite from the Kola Peninsula can be shipped through the Baltic-White Sea and Volga-Baltic waterways to nearly all the superphosphate plants of European Russia.

A bonus benefit realized from this system will be additional water brought into the upper Volga from Lake Kubeno and the Sukhona River, the major left-bank tributary of the Northern Dvina. Water from Lake Kubeno and the Sukhona River is to be dumped into the Cherepovets Sea at the rate of about 3.5 cubic kilometers per year, thereby increasing the flow of the Volga. This increase will enhance navigation and electric production in the power stations on the upper Volga that will not benefit from the Pechora-Vychegda diversion project that will bring water into the Volga via the Kama River downstream from Kazan. The Cherepovets Sea on the Sheksna will fill the old Northern Dvina Canal and provide for a better connection between the old Mariinsk and Northern Dvina Canal systems. Additional improvements are to be made later along the Northern Dvina waterway.

The Urals

Region	Area (sq mile)	Population	People (sq mile)	% Urban
Perm Oblast	63,500	2,993,000	47.6	59
Komi-Permyak N.O.	12,800	217,000	17.6	10
Udmurt A.S.S.R.	16,400	1,332,000	82.4	44
Bashkir A.S.S.R.	56,200	3,342,000	60.4	38
Sverdlovsk Oblast	75,400	4,044,000	54.4	76
Chelyabinsk Oblast	34,400	2,977,000	87.8	76
Orenburg Oblast	48,500	1,831,000	38.3	45
Total	294,400	16,519,000		

8

The Urals

Topography

The flat plain of the Pechora Basin ends abruptly on the east with the high ridge of the Ural Mountains, or "Stone Belt," as the Russians often call it. In the north about 25 miles inland from the Kara Sea the Urals rise from the flat tundra to a height of over 4000 feet in Konstantinov Kamen. From here southward to a latitude of about 65 degrees, the Urals extend as one continuously high and narrow ridge which is a truly wild and rocky region. This section is well above the tree line and has been heavily glaciated. Local mountain glaciers still exist in some of the protected upper valleys. On either side the ridge drops off abruptly to an extremely flat plain that has recently been washed by the waters of the Arctic Ocean. This northern section, at approximately 65 degrees latitude, contains the highest elevation in the Urals, Narodnaya Gora, or "People's Mountain," which reaches an elevation of 6183 feet.

South of here the Urals split into two or more ranges and become softer in outline as pine, fir, and larch forests begin to cover the slopes. From 61 degrees latitude southward to approximately 55 degrees, in the region known usually as the Middle Urals, the mountains are comprised of from two to ten ranges, all rather ill-defined, broken, and low

in elevation with only occasional peaks rising to four or five thousand feet. The original vegetation in this region was a mixed forest grading from coniferous forest in the north to wooded steppe in the south. At present much of the area is wooded by second-growth birch and aspen. This middle section has become by far the most important area in the Urals for settlement and industry, and agriculture is carried on to a considerable extent.

In many places this middle section is not mountainous at all; branches of the Trans-Siberian Railroad cross the range without difficulty. Neither do the mountains in this section drop off abruptly on either side. This is particularly true in the west where the land rises gradually eastward from the Volga River in a broad mountain foreland. Much of the foreland has been rather deeply dissected by streams, which in some places have eroded the upland into a series of rounded hills and in others have cut canyon-like stream valleys several hundred feet below plateau- and mesa-like divides. The northern part of this foreland in the Kama River area is known as the Uvaly, or "Lumps," the central section is the Ufa Plateau, a tableland deeply dissected by the Ufa River and its tributaries, and farther south the upland is known as the Obshchiy Syrt, which means "upland erosion surface."

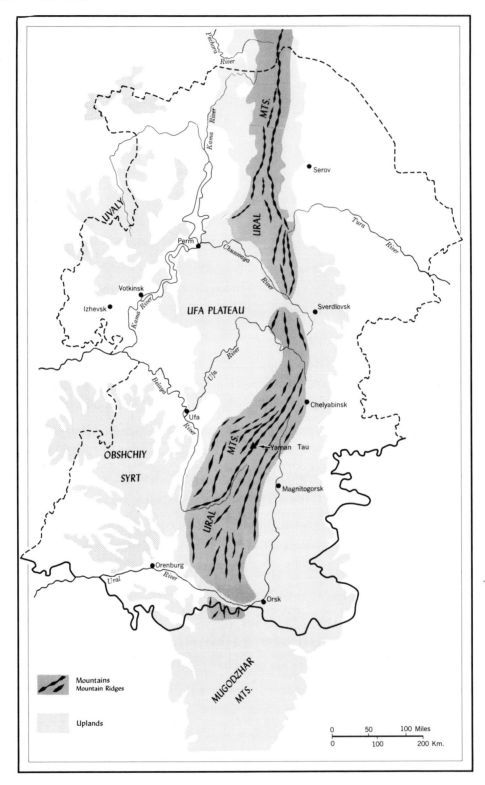

Figure 8-1   Landforms of the Urals Region.

The Southern Urals, south of 55 degrees latitude, continue to fan out in a series of indistinct ranges that here and there rise to mountainous proportions, among which the highest peak, Yamantau, reaches an elevation of 5375 feet. South of the Russian-Kazakh border the mountains trail out in a broad, eroded, semiarid upland known as the Mugodzhar Mountains, whose highest elevations are little more than 2000 feet.

In all sections the mountains drop off more abruptly on the east than they do on the west. The drainage divide lies along the eastern part of the region and the major rivers drain westward into the Pechora and Volga systems. The Pechora River drains the northern section of the Urals, and the main streams in the center are the Kama, Chusovaya, Belaya, and Ufa rivers. The Ural River drains to the south into the Caspian Sea, and the left bank tributaries of the Tobol River drain eastward through the Tobol into the Irtysh and finally through the Ob to the Arctic Ocean.

Definition of Region

The Urals extend more than 1200 miles from the Arctic Ocean to the Mugodzhar Mountains, but the discussion here will be limited to the central and southern portions south to the boundary of the Kazakh Republic, the area that presently contains much of the industrial growth and the population. Politically, the following regions are in-Okrug; in the northeast, Sverdlovsk Oblast; which includes the Komi-Permyak National Okrug; in the northeast, Sverdlovsk Oblast; in the extreme west, bordering on the Volga region, the Udmurt A.S.S.R.; and to the south the Bashkir A.S.S.R. Joining the Bashkir Republic on the east is Chelyabinsk Oblast and in the south is Orenburg Oblast. North of the boundaries of Perm and Sverdlovsk Oblasts the Urals are merely a thin ridge of high rocky, treeless crags which form the boundary between the Komi A.S.S.R. on the west and Tyumen Oblast on the east.

This area is practically uninhabited and will not be considered other than as the bounding edge between these two political units.

Settlement and Population

From the time of Ivan the Terrible, when Yermak crossed the Urals with his little band of Cossacks to explore and conquer Siberia, down to the time of the Revolution the Urals were looked on as just about the edge of civilized Russia. But since the Revolution, and particularly since World War II, the Urals have become an integral part of the core of the country, intimately tied industrially to the Central Industrial Region and the eastern Ukraine. The Central and Southern Urals in 1959 contained 16,519,000 people, which gives a population density to the area of approximately 50 people per square mile. The people in Sverdlovsk and Chelyabinsk Oblasts are more than three fourths urbanized, and Perm Oblast is over one half urbanized; the remainder of the territory is still quite rural. The Udmurts and Komi-Permyaks are Finno-Ugrian peoples and the Bashkirs are Turkic. The Udmurts still comprise about one-half of the total population of the Udmurt A.S.S.R., but the Bashkirs now account for less than one third of the population of their republic. Russians have been moving into the larger cities and mining areas in great numbers, particularly in the newly opened oil fields of the Bashkir A.S.S.R.

Mineral Resources and Industries

The rich mineral deposits of great variety explain the buildup of population and industry in the Urals. They range through the entire gamut of resources from ores for various forms of metallurgy to the mineral fuels. There is a saying in Russia that if a schoolboy is asked where a certain mineral is found, if he says, "the Urals," he is correct,

Figure 8-2   Political units and cities in the Urals.

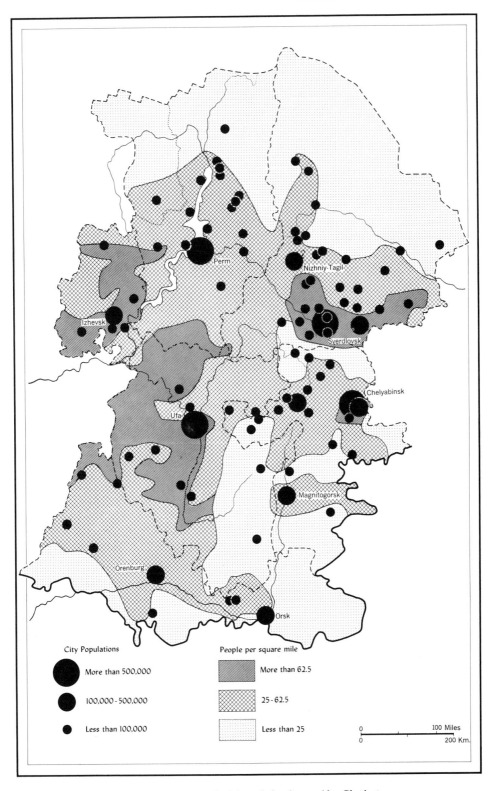

Figure 8-3   Population densities and city sizes.   After Cherdantsev.

The Urals are an old Paleozoic mountain range, corresponding in geological age to the Appalachians in the United States, that have undergone extensive folding, thrust faulting, and some volcanic intrusion on the eastern slopes. The mountains may have been 12,000 feet or more in elevation at one time, but long periods of erosion have worn them down to the bare stumps that remain today. The average elevation at present is little over 1600 feet. In general the Paleozoic sedimentary rocks are still in place on the western slopes, whereas considerable amounts of the underlying intrusive volcanic material is exposed at the surface in the eastern and central portions. Hence a great variety of both sedimentary and igneous rocks are exposed at the surface, and a great potential for mineral deposits exists.

Nonferrous Metals   The Urals have traditionally stood out among mining regions of the Soviet Union because of their nonferrous metals. Copper, zinc, lead, silver, gold, platinum, and asbestos, as well as semiprecious stones, such as emeralds, have been mined for years in the Urals, and until recently were mined almost exclusively there. Copper and some other metals are now found in greater abundance in other regions. Most recently the production of bauxite has become very important in the Urals, surpassing the earlier Tikhvin development in Leningrad Oblast. At present the Urals produce most of the aluminum ore in the country, but other areas are being opened up in Transcaucasia, Middle Asia, Kazakhstan, and Siberia.

Copper ores are scattered up and down the length of the Urals, but the most important copper-smelting centers are two small towns northwest of Chelyabinsk—Karabash and Kyshtym. A newly discovered deposit at Gay, 20 miles north-northwest of Orsk began producing in 1960 and is scheduled to produce more copper in 1965 than the entire Urals did in 1960. Its reserves are said to be second only to those of Dzhezkazgan in Kazakhstan. Bauxite is also scattered through the Middle Urals, but the largest deposits and most developed areas are north of Serov in the so-called Krasnaya-Shapochka, or "red-cap," mines. Much of this ore is shipped southward to Kamensk-Uralskiy, where the largest alumina smelters in the country are located. Some of the alumina is transformed to aluminum at Kamensk-Uralskiy, but some of it is shipped to Transcaucasia, particularly to Yerevan, where large quantities of hydroelectricity are available.

Ferrous Metals   Although traditionally the nonferrous metals have distinguished the Urals, iron ore has provided the main basis for industrial growth during the last 30 years. There are several good deposits of iron ore. Major mining developments at present are located at Magnitnaya, near the city of Magnitogorsk; at Blagodat and Vysokaya, on either side of the city of Nizhniy Tagil; and at the smaller, but high-grade deposit at Bakal, which supplies the special steel mills at the old city of Zlatoust.

Higher grade ores at both Bakal and Magnitnaya are nearing exhaustion; large new steel plants built in Magnitogorsk, Nizhniy Tagil, and other towns will depend more and more heavily on newly discovered abundant low-grade ore deposits on the eastern and southern flanks of the Urals in western Siberia and in northern Kazakhstan. Within the Urals, the outstanding deposits are at Kachkanar and in the Orsk-Khalilovo district. The Kachkanar ore contains only 16 to 18 per cent iron, but some of the largest beneficiating plants in the world concentrate it for shipment to iron and steel mills.

Ferrous alloys such as manganese, nickel, tungsten, and chrome are found in some quantities in the Urals, with nickel and chrome being especially abundant in the Orsk-Khalilovo area. The Russians claim that they have found the largest deposit of chrome in the world across the Kazakh border at Chrome-Tau. A new steel industry is being established in this southern extension of the Urals to utilize the iron ore,

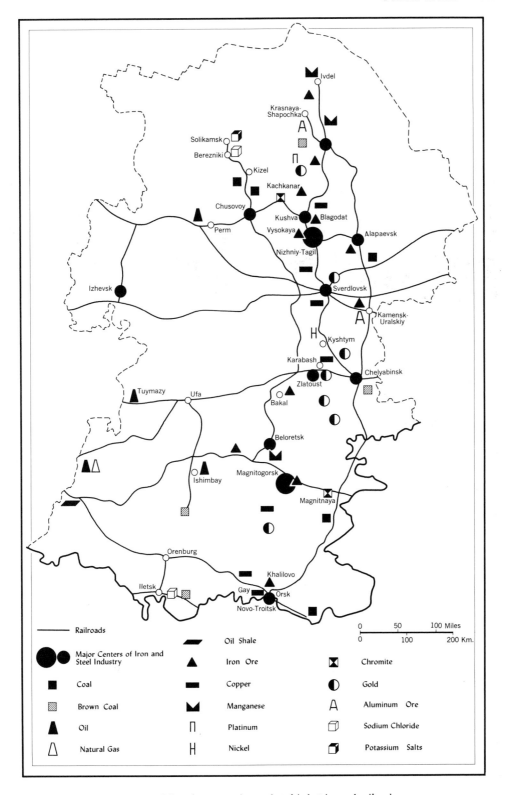

Figure 8-4 Mineral resources, iron and steel industries, and railroads.

Figure 8-5   The oilfields of Bashkiria.   Note the tableland character of the terrain in the Ufa Plateau.   Novosti Press.

nickel, and chrome deposits for the production of high-grade nickel-chrome steels.

Fuels   Unfortunately, the Urals are poor in coal. The region contains 0.5 per cent of the country's energy resources and regularly consumes 15 per cent of the country's energy production. The best deposits of coal are in the northwest at Kizel, but even these are not of coking quality. Other than the Kizel coals, the Urals are limited to scattered deposits of lignite, generally along the eastern flanks of the mountains and particularly in Chelyabinsk Oblast. Coal must be shipped in for the steel and other metallurgical mills from the Kuznetsk Basin, more than a thousand miles to the east, and from Karaganda, more than 600 miles to the southeast in Kazakhstan.

Except for the heavy metallurgical industries, the fuel problems in the Urals may largely be solved by oil and gas, which lie in some abundance on either slope of the Urals, and which can be piped in from the gas fields of Uzbekistan in Middle Asia over 2000 miles to the south. The most important oil fields in the country lie between the

Volga River and the Ural Mountains on the western flanks of the fold. In the Urals region these fields are concentrated particularly in the Ufa Plateau in the Bashkir Republic, to the west and south of the capital city of Ufa. The Ishimbay fields lie south of Ufa, and the Tuymazy fields lie to the west of Ufa. Oil pipelines have been constructed from both these areas to the city of Ufa, which is a major refining center. The Bashkir Republic is the second most important producer of oil in the Soviet Union after the Tatar Republic to the west. Actually oil was first discovered in this western foreland farther north in an operation drilling for potash salts in Perm Oblast. These northern deposits have proved to be minor, however, and production here has not kept up with that in the south.

Only minor gas deposits occur with the oil in the western Urals, but it appears that perhaps a major deposit of gas exists on the eastern side of the mountains in the Ob basin near the town of Berezovo. The gas deposits of the Komi A.S.S.R. near the city of Ukhta have already been mentioned in the discussion of the European North. With the completion of pipelines from the Komi and Berezovo fields and from the Middle Asian fields to the major cities of the Urals, it is planned that by 1965 half of the fuel needs of the Urals can be met by oil and gas. This compares to only 12 per cent in 1958 when coal supplied 80 per cent of the fuel needs.

Other Minerals Major deposits of potassium and magnesium salts are located near Solikamsk on the upper Kama River, and potash and other chemical industries based on these salts were established early in Solikamsk and Berezniki. Far to the south, sodium chloride deposits are found near the town of Iletsk in Orenburg Oblast. Sulfur and pyrite deposits, the bases for the all-important constituent of the chemical industries, sulfuric acid, are scattered throughout the central Urals.

With advances in technology some of the rare metals found in this old rock complex of the Urals now are becoming very important. A good illustration are the columbium deposits, which supply the light metal for jet engines.

Agriculture and Lumbering

As might be deduced from the description of the physical landscape, agricultural possibilities in the Urals definitely are limited, and agriculture plays a role in the economy secondary to mining and industry. Nevertheless, agriculture has been developed wherever topography, soils, and climate make it feasible. In the middle Urals the cool humid climate and forest soils have allowed the development of general farming concentrating on flax, dairying, small grains, hay, and livestock raising. To the south this complex gives way to the extensive growing of spring wheat and the grazing of sheep and cattle in the dry steppes of Orenburg and Chelyabinsk Oblasts. In the south the soils are better, but drought becomes a limiting factor. The Bashkir A.S.S.R. has perhaps the best combination of black soils and moderately humid climate. Here sugar beets recently have been introduced into the crop complex.

Lumbering is an important economic activity in the Urals, particularly in the northwest in the upper Kama River basin. Much lumber is floated down the Kama into the Volga for distribution in the southern steppes, and sawmilling and paper milling are important industries in many of the cities in Perm Oblast and the Udmurt A.S.S.R. Three paper mills on the upper Kama regularly produce about one fourth of the country's paper.

Cities and Industries

With the predominance of mining and the relative unimportance of agriculture, urbanization took place in the Urals almost as soon as settlement began. Rudimentary industries were established during the time of Peter the Great, and the metal industries really became established during the reign of Catherine the Great. The cities and industries grew steadily, though slowly, until the Revolution; since the Revolution they have grown much more rapidly, particularly during and since World War II. During the war the Urals had to supply much of the materials that previously had been supplied by the Ukraine. Entire factories in the west were evacuated on railway cars and shipped to the Urals to be set up again in new locations. Since the war these industries have not been dismantled; they have continued to grow, and new industries have been added to them. Old metallurgical plants have been reconstructed and modernized at Chusovoy northeast of Perm, at Serov, at Zlatoust, at Beloretsk southeast of Ufa, at Sverdlovsk, and at Izhevsk. The Urals now produce one third of the pig iron of the country and almost one third of the steel.

Machine building industries have lagged somewhat behind the iron and steel industries; 65 per cent of the rolled steel produced in the Urals is shipped out for use

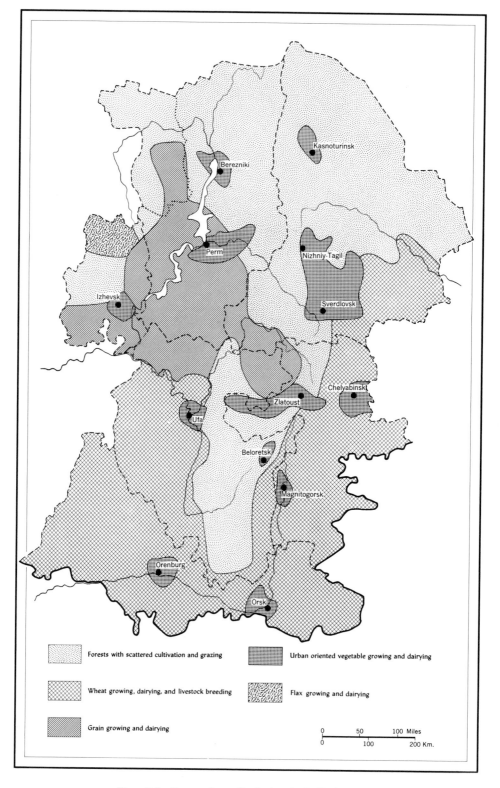

Figure 8-6   Forest and crop distributions in the Urals.   After Lyalikov,

elsewhere. Nevertheless the machine-building industries are second in importance to primary metallurgy.

Sverdlovsk Sverdlovsk still is the largest city in the Urals although some others are growing at faster rates. In 1959 Sverdlovsk had a population of 779,000. It is the old city of Yekaterinburg, named after Catherine the Great because it developed during her reign. It has often been referred to as the "Capital of the Urals," although, of course, the Urals never have been a political unit. Sverdlovsk has some steel industry, but there is more concentration on a variety of machine industries, particularly the electrical machine industries and equipment for mining and metallurgy. It also has chemical and woodworking industries. Seven railroad lines make it the most important rail junction in the Urals.

Chelyabinsk Second in size is Chelyabinsk, which in 1959 had a population of 689,000. It has grown considerably faster during the Soviet period that has Sverdlovsk, but it is interesting to note that the 1959 census found its population to be considerably less than had been estimated previously. Calculations based on earlier growth rates had estimated its population to be greater than that of Sverdlovsk. Apparently the growth rate of Chelyabinsk has slowed down during the last few years.

Chelyabinsk early labored under an infamous reputation during the Russian Empire days as the transfer point for exiled peasants awaiting shipment into Siberia. It was largely a barracks town for transients laying over and awaiting assignment to new regions; and, of course, most of them were in a confused, depressed state of mind and they left with very bad impressions of the town. With the coming of the Trans-Siberian Railroad in 1890, Chelyabinsk got a great boost in importance and soon replaced Tyumen as the gateway to Siberia.

The city is situated on rather level terrain on the eastern slopes of the Urals, and has more room for expansion than many of the older cities within the Urals. Early in the 1900's Chelyabinsk went through a growth period in which flour milling, based on local wheat growing, was the most significant industry. But today Chelyabinsk has evolved into another important machine-building town like Sverdlovsk. It also has some steel industry and nonferrous metallurgy, as well as chemical industries based on local low-grade coal. When the gas pipeline is completed from Uzbekistan, the chemical industries will expand greatly. Its machine industries range from fine machine tools to aircraft industries, but Chelyabinsk probably still is best known for its tractor works, which, like Volgograd's, are outstanding in the Soviet Union. Much of the agricultural machinery that services southwestern Siberia and northern Kazakhstan is built in Chelyabinsk.

Perm Third in size is the old city of Perm which in 1959 had a population of 629,000. For a period of about 20 years, up until 1957, the city was renamed Molotov. Perm has shared in the general growth of population and industry in the Urals and serves as the major center for the northwestern portion of the industrial region in the Kama River area. It has some metallurgy, some oil refining, chemicals, machine industries, and so forth.

Ufa Fourth in size is Ufa, the capital of the Bashkir Republic, with a population of 547,000. As has been mentioned, Ufa serves as the refining center for the important oil fields in the region, and it is also an important city for machine building.

Nizhniy Tagil Fifth in size is the old city of Nizhniy Tagil, which under the Soviets has been revitalized into one of the two major iron and steel centers in the Urals. In 1959 Nizhniy Tagil had a population of 339,000.

Magnitogorsk Sixth in size is Magnitogorsk, which is the second of the two most important iron and steel centers in the Urals. Magnitogorsk now has a population

Figure 8-7   The Chelyabinsk tractor plant.   Most of the tractors produced in the Soviet Union are still of the heavy caterpillar type with enclosed cabs.   Novosti Press.

of 311,000, which makes it somewhat smaller than Nizhniy Tagil. Magnitogorsk did not exist at all before 1931, however. It was established next to Magnitnaya Gora, the important iron deposit in the hill just outside of town, as part of the widely publicized Urals-Kuznetsk Combine to utilize the iron ore in the Magnitogorsk area and the coal in the Kuznetsk Basin 1200 miles to the east.

Iron and steel mills were built at both ends so that railroad cars could carry coal westward and iron ore eastward. As usual, the most important steel mills were built at the end closest to the markets, in this case Magnitogorsk. By 1939 Magnitogorsk had developed into one of the major metallurgical centers in the U.S.S.R.

During this short 8-year period the town

grew like Topsy with no planning whatsoever. Iron and steel mills were erected and laborers were shipped into the area with no living accommodations provided for them. People were living in caves and lean-tos strung without pattern. The citizens of Magnitogorsk are still trying to eliminate the chaos of the past and rebuild the city on a rectangular pattern. Magnitogorsk sits at the southern end of the Urals in the steppes along the Ural River. A dam across the river creates a reservoir that provides sufficient water to the mills and homes of Magnitogorsk, but it is not as pleasant a place to live as are cities further north in the Urals.

Magnitogorsk and Nizhniy Tagil today are nearly equal in size and are approximately equal in importance in ferrous metallurgy. They are by far the two most outstanding

Figure 8-8   Steel smelting at Magnitogorsk.   Novosti Press.

iron and steel centers in the Urals. Although such larger cities as Sverdlovsk and Chelyabinsk also have steel industries, they apparently do not produce pig iron, and steel does not dominate the scene as it does in Magnitogorsk and Nizhniy Tagil.

Izhevsk Seventh in size is Izhevsk, the capital of the Udmurt Republic, with a population of 285,000. Its foremost industry is the iron and steel industry, but such things as machine building and food industries are important.

Orenburg Eighth in size is Orenburg, in the steppes to the southwest, with a population of 267,000. Orenburg grew up as one of a series of Russian fortifications against the steppe peoples to the southeast, and eventually became the center of a rather important agricultural region. After the successful polar flight from Moscow to Los Angeles by Chkalov and his companions in 1938, Orenburg was renamed Chkalov. However, in 1957, when several towns reverted to their pre-Revolutionary names Chkalov again became Orenburg. Orenburg serves simply as the center of an important agricultural area in the dry steppes along the southern Urals, where the main economy is spring wheat growing and sheep and horse raising.

Orsk Ninth in size is Orsk with a population of 176,000. It also lies in the steppe, to the east of Orenburg, and originally was primarily a center of a farming area. With the development of the Orsk-Khalilovo metallurgical district, Orsk promises to grow rapidly into an industrial city. For a number of years it has been the northern terminus of an oil pipeline from the Emba oil fields in the North Caspian Lowland. It refines oil for distribution to the agricultural areas of southwestern Siberia and northern Kazakhstan. A new city, Novotroitsk, is being built in the vicinity of Orsk to serve as the iron and steel center for this important metallurgical

region. Its integrated iron and steel plant will specialize in high grade chrome and nickel steels. A huge thermal power plant with a capacity of 2,500,000 kilowatts is being built in the vicinity to be fueled in winter by fuel oil from the refinery in Orsk and in summer by natural gas from Bukhara in Middle Asia.

Other Cities Tenth in size is the old city of Zlatoust, with a population of 161,000. Zlatoust is the site of one of the early steel mills in the Urals, utilizing the high-grade iron ore from the Bakal mines. It still specializes in high-grade steel, and this is the major industry in the town. Its steel compares to high-grade Swedish steels. The same size as Zlatoust is Kopeysk, a suburb of Chelyabinsk. Kamensk-Uralskiy comes next with a population of 141,000. It already has been mentioned as the largest center of alumina production in the Soviet Union.

One other industrial area that should be mentioned is the Berezniki-Solikamsk area on the upper Kama River north of Perm. Berezniki in 1959 had a population of 106,000. The two towns are heavily concentrated on chemical industries, based on the potash and magnesium salts in the Solikamsk area. This is the oldest developed area of potash salts in the country and still is the major producer, the western Ukraine being a poor second.

River Navigation

With the building of dams and reservoirs on the Kama River in conjunction with the great Volga scheme, towns such as Perm and Berezniki are serving important port functions as well as industrial functions. These navigation functions may be greatly enhanced in the future if the proposed Vychegda-Pechora reservoir and canal system is constructed to bring Vychegda and Pechora River water into the Kama.

The Caucasus and the North Caucasian Foreland

Region	Area (sq mile)	Population	People (sq mile)	% Urban
Within the R.S.F.S.R.				
Krasnodar Kray	32,700	3,762,000	117.0	39
Adyge A.O.	1,700	285,000	165.0	33
Stavropol Kray	31,400	1,883,000	60.8	30
Karachai-Cherkess A.O.	5,500	278,000	51.2	24
Kabardino-Balkar A.S.S.R.	4,900	420,000	87.0	38
North Osetian A.S.S.R.	3,100	451,000	145.9	53
Chechen-Ingush A.S.S.R.	7,600	710,000	95.2	41
Dagestan A.S.S.R.	19,700	1,063,000	54.6	30
Georgian S.S.R.	27,200	4,044,000	150.2	42
Abkhaz A.S.S.R.	3,400	405,000	119.0	37
Adzhar A.S.S.R.	1,200	245,000	204.0	43
South Osetian A.O.	1,500	97,000	64.6	25
Armenian S.S.R.	11,600	1,763,000	153.3	50
Azerbaydzhanian S.S.R.	33,800	3,698,000	110.6	48
Nakhichevan A.S.S.R.	2,100	141,000	67.0	27
Nagorno-Karabakh A.O.	1,700	131,000	77.0	21
Total	172,000	17,794,000		

9

The Caucasus and the North Caucasian Foreland

In the latter part of the eighteenth century, under the reign of Catherine the Great, when advances were being made all along the Black Sea Coast and toward the west against the Turks, the Austrians, and the Poles, a simultaneous drive was going to the southeast between the Black and Caspian Seas toward the Caucasus. Rostov-on-the-Don was founded in 1761 as an outpost against the Turks, and in 1794 a major settlement was established at Yekaterinodar, the modern Krasnodar. Far to the southeast, in 1784, a fort was set up at Vladikavkaz, the modern Ordzhonikidze. After the turn of the century the Russians moved into Transcaucasia primarily by invitation and default. In 1801 Alexander the First, who was becoming looked on as the "Savior of Europe" because of his resistance against Napolean, was invited by the Georgian prince to protect the area from the Moslem Persian Shah. Thus the Russian armies crossed the Caucasus and gained a foothold in Tbilisi, the capital city of Georgia, from whence they moved to Baku in 1806 and to Yerevan in 1828. Here Russia met the growing influence of the British in Persia, and a stalemate resulted, which with minor boundary changes, remains to this day.

Thus by 1828 the Russian Empire had acquired an extensive chunk of land peopled largely by non-Russian groups who had national traditions in the local area of over 2000 years duration. The Georgians and Armenians seldom have enjoyed the status of independent countries, but they are both proud old nationality groups who consider themselves culturally ahead of the Russians, the Turks, and the Persians, the three great powers that have surrounded them from time immemorial. Since the Revolution the Transcaucasians have voiced their desires strongly and have played significant roles in national political maneuvering. During the chaotic period of the Civil War following the Revolution, each of the major nationality groups set up a "White Republic" and declared its independence. These "White" governments ultimately were crushed by the Bolsheviks, and the entire Transcaucasian area was included in the newly constituted Soviet Union in 1923 as the Transcaucasian Soviet Federated Socialist Republic. Agitation for national recognition continued, however, and when the Soviet Union was reconstituted in 1936 each of the three major nationality groups was accorded union republic political status. Thus an area containing approximately 8 per cent of the total population of the U.S.S.R. accounts for three of the fifteen union republics.

Population

Ethnographically the Caucasus are extremely complex; many small nationality groups have occupied separate valleys and basins for centuries without significant contact with one another or with the outside world. Each of these ethnological groups has maintained a more or less distinct identity, and, under the Soviet policy to recognize nationality groups, has been accorded some sort of political status. Although several of the nationality groups on the north slopes of the Caucasus lost their political identities during World War II as punishment allegedly for collaborating with the Germans, in 1957 the political units were reconstituted almost exactly as they had been before the war. Hence, once again the Caucasus are a crazy quilt of union republics, autonomous republics, and autonomous oblasts.

To simplify a bit, the area north of the crest of the Great Caucasus is essentially a Russian area, and it lies within the Russian Republic. But within it exist several non-Russian nationality groups who have been given political recognition either as autonomous oblasts within krays or as autonomous republics. Many of these are nestled in the valleys on the northern slopes of the Great Caucasus. Besides there are many small groups in the mountains whose numbers have not warranted separate political categories. In Dagestan, for instance, there are many, many, small groups of peoples who differ from one another, but whose numbers individually do not warrant separate political status. They have been lumped together simply as "Dagestani peoples" and have been placed within the Dagestan A.S.S.R.

South of the Great Caucasus, three large nationality groups have been given union republic status: the Georgians, the Armenians, and the Azerbaydzhanians. Again, within these republics live minority groups who differ from the majority groups enough to warrant separate political identity. Within the Georgian Republic lie the Abkhaz

A.S.S.R., the Adzhar A.S.S.R., and the South Osetian Autonomous Oblast. And under the jurisdiction of the Azerbaydzhan S.S.R. are the Nagorno-Karabakh Autonomous Oblast and the Nakhichevan A.S.S.R. The Nakhichevan A.S.S.R. is an isolated segment of land surrounded by the Armenian S.S.R.

Table 9–1   Numbers of People by Nationality by Union Republic, 1959[a]

	Number of People	Per Cent of Total
Georgia SSR	4,044,000	100.0
Georgian	2,601,000	64.3
Osetian	141,000	3.5
Abkhazian	63,000	1.6
Armenian	443,000	11.0
Russian	408,000	10.1
Azerbaydzhanian	154,000	3.8
Greek	73,000	1.8
Ukrainian	52,000	1.3
Jew	52,000	1.3
Kurd	16,000	0.4
Armenia SSR	1,763,000	100.0
Armenian	1,552,000	88.0
Azerbaydzhanian	108,000	6.1
Russian	56,000	3.2
Kurd	26,000	1.5
Azerbaydzhan SSR	3,698,000	100.0
Azerbaydzhanian	2,494,000	67.5
Russian	501,000	13.6
Armenian	442,000	12.0
Lezghian	98,000	2.7

[a] Source: *Narodnoe khozyaystvo SSSR v 1959 godu*, pp. 16–20.

and Iran, but it is attached politically to the Azerbaydzhan Republic because it is peopled primarily by Azerbaydzhanians and because there are adequate communication and transportation lines between it and the parent republic. The Nagorno-Karabakh Autonomous Oblast, however, which lies within Azerbaydzhan territory and is peopled by Armenians, is attached politically to the

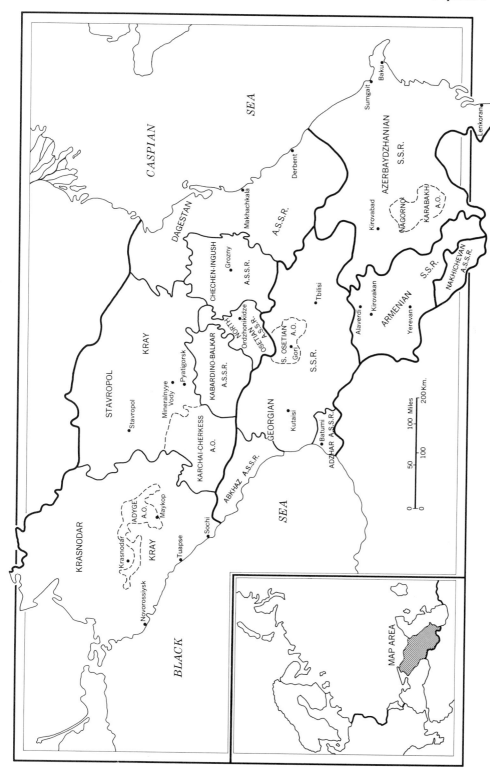

Figure 9-1   The Caucasus.

Azerbaydzhan Republic because it has no good connections with the Armenian Republic. It is the highest part of the Armenian Plateau, which has been deeply dissected by stream canyons, and transportation routes out of the area are tortuous.

In toto, the North Caucasian Foreland has a population of approximately 8,300,000 and Transcaucasia a population of about 9,500,000. Densities of population vary widely from place to place, because of topographic and climatic conditions, from around 55 per square mile in Dagestan to over 150 per square mile in Georgia and Armenia. In the high mountains, of course, population is sparse or absent, whereas the humid lowlands of western Georgia in places contain 300 to 400 people per square mile. North of the Great Caucasus the population is predominantly Russian, whereas south of the Caucasus the population is primarily non-Russian. Russians account for only 10 per cent of the total population of Georgia, 14 per cent of Azerbaydzhan, and 3 per cent of Armenia.

Physical Characteristics and Agriculture

The Caucasus Mountains are a high, continuous range of young, rugged mountains of Tertiary age, which have been folded along a west, northwest-east, southeast axis by pressures from the north and the south. Basically they are two folds separated by a synclinal valley. But the simple line of folding has been complicated by faulting and outbreaks of vulcanism and also by a transverse axis of folding, which runs roughly south to north through the west-central portion of the area. The higher northern fold, the Great Caucasus, stands out clearly in its overall form; rising in a broad bulge from the North Caucasian Foreland, it plunges steeply to the synclinal valley on the south. But the Lesser Caucasus south of the synclinal valley are harder to distinguish because they merge with portions of a general upland, the Armenian Plateau, in the

southern part of Armenia and adjacent Turkey and Iran. The Surami Range follows the north-south axis of folding through eastern Georgia across the Lesser Caucasus and the synclinal valley and divides the valley into two separate basins facing west and east on the Black and Caspian Seas. North of the Great Caucasus the north-south axis of folding can be picked up again in a broad, gentle upwarp in the center of the North Caucasian Foreland.

On either flank of the Great Caucasus, and to some extent in the Lesser Caucasus too, a broad belt of Cretaceous and Jurassic limestones has been conducive to the formation of extensive karst topography honeycombed by innumerable caves and sinks. Some of the caves contain ice and were used as early as the twelfth century by the Georgian Khans for refrigerating wines. Large underground streams have been tapped for domestic water supplies in such areas as Pyatigorsk and Ordzhonikidze on the northern slopes of the Great Caucasus. Abkhazia, in northwestern Georgia, is most noted for its caves and karst. The Black Sea coast between Novorossiysk and Sochi is full of sea caves and coves, from which pirates have preyed on Black Sea shipping for centuries. Caves also exist to some extent in the volcanic basalt and tuff of the Armenian Plateau in southern Georgia and Armenia. Here, in addition to natural caves, many enclosures have been hollowed out by man for purposes of shelter, military protection, and worship.

The high range of the Great Caucasus extends unbroken for a distance of more than 500 miles from the northeastern shore of the Black Sea to the Apsheron Peninsula jutting into the Caspian and forms a nearly complete barrier to climatic and cultural exchange between north and south. It protects the basins and valleys of the Transcaucasus from the wintry blasts of cold air that sweep across the flat, sloping plain of the North Caucasian Foreland. The only railroads connecting the Transcaucasian republics with the rest of the Soviet Union skirt either end of the Caucasus along the shores of the Black and Caspian Seas. Three roads cross the mountains, all in close proximity to one another in the Georgian Republic; they are known respectively as the Georgian, Sukhumi, and Osetian military highways. Built early after the acquisition of the Transcaucasian areas, these roads had to be guarded by Russian military personnel from wild bands of tribesmen who lived in

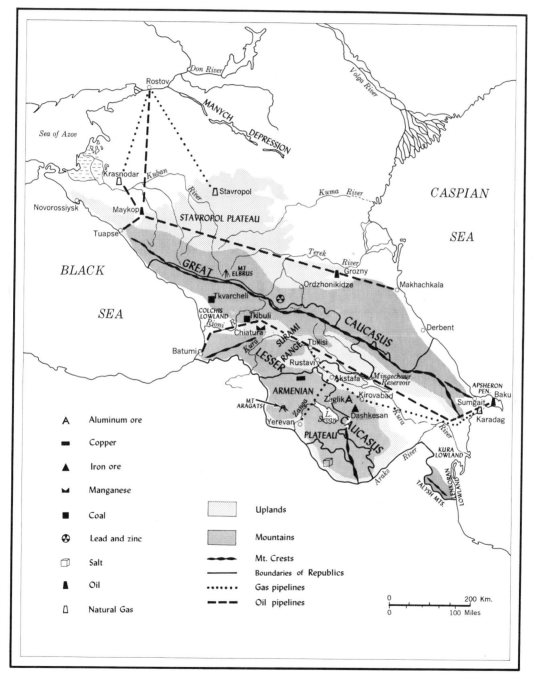

Figure 9-2. Landforms and minerals in the Caucasus.

the mountains and pillaged travelers along the roads. Today these military roads are unguarded and the greater part of them have been paved in two-lane highways. They follow tortuous routes, however, in many places hanging on sheer cliffs, and traffic over them is very light. Hence the Transcaucasus are quite separate from the North Caucasian Foreland.

Russian geographers, in their reluctance to violate political boundaries, usually divide this area along the boundary between the Russian Republic and the Transcaucasian republics, which mainly follows the crest of the Great Caucasus. Many Russian textbooks treat the North Caucasian Foreland with the lower Don region as one unit and the Transcaucasus as another unit. But as has been pointed out in the discussion of the Povolzhye, with the completion of the Volga-Don Canal the lower Don has become an integral part of the navigational system along the Volga. Also the lower Don region does not significantly differ from the adjacent area along the Volga; physically it is just as closely related to the Volga area as it is to the North Caucasian area. Western Rostov Oblast has been treated with the Ukraine because of its common economic ties with the Donets Basin.

Historically the North Caucasian Foreland has been considered an integral part of the Caucasus Region because the entry into the two areas was a continuous one through the northern plain and eventually across the mountains into the southern valleys. The area thus came into the Russian Empire somewhat as a unit. Physically and agriculturally, however, the northern plain is so different from the mountains and valleys to the south, that the region will be discussed in two parts.

The North Caucasian Foreland   The flat, dryish plain of the lower Don approaches sea level east of the Sea of Azov in an east-west trough known as the Manych Depression that served as a spillway during Pleistocene times from an enlarged Caspian Sea

to the head of the Sea of Azov. From the Manych Depression southward the plain rises gently toward the foothills of the Great Caucasus in what is known as the North Caucasian Foreland. A broad warping of small vertical magnitude along the north-south axis of folding has bulged the south-central portion of the sedimentary strata a few hundred feet higher than the plain to the east or the west to form what is known as the Stavropol Plateau. This upwarp has undergone a little more stream erosion and is a little hillier than are other parts of the plain. The slight increase in the roughness of the topography does not effect a change in agriculture, however, as much as does the decrease in moisture from west to east.

The entire plain is strongly influenced by continental air masses which produce droughty conditions and seasonal extremes in temperature. During much of the winter air circulates across the region from east to west around the southwestern extremity of the Siberian high-pressure cell. January temperatures average between 20 and 30°F, and a strong push of the Siberian air westward can plunge temperatures on individual nights to —15°F and send cold air spilling over the lower western portion of the Great Caucasus to bring freezing conditions to the otherwise mild seacoast around Novorossiysk. Such "bora wind" conditions frequently whip up the waves of the Black Sea to produce an ice spray over the piers, moorings, and buildings along the beach.

Cyclonic storms, active over the Black Sea during the winter, bring considerable precipitation to the western part of the plain. The northern slopes of the mountains in Krasnodar Kray may receive as much as 25 feet of snow. These storms generally follow a northeasterly course across Krasnodar Kray and Rostov Oblast and have little effect on the plain east of the Stavropol Plateau.

During the summer there is generally a sluggish flow of air across the region from north to south around the eastern end of the Atlantic high. Temperatures average between 65 and 70°F during July, but maxi-

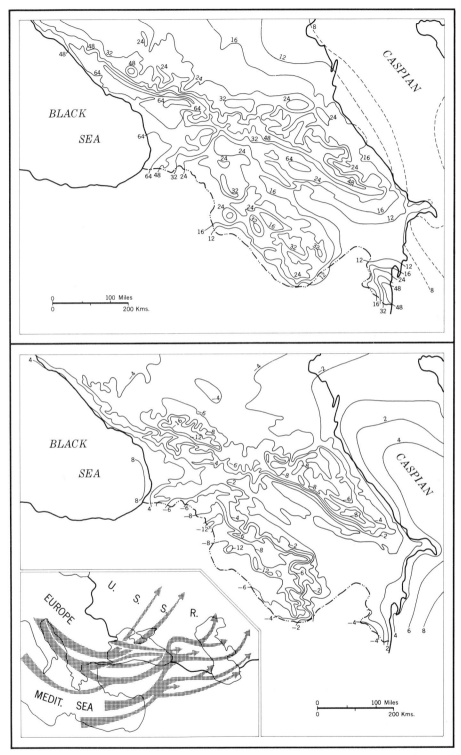

Figure 9-3   Upper map: Annual precipitation in inches.   Lower map: Average January temperatures in degrees centigrade.   Inset: Cyclone trajectories affecting the Caucasus.   From Klimat SSSR, Kavkaz.

mum temperatures over 100°F are experienced. Surface heating, combined with influxes of moisture from the Black Sea, set off frequent thundershowers, which bring a summer maximum of rainfall to the plain. June typically is the rainiest month of the year. The thundershowers are most active in the western part of the plain, but their occurrence does not decrease so sharply eastward as does the occurrence of cyclones during the winter. Hence the summer maximum is most pronounced in the east, although the western part of the plain receives more rainfall than the east during both halves of the year. The precipitation in the west is more evenly distributed throughout the year, and along the immediate Black Sea coast the influence of the winter cyclones becomes predominant and a winter maximum of precipitation is experienced.

Annual precipitation in the west averages between 20 and 25 inches; it decreases steadily northeastward to between 10 and 15 inches in northern Dagestan. Thus the west is subhumid and the east is semiarid. Such climatic conditions have been conducive to the development of a grass and desert shrub type of natural vegetation which has made for the development of Chernozem soils in the west and steppe and desert soils in the east. These soils are all quite fertile and except where they are saline, are adaptable to agriculture as long as the moisture is sufficient. Throughout Krasnodar Kray the rainfall normally is sufficient for crop growth of a wide variety without irrigation, but in the eastern portion of the plain cultivation without irrigation is impossible. Streams heading in the snow fields of the Caucasus afford some opportunity for irrigation.

The two major streams on the plain head in the central portion of the northern slopes of the Great Caucasus and flow out in either direction to the Black and Caspian Seas. Flowing northwestward into the Sea of Azov is the Kuban River, whose drainage basin is practically coextensive with Krasnodar Kray. This region is often referred to simply as "The Kuban." With its rich, black soils and its relatively warm, humid summers, the Kuban rivals the central Ukraine in agricultural possibilities. In fact, with the enthusiasm generated by Khrushchev's corn planting program since 1955, the chairman of the Economic Council of Krasnodar Kray has posed a contest with Iowa in corn production. At present Krasnodar Kray does not compare to Iowa in corn production, and it probably never will closely rival it; the summers average about 5°F cooler and the annual precipitation 5 to 10 inches less than in Iowa. The Kuban suffers from frequent incursions of the dry "sukhovey" winds from the Caspian deserts in summer, which are very dessicating to a crop such as corn that reaches its most rapid stage of succulent growth in midsummer. The region is much more suited to its traditional crops, wheat and sunflowers.

The Kuban is the eastern node of the sunflower belt which wraps around the head of the Sea of Azov and extends into the eastern Ukraine. In addition both winter and spring wheat are grown, and sugar beets are being introduced into the area in ever-increasing quantities. The Kuban is now the second most important sugar beet-growing area in the Soviet Union, after the main belt in the Ukraine and the Central Black Earth Region. The cultivated area of sugar beets in the Kuban tripled from 1957 to 1959, and it is planned that it will more than double again by 1965. Rice is grown in the swampy delta of the Kuban River where it empties into the Sea of Azov.

The Terek River flows eastward into the Caspian through a semiarid region with somewhat poorer soils than those in the Kuban area. Some irrigation agriculture is carried on along the lower Terek, particularly rice growing in the delta of the river, but much of the region is a dry grazing land. North of the Terek the entire area is given over to extensive grazing of sheep and camels.

Transcaucasia   The plain extends southward in a long, sweeping upslope and then

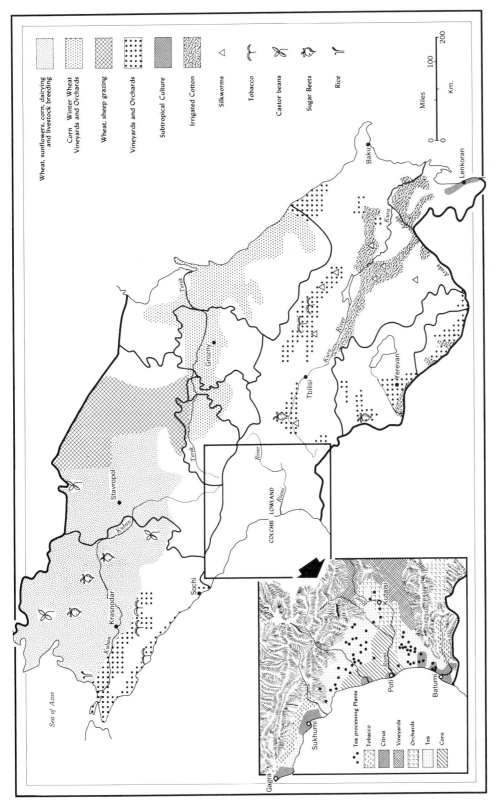

Figure 9-4 Crop distributions in the Caucasus. After Cherdantsev and Lyalikov.

Figure 9-5   Tangerine picking in Georgia.   Novosti Press.

ends abruptly against the base of the Great Caucasus, whose glaciated volcanic peaks tower to heights above 17,000 feet. Mt. Elbrus, the highest of the peaks, reaches an elevation of 18,481 feet. Its horn-like crest is surrounded by mountain glaciers nestled in cirques that lead down to deep U-shaped valleys spotted here and there by glacial tarns. The steep southern slopes of the Great Caucasus frown down on the Kura-Rioni Syncline beyond which lie the Lesser Caucasus and the Armenian Plateau.

The Lesser Caucasus, which do not reach elevations over 8000 feet, in many places merge imperceptibly with the Armenian Plateau to the south, a stream-dissected upland that lies between 3000 and 7000 feet in elevation. Much of the material making up the plateau is of volcanic origin, and the plateau is surmounted here and there by much higher, more recent volcanic cones. The highest of these cones in the Soviet

Union is Mount Aragats, west of Yerevan, which has an elevation of 13,500 feet. These cones get higher across the border in Turkey where Mount Ararat reaches an elevation of 16,945 feet. Mount Ararat is about 40 miles south of Yerevan, but in the dry crystal-clear air it is plainly visible from Yerevan most days of the year. These volcanic peaks reach well above the perpetual frost line, so that they are snow capped year around and lend a grandeur to the scenery of the area.

The low, transverse Surami Range along the north-south axis of folding divides the Kura-Rioni Syncline into two separate basins drained to the east by the Kura River and to the west by the Rioni. These two low-lying alluvial plains at either end of the syncline are the only extensive areas of flat land in Transcaucasia. The Colchis Lowland, as the western basin is known, is a low, swampy, partially filled in extension of the eastern end of the Black Sea. Waves have built a sand bar across the mouth of the Rioni River that has forced the stream to dump its sediment in the embayment. Thus the valley floor is very flat, and drainage is exceedingly poor. Summers here are hot, averaging between 75 and 80°F, and the winters are mild with only occasional light frosts. Cyclonic storms from the Black Sea in the winter bring heavy rains to the area, and thunderstorms develop in the warm, moist air of the basin in summer. These storms combined make this the most excessively humid area in the entire country. Much of the basin receives more than 60 inches of rain annually, and Batumi, in the foothills to the southwest, receives 93 inches. Throughout most of the basin there is a little more rain in summer than winter, but Batumi records a fairly pronounced winter maximum.

The humid subtropical climate allows the area to specialize in crops that are exotic to the rest of the Soviet Union. Citrus and tea are the most important cash crops, although thus far the growing and marketing of these crops has not been developed to the point that it might be. A great demand for these products in the Soviet Union induces importation from other countries, but it is hoped that at some time in the future the Georgian region can supply most of these items for the rest of the Soviet Union. Tea is the national drink in the Soviet Union, afternoon tea pouring being as much of a ceremony as it is in England. Thus a great effort is being made to expand tea production in the Colchis area. Citrus fruits are still very scarce in the city markets, and the quality is always very poor. Therefore there is great demand for expansion of agricultural production in the Georgian region. Other crops are grapes, tobacco, and a variety of fruits and vegetables. Mulberries are grown for the silk industry, and corn has long been

Figure 9-6 Tea picking in Georgia. Novosti Press.

the staple grain for human consumption. Rice is also a basic food and is grown extensively.

Drainage is the biggest problem to agriculture in the Colchis Lowland. Before World War II the Soviets began a project to drain much of the lowland, which combined the digging of canals with the planting of eucalyptus trees along their banks to transpire large quantities of water from the ground into the air. How far this project has progressed and how successful it has been is not known.

The Kura Lowland to the east, fronting on the Caspian Sea, is a considerably more extensive lowland than is the Colchis Lowland, but climatically it is entirely different. It is primarily a steppe region with dry steppe-like soils that necessitate irrigation for the intensive raising of crops. The Kura River heads on the western slopes of the Surami Range and cuts across the range to the east where it enters the broad synclinal valley to flow for more than 200 miles through the flat alluvial steppe to the Caspian Sea. Wherever water is available for irrigation, land has been planted in cotton, alfalfa, corn, and orchards and vineyards. Rice is grown in the delta and in other marshy areas along the river. Cotton and alfalfa each occupy about one fourth of the irrigated area and corn occupies about 15 per cent. This is the second most important cotton-growing area in the country, after Middle Asia. Mulberry trees typically line the irrigation canals to provide the basis for an important silk industry. Some wheat is grown without irrigation in the moister foothills surrounding the basin, but the largest portions of the lowland still are dry winter grazing lands. The area under irrigation was increased to about 500,000 acres with the opening of the Mingechaur Reservoir on the Kura River in 1953.

Transhumance of livestock still is practiced in the Kura River area; the sheep and cattle being pastured on the "kishlag," or winter pastures, on the steppes of the lowland in the winter and in the "eilag," or mountain pastures, of the Armenian Plateau in the summer. The livestock are driven seasonally over a distance of a hundred miles or more. The sheep are brought into the Kura Lowland early in the fall where they are shorn and sorted for slaughtering, and the breeding herd is retained to feed on the local pastures and alfalfa hay during the winter.

The wettest part of the Kura Lowland is the extreme southeast around Lenkoran where some citrus and tea as well as some rice are grown. This area is a wet, swampy, and subtropical area, the culture is more oriental than western, and the main beast of burden still is the water buffalo.

The other region of significant cultivation in Transcaucasia is the Araks River Valley cut in the Armenian Plateau along the southern boundary of the country. Beginning at an elevation of around 3300 feet in the basin around the Armenian capital of Yerevan, this agricultural area continues down the short Zanga River and southeastward along the flood plain of the Araks. The entire area is steppe-like, and very little agriculture can be carried on without irrigation. Irrigation water is available from Lake Sevan and from small streams heading in the snow fields on the volcanic peaks dotting the area. The chief crop is cotton, as it is in the Kura Lowland, with a good deal of acreage being given over to alfalfa as a rotation crop. A great variety of vegetables and fruit are grown, particularly in the Yerevan Basin, for local consumption.

Other than in these three low-lying valleys, agriculture is limited largely to grazing, particularly of sheep. The Armenian Plateau is a dry, rolling upland of volcanic soils that sustains fairly good summer pastures. But in general the soils there are too thin and stony and the climate is too dry for cultivation. Armenia is known as the land of stone, because of the prevalence of bare volcanic rock.

At the altitudes at which much of the plateau lies, the climate is no longer subtropical; temperatures approximate those of the North Caucasian Foreland, going well below 0°F in winter and above 100°F in the summer. The air here is dry and stable, however, and the skies are generally sunny, so that the weather differs considerably from that on the northern plain.

Water Power and Mineral Resources

Besides the climatic resources for special types of agriculture, the Caucasus have a great water power potential and several important mineral resources. The steepness of the mountain streams gives this region greater hydroelectric potential than the whole of the European Plain of Russia. Power potentials are enhanced by the fact that in general the major streams do not freeze during the winters and they are fed by snow fields and high-level lakes that maintain consistent flows. A number of hydroelectric stations already have been constructed, the chief ones being at Mingechaur on the Kura River along the Sevan-Zanga Cascade.

The Mingechaur dam and reservoir was the largest water construction project to be completed in the Soviet Union during the fifth five-year plan, 1950–1955. Its building required particular engineering skill since the dam was strung across a gorge flanked on both sides by weak gypsum clays. The power plant has a capacity of 350,000 kilowatts. Irrigation water has been supplied to large sections of the Kura Lowland.

The Sevan-Zanga Cascade is a project involving a series of dams and reservoirs on the small Zanga or Razdan River which drains Lake Sevan southward through Yerevan to the Araks River. The Zanga River is only 65 miles long, but in that distance it drops 3300 feet from Lake Sevan, at an elevation of 6350 feet, to its junction with the Araks. Also, its flow is very consistent since it drains the large lake, so the natural conditions are ideal for the development of waterpower. Originally it was planned over the next 50 years to drain Lake Sevan down to a level 160 feet below the present surface and thereby reduce its area to about one

seventh of the original size. At this point it was calculated that a balance would be reached between run-in, evaporation, and water necessary for power development on the Cascade. At the present time about nine tenths of the annual run-in is evaporated. A tunnel 4 miles long has been dug connecting the lake with the Zanga River downstream from the natural outlet to increase the drainage, and Ozernaya Station has been constructed at the end of the tunnel to generate electricity completely underground. A couple of other stations also have been constructed farther downstream. Since 1960, however, with the completion of a pipeline from the gas fields of Karadag to Yerevan, a much more modest proposal for the Sevan-Zanga Cascade has been made that will reduce the surface area of the lake over the 50-year period by only 13 per cent. It is now envisioned that much of the energy needed in the Yerevan area can come from natural gas rather than from water power, which originally seemed to be the only potential source of energy for the establishment of important aluminum and synthetic industries in the city, the Armenian Plateau being devoid of mineral fuels.

Outside of Armenia, the mineral fuels, particularly oil and gas, are outstanding among the mineral resources of the Caucasus. For nearly a hundred years Baku was the leading oil producer in the Soviet Union, and around the turn of the century it was the leading oil producer in the world. Also, important oil fields lie along the northern slopes of the Caucasus in the Grozny area and around Maykop in Krasnodar Kray. Minor deposits exist in eastern Georgia on the southern slopes of the Great Caucasus. Many of these Caucasian fields now are on the decline, and an absolute decline in production has occurred at Baku since World War II. Relative to the country as a whole the Caucasus have become much less significant. They now produce less than 15 per cent of the country's oil, whereas before the Revolution they produced almost all of it. Through deeper drilling and drilling offshore in the Caspian, production at Baku is being increased approximately to its pre World War II level, but no significant increase beyond that point is expected.

Since 1955 large gas fields have been opened up both along the northern Caucasus around Stavropol and Krasnodar and in Transcaucasia southwest of Baku. The Stavropol-Krasnodar fields are some of the largest in the country, and pipelines are rapidly being constructed from these fields northwestward through Rostov and the Donets Basin to Moscow and Leningrad. A gas pipeline now extends from the Karadag Field southwest of Baku, up the Kura River through Kirovabad and Akstafa to Tbilisi, and from Akstafa southwestward to Yerevan. It is hoped that through the greater use of natural gas in Transcaucasia the import of coal from the Donets Basin can be eliminated. The only coal of any significance in Transcaucasia lies in two neighboring areas in the Colchis Lowland at the towns of Tkibuli and Tkvarcheli. These fields are not extensive enough nor of a high enough grade to serve as a basis for large-scale industry, but they do supply much of the local needs for coal.

The second largest deposit of manganese in the Soviet Union is located at Chiatura in the Colchis Lowland. The Ordzhonikidze area on the northern slopes of the Great Caucasus has long been important for its lead and zinc mines. Copper has been mined in Armenia for a number of years. Alunite mines have been opened up at Zaglik near Kirovabad, in the Azerbaydzhan Republic, and important salt deposits occur in Nakhichevan A.S.S.R. Besides these important minerals, deposits of molybdenum, cobalt, and other minerals exist.

Industries

The Caucasus are still primarily agricultural, but the mineral resources provide a potential basis for considerable industry, and many of the cities are becoming industrial-

ized. Oil for a long time has provided the basis for industry in Baku, Grozny, and Krasnodar and in the refining towns of Batumi and Tuapse on the eastern Black Sea coast. An oil pipeline running the length of the Kura-Rioni syncline from Baku to Batumi has been serving the area for many years. Also, very early a pipeline was constructed from the oil fields around Maykop across the low northern end of the Caucasus to Tuapse. The oil-refining towns of Tuapse and Batumi ship refined products to the industries of the Ukraine via tanker across the Black Sea.

Also of long standing in Transcaucasia are the textile industries—cotton, wool, and silk. The raw materials for all these textiles are derived locally, and the industries are widely scattered through the major cities of the area. Tbilisi stands out in the silk industry, and Gori, the birthplace of Stalin northwest of Tbilisi, is foremost in cotton textiles.

Since World War II, as part of a drive to make the Transcaucasus semi-independent of the rest of the country, a small-scale primary iron and steel industry has been developed, and chemical industries are growing rapidly. The new town of Rustavi was established southeast of Tbilisi as an iron and steel center to serve the needs of Transcaucasia, particularly steel pipe for oil wells and for pipelines. Rustavi has now reached a population of 62,000 people, which is larger than the 50,000 for which it supposedly was built. It derives its iron ore from Dashkesan nearby and its coal from the Colchis Lowland. Deriving all its raw materials from Transcaucasia and selling all its products in Transcaucasia makes it a self-contained industry.

The chemical industry has been important to some extent in Baku for a number of years, but it is becoming very important now in two other cities, Yerevan and Sumgait. Yerevan early became one of the major centers of the synthetic rubber industry because of its hydroelectric power, which, with local limestone, was used to produce calcium carbide and acetylene, the raw materials for special purpose chloroprene rubber. The industry is being expanded and diversified into all sorts of plastics and synthetics, and the basis for these industries is rapidly being shifted to natural gas, which since 1960 has been piped in from Karadag.

A new city, Sumgait, has been established on the northern side of the Apsheron Peninsula, northwest of Baku, primarily as a chemical industrial center. Sumgait uses the by-product gases from the oil-refining Baku area and will use some of the natural gas from Karadag. It also is scheduled to produce a wide range of plastics and synthetics as well as some steel and aluminum. Besides Baku, Sumgait, and Yerevan, chemical industries are important in Makhachkala, the capital city of Dagestan; Derbent, a Caspian seaport in Dagestan; Grozny; Kutaisi; Kirovabad; and Kirovakan and Alaverdi in Armenia.

One of the most rapid developments in Transcaucasia at the present time is the aluminum industry. Alumina is shipped from the Urals to Yerevan and Sumgait for refining into aluminum because of the abundant water power supplies at Yerevan and oil and gas power supplies at Sumgait. The aluminum industry in Transcaucasia is being expanded greatly because of recently discovered deposits of alunite in Azerbaydzhan at Zaglik near Kirovabad. Much of the alunite is refined to alumina at Kirovabad and is then shipped to Yerevan and Sumgait for final refining into aluminum. An aluminum plant is now under construction in Kirovabad.

Machine industries of all types are rapidly being established in the Caucasus to supply local markets and to make use of local metallurgical products. The machine-building industries are located primarily in the larger cities, such as Baku, Tbilisi, Yerevan, Kutaisi, Stavropol, Krasnodar, and Novorossiysk. During the last decade an automobile assembly plant has been established at Kutaisi, the main city of the Colchis Lowland. The cement industry long has been important in Novorossiysk, along the Black Sea coast; Novorossiysk is the largest producer of cement in the Soviet Union. The lead and zinc in-

dustries of the Ordzhonikidze area have already been mentioned.

Cities

Baku The largest cities in the region are the three capitals of the Transcaucasian republics. Baku is first with a population of 968,000, which makes it fourth in size in the U.S.S.R. Baku is an ancient city which served as a stopover point along a constricted segment of the trade route between the Orient and Europe around the southern end of the Caspian Sea. It grew rapidly in the latter part of the nineteenth century under the impetus of oil production, and because of oil has been maintaining this growth ever since. Although oil production declined during World War II by roughly 50 per cent, it has been increased slowly since then by deeper drilling and by drilling offshore. Three causeways have been constructed to link offshore islands with the mainland, and entire oil-drilling villages have been constructed on floating platforms. The oil workers come into Baku only on weekends. Besides oil refining, Baku has developed booming industries in chemicals and machine building. Since 1936 it has served the additional function of capital of the Azerbaydzhan Republic.

Had it not been for oil, Baku undoubtedly would not have gained the eminence that it has today, for it sits on the barren windswept southern shore of the Apsheron Peninsula where the rainfall is less than 8 inches per year. Water supply is a serious problem in the large city. Before 1917 drinking water had to be brought in from the Kura River by tankers. Then a pipeline 120 miles long was constructed to bring in good mountain water for drinking, but it did not supply anything for irrigation. There are no lawns in the city. Plans are underway for diverting more water for domestic purposes in Baku so that greenery can be grown, but at the present time the city is an unpleasant place in the Soviet Union. The lead and zinc in-

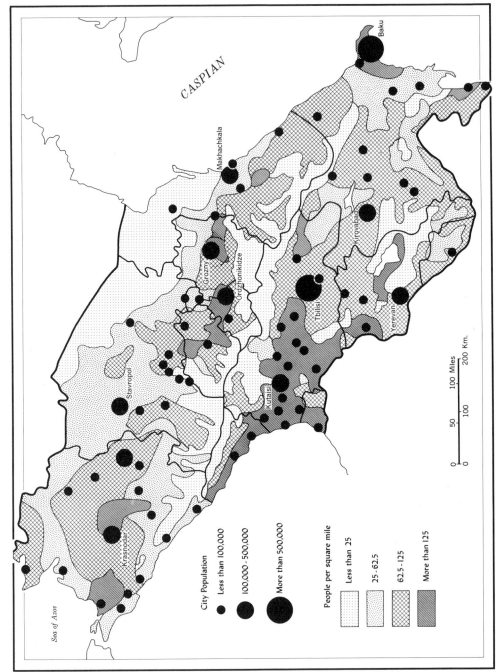

Figure 9-7 Population densities and city sizes.   After Cherdantsev.

summer and subject to strong winds throughout many months of the year. During summer hot, dry winds funnel around the eastern end of the Great Caucasus and blow dust across the city from the steppes to the north. It is said that in Baku even horses in the streets must wear goggles! The name Baku comes from the Persian term "Bad Kube," which means "a blow of the wind."

Tbilisi Tbilisi is second in size with a population of 695,000, which makes it twelfth in size in the Soviet Union. It has long been the center of Georgian culture and now is the capital of the Georgian Republic. Unlike Baku it is a lovely city sitting in the rolling hills and low mountains where the Kura River crosses the Surami Range. Tbilisi is not a heavy industrial town as Baku is, for it has no major local resources, but it has much diversified light industry. Most important are the textile industries, concentrating on silk, and machine industries and food industries.

Yerevan Third in size is Yerevan, the capital of the Armenian Republic, with a population of 509,000. Like Tbilisi, it has been the cultural center of an important nationality group which has occupied the area for over 2000 years. Under the Soviets it has flourished because of its function as the capital of the Armenian Republic and because of rapid industrialization. It is a lovely old city, sitting at an elevation of 3300 feet in a basin surrounded by higher land on three sides that opens on the south onto the Araks River Valley. Dotted across the Armenian Plateau within sight of the city are several snow-capped volcanic peaks, the highest of which is Mount Ararat across the border in Turkey. Irrigated crops of fruits and vegetables surround Yerevan and serve the urban market. As has been pointed out, Yerevan is rapidly undergoing industrialization in such industries as chemicals, aluminum, and machine building. These industries originally were based primarily on the hydroelectric power of the Sevan-Zanga Cascade, but recently natural gas from Karadag has augmented this. It appears that Yerevan is destined to become one of the main industrial cities of the Transcaucasus; it may, therefore, eventually equal Tbilisi in population.

Figure 9-8 Formal gardens in Tbilisi. Note the hilly setting on the slopes of the Surami Range. The paths of the gardens are surfaced with red volcanic cinders. Photograph by the author.

Krasnodar   The next four cities in order of size are on the northern plain: Krasnodar, Grozny, Ordzhonikidze, and Stavropol. Krasnodar now has a population of 313,000. It is the economic center of the rich Kuban farming region of Krasnodar Kray, and for a long time it has had a minor oil-refining industry, and gas fields have been discovered nearby.   The bulk of the industry, however, still reflects the agricultural base.

Grozny   Grozny, a city of 242,000 population, on the other hand, is an industrial city based almost entirely on oil refining.   It does serve as a main regional center of a relatively poorer agricultural region and as the capital city of the Chechen-Ingush A.S.S.R.   But it owes its eminence to the fact that there is local petroleum available, and it got its start in the oil-refining industry.

Ordzhonikidze   Ordzhonikidze, with a population of 164,000, is outstanding for its lead and zinc industries.   It also serves as the seat of government for the North Osetian A.S.S.R. and as a regional center for that area.   Much of its industry has located here because of considerable amounts of hydro-electric power derived from the headwater streams of the Terek River which cascade down the mountains at steep gradients from Mount Kazbek, one of the high, snow-capped peaks of the Caucasus.

Stavropol   Stavropol, with a population of 141,000, is almost a replica Krasnodar on a smaller scale.   The city sits at the crest of the arch of the Stavropol Plateau in the midst of a relatively good farming region, and what industries it has largely reflect the farming resource.   Like Krasnodar, since 1955 large gas fields have been discovered in the area that promise to add to the industries of Stavropol.

Kutaisi   The next city in size is Kutaisi, the economic center and rail center of the Colchis Lowland, with a population of 128,000.   It has diversified light industries, none of which are outstanding.   During the last few years an automobile assembly plant has been established in Kutaisi that is to serve the entire needs of Transcaucasia.

Makhachkala   Ninth in size is Makhachkala, the capital city of the Dagestan A.S.S.R., with a population of 119,000.   Besides being the seat of government for the Dagestan Republic, Makhachkala is an important seaport on the western coast of the Caspian.   As the eastern terminus of an oil pipeline, it serves as the transshipping point for oil coming by steamers from Baku and continuing by pipe westward through Grozny to Rostov and the Ukraine.

Kirovabad   The tenth city in size is Kirovabad, in the middle Kura River valley in Azerbaydzhan, with a population of 116,000 people.   The economic center of the Kura valley, its importance has been enhanced by the establishment of alumina industries based on the alunite ore to the south.   Also, since 1960 the natural gas pipeline from Karadag to Tbilisi has been built through Kirovabad, thereby serving its needs for fuel.

Other Cities   Besides these cities there are a number of significant smaller cities with populations between 50,000 and 100,000, such as the oil-refining towns of Maykop and Tuapse in Krasnodar Kray and Batumi in the Georgian Republic, the iron and steel city of Rustavi, the chemical city of Sumgait, and the cement-manufacturing town of Novorossiysk.

The resort towns of Sochi and Sukhumi along the eastern shore of the Black Sea and Mineralnye Vody on the northern slopes of the Great Caucasus serve recreational and health needs of the entire nation, and are visited by hundreds of thousands of people each year.   Like Yalta and other towns of the southeast Crimean coast, the steep slopes of these cities are dotted with whitewashed health resorts and sanitoria.

Sochi is the largest of these resort cities, with a 1959 population of 95,000.   It sits on a hilly section of land where the mountains plunge abruptly to the Black Sea, and although it is very picturesque, the beaches are narrow and filled with cobbles. Level land in Sochi is so lacking that the city cannot be served directly by air; planes must land at Adler about 20 miles to the south on a small river delta, and passengers must be conveyed to Sochi by open-air bus over a bumpy, winding mountain road. In 1961 the city limits of Sochi were extended southward to include Adler, which brought the population of the Sochi metropolitan area somewhat over 100,000 people. In Sochi are all that the Russians consider to be significant to the self indulgence of the idle vacationer: glistening white resort hotels perched on the hills high above the Black Sea, funicular railways, and large expanses of parks with their circus, opera house, and cinema. Besides these strictly resort amenities there is a subtropical botanical garden whose paths are constantly jammed by pedestrians, many of whom are visiting the city in large groups and insist on posing for group pictures.

Sukhumi is better known for its botanical garden for scientific studies than it is for its resort facilities. Mineralnye Vody is noted for its warm mineral baths fed by hot springs issuing from subvolcanic areas.

Soviet Middle Asia and Southern Kazakhstan

	Area (sq mile)	Population	People (sq mile)	% Urban
Within the Kazakh S.S.R.				
West Kazakhstan Kray				
Guryev Oblast	10,900	288,000	2.6	56
Aktyubinsk Oblast (southern)[a]	55,000	—	—	—
South Kazakhstan Kray	206,400	1,810,000	8.8	—
Kzyl-Orda Oblast[b]	91,000	327,000	3.6	47
Chimkent Oblast[b]	58,700	921,000	15.8	36
Dzhambul Oblast	56,700	562,000	10.1	36
Alma-Ata Oblast	89,000	1,403,000	16.1	53
Karaganda Oblast (southern)[a]	54,000	—	—	—
Turkmen S.S.R.	191,000	1,516,000	8.0	46
Uzbek S.S.R.[b]	160,000	8,106,000	51.3	34
Kara-Kalpak A.S.S.R.	64,500	510,000	7.9	27
Tadzhik S.S.R.	55,900	1,980,000	35.7	33
Gorno-Badakhshan A.O.	24,800	73,000	2.9	11
Kirgiz S.S.R.	77,700	2,066,000	26.9	34
Total	899,900	17,169,000		

[a] Estimated areas of parts of Aktyubinsk and Karaganda Oblasts included in southern Kazakhstan. No attempt has been made to divide the population figures for these oblasts, since the population is very sparse in the southern parts.

[b] In January 1963, 14,400 square miles of territory were transferred from Chimkent and Kzyl-Orda Oblasts of Kazakhstan to the Uzbek S.S.R.

10

Soviet Middle Asia
and Southern Kazakhstan

Stretching all the way from the Volga River to China, Kazakhstan and Soviet Middle Asia comprise approximately one and one half million square miles, an area equal to about half that of the United States. Politically this region is composed of five union republics, which are further subdivided into oblasts, autonomous republics, and autonomous oblasts. The Kazakh Republic alone contains a million square miles, and except for the Russian Republic, is larger in area than all the other republics combined. East and west it stretches for a distance of more than 1800 miles, and north and south for a distance of over 1000 miles.

The Soviets usually treat the Kazakh Republic as a separate region whereas they combine the other four republics under the term "Soviet Middle Asia." The Kazakh Republic alone does not make a good regional unit, however, since it is neither a homogeneous nor a contiguously populated area. The more populous northern and southern portions are divided in the middle by a wide expanse of drier, less populated land. The northern part of Kazakhstan is more closely related physically and culturally to adjacent western Siberia than it is to the rest of the Kazakh Republic, and the southern part of the Kazakh Republic is more closely related to the adjacent Middle Asian

republics. Therefore, the Kazakh Republic will be treated in two separate parts: the southern oblasts with the Middle Asian republics, as shown on the table at the beginning of this chapter, and the northern and central oblasts with adjacent western Siberia in the following chapter. Such a division cuts across the newly formed West Kazakhstan Kray. It will be expedient, however, occasionally to consider the Kazakh Republic in its entirety.

If there is a theme that unites the Middle Asian republics and southern Kazakhstan it is a climatic one, that is, drought, because this entire area is afflicted to some degree by lack of water. Only the mountain slopes in the far south have sufficient moisture. Much of the area receives less than 8 inches of precipitation per year, and a large section in the central portion southeast of the Aral Sea, as well as smaller areas along the eastern shore of the Caspian and the western shore of Lake Balkhash, receive less than 4 inches per year. Thus, except for the higher mountains, the area is entirely desert and steppe. This leads to a certain degree of homogeneity in landscape, land utilization, and culture in spite of variations induced by the complex makeup of such factors as geological structure and ethnology. Also, the entire region, which originally was a non-

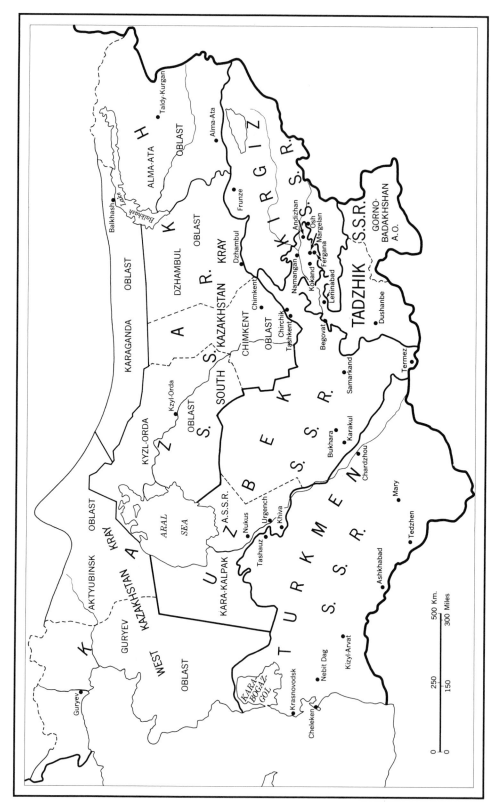

Figure 10-1   Soviet Middle Asia and Southern Kazakhstan.

Russian area, during the last century has undergone a common history of Russian acquisition and organization.

Territorial Acquisition and Organization

Kazakhstan and Middle Asia were incorporated into the Russian Empire by the gradual establishment of bases in northern Kazakhstan, from which the Russians, in a series of rapid thrusts to the southeast, subjugated the indigenous peoples during the latter half of the nineteenth century. The Russians captured Yangi, now Dzhambul, in 1864, Tashkent in 1865, Khodzhent, now Leninabad, in 1866, Bakhara and Samarkand in 1868, and the last remaining Khanates of Khiva in 1873 and Kokand in 1876. These forays to the southeast mainly were to sub-

jugate the war-like nomadic horsemen who periodically marauded the Russian settlers to the northwest and frequently carried off hostages to be sold as slaves in Khiva or Bukhara. Once these hotbeds of disturbance were subjugated, the Russians found themselves in semicontrol of the entire area. Once again the Russians came into contact with the British influence, in India, and in 1888 a frontier was agreed on that established Afghanistan as a buffer country between Russia and India. Some of the Moslem colonies, such as Bukhara and Khiva, remained nominally independent under the Russian regime until 1920, when finally the Bolsheviks won the Civil Wars in the area and established Soviet rule.

Like the Transcaucasus, Middle Asia between the years of 1917 and 1921 was split between the "Reds" and the "Whites," and

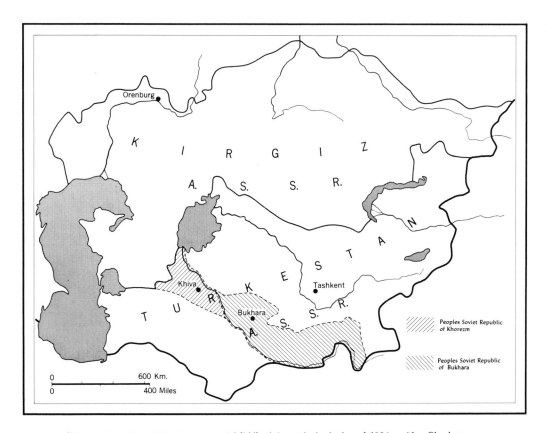

Figure 10-2   The political structure of Middle Asia at the beginning of 1924.   After Cherdantsev.

Figure 10-3   Uzbek men drinking their afternoon tea on a carpet-covered raised platform beside a shady irrigation ditch north of Tashkent.   Photograph by the author.

Figure 10-4   Tadzhik men playing chess in a tea garden near Dushanbe.   Novosti Press.

"White Republics" were established for a short time to oppose the Bolsheviks. However, after a few bloody skirmishes the White resistance was broken and the entire area was incorporated into the newly formed Soviet Union. Shortly after the Revolution in 1917 the area occupied by the Kazakhs was constituted as the Kirgiz A.S.S.R. under the Russian Republic, and the remainder of Middle Asia, except for the semi-independent Khanates of Khiva and Bukhara, was constituted as the Turkestan A.S.S.R., also under the Russian Republic. With the final subjugation of Khiva and Bukhara in 1921, these two areas were constituted as "soviet people's republics" within the Russian Republic. The terms "Kirgiz" and "Kazakh" were confused in the minds of the Russians, so that the large area occupied by the Kazakhs was designated as the Kirgiz A.S.S.R. in spite of the fact that the Kirgiz nationality group occupied only a small area in the northern part of the Tyan Shan Mountains. Later, in 1924 when the area was reconstituted into five union republics, the confusion was eliminated, and the bulk of the area was placed within the Kazakh Republic.

Population

Today southern Kazakhstan and Middle Asia contain somewhat more than 17 million people who are a mixture of native peoples and other groups, particularly Russians and Ukrainians, who have moved in (Table 10–1). The five most populous native groups give their names to the five republics. The natives in many cases are remnant mix-

Figure 10-5   The felt-covered yurt *is the summer home of Kirgiz shepherds in the mountain pastures of the Tyan Shans. Novosti Press.*

Figure 10-6   The interior of the home of a Kazakh collective farmer.   The samovar in the foreground provides hot water for making tea, which is drunk out of bowls.   Novosti Press.

tures of the waves of Oriental peoples who have swept across the region through the ages from the east and the south. The Kazakhs, Kirgiz, Turkmen, and Uzbeks all are classified as Turkish groups of people, but there are distinguishable physical differences among them. The Kazakhs have yellow skin and broad, flat faces, which indicate a strong tie with the Mongolians, whereas the Uzbeks, with long, bony faces and a dusky-colored skin, more closely resemble the Indians and Iranians to the south. The Tadzhiks are closely related to the Iranians.

Middle Asia is now being invaded from a new direction—the west. Russians make up much of the population in the larger cities and most of the labor force in the factories. Russians now make up almost 43 per cent of the population of the Republic of Kazakhstan. In the capital city of Alma-Ata, one sees scarcely anyone but Russians. With this influx of Russians into certain parts of the area, it is quite possible that some changes in the political setup will be made in the near future.

In the oases of Middle Asia where the

Table 10–1   Numbers of People by Nationality by Union Republic, 1959[a]

	Number of People (thousands)	Per Cent of Total
Uzbek S.S.R.	8,106	100.0
Uzbek	5,038	62.2
Russian	1,091	13.5
Tatar	445	5.5
Kazakh	335	4.1
Tadzhik	311	3.8
Karakalpak	168	2.1
Korean	138	1.7
Jew	94	1.2
Kirgiz	93	1.1
Ukrainian	88	1.1
Turkmen	55	0.7
Kazakh S.S.R.	9,310	100.0
Kazakh	2,795	30.0
Russian	3,974	42.7
Ukrainian	762	8.2
Tatar	192	2.1
Uzbek	137	1.5
Belorussian	107	1.2
Korean	74	0.8
Uigur	60	0.6
Pole	53	0.6
Dungan	10	0.1
Kirgiz S.S.R.	2,066	100.0
Kirgiz	837	40.5
Russian	624	30.2
Uzbek	219	10.6
Ukrainian	137	6.6
Tatar	56	2.7
Kazakh	20	1.0
Tadzhik	15	0.7
Uigur	14	0.7
Tadzhik S.S.R.	1,980	100.0
Tadzhik	1,051	53.1
Uzbek	454	23.0
Russian	263	13.3
Tatar	57	2.9
Ukrainian	27	1.4
Kirgiz	26	1.3
Kazakh	13	0.6

Table 10–1   Numbers of People by Nationality by Union Republic, 1959[a] (Continued)

	Number of People (thousands)	Per Cent of Total
Turkmen S.S.R.	1,516	100.0
Turkmen	924	60.9
Russian	263	17.3
Uzbek	125	8.3
Kazakh	70	4.6
Tatar	30	2.0
Ukrainian	21	1.4
Armenian	20	1.3
Total, Middle Asia and Kazakhstan[a]	22,978	100.0
Slavic Groups	7,250	31.5
Russians	6,215	27.0
Ukrainians	1,035	4.5
Titular Native Groups	12,518	54.5
Uzbeks	5,973	26.0
Kazakhs	3,233	14.0
Tadzhiks	1,377	6.0
Turkmen	979	4.3
Kirgiz	956	4.2
Other	3,210	14.0

[a] *Source: Narodnoe khozyaystvo SSSR v 1960 gody*, pp. 17–20.
[b] Includes all of Kazakhstan.

native populations are more dominant there is very little connection between the native life in the rural villages and the Russian life in the larger cities. The natives live and work the land much as they did before the Revolution, whereas in the cities the factories are being run as they are back in Moscow. Most of the natives still live in adobe huts with thatched roofs. The donkey is the universal beast of burden and the donkey cart the chief means of transport of produce.

The population of Kazakhstan and Middle Asia is distributed very unevenly. In general it is concentrated in areas that afford high

Figure 10-7   The adobe walls and thatched roofs in the native quarter, Tashkent.   Courtesy of Robert H. Dawson.

potentials for agriculture. Such areas are determined primarily by factors of soil and climate, which in turn are very closely related to topography. A few major centers of population and a considerable number of scattered minor settlements owe their existence to the mining of mineral resources, and this is closely related to the geology of the region.

Physical Characteristics

Topographically and geologically the area is quite varied, ranging from broad alluvial plains lying below sea level through old worn-down mountain and plateau areas to the young rugged mountains along the southeastern border.

The Caspian Basin In the northwest is the low-lying area surrounding the northern and eastern sides of the Caspian Sea. The northern end is part of the old Caspian Lake bed which lies below sea level and is as flat as a floor. The climate here is strictly desert, and many salt flats and remnant salt

Figure 10-8 Contrasting modes of transportation along a blacktop highway among the loess hills north of Samarkand. Photograph by the author.

Figure 10-9 Typical mode of transportation in the native villages outside Alma-Ata. An old Kazakh man rides his donkey pulling a cartload of hay. Photograph by the author.

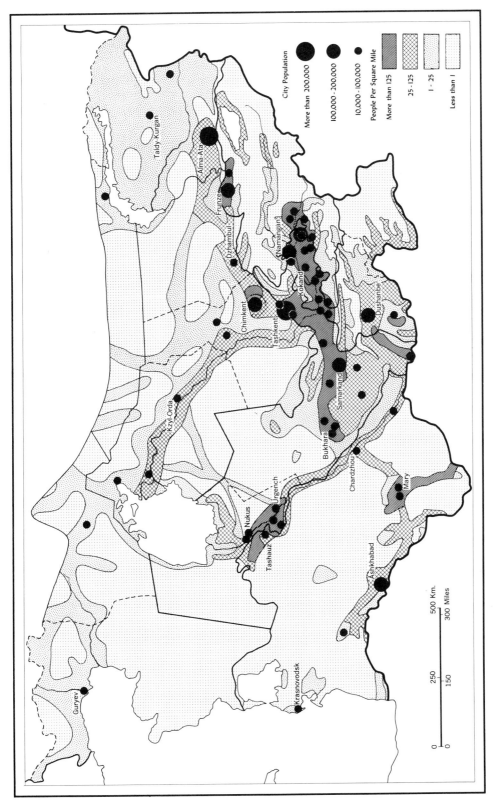

Figure 10-10 Population densities and city sizes. After Cherdantsev.

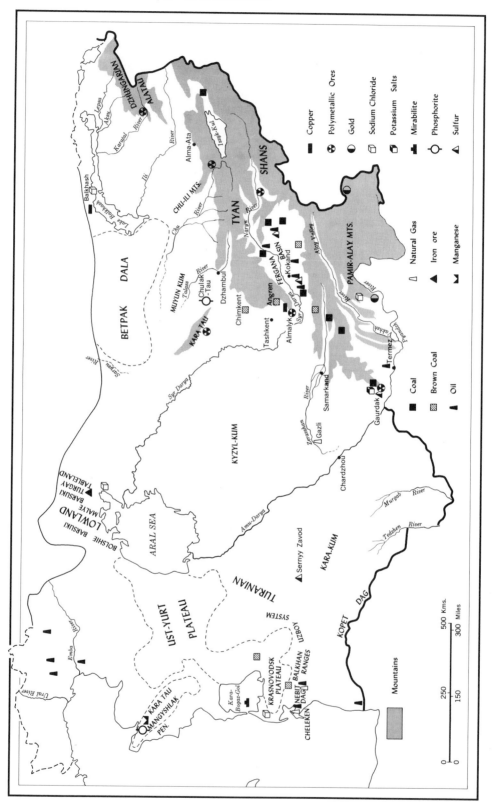

Figure 10-11   The physical landscape and mineral resources.

lakes exist on the plain. Agriculture here, except for extensive grazing of sheep and camels, is quite impossible. The Ural and Emba Rivers, crossing the area on their way from the meager headwater areas in the southern Urals and Mugodzhar Mountains, barely flow to the Caspian during low-water stage in late summer. Between the two rivers the flat plain is gently interrupted by the slight rises of innumerable salt domes, which are the bases of the Emba oil fields. These flat salt domes are similar to those along the east Texas and Louisiana Gulf Coasts in the United States.

Southward along the eastern shore of the Caspian, the level plain ends abruptly against the Mangyshlak Peninsula in the Kara Tau, or "Black Mountain," which is a fault block plateau or horst with steep cliffs on both sides and is split down the middle by a graben that runs the entire length of the peninsula. Elevation here varies from a high of 1742 feet above sea level to 435 feet below sea level in a down-faulted depression in the southeastern part of the peninsula.

Farther south, Kara-Bogaz-Gol, or "Black Mouth Bay," is bordered on almost all sides by steep cliffs of surrounding plateau surfaces that reach heights of a few hundred to one thousand feet above sea level. The gulf itself lies about 100 feet below sea level. Kara-Bogaz-Gol is almost completely cut off from the main body of the Caspian by sand bars which have grown from either side to within about 600 feet of each other, so that the strait between the Caspian and the gulf is now only 600 feet wide and about 10 feet deep. The gulf averages about 30 feet in depth, and according to the Russians it has a surface level that often falls as much as 12 feet below the level of the Caspian. Thus there is a considerable current which flows from the Caspian into the gulf, and the gulf acts as a final evaporation pan for the Caspian. It has been calculated that between 10 and 20 cubic kilometers of water are evaporated from Kara-Bogaz-Gol annually. The salt content here is understandably very high.

South of Kara-Bogaz-Gol is a peninsula

formed by the Krasnovodsk Plateau that rises several hundred feet above the Caspian and again plunges off to the sea in very steep cliffs. The city of Krasnovodsk clings to the base of the cliff on a narrow coastal plain bordering the Caspian. Southeast of the Krasnovodsk Plateau lie several anticlines of thick limestone that are known as the Balkhan Ranges, which reach maximum elevations of a little over 5000 feet. The ranges are surrounded by a broad "takyr," or salt flat, which represents an old lake bed. The shallow basin was undoubtedly filled with water at one time during the glacial period when a connection existed between the Aral Sea and the Caspian. There are terraces along the slopes of the Balkhans as high as 230 feet above the present surface of the plain. A series of dry stream channels known as the "Uzboy System" leads through the plain and only a few hundred years ago served as a spillway from the Aral Sea to the Caspian. Nebit-Dag and other low hills rising 150 feet or more above this vast "solonchak" are topographic expressions of dislocated tertiary sediments which yield a considerable quantity of petroleum.

West of Nebit-Dag, or "Oil Mountain," lies Cheleken Island, or, since the drop in water level in the Caspian, actually Cheleken Peninsula, another fault block that rises abruptly from the Caspian to elevations of over 300 feet. It has been described as a broken plate, a tertiary, oil-bearing, highly faulted section of sandstone and other deposits underlain by young volcanic magma. Mud volcanoes and petroleum seeps abound and have turned the sand into an asphalt-cemented rock that has split into basaltic-like prisms to form spectacular mesas and buttes. Gases are emitted from some of the mud volcanoes, and gas bubbles constantly rise through the water from the bottom of the Caspian. This sort of activity continues southward to the western end of the Kopet Dag.

This entire coast of the Caspian from the northern end southward all along the eastern side is completely desert, and the landscape is very barren. In spite of the fact that everywhere elevations are relatively low, local relief is considerable, and changes in elevation are abrupt. There are no streams of any note except in the northern end, where the Ural River flows into the Caspian from the Ural Mountains, and the Emba comes in from the northeast off the Mugodzhar Mountains. The region is little utilized other than the oil-bearing areas of the Emba fields in the north and Nebit-Dag in the south. The few towns that exist along the coast of the Caspian have been established for fishing and trading. All are small and all have acute water supply problems. The largest of these, Krasnovodsk, is supplied with drinking water by tanker across the Caspian from the Kura River in Transcaucasia. It has been suggested that a 600-mile-long canal be constructed from the lower Amu-Darya to Krasnovodsk utilizing the old Uzboy System, thereby supplying water to Krasnovodsk and providing irrigation water for several million acres of land in the intervening area. But it is quite clear to all who have studied the situation that there simply is not enough water in the Amu-Darya to create such a canal system, and since the death of Stalin no more mention has been made of the project. Perhaps more realistic is a planned extension of the Kara-Kum Canal from Ashkhabad to Krasnovodsk. This canal, which leads off water from the upper Amu-Darya, has already been completed to Ashkhabad.

Between the Caspian and Aral Seas lies the Ust-Yurt Plateau, a dry, flat, barren upland of nearly horizontal sedimentary strata which lies at an elevation of nearly 1000 feet. Its eastern edge plunges in a fault scarp several hundred feet to the Aral Sea at its base. No streams of any significance head in this area, and no water is available to be brought in for irrigation. Hence it is destined to remain an almost unused area.

The Turanian Lowland   East of the Ust-Yurt Plateau lies a broad, elongated synclinal trough that stretches in a southsouthwest-northnortheast direction from the Kopet Dag along the Iranian border northward into western Siberia. This large plains region is known as the Turanian Lowland, but different sections of it are known by different names.

In its midsection lies the Aral Sea, the fourth largest lake in the world, with a surface area of almost 25,000 square miles. It is a shallow sea, with depths of only 30 to 60 feet throughout much of its extent, and it contains literally thousands of islands. The name Aral Sea means "island" sea. The Syr-Darya is building a large delta into the lake in the northeast, and the Amu-Darya is building a large delta from the southern side. Apparently, until only a few hundred years ago the Aral Sea drained southwestward through the Uzboy System into the Caspian; hence, the Aral Sea has less than 1 per cent salt. The Caspian by comparison has about 14 per cent salt. Precipitation in the Aral Sea area totals less than 4 inches per year, and if it were not for the inflow of the two large rivers fed by the melting snows of the high mountains to the southeast, the sea would immediately dry up. As it is, the two rivers are unable to supply as much water as is evaporated each year, and the sea is gradually diminishing. The greatest depth, 228 feet, is along the western edge at the base of the fault scarp of the Ust-Yurt Plateau. Hence the basin ends abruptly at a fault scarp on the west, but rises gradually eastward into the sands of the Kyzyl-Kum and Kara-Kum.

North of the Aral Sea the trough is continued as the Turgay Lowland or Turgay Tableland, which extends north of the area under consideration into northern Kazakhstan and southwestern Siberia. The area is a stripped sedimentary plain dotted by mesa and butte remnants of higher strata standing in vertical cliffs above the clay and salt flats occupying much of the basin floor; hence, the name "Turgay Tableland." Ridges of sand dunes oriented south-southwest—north-northeast occupy parts of the intervening lowlands among the tablelands.

The most extensive of these dune areas are the Bolshie, or great, Barsuki, northwest of the Aral Sea, and the Malye, or small, Barsuki, north of the Aral Sea. It is thought that important I.C.B.M. bases have been built in this remote and empty area. South of the Aral Sea the Turanian Lowland continues through the western part of the Kara-Kum, or "black sands," desert to the foothills of the Kopet Dag on the Iranian border.

The Eastern Sand-Ridge Deserts and Uplands Southwest of the Amu-Darya lies the Kara-Kum, the most extensive sand desert in Middle Asia. About nine tenths of the area is covered by elongated ridges of sand topped by smaller, shifting barchan dunes of loose sand. Most of it is quite unfit for agriculture. Only the southern margins bordering on the mountains along the south and the northern section near the mouth of the Amu-Darya have rich alluvial soils that are supplied with irrigation water and support a thriving agriculture.

Across the Amu-Darya to the northeast is the Kyzyl-Kum, or "Red Sand Desert," which occupies much of the area lying between the Amu-Darya and the Syr-Darya. The Kyzyl-Kum is higher, rockier, and more devoid of sand than is the Kara-Kum, and shows more variety in its relief. Stubby, worn-down outcrops of old Paleozoic formations reach elevations of over 3000 feet in the central and southwestern portions. Like the Kara-Kum, the Kyzyl-Kum is a very dry desert which is little utilized except along the margins where some irrigation water can be derived from either the Syr-Darya or the Amu-Darya.

Northeast of the Syr-Darya is the Kara Tau, or "Black Mountain," extending northwestward from the Tyan Shans and overlooking the Muyun Kum to the northeast. The Muyun Kum, or "Sandy Desert," is a ridged sand desert similar to the Kara-Kum, but it is much more restricted in area and somewhat higher in elevation. The Muyun Kum is bordered on the west and east by the Talass and Chu Rivers, which head in the Tyan Shans to the south and flow northwestward to end in the sands. The Chu Valley separates the Muyun Kum on the south from the Betpak-Dala to the north.

"Betpak-Dala" means "Cruel, Crafty Steppe." It derives its name, it is thought, from the fact that it is an extensive trackless surface that on hot days abounds in mirages which lead the unwary traveler astray. This dry plateau rises from an elevation of about 450 feet at its southern edge along the Chu River northward to elevations of about 1500 feet where it merges with the higher Kazakh Folded Country north of Lake Balkhash. On the northwest it drops off in an escarpment approximately 150 feet high to the Sarysu River. In its western portion it is composed primarily of horizontal layers of clay and sandstone, predominantly of Tertiary age, but to the east the area is one of "melkosopochnik," which is a Russian term designating old worn-down hills composed of granites, syenites, porphyries, diorites, and some sedimentary Paleozoic strata. The Betpak-Dala, or "Hungry Steppe," has a cracked-clay and salt-encrusted surface that supports only a sparse vegetation and has very little prospects for development. The area should not be confused with the less extensive "Hungry Steppe" southwest of Tashkent where an irrigation project has produced the so-called "Pakhta Aral," or "cotton island," southwest of the Syr-Darya.

Lake Balkhash occupies a large landlocked basin approximately 350 miles long at an elevation of about 1100 feet above sea level. The lake itself has a surface area of approximately 6680 square miles and an average depth of only 20 feet. But terraces along the northern side, rising to elevations approximately 400 feet above the surface of the lake, attest to the fact that the lake was higher at one time and reached as far eastward as the basin of Ebi-Nur in China. Apparently the waters of the lake are of geologically recent origin, since the salt content is quite low. The western end, which is fed by the Ili River, is fresh enough to be used for irrigation and drinking. The lake seems to be in the process of drying up and becoming more salty, however. Large alluvial fans built by small streams flowing northward out of the northern ranges of the Tyan Shans have stretched across the basin of the lake and have cut off segments of its eastern end. These isolated segments are becoming quite salty. A sand bar practically severs the present lake in its midsection, thereby dividing a relatively fresh body of water in the western end, where fresh water is added by the Ili River, from a relatively salty body of water in the eastern end, where the Karatal, Aksu, and Lepsa Rivers are insufficient to counterbalance evaporation. The eastern end serves as the final evaporation pan for the entire lake.

The High Mountains   Everywhere on the south and east, Middle Asia is bounded by high, rugged mountains. In the west, bordering on Iran, are the Kopet Dag, or "Dry Mountains," a fault-block range which is cut sharply on its northeastern side by a major fault system that runs in a straight line from southeast to northwest along the Transcaspian Railroad through the cities of Ashkhabad and Kizyl-Arvat and continues on northwestward through Nebit-Dag and the Balkhan Mountains to the Caspian. The Kopet Dag reaches elevations of around 7500 feet in the Soviet Union, but the area is so dry that even in their highest elevations the mountains are practically devoid of vegetation. Erosion, in the process of stripping the sedimentary layers down their dip slopes toward the southwest, has produced a series of jagged, overhanging cuesta escarpments facing northeastward overlooking the sandy deserts of the Kara-Kum. The spectacular scenery standing out in bold relief in this dry climate has induced the Soviets to establish the city of Ashkhabad as one of the film-making centers of the Soviet Union. "Western-type" movies are produced here, utilizing the magnificent backdrop of the Kopet Dag. No streams of any proportions originate in the Kopet Dag, but several small streams provide water for local domestic use

and restricted irrigation in areas such as Ashkhabad. Also, wells and underground canal systems constructed centuries ago by the Persians are still utilized to provide limited water supplies.

Eastward from the Kopet Dag rise the Hindu Kush. Although they lie entirely in Afghanistan, they provide the water shed for small streams flowing northward into Soviet Middle Asia. The two largest of these streams, the Murgab and the Tedzhen Rivers, end in the sands of Turkmenistan and form the two oases around the cities of Mary and Tedzhen.

The Hindu Kush rise in eastern Afghanistan to join the Pamir Knot, which straddles the boundaries of Afghanistan, Pakistan, China, and the Soviet Union. On the Soviet Union side, the Pamirs fan out to the west in a series of east-west oriented ranges, known as the Pamir-Alay. These are the highest mountains in the Soviet Union, containing the peaks of Mount Stalin at an elevation of 24,590 feet and Mount Lenin at an elevation of 23,363 feet, both in the Tadzhik Republic. In the western extremities the Pamir-Alay Ranges are deeply dissected by the headwaters of the Amu-Darya, especially by the two main headwater streams, the Vakhsh and the Pyandzh. Throughout much of its course, the Pyandzh forms the international boundary between the Soviet Union and Afghanistan. The Vakhsh and several smaller streams flow southwestward through a gently rolling upland in southwestern Tadzhikistan, and provide irrigation water to transform the steppe into the primary agricultural area of the Tadzhik Republic.

The Trans Alay Range forms the northernmost range of the Pamir-Alay Mountains, and northward across the Alay Valley the Alay Range forms the southernmost range of an extensive mountain system known as the Tyan Shans. The Tyan Shans stretch all the way from northern Tadzhikistan, through the Uzbek and Kirgiz Republics, and through eastern Kazakhstan east of Lake Balkhash into China. The individual ranges in this system are oriented primarily west-east, and generally they are rather widely spaced with broad steppe-like mountain basins in between. The broadest of these mountain basins is the Fergana Basin just north of the Alay Range. This flat-floored alluvial basin, extending approximately 100 miles east-west and 10 to 25 miles north-south, is a major agricultural area of Middle Asia. It is a steppe area and requires irrigation.

North of the Fergana Basin the main ranges of the Tyan Shans form a bold escarpment on the north overlooking a string of important irrigated areas and cities built on the alluvial fans at their base. Many small streams flowing northwestward out of the mountains bring the all-important water to these settlements. Issyk-Kul, as well as several smaller lakes, lie within these ranges. The headwaters of the Syr-Darya, particularly the Naryn, head along the southern slope of the ranges and flow the entire length of the Fergana Basin before entering the desert to the northwest. These lakes and streams are fed by melting glaciers during the summer and reach their greatest flow at that time, a fact that is very significant to the agriculture in the area. Most of the precipitation in these mountains comes during the wintertime in the form of snow when cyclonic storms from the Mediterranean and Black Seas penetrate the Middle Asian region. The precipitation in the form of snow is stored until it is needed for irrigation in the summer. Were it not for this natural storage, agriculture in this area would be extremely limited.

The Tyan Shans in general are folded mountain ranges, but faulting has occurred, and some volcanism has broken out along various fault lines. Issyk-Kul, or "hot lake," gets its name from the fact that volcanic activity in the immediate surroundings produces warm water in certain portions of the lake. Several fault-block ranges branch out in a general northwesterly direction from the northern side of the main line of the Tyan Shans. The most westerly of these, Kara Tau, has already been mentioned as the divide between the Kyzyl-Kum and the

Muyun Kum northeast of the Syr-Darya. Lying in a desert climatic area, the Kara Tau stand out conspicuously although the elevations are no higher than 5700 feet. The dark and somber sedimentary rocks making up the fault block have formed imposing escarpments facing northeast under the erosional process of stripping down the dip slope toward the southwest. Similar to the Kara Tau are the Chu-Ili Mountains, lying between the Chu and the Ili Rivers, extending northwestward from Alma-Ata toward Lake Balkhash. Their highest elevation is a little over 3500 feet.

After a major break where the Ili River flows westward out of China, the Tyan Shans rise once again in the Dzhungarian Alatau to elevations of 16,500 feet. As indicated by the name, these mountains also are snow-capped year round. The term "Alatau" means "mottled mountains" and comes from the fact that in the summertime from a distance the mountains appear mottled because of patches of snow on their slopes. The Dzhungarian Alatau are the northernmost range of the Tyan Shans, and are separated from the Tarbagatay Mountains to the north by the broad Dzhungarian Gate east of Lake Balkhash. The Dzhungarian Gate has long afforded a low-level route of travel from Sinkiang, China, into

Figure 10-12 Mountain streams building rocky alluvial fans along the northern base of the Tyan Shans provide water for irrigation of orchards east of Alma-Ata. Photograph by the author.

Middle Asia and thence to the Middle East and Europe.

North of the Dzhungarian Gate, the Tarbagatay Range, rising to 9500 feet, represents the eastern extremity of an extensive area of old, worn-down mountains north of Lake Balkhash. This area, the Kazakh Folded Country, is discussed with northern Kazakhstan in Chapter 11 as are the chains of high mountains that continue northeastward into Siberia.

Figure 10-14   The "fences" around the fields and barnlots near Tashkent are loess walls.   Photograph by the author.

Hydrology and Soils

Water is the key word in Soviet Middle Asia, as it is in most dry regions of the earth. With water the native population can carry on an extensive irrigation agriculture; without it, they must struggle as best they can with dry-farming procedures in the moister areas and with extensive grazing in the drier areas. As has been pointed out at the beginning of this chapter, the entire plains area of Soviet Middle Asia is dry. Certain areas are moister than others, but none classifies as humid. The streams that originate on the plain flow primarily only as spring freshets when the thin snow cover is melting; many of them dry up completely before the summer is over. All end either in one of the three great interior drainage basins, the Caspian Sea, the Aral Sea, or Lake Balkhash,

or in some salt-encrusted playa lake bed. None of the runoff from this area reaches the sea; evaporation eventually accounts for all the precipitation that falls in the area.

Perennial streams are limited primarily to those whose headwaters lie in the high mountains and are fed throughout the summer by the melting snows and glaciers. In the south the two outstanding streams of this nature are the Amu-Darya and the Syr-Darya, the two great rivers of Soviet Middle Asia that flow into the Aral Sea. But many smaller streams flow out of the southern mountains, some of which already have been named. Of these, the most important to irrigation are the Ili and Chu Rivers in the east, the Zeravshan between the Syr-Darya and the Amu-Darya, the Murgab and the Tedzhen in the Turkmen Republic, and the Vakhsh in the Tadzhik Republic.

The Ural River in the northwest does not have much of a water shed in the southern Urals, but it does find its way to the Caspian all year round. The other stream of significance northeast of the Caspian, the Emba River, heads in the low Mugodzhar Mountains and barely makes it to the sea in late summer.

The inorganic soils of the area are adaptable to a variety of crops wherever irrigation water is available and the surface material is not too sandy or rocky. Large areas of the lower portions of the alluvial fans spread-

Figure 10-13   The Bakhmal (velvet) Mountains northeast of Samarkand, loess-mantled low ranges along the River Zeravshan.   Courtesy of Robert H. Dawson.

ing out from the mountains toward the northern lowlands are deeply covered by loess on which mineral-rich sierozem soils have developed. The loess appears to be material which has been reworked by the wind after it was originally laid down by streams either in the fashion of alluvial fans or in glaciolfluvial deposits during the Pleistocene Period. This is one of the most extensive belts of loess in the world; in places it reaches thicknesses of several hundred feet. The loess stands in vertical cliffs because of its loosely compacted porous nature and is an ideal soil for farming and for making adobe walls for houses and fences. Hence it is not difficult to understand why very early civilizations developed in some of these river valleys.

Other than in the loess belt, fine, fertile soils are found in delta areas and in other sections of floodplains of the major rivers. The most extensive area of good river alluvium is near the mouth of the Amu-Darya.

Some of the coarser soils near the heads of alluvial fans are adaptable to vegetable and fruit crops, and are ideally situated with respect to sources of water. The most highly developed area of this type is around Alma-Ata against the very base of the Tyan Shans.

Agriculture

The agriculture of southern Kazakhstan and Soviet Middle Asia can be characterized broadly into three types: (1) extensive grazing throughout much of the area, (2) dry farming of grain in the moister portions of loess-covered foothills of the southern mountains, and (3) intensive irrigation farming of cotton, alfalfa, some grain, and many vegetables and fruits wherever good soil and irrigation water are available.

Grazing Some grazing of livestock is carried on nearly everywhere, but it becomes the predominant economy in the drier lowlands and in the high mountains where cultivation is largely impossible. The entire lowland from the Caspian Sea to the eastern

end of Lake Balkhash and extending to the southern border of the Turkmen Republic, except for scattered regions of irrigation, is utilized only for grazing. Even grazing is poor throughout the drier areas, in many areas being limited to spring and early summer after the melting snows have produced an abundance of ephemeral vegetation. Thawing and refreezing of winter snow, as well as ice storms, may form a hard crust of ice over the surface of the plains, which makes it impossible for the livestock to reach the grass underneath during prolonged periods in the winter. On the other hand, in the immediate forelands of many of the mountains of the southeast, foehn winds during the winter frequently produce relatively balmy spells of weather with temperatures above freezing, which dispel the snow and provide open grazing through the winter. This is particularly true in the region between the Dzhungarian Gate and the eastern end of Lake Balkhash, where a foehn wind, called the "ebe," frequently flows westward down slope from the Sinkiang Basin in China.

Sheep and camels predominate in the lowland deserts. Cattle, sheep, and goats utilize the desert pastures in winter and spring but must be driven to the mountains during the summer. Transhumance is practiced on a grand scale.

The Karakul sheep are admirably suited to desert conditions, having originated in the Karakul, or "Black Lake," Oasis at the end of the Zeravshan River. Karakul are black, curly-haired sheep that are raised for the skins of the new-born lambs, which bring very high prices on the world market. They are raised in various places scattered about the desert and in the mountains to some extent, but they are concentrated in the Zeravshan area. The Kara-Kalpak A.S.S.R. south of the Aral Sea owes its name to these sheep. The term "Kara-Kalpak" refers to the large Karakul hat worn by the natives in this area. Today factories in Tashkent and in some of the other cities of Middle Asia are turning out synthetic Karakul cloth.

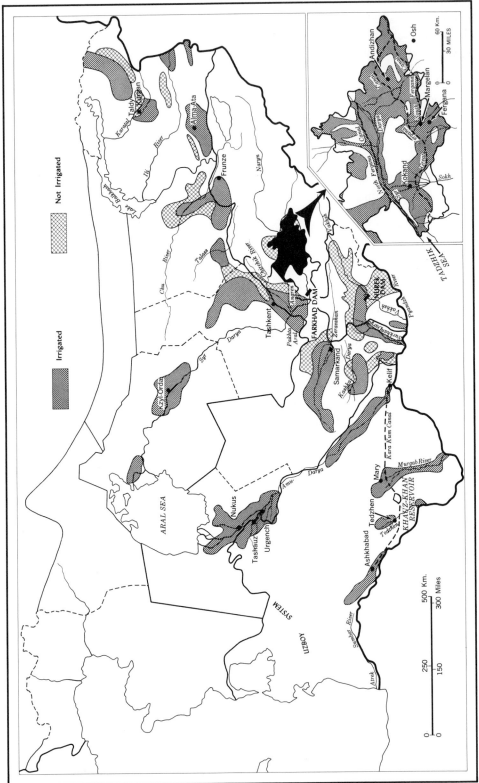

Figure 10-15 Cultivated land.

Camels have been used extensively as beasts of burden from time immemorial in the deserts of Middle Asia, particularly along the caravan route from China to Europe. Such cities as Tashkent and Samarkand were long important as stopover points along the "silk road" between China and Europe, and the camel very early became established as the best means of transport across the Middle Asian deserts. Today camels seem to be decreasing in importance; they are no longer seen in the vicinity of the larger cities. Cattle and sheep are becoming the predominant animals, for their meat, and the donkey is the chief beast of burden in the cultivated areas of Middle Asia.

A great effort is being made to rely less and less on the native vegetation and more and more on forage and hay crops raised in rotation with cotton and grain. Alfalfa is the chief rotation crop with the cotton in the irrigated areas and produces an abundant supply of forage, being harvested usually about five times per year. Along with this reliance on domestic crops, the Soviets are attempting to settle the nomadic herdsmen and to make farmers out of them. Recently there have been reports that herdsmen from the high mountains are being resettled with their families on irrigated plains to open up new cotton-alfalfa-beef cattle areas.

Although the native vegetation over much of the desert area is rather poor for grazing, it is very important to the stabilization of the blowing sands. Little of the desert actually is devoid of vegetation, even in the most sandy areas of the Kara-Kum. Besides many species of brushy plants and ephemeral grasses and flowering herbs, there is a stunted tree that appears to be unique to this desert area. This is the Saxaul, a gnarled tree approximately 20 feet high of very heavy, iron-hard wood that burns like charcoal. The Saxaul has two main species: the white, or sand, Saxaul which grows on top of the sand dunes, and the black Saxaul which grows in the alkaline flats between the sand dunes. Maintaining itself practically without water, the Saxaul has been very important both in the stabilization of the sand dunes and as a source of firewood for the nomadic herdsmen. After all, this is a cold region in winter to be weathered in makeshift camps. Lying wide open to cold blasts of Siberian air from the northeast, much of the area averages well below freezing in January. As far south as Tashkent, the January average is only 30°F, and at times the temperature plunges to zero or below. In the past the Saxaul tree has been utilized so extensively for fuel that in certain areas it has been threatened by extinction. There is now an effort to save the Saxaul tree and to reforest certain areas with it to stabilize the drifting sands. Stabilization of the sands becomes especially necessary where canals and railroads are constructed.

Dry Farming Wheat and some other grains are dry farmed in the moister portions of the loess-covered foothills in the south where precipitation averages between 10 and 15 inches per year. In these areas the rain comes primarily in late winter and early spring, which is quite advantageous for wheat growing. Dry farming of grain has been carried on in the loessial foothills for a long time, but under the virgin lands program additional areas are being opened up.

Figure 10-16 "Main street" in a village of 5000 people on a new state farm in the loess belt north of Alma-Ata. The building in the left foreground is the village store. Photograph by the author.

Figure 10-17 Women coming with their buckets and yokes to obtain water at the village pump on a state farm north of Alma-Ata. The new rural dwellings of unpainted boards and sheet metal roofs are typical of new single-family dwellings throughout the Soviet Union. Photograph by the author.

The loess belt is a dry, hot, dusty place in the summer, and it is not easy to recruit people to settle the new state farms. In the words of Berg, "In summer the towns of Middle Asia may be recognized from a distance by the loessial dust which hangs over them. This dust is a characteristic feature of all the settlements of Middle Asia. Carried by winds and convectional currents, the fine dust rises to a height of at least 6000 meters. Often during the dry period of the year when gales are blowing, the whole sky is covered by a continuous turbid shroud. In general a whitish, foggy atmospheric coloration is very characteristic to the landscape here." The so-called "Afghanets," a dry, dusty southwest wind, blows from 40 to 70 days per year in the vicinity of Termez on the Afghan border.

Irrigation Agriculture Wherever irrigation water is available, the rich loess soil has been utilized intensively for irrigated crops. Also, some of the more stony soils in the higher parts of the alluvial fans have been irrigated for the growing of fruit trees, grapes, and berries, which do not make heavy demands on the soil. These irrigated areas form a discontinuous belt along the northern slopes of the Tyan Shans all the way from Taldy-Kurgan in the east through Alma-Ata, Frunze, and Dzhambul to Tashkent, and on westward across the Kara Kum along the northern bases of the Hindu Kush and Kopet Dag.

Irrigation developed the earliest along the River Zeravshan, but the largest continuous area of irrigation today is the Fergana Basin between two prongs of the Tyan Shans. Other extensive areas lie ir southwestern Tadzhikistan, utilizing the waters of the Vakhsh and several lesser rivers, and around Tashkent, utilizing the waters of the Chirchik and Angren rivers before they enter the Syr-Darya. Other extensive regions of irrigation exist along the Amu-Darya and Syr-Darya. The largest of these by far is along the lower Amu-Darya in the so-called Khorezm or Khiva Oasis. A line of oases of lesser size are strung along the Trans-Caspian Railway from Mary through Tedzhen and Ashkhabad to Kizyl-Arvat. These oases utilize separate small streams flowing northward out of the Hindu Kush and Kopet Dag.

The specialty crop for which the irrigated areas of Middle Asia are best known is, of course, cotton. But many other crops are raised that also utilize the long hot summers and good loess soils. Although the Soviets have forced a continual expansion of cotton acreage in the irrigated areas at the expense of wheat, a considerable amount of irrigated land is still occupied by grain crops, particularly wheat and rice—the staple food of Middle Asia—and by a great variety of fruits and vegetables. Certain regions are known for their vineyards and wine-making. And recently, sugar beets have been introduced into the area rather heavily. Other specialty crops are raised, such as tobacco and kenaf, a fiber crop for use in making ropes and burlap bags. Not all these crops are scattered throughout the entire region; the physical environment does vary from place to place, and certain regions are conducive to the growing of other crops. Cotton growing is limited to the regions with the longest, hottest growing season, which eliminates it from the northeastern slopes of the Tyan

Shans. A brief summary of the main irrigated areas of Middle Asia and characterizations of their crop complexes follows.

Beginning in the east, the first irrigated region is around Taldy-Kurgan, in eastern Kazakhstan just south of the eastern end of Lake Balkhash. Most of the irrigated acreage here is occupied by grain, primarily wheat and barley, with some rice growing. But the crop for which the area is becoming known is sugar beets, which have been introduced recently by in-migrating Russians and Ukrainians.

Southwestward, along the slopes of the Tyan Shans, is a significant area of irrigated agriculture around the large city of Alma-Ata. Much of this irrigation is carried on in the rather rocky alluvial fans at the very base of the Tyan Shans. Also, the region lies at an elevation of about 2000 feet above sea level, and this together with its exposure to the north produces a climate that is too cool for cotton. Fruit and vegetable growing are developed to a high degree around Alma-Ata, and the city provides a ready market for such produce. The name "Alma-Ata" means "Father of Apples." Supposedly this area is where apples originated. There are many apple orchards on the collective farms surrounding the city. Some rice is grown northwest of Alma-Ata near the mouth of the Ili River.

Moving westward, the next important river valley is the Chu, which stretches northwestward from the city of Frunze, the capital of the Kirgiz Republic. About 90 per cent of the irrigated acreage in the Chu Valley is planted to grain crops, particularly winter wheat and barley, but the Valley is better known for its sugar beets. Like the Taldy-Kurgan area farther east, sugar beets have been introduced recently into the Chu Valley by Russian and Ukrainian settlers. The Chu Valley is now the most important sugar beet raising area in Middle Asia and has been dubbed "Sugar Beet Valley."

Westward from the Chu Valley across the Muyun-Kum is a small river along the eastern base of the Kara Tau. This is the Talass River, and its valley is the beginning of the cotton belt. The Talass is not a large stream and the irrigated area it supports is not extensive. The chief crop here is cotton, but some grain and sugar beets are grown near the city of Dzhambul. Also, a little rice is grown in this area.

Except in some mountain spurs along the western end of the Tyan Shans, the cotton belt continues unbroken from the Talass River Valley westward down the Chirchik and Arys Rivers to the Syr-Darya. Along the Syr-Darya, irrigated agriculture stretches both upstream and downstream for a long distance. The broadest area of irrigation is in the middle section from the small town of Turkestan southeastward to Tashkent and then eastward into the broad Fergana Basin. Throughout this entire region cotton reigns supreme, but other crops are raised, particularly alfalfa as a rotation crop with the cotton. In the Fergana Basin a considerable amount of irrigated wheat and barley are grown, and in both this area and in the vicinity of Tashkent, rice is grown. Around the larger cities vegetables and fruits of all types are grown for the urban markets. Grapes for wine are grown throughout the area. Such specialty crops as kenaf are being introduced. Mulberry trees have been grown for centuries along the irrigation canals and provide the basis for a silk industry. Downstream on the Syr-Darya in a long strip of irrigated land centered on Kzyl-Orda, and again near the delta of the Syr-Darya, are extensive areas of rice growing.

A separate area of irrigation lies along the Zeravshan River, which flows westward out of the Tyan Shans across the southern Kyzyl-Kum toward the Amu-Darya. The Zeravshan has already been mentioned as the location of the earliest river civilization in Middle Asia. For a distance of about 200 miles along the Zeravshan irrigated cotton extends in an almost unbroken belt 10 to 25 miles wide. In its middle and eastern portions this belt is flanked on either side by unirrigated wheat and barley. The irrigated strip extends westward beyond Bukhara

Figure 10-18   Orchards, fields, and rice paddys in the Fergana Valley.   Novosti Press.

to the region of Karakul, which has been mentioned before as the origin of the Karakul sheep. Although this area along the Zeravshan is heavily concentrated on cotton and wheat, other crops, such as rice, tobacco, and certain fiber crops are raised, as well as grapes and other fruits and vegetables for the local market.

Several extensive areas of irrigated agriculture exist along the Amu-Darya and some of its tributary valleys. In the upstream portions of the river system lies the irrigated region in southwestern Tadzhikistan on the low plateau which is crossed by the Vakhsh River and other tributaries of the Amu-Darya. Long staple cotton and grain are the chief crops in this area. Some rice is grown for local consumption. Adjacent to

this area on the west is the region in the very southernmost part of the Uzbek Republic that is watered by the Surkhan-Darya, the Kashka-Darya, and some other minor streams. The Surkhan-Darya Valley grows considerable irrigated cotton, and a small area of cotton exists in the Kashka-Darya Valley. The Kashka-Darya Valley also grows a considerable amount of irrigated grain. Specialty crops such as rice, tobacco, grapes, etc. are scattered throughout the region.

The irrigated region along the Amu-Darya extends downstream past the city of Chardzhou, where it ends in the sand, and no more agriculture is found until near the city of Urgench on the lower portion of the river. Downstream from Urgench, except for the swampy, reed-covered delta, the river plain supports an extensive area of irrigated agriculture whose origin dates back to ancient times. This is the famous Khiva Oasis, which at the present time is divided between Khorezm Oblast and the Kara-Kalpak A.S.S.R. within the Uzbek Republic and Tashauz Oblast in the Turkmen Republic. This area is hot and dry with excellent soils that have been deposited by repeated floodings of the river through the ages. The region probably is more highly concentrated on cotton growing than in any of the other areas mentioned. Alfalfa serves as the rotation crop. The area is also one of the major rice-growing regions of Middle Asia.

The remaining areas of irrigation lie along the northern bases of the Hindu Kush and Kopet Dag on the southern border of the Turkmen Republic. The largest of these are the Murgab River Valley, with its chief city of Mary, in the east, the Tedzhen River Valley, with its major town of Tedzhen, in the middle, and the area around Ashkhabad, the capital city of the Turkmen Republic, in the west, which is fed by several minor streams. Cotton is grown in all three areas, but it is predominant in the Murgab River Valley. The Tedzhen River Valley is predominantly irrigated grain, and the Ashkhabad region is a mixture of cotton and grain.

One other very small valley that the Russians sometimes mention as having potentialities for citrus growing lies along the Sumbar River which flows through the western end of the Kopet Dag into the Atrek River and finally into the Caspian Sea. This region is a very limited area of irrigated agriculture and does not have enough water or level land to become a major producing area in the future; but it has very mild winters, being protected by the Kopet Dag from the cold air to the north, and the Russians frequently have pointed out that this area is one region in Middle Asia where citrus crops might be grown. At present, what little land is irrigated is put in orchards and vegetable gardens.

Water Construction Projects

It bears repeating that water is the lifeblood of Middle Asia. Because rain does not fall in adequate amounts on the plain, many man-made constructions have had to be devised to distribute the water from the mountains where it falls to the plains where it is needed for agriculture. Some of these man-made constructions date back to the ancient civilizations that occupied the area before the time of Christ, but the Soviets are adding many more of their own. In general the ancient constructions dealt with the smaller streams or the more easily controlled lower portions of the bigger streams, because the inhabitants did not have the technology to harness the very large rivers at the most strategic points where they issue forth from the mountains. Such rivers as the Zeravshan were ideal for the agricultural practices of the ancients, but the Soviets are greatly expanding the irrigated area of Middle Asia by constructing large dams in the gorges where the major streams, such as the Amu-Darya and the Syr-Darya, leave the mountains and enter the plains. Most of these dams and reservoirs are for the purpose of irrigation, but some of them also have power stations, and a few facilitate river navigation. In general, river navigation in Middle Asia is insignificant because of shallow water and the shifting nature of the channels in the sands.

The Fergana Basin The first major water construction project in Middle Asia under the Soviet regime was the so-called Great Fergana Canal, which was completed in 1939. Until this time the Fergana Basin was rather poorly utilized with water being tapped only from minor streams to irrigate local areas, primarily along the southern side of the basin. A myriad of small streams flowing down the northern slopes of the Alay Range into the southern portion of the Fergana Basin have built a string of alluvial fans sloping northward into the Basin and afford ideal conditions for gravity-flow irrigation. Many of these small streams have been utilized for centuries because they were easy to control, but the large Syr-Darya which flows the full length of the basin was not used. During the first two five-year plans the Soviets initiated a large project to tap the waters of the Syr-Darya and to irrigate much more of the floor of the Fergana Basin. The Great Fergana Canal project became one of the three big construction projects in the country, along with the Dnieper Dam and Magnitogorsk, which were held up as symbols of new national strength to capture the imaginations of young volunteers to work on the projects during their spare time and on weekends without pay. The main canal system is about 200 miles long and completely encircles the Fergana Basin. Many feeder canals distribute the water over much of the Basin floor. Only the lowest central portion of the Basin still is not utilized, because it is too sandy and salty for cultivation.

In 1943 construction began on the large Farkhad Dam opposite the city of Begovat at the western mouth of the Fergana Basin where the noisy Syr-Darya rushes through a gorge in the Mogol Tau on its way to the Hungry Steppe to the west. The Farkhad Dam was constructed primarily to provide hydroelectricity to the many industries that are being located in Middle Asia, particularly to a variety of chemical and synthetic industries being established there. It also provides more water for irrigation to expand the Pakhta Aral or "Cotton Island" in the Hungry Steppe.

There is a romantic legend behind the naming of the Farkhad Dam. According to Uzbek lore, a capricious princess once lived on the high cliff that overlooks the dam site. She agreed to give her hand in marriage to the one of her many suitors who performed the greatest deed. Being in sympathy with the poor people who were in dire need of irrigation water, she announced that she would marry the man who could bring water to the Hungry Steppe. One cunning young nobleman ordered the steppes

to be covered with mats of chi grass. When the sun rose in the morning its glare from the chi grass looked very much like the reflection from a water surface. The princess agreed to marry the hero on the spot. Meanwhile (and here the legend takes on a definite Soviet slant), a simple hero of the common people had brought water to the steppes by his honest toil. (The legend does not explain exactly how he did this by his honest toil.) But it was too late, the princess already had married the deceiver. Farkhad, as the honest peasant was called, learning of the trickery, threw his heavy ketmen, a hoe-like spade, into the air, which fell on his head and split his skull. An opera has been written about this unfortunate but noble Uzbek peasant. Now Farkhad is bringing water to the desert.

Just upstream from the Farkhad Reservoir on the Syr-Darya the Kayrak-Kum "hydro-knot," with its "Druzhba Narodov" (Friendship of Nations) hydroelectric station, was completed in 1957 to form a reservoir known as the "Tadzhik Sea," 70 kilometers long within the neck of Tadzhikistan that extends into the western end of the Fergana Basin. The reservoir feeds twelve networks of irrigation canals, which are still being extended, to bring extra water to 400,000 hectares of arid lands, 300,000 of which lie in the Golodnaya (Hungry) Steppe west of the Fergana Basin in the Uzbek Republic. The Sangar pumping station on the Kayrak-Kum Reservoir began operations in 1959 to lift water 56 meters to irrigate the Sangar region in northern Tadzhikistan. This region will be fully reclaimed after the construction of 250 kilometers of canals and 860 installations. These new canals will connect with the western end of the Great Fergana Canal. The Kayrak-Kum hydroelectric plant has a capacity of 126,000 kilowatts.

Between 1957 and 1959 the Kokand "hydro-knot" was constructed at the head of the large alluvial fan on which Kokand sits to collect water from all the distributory channels of the Sokh River to provide for the irrigation of an additional 60,000 hectares of land in the south-central part of the Fergana Basin. A silt basin above the "knot" catches the coarse, rocky alluvium before it clogs the canals feeding irrigation water both right and left from the "hydro-knot."

During the seven-year plan, widening of the Great Fergana Canal and other improvements of the system are to allow for the irrigation of another 100,000 hectares of land in the Fergana Basin.

The Kara-Kum Canal   The largest irrigation project under way at present is the Kara-Kum Canal, which leads water from the Amu-Darya at Kelif westward through the oases at Mary and Tedzhen to Ashkhabad. Hence it will bring water to the entire area of thirsty southern Turkmenistan, which until now has been supplied only in local areas by small streams. The canal was completed to Ashkhabad in 1962. There are long-rang plans to extend the canal to Krasnovodsk on the Caspian. Whether or not this is possible is a question. This is a major undertaking involving the building of a canal through 650 kilometers or more of shifting sands, which during any windstorm may destroy the work already completed. Apparently the Soviets have solved the problems of wind and sand and are successfully bringing additional water to hundreds of thousands of hectares of land in this region, but not without expensive special installations.

The Amu-Darya carries 250 million cubic meters of silt and sand per year and 8 million cubic meters enter the canal. This is why the canal starts in the form of three wide branches. A quarter of the sediment

Figure 10-19   The Kara-Kum Canal cuts through the sand dunes near Mary.   Novosti Press.

remains in these branches, and seventeen excavating pumps continually remove it. The rest settles in the Kelif Lakes, so that after the last of them the canal is clear. The Kelif Lakes are a series of eight stagnant lakes connected by shallow channels that occupy the Kelif Uzboy, the bed of an old tributary of the Amu-Darya, which has been all but swallowed up by the shifting sands of the Kara-Kum. Three of the lakes have already ceased to exist since the canal has brought extra silt to them. Now that the Amu-Darya water has returned to the Kelif Uzboy, life has reappeared on the lakes, which are overgrown with reeds and water plants and swarm with birds. The water plants are a serious problem to the canal; tractors are employed to pull the weeds from the bed of the canal, and special floating cutting machines are used. Because this is very expensive, the Russians are planning to import a species of fish from China to feed on the water plants.

Only one third of the Amu-Darya waters that enter the Canal reach the Murgab oasis at Mary; the rest is lost in evaporation and filtration or is used for irrigation. To supplement the water from the Canal, the Sagr-Yazy Reservoir was constructed on the Murgab River in 1953.

The Tedzhen River carries 90 per cent of its annual flow in the spring when the rains come and the snow begins to melt in the mountains. To remedy the shortage of irrigation water in summer, the Tedzhen Reservoir was constructed in 1950. But it is too small, and already it is clogged with sand and silt. Subsequently two other reservoirs have been constructed on the Tedzhen.

A large reservoir, the Khauz Khan, is being built on the Kara-Kum Canal between the Murgab and Tedzhen Rivers to reconcile the even flow in the canal throughout the year with the peak spring and summer usage in the irrigation systems. The winter flow of the canal can be stored in the reservoir until it is needed for irrigation in spring and summer. Also, the reservoir will store the overflow of water from the Tedzhen

River whose reservoirs still are unable fully to control its floods in excessively rainy seasons. A "hydro-knot" above the first Tedzhen reservoir will direct the excess flow during spring into the Khauz Khan Reservoir. Thus, the entire flow of the Canal and the Tedzhen River can be used for irrigation. The Khauz Khan Reservoir is to be completed in 1970 with a capacity of 1.3 billion cubic meters.

The Great Turkmen Canal A still larger project that has been talked about, but which seems to be unrealistic, is the Great Turkmen Canal. As proposed, it would lead off from the Amu-Darya near its mouth at the city of Nukus southwestward, utilizing the old Uzboy System, to carry water all the way to Krasnovodsk on the shores of the Caspian. This would involve building a canal some 680 miles long with branch canals totaling more than 750 miles. According to the Soviets, such a system would enable over three million acres of land to be irrigated, and besides there would be provisions for hydroelectric stations along the canals and for some navigation. As has been amply pointed out by various authors, the Amu-Darya simply does not have enough water for such a project, particularly in light of the irrigation water that is being led off upstream by the Kara-Kum Canal. In 1951 the Soviets announced with much fanfare that they were starting construction of the canal, but in 1953 after the death of Stalin all such talk ceased. Apparently the Soviets decided that the project was not feasible.

The Caspian Sea Problem One of the main reasons for wanting to bring Amu-Darya water into the Caspian was to maintain the level of the Caspian, which since 1929 has dropped 2.5 meters to its lowest level in 350 years. A continued drop of similar magnitude will lay bare much of the northern end of the sea bed, which now is covered by water to an average depth of only 5.4 meters. The falling water level and accompanying recession of the shore line has greatly affected shipping facilities; the fishing industry, and the sodium sulfate industry in Kara-Bogaz-Gol, all of which are of national significance. The Caspian each year carries approximately 40 per cent of the maritime traffic of the U.S.S.R., chiefly in the form of petroleum, and provides 90 per cent of the world's sturgeon catch, 95 per cent of the world's black caviar, and about 100,000 seals, not to mention other types of fish.

Since 1929 the delta of the Volga has extended outward into the Sea by more than 30 kilometers, the eastern part of the delta has become "dead," and only one navigable channel remains in the western part of the delta. During the same time the annual fish catch in the Caspian dropped from 510,000 tons to 190,000 tons. Extraction of sodium sulfate from Kara-Bogaz-Gol has been threatened by lack of water.

Several elaborate schemes have been devised to restore and stabilize the water level of the Caspian, all of which show more promise than that of bringing in water from the Amu-Darya. At the All-Union Conference on the Caspian Sea Problem on April 11, 1960, the Pechora-Vychegda river diversion project was revitalized, and discussion was begun on possible regulatory measures in the Caspian Sea itself. It was pointed out that the drop in the level of the Caspian since 1929 was due primarily to two factors: (1) a warming, drying climate, and (2) man-made dams and reservoirs on the Volga River, which supplies 78 per cent of the Caspian water. Loss of Volga River water, through irrigation and evaporation from large reservoir surfaces before it enters the Caspian, is the primary factor in the reduction of the level of the Caspian. The construction of a large reservoir in northeastern European Russia joining headwaters of the Pechora, Vychegda, and Kama Rivers would allow approximately 41 cubic kilometers additional water to flow down the Volga annually, an amount equal to approximately one sixth the present flow of the Volga. This not only would help to stabilize the level of the Caspian, it would increase the water flowing through the turbines of the hydroelectric power stations along the Volga, thereby increasing their electrical output. It has been pointed out that the Pechora-Vychegda Diversion Project would cost about one half the cost of the Kuybyshev Dam and power station and that the additional flow in the Volga produced by it would increase the aggregate electrical output of all the Volga power stations by an amount equal to the present output of the Kuybyshev station. Hence, the electricity derived from the project alone would justify the project economically.

A grand scheme to regulate the water level of the Caspian locally has been proposed to supplement the addition of northern water. It provides for a series of dams across the northern Caspian, totalling 460 kilometers in length with an average height of 6.5 meters, which would separate the shallow northern end from the rest of the Caspian and would allow the water level in the north to be maintained about 2.5 meters above that in the south. It is stated that several fringe benefits would accrue from this project, such as generation of power along the dam and exposure of more oil-bearing strata by an additional drop of water in the south.

This is indeed a grandiose scheme; such a dam would be very expensive. One Russian scientist has argued that there is no need for attempting to stabilize the water level at even the present level of the Caspian. He points out that the dropping water level continually is exposing more farm land in the North Caspian Lowland, which could become very productive if irrigated by water to be brought down the Volga from the Pechora and Vychegda. He contends that this extra water could be put to much better use through irrigation of crops than through maintaining the level of the Caspian. He says that these additional crops would far outweigh the fish loss, which largely has been due to mismanagement and not to the falling sea level. He points out that already very little sodium sulfate is taken from Kara-Bogaz-Gol; that it is now mined from the floor of the Caspian itself. Hence there is no need to keep up the water supply of Kara-Bogaz-Gol. In fact, there is no easier way to reduce the evaporation of about 20 cubic kilometers of water annually than by causing the gulf to dry up. Also, he points out the very obvious fact that all shipping, fishing, and industrial installations along the shores of the Caspian have constantly relocated their facilities to adjust to the lowering levels, and a rise to former levels would not solve their problems, but would simply cause them all to relocate once more.

Hence the Caspian Sea Problem is still being debated. It now looks as though the Pechora-Vychegda diversion project will be carried out in the near future, but whether all the added water will be dumped in the Caspian is still undecided. It has been calculated that all this northern water would not raise the Caspian to its 1929 level. If the Caspian level is stabilized, it will have to be at a level that is lower than the present one. The construction of any large dam system in the Caspian appears to be very doubtful. Perhaps the level of the Caspian will be allowed to continue to fall, and the Pechora-Vychegda waters will be put to good use to increase electrical output and enhance navigation on the Volga and to irrigate more land along the lower Volga.

Other Projects Besides the major water projects just mentioned, there are many projects that have been either initiated or improved during the Soviet period which involve other portions of the Amu and Syr-Darya as well as many other streams. Examples are the large stone dam, Tas-Buget, on the middle Syr-Darya near Kzyl-Orda, the Katta Kurgan Canal along the River Zeravshan, the complex irrigation works in the Khiva Oasis along the lower Amu-Darya, and the many projects involving the Ili, the Chu, and other streams flowing northward out of the Tyan Shans, and the tributaries of the Amu-Darya in southwestern Tadzhikistan. Two of the larger of these projects now under construction are the

Amu-Karakul Canal and the high Nurek Dam.

The Amu-Karakul Canal starts on the Amu-Darya above the Chardzhou railway bridge and extends 54 kilometers in a northeasterly direction across the Kyzyl-Kum to Karakul, the oasis at the end of the Zeravshan River. It will supplement the waters of the Zeravshan that are not sufficient to irrigate all the rich loess area stretching from Samarkand through Bukhara to Karakul. Construction began on the Canal in 1959; no completion date has been announced.

The large Nurek Dam and reservoir on the Vakhsh River southeast of Dushanbe in southern Tadzhikistan is under construction with completion set for sometime after 1965. The dam will be 1 kilometer long and 300 meters high. The power station, with a planned capacity of more than 2,500,000 kilowatts, will be the largest in Middle Asia. Part of the electricity is to be utilized in an aluminum plant that is to be built in the vicinity to produce alumina from the kaolin overburden of the Angren coal beds in the Fergana Basin. Water from the reservoir will allow for the irrigation of 100,000 additional hectares of cotton land on the Uaban-Obi-Kiik Massif in southwestern Tadzhikistan. In the same general area, west of the Vakhsh River, additional dams are being built on the Surkhan-Darya and Kashka-Darya, as well as on the upper Zeravshan, for the expansion of irrigation and production of hydroelectricity in southwestern Tadzhikistan and southeastern Uzbekistan.

In the Tashkent area, complex works on the Chirchik and Angren Rivers, tributaries to the Syr-Darya, provide water for irrigation and domestic use. The large Chardara Reservoir on the Syr-Darya itself has recently been constructed to supplement the water supply in the new cotton area southwest of Tashkent.

In the mountains south of the large city of Alma-Ata, numerous glacial-fed streams join to form the Alma-Atinka River, which in turn creates the Big Alma-Atinka Lake at an elevation of some 2500 meters. Nine hydroelectric plants are to be constructed to utilize the water flowing down the northern slopes of the mountains from this high lake.

Mineral Resources

Besides the unusual resources for agriculture, southern Kazakhstan and Middle Asia have some minerals that are used to supplement those of the rest of the Soviet Union. The sedimentary basins of the Caspian and Turanian Lowlands contain considerable deposits of petroleum, natural gas, various salts, and sulfur, and the Tyan Shans contain a variety of metallic ores. A brief summary of the major mineral deposits follows, but minor quantities of other elements exist.

Oil has been produced for over 50 years at the Emba oil fields in the Kazakh Republic along the northern shore of the Caspian and in the vicinity of Nebit Dag south of Kara-Bogaz-Gol in the Turkmen Republic. Also, minor quantities of oil have been produced in the Fergana Valley. These three areas of oil production do not appear to be areas of major oil reserves, and hence no great increase in development can be anticipated. Their production has held steady or increased slowly through the years, however, and the fifteen-year plan for oil development indicates that this trend will continue. In 1961 it was announced that oil was being produced in the extreme southwest corner of the Turkmen Republic and that a 17-kilometer pipeline was transporting the crude oil to Caspian tankers.

Since 1955 natural gas deposits near Nebit Dag and at Gazli, near Bukhara in the Kyzyl-Kum, have been discovered. The deposits at Gazli appear to be very large, rivaling those of the northern Caucasus and the Ukraine, and production here is scheduled to leap from zero in 1958 to 60 billion cubic meters in 1972. Two large pipelines are being laid from this area all the way to the Urals to supply gas to that fuel-impoverished heavy-industry area. Also, a gas pipeline is being laid eastward from Bukhara through Tashkent and on through all the important cities lying along the northern base of the Tyan Shans. A third line takes gas to the Fergana Basin.

A number of small coal deposits occur in the Fergana Basin and the surrounding mountains. Some deposits contain hard coal, but the major producer at present is the Angren brown coal deposit in the western part of the Fergana Basin. Here has been built the largest underground gasification plant in the country. Since supplies are limited and quality is low, coal mined in Middle Asia serves only part of the local needs and must be supplemented by coal from the Karaganda Fields in northern Kazakhstan and from the Kuznetsk Basin in western Siberia.

So far, no significant iron mining has been developed in Middle Asia and southern Kazakhstan. It appears that perhaps the only possibilities for development are the recently discovered low-grade ore deposits in the Turgay Lowland just north of the Aral Sea. These ores conceivably might be utilized along with Karaganda coal to establish an iron and steel industry somewhere along the lower Syr-Darya, but no definite plans have been formulated.

A manganese deposit was opened up on the Mangyshlak Peninsula during World War II to compensate partially for the loss to the Germans of Nikopol in the Ukraine, but no mention has been made of this development since the war.

Mining in Middle Asia is probably the best developed in the nonferrous metals. Copper has been mined for a long time at the major deposit near Balkhash on the northern shore of Lake Balkhash and at the minor deposit near Almalyk in the Tyan Shans southeast of Tashkent. Lead and zinc mines in the Karatau and other spurs of the Tyan Shans supply smelters in the city of Chimkent. Recently a molybdenum combine has been added at Almalyk. Although the magnitude of mining operations in Middle Asia and southern Kazakhstan for each type of metal is surpassed by mining operations in the Urals or in northern Kazakhstan, neverethless mining in Middle Asia is a significant part of the local economy.

Important deposits of nonmetallic minerals scattered about Middle Asia now are being developed as a strong base for new chemical industries. Particularly important are deposits of various mineral salts, phosphate, and sulfur. Sodium chloride is derived from widespread surface deposits associated with the Caspian Sea, the Aral Sea, and Lake Balkhash, as well as with scattered playa lake beds in the Turanian Lowland. Sodium sulfate, mirabilite, or Glauber's salt, important in the pharmaceutical industries for the manufacture of such things as Epsom Salts, is gathered in large quantities from the waters of Kara-Bogaz-Gol.

Important phosphate deposits exist on the Mangyshlak Peninsula and at Chulak-Tau north of Dzhambul. Phosphate from the Chulak-Tau deposit, combined with sulfuric acid from scattered sulfur deposits, is being used to produce mineral fertilizers at the superphosphate plants in Dzhambul, Chardzhou, Kokand, and Samarkand. The most important sulfur deposits are found at Sernyy Zavod, or "sulfur plant," in the desert of central Turkmenistan, at Gaurdak, near Termez on the Afghan border, and in the hills surrounding the Fergana Basin.

These mineral deposits, along with agricultural produce, have laid the basis for some industrialization of Middle Asia and for the rapid development of certain urban areas.

Industries and Cities

Industry is coming to Middle Asia in the form of diversified light industries in the larger cities, mainly in the Republic capitals, to serve the growing market, and metallurgical industries in new or rapidly expanding old towns located near important mineral resources. The industries in the larger cities are designed to turn out finished products for the local markets and are concentrated on machine building, textiles, and food industries. Tashkent, the capital of the Uzbek Republic, and Alma-Ata, the capital of the Kazakh Republic, have grown rapidly under the impetus of such industries. On the other side, Begovat is a good example of a new small city that has developed because of its function as a mining and metallurgical center to serve the industrial needs of Middle Asia. Perhaps the industries of Middle Asia can be summarized best by a discussion of the major cities.

Tashkent The metropolis of Middle Asia is Tashkent. With a population in 1959 of 912,000, it is seventh in size in the Soviet Union. Tashkent has served an important historical role since the seventh century as the main stopover point in Middle Asia for the caravan routes between China and Europe. It has shared with Samarkand and Bukhara the function of the seat of the governmental control over Moslem Middle Asia. In 1865 the Russians took over the area and established a new town outside the old Moslem center. Since that time, and particularly during the Soviet regime, the new city of Tashkent has grown and engulfed the old city, and in the process of transformation many of the old adobe huts have been torn down and replaced by brick and concrete-section apartment buildings. But many new individual homes are being economically built by Uzbeks of adobe bricks made from extensive loess deposits.

Today Tashkent is a thriving, bustling city of streetcars and taxis peopled by Russians as well as by Uzbeks. It sits in the heart of a rich cotton-growing area at a strategic position on the northwest corner of the Tyan Shans around which all transportation routes must funnel. It has been selected by the Soviets as the primary manufacturing city of Middle Asia, and machine-building industries and textile industries have been developed to the highest degree. Thus it serves more than the function of political capital of the Uzbek Republic, it is the com-

Figure 10-20 Large cranes swing prefabricated reinforced concrete slabs into place to be bolted together to form new apartment houses on the outskirts of Tashkent. Photograph by the author.

mercial capital of the entire Middle Asian area.

Tashkent sits at a rather low altitude, 1610 feet, and has long, hot, dry summers. Its annual rainfall is only 14.6 inches, and practically all of it comes during the winter months, with March and April having maximum rainfall. Thus it has a Mediterranean-type rainfall regime, with cyclonic storms moving in from the Mediterranean area during the wintertime, but its temperature range of 50°F between January and July reflects its continental location. January averages 30°F, and there are nights during the winter when temperatures plunge below zero. Since the growing season is hot and dry, irrigation is necessary for all agriculture, as well as the growing of trees and lawns is Tashkent. Small ariqs or water-distributing ditches gurgle along both sides of every street in the city. Often the ditch is a cemented trench from 1 to 2 feet wide and of about equal depth running between the sidewalk and the street, but sometimes it is simply a shallow channel in the earth that is allowed to wander at will alongside the footpaths.

Although factories and apartment buildings have been built in Tashkent, many of the Uzbek residents have maintained much of their old way of life. The native bazaar is still a main feature of the commercial life of the city, as it is in most Middle Asian cities. Farmers bring their produce to the market early in the morning and spend the day selling their own vegetables and fruits. As long as the farmer does not hire someone else to sell his produce for him, private retailing is not considered to be capitalistic. The labor forces in the larger factories are made up largely of Russians and Ukrainians who have moved into the area. Thus there is a considerable racial and social split between the society manning the larger factories and the society carrying on agriculture and much of the retail trade.

Alma-Ata Second in size among the cities of Soviet Middle Asia is Alma-Ata, the capital of the Kazakh Republic, which in 1959 had a population of 456,000. Unlike Tashkent, Alma-Ata is a newcomer to Middle Asia, and is a Russian, not a native, city. It was founded in 1854 as the Russian fort of Vernyy, and only recently has been selected as the capital of the new Kazakh Republic. In 1926 its population was only 45,000. Its rapid growth has taken place largely since it became the capital. Its present form reflects the rather chaotic growth that has taken place. Temporary structures have been thrown up in a hurry

Figure 10-21 An Uzbek woman and boy resting beside an ariq in Tashkent. Photograph by the author.

to keep up with the influx of population. The town does not have the look of a metropolitan center as does Tashkent, but nevertheless it is becoming a large city, and it has certain natural advantages over Tashkent. It lies at a somewhat higher elevation than does Tashkent, being nestled directly within the foothills of the Tyan Shans, whereas Tashkent sits out on the desert 50 miles or more from the mountains. Thus Alma-Ata is cooler than Tashkent, has a magnificent backdrop of mountain scenery, and is better watered by the many little rushing torrents which criss-cross the alluvial fan surfaces on their way from the snow-capped mountains in the south to the desert surrounding Lake Balkhash in the north. Again, many gurgling irrigation ditches run along all the streets, and a great tree-planting campaign has been carried on along the streets and in the parks of the city. The residents of Alma-Ata proudly announce that there are ten trees for every person in the city. In most cases, the trees have been planted very close together, within 4 or 5 feet of one another; consequently they are small and scraggly. Walking through a park is often more like beating one's way through a thicket than strolling beneath stately trees. Nevertheless, now there is deep shade where previously the sun beat down on a dry and rocky landscape; so the citizens contend with a measure of truth that they have transformed a barren area into one of pleasant greenery. Russians far outnumber the native Kazakhs in Alma-Ata, and native faces are not seen in the factories. Like Tashkent, Alma-Ata has a widely diversified industrial base, with machine building being of first importance.

Dushanbe   Third in size in Middle Asia is Dushanbe, the capital of the Tadzhik Republic, which in 1959 had a population of 224,000. Dushanbe exemplifies the rapid growth of an old native village after it became the seat of government for a newly established republic. From 1927 until 1961 it was known as Stalinabad, but with the fur-

ther downgrading of Stalin in 1961 it reverted to its old Tadzhik name. The city sits on the southern side of the Zeravshan Range of the Tyan Shans on the upper portions of the plateau in southwestern Tadzhikistan. It serves as the governmental and commercial center for a relatively rich cotton-growing region, and cotton textiles are its primary industry. Machine building and food industries also are important.

Frunze   Fourth in size is Frunze, the capital of the Kirgiz Republic, with a population of 220,000. Frunze sits on the northern slopes of the Tyan Shans among the headwaters of the Chu River. It thus lies within a rich agricultural area specializing in grains and sugar beets. Its industries are concentrated on machine building, textiles, and food processing.

Samarkand   Fifth in size is Samarkand, with a population of 196,000. Samarkand is situated on the Zeravshan River which was the cradle of civilization in Middle Asia. The modern city sits on hills of thick loess deposits which cover the remains of many former cities dating back as far as 3000 B.C. During the fourteenth and fifteenth centuries Samarkand served as the center of Tamerlane's far-flung empire, which at times encompassed all the territory from eastern China to Persia. During this time, many magnificent mosques were built to commemorate important individuals. Ruins of these beautiful mosques still dominate the urban scene, their blue tiles sparkling in the desert sun. Some of the mosques are now being reconstructed out of bricks made from the loess clay in the same manner as were the originals. Archeologic excavations are unearthing predecessor cities.

In 1868 the Russians established a new town next to Samarkand which has grown and gradually engulfed the old city. It might be said that Samarkand at present is a small-sized Tashkent that lags behind Tashkent in transformation by a period of 10 or 15 years. Samarkand still has the native aspects to a much greater degree than does

Tashkent, but as fast as it can be accomplished the native quarters are being torn down and apartment buildings constructed. Some light industries have come to Samarkand, particularly the textile industries.

Ashkhabad Sixth in size is Ashkhabad, the capital of the Turkmen Republic, with a population of 170,000. Ashkhabad sits at the northern base of the Kopet Dag on the southern edge of the Kara-Kum. It is thus in a remote and barren desert area with only a limited amount of irrigation agriculture developed around it. If it were not for its function as the capital city of the Turkmen Republic, Ashkhabad would not have prospered significantly, since it is off base from the main activity in Middle Asia. It is connected with the port of Krasnovodsk on the Caspian and with the major cities of Middle Asia to the east by the Trans-Caspian Railroad. If it were not for this single lifeline, it would be isolated indeed. Its function as one of the main film-making centers in the Soviet Union already has been mentioned. Also, it has some textile and machine-building industries.

As was the case in Transcaucasia and in the Baltic and Belorussian Republics of the northwest, it can be seen clearly here in Middle Asia that the function as a governmental seat is of prime importance to the development of a town. Among the six largest cities in Middle Asia, five are the capitals of the five republics. Only Samarkand does not serve that function at the present time. Samarkand, of course, got its start as the center of early civilization and later benefited greatly as the governmental seat of a loosely constructed empire, so in a sense it too might be considered to have grown because of its governmental function.

Other Cities A number of cities having populations between 50,000 and 160,000 serve as regional centers of commerce and industry and as processing centers of local produce. Many of these are situated in agricultural areas where raw materials for textile and food industries are available. Others

Figure 10-22 The Tomb of Tamerlane in Samarkand. Photograph by the author.

are located near mineral resources. They are concentrated either in the Fergana Valley or along the northern slopes of the Tyan Shans. The rest of the area, that is the deserts and the high mountains, is almost devoid of urban settlement.

Along the base of the Tyan Shans lies a string of cities besides the three capitals already mentioned, chief among which are Chimkent, with a population of 153,000, Dzhambul, with a population of 113,000, and Chirchik, with a population of 66,000. These three cities lying within 200 miles of one another on the northwestern corner of the Tyan Shans are industrial centers concentrating on chemical industries and nonferrous metallurgy. Chimkent is reported to have the largest lead smelter in all of Eurasia. Dzhambul recently has become the main superphosphate manufacturing center for the agricultural regions of Middle Asia, utilizing the phosphate deposits at Chulak-Tau just northwest of Dzhambul. The lead, zinc, copper, and other ores used in the smelters of these cities partially are derived locally from the Tyan Shans and Karatau and partially are shipped in from the Kazakh Folded Country and the Altay Mountains in the north. Chirchik, on the Chirchik River just northeast of Tashkent, produces chemical fertilizers and agricultural machinery for the farmlands of Middle Asia.

A considerable number of cities of intermediate size lie within the Fergana Basin. Many of these are old cities that have served as cultural and commercial centers of a rich agricultural area for centuries; in large part that is their function today. Their industries are largely based on the processing of local cotton, silk, and a variety of foods. Also, at the town of Fergana, some oil refining has been carried on for 50 or more years utilizing the small local reserves of petroleum. The main cities are Andizhan, with a population of 130,000, Namangan, with a population of 122,000, the famous old Moslem center of Kokand, with a population of 105,000, Fergana, with a population of 80,000, Leninabad, with a population of 77,000, Margelan, with a population of 68,000, and Osh, with a population of 65,000. Most of these cities lie within the Uzbek Republic, although the Fergana Basin is politically divided among the Uzbek, the Kirgiz, and the Tadzhik republics on the basis of the distribution of ethnic groups. The endeavor to keep nationality groups on the correct sides of the boundaries coupled with the endeavor to include the mountain watershed areas with the corresponding parts of the basin to which they supply water has made for an intricate boundary delineation in the area. Leninabad lies within the Tadzhik Republic, and it is one of the principal Middle Asian centers for cotton and silk textile industries.

The leading cotton textile centers in Middle Asia are Tashkent, Leninabad, Dushanbe, Fergana, and Ashkhabad; the leading silk textile centers are Leninabad, Osh, Margelan, Dushanbe, and Ashkhabad. Leading wool textile centers are Alma-Ata, Frunze, and Dushanbe.

A few other scattered cities might be mentioned because of significant functions as regional centers or as industrial centers. At the western entrance to the Fergana Basin, where the Syr-Darya cuts a deep and narrow gorge through a low range of hills, stands the new city of Begovat, which, like Rustavi in Transcaucasia, has been established by the Soviets as a steel center to serve an outlying area of the Soviet Union. Although no population figures for Begovat were given in the 1959 census data, the town is supposed to grow to a size of approximately 50,000 people, all of whom are to be connected with the steel works, which is to produce enough steel to serve the Middle Asian region. The present steel plant was constructed in 1944. So far, all the steel has been produced from scrap or from pig iron shipped from the Kuznetsk Basin. Coal is derived partially from Karaganda and partially from local supplies in the Fergana Basin.

Along the three great rivers of Soviet Middle Asia—that is, the Amu-Darya, the Syr-Darya, and the Zeravshan—are located several cities besides those already mentioned. These cities serve as centers of important agricultural areas concentrating primarily on cotton. Where the Trans-Caspian Railroad crosses the Amu-Darya stands the city of Chardzhou, with a 1959 population of 66,000. Chardzhou serves as an important trans-shipping point between the railroad and the river as well as an important collection point for cotton. Downstream on the Syr-Darya, near the delta in the extensive irrigated cotton-growing area of the Khiva Oasis, are the cities of Urgench, with a population of 44,000, Nukus, with a population of 39,000, and Tashauz, with a population of 38,000. Along the middle Syr-Darya in an important rice-growing area is the town of Kzyl-Orda, with a population of 66,000. For a short time Kzyl-Orda served as the capital city of the former Kirgiz A.S.S.R. Near the western end of the Zeravshan River stands the ancient city of Bukhara with a present population of 69,000. It is the center of an important irrigated cotton-growing area and the Karakul sheep-grazing region.

On the north end of the Caspian Sea, at the mouth of the Ural River, is the oil refining town of Guryev, which in 1959 had a population of 78,000. It serves as the center of the Emba oil fields, and an oil pipeline leads northeastward from Guryev to Orsk at the southern end of the Urals. Guryev also is an important fishing center.

Far to the south on the eastern shore of the Caspian, near the oil fields of Nebit-Dag, stands the town of Krasnovodsk, which is the third important oil refining town of Middle Asia. It also serves as an important fishing port and as the western terminus of the Trans-Caspian Railroad. The three cities, Guryev, Krasnovodsk, and Fergana, serve as the oil-refining centers in the three respective oil-producing areas of Middle Asia and southern Kazakhstan.

Transportation and Trade

In this far flung area of isolated settlements transportation lines become of utmost importance, and in this arid region the burden falls even more heavily on the railroads than it does in the rest of the Soviet Union.

The streams by and large are unsuitable for navigation. The major streams head in high mountains where rapids and gorges prevent traffic, and when they issue forth on the dry, sandy plains they spread out, become shallow, and divide into many separate, shifting channels with extremely fluctuating levels of flow during different times of the year. There is local navigation on the Amu-Darya, but this stream leads nowhere at either end. A bit of navigation may be carried on during high-water stage in early summer on the Ural River between the Caspian and the Urals, and small boats ply the Ili River south of Lake Balkhash. Other than this, stream navigation largely is lacking.

Soviet policy since the beginning of the five-year plans has brought about both a great increase in the production and consumption of Middle Asia and southern Kazakhstan and a strict specialization of crops raised in the area. Both factors have thrown an increasingly heavy burden on the railroads. The fact that these heavily populated irrigated areas are separated from other populous areas of the Soviet Union by wide expanses of steppe and desert, together with the increasing specialization of the agricul-

ture, has brought about some of the longest rail hauls in the Soviet Union. Although the Middle Asian republics now produce more than 90 per cent of the country's raw cotton, the Central Industrial Region around Moscow still produces almost 80 per cent of the country's cotton textiles. Hence much of the raw cotton of the country must be shipped more than 2000 miles to be processed. Also, with the intense specialization on cotton in Middle Asia grain must be shipped into the area all the way from northern Kazakhstan and western Siberia and from even more removed areas such as the Trans Volga and the Caucasus.

An increasing demand for lumber products associated with the great buildup of industries and cities in Middle Asia has greatly increased long hauls of lumber from western and eastern Siberia as well as from the Volga and Urals areas. The industrialization of Middle Asia has brought about an increasingly heavy movement of coal and petroleum products between different regions within Kazakhstan and the Middle Asian republics. A large volume of trade with regions outside the area has been generated by the total absence of pig iron production in the Middle Asian republics and the inadequate assortment of locally produced, rolled steel products. The Begovat plant imports large quantities of pig iron from the Kuznetsk Basin and, in turn, exports steel ingots to the steel plant at Temir-Tau near Karaganda. At the same time, Middle Asian industries are forced to import considerable quantities of rolled steel products from different portions of the country.

In an effort to increase cotton production per acre, large amounts of mineral fertilizers are being added to the irrigated lands. And although the superphosphate plants of Dzhambul and Chardzhou and the nitrogen fertilizer plants of Chirchik have greatly expanded production in recent years, their production has not kept pace with the increased demand for these products. In 1955 Middle Asian plants produced only 46.5 per cent of the artificial nitrogen fertilizers and

70 per cent of the phosphate fertilizers applied to the agricultural areas of Middle Asia. The rest had to be shipped in from European Russia.

Before the turn of the century, when the interregional trade of the area largely was undeveloped and the bulk of the irrigated acreage was occupied by wheat and other food crops for local consumption, the camel caravan served as the main means of transportation of the small quantities of high-cost goods that were exchanged over long distances. Since that time, interregional trade has increased a hundredfold, and railroad lines have been constructed. The railroads now carry more than 90 per cent of the total freight. Until 1906 the Trans-Caspian Railroad, connecting the towns along the foothills of the southern mountains between Krasnovodsk and Tashkent, was the only railroad in the area, and its only connection with the rest of the country was by ferry across the Caspian from Krasnovodsk to Baku. This railroad served primarily to bring in oil from Baku to fuel-deficient Middle Asia and to export raw cotton from Middle Asia westward across the Caspian to European Russia. At this time the Turkmen oil fields around Nebit-Dag were producing very little so that the small need for oil products in Middle Asia had to be provided for primarily from the Caucasus oil fields. Also, at this time, the cotton export trade in Middle Asia was not very flourishing, and much of the cotton textiles that were produced in the Central Industrial Region were produced from raw cotton imported from Egypt, India, and the United States.

Then in 1906 a line leading directly northwestward from Tashkent to Orenburg was completed. This linked up with railroads leading to the west and provided a direct route for increasing shipments of cotton northwestward and grain and lumber southeastward. By the end of the 1920's this Kazalinsk Line, as it came to be known, was so overburdened that new efforts were made to complete the Turk-Sib Railroad to relieve the congestion and at the same time to make

possible an increase of shipments of cotton, grain, and lumber to provide for an even more intense specialization of cotton growing in Middle Asia.

The Turk-Sib Railroad, running from Semipalatinsk to Arys, had been started in 1912, but it was abandoned during World War I and the ensuing chaos of the civil war and was begun again only in 1927. Finally completed in 1931, the Turk-Sib Railroad provided a link around the eastern end of Lake Balkhash between the cities of Middle Asia and the Trans-Siberian Railroad in southwestern Siberia. It was built specifically to induce a movement of raw cotton northeastward into newly developing industrial centers in Siberia and to bring about a shift in the supply areas of lumber and grain for Middle Asia. Until this time much of the grain consumed in Middle Asia was raised in the Trans-Volga region, the northern Caucasus and Transcaucasia, the Urals, and the Ukraine, with only about one tenth of the grain consumption of Middle Asia being supplied by western Siberia. Also, most of the lumber consumed in Middle Asia came from either the Volga area or the Urals. It was hoped that the Turk-Sib Railroad would induce a change in these supply areas so that western Siberia, particularly the Kulunda Steppe, would supply much of the grain needs of Middle Asia and the slopes of the Altay Mountains and the plains of western Siberia would supply much of the lumber needs. By developing textile industries in the growing cities of Siberia, raw cotton shipment northwestward on the Kazalinsk Line could be reduced, and the shipment of cotton textiles from the Central Industrial Region to Siberia over the heavily burdened Trans-Siberian line could be halted.

These shifts in interregional trade came about agonizingly slow, and it appeared for a time that the Turk-Sib Railroad was going to be an economic failure. The production of lumber did gradually pick up in Siberia, however, and the lumber demands of Middle Asia grew rapidly as industrialization and urbanization took place. The opening of the

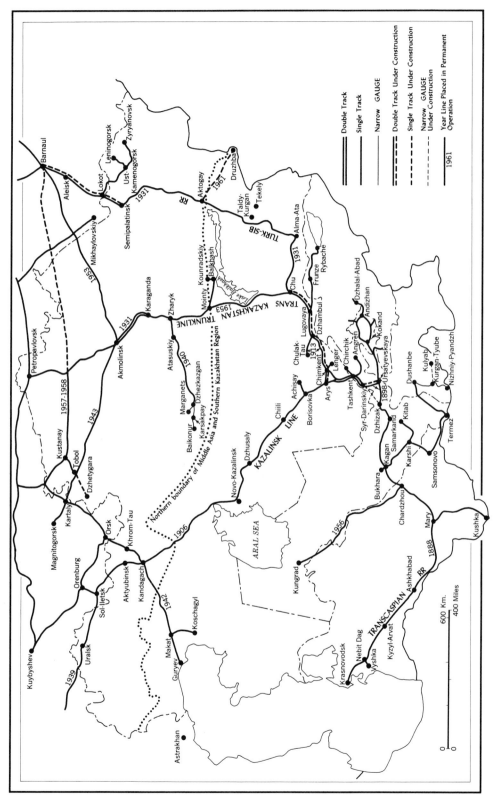

Figure 10-23   The development of the transportation system.   Adapted from Taaffe.

virgin lands in southwestern Siberia and northern Kazakhstan since 1954 has greatly increased grain production in that area, so that now the aims of the Turk-Sib Railroad have largely been accomplished, and a new line to the west of it has been built to supplement its function. In 1953 the last link of the so-called Trans-Kazakhstan Trunk Line was completed between Mointy and Chu around the western end of Lake Balkhash. This provides a direct route from the new grain-growing areas of northern Kazakhstan and western Siberia through the area of heavy industry around Karaganda to the major cities of Middle Asia. Northern Kazakhstan, whose wheat acreage increased from approximately 10 million acres in 1953 to between 45 and 50 million acres in 1956, now fills most of the wheat needs of Middle Asia.

Since the early 1930's a number of paralleling and branch rail lines have been constructed either to link major cities more directly or to provide access into new mining and industrial areas. A rail line paralleling the Amu-Darya has been constructed, from its junction with the Trans-Caspian line at Chardzhou, to Kungrad near the mouth of the river. Much pressure has been brought to bear on the national government by the Uzbek Republic to extend this line northwestward to Guryev and thereby provide another direct link to the northwest with European Russia.

The construction of many of these lines, including the first one, the Trans-Caspian, which was constructed in record time under the impetus of war against the Turkmen uprisings, was accomplished in the face of overwhelming natural hazards in the form of shifting sands and lack of water. Accounts of their construction provide interesting reading.

One of the most publicized railroad lines recently to be completed in the area is the Aktogay-Sinkiang-Lanchow Railroad, which leads off from the Turk-Sib Railroad at Aktogay and provides a new direct link between the U.S.S.R. and China through the Dzhungarian Gate east of Lake Balkhash. The Russians recently celebrated the completion of their section of the line by the establishment of the new town of Druzhba, or "Friendship," where the railroad crosses the Russian-Chinese border.

Reading List

Alampiev, P., *Soviet Kazakhstan,* Foreign Languages Publishing House, Moscow, 1958, 186 pp.

Burke, Albert, *A Political Economic Survey of Soviet Central Asia,* PhD Dissertation, University of Pennsylvania, 1959.

Central Asian Review, Central Asian Research Center, 66 Kings Road, London SW 3.

Lewis, Robert A., "The Irrigation Potential of Soviet Central Asia," *Annals of the Association of American Geographers,* March 1962, 99–114.

Luknitsky, Pavel, *Soviet Tadjikistan,* Foreign Languages Publishing House, Moscow, 1954, 254 pp.

Pierce, Richard A., *Russian Central Asia 1867–1917: A Study in Colonial Rule,* Russian and East European Study Series, University of California Press, 1960, 306 pp.

Skosyrev, P., *Soviet Turkmenistan,* Foreign Languages Publishing House, Moscow, 1956, 231 pp.

Taaffe, Robert, *Rail Transportation and the Economic Development of Soviet Central Asia,* Department of Geography Research Paper No. 64, University of Chicago, 1960, 186 pp.

——— "Transportation and Regional Specialization: The Example of Soviet Central Asia," *Annals of the Association of American Geographers,* March 1962, 80–98.

Vitkovich, Victor, *A Tour of Soviet Uzbekistan,* Foreign Languages Publishing House, Moscow, 1954, 246 pp.

Western Siberia and Northern Kazakhstan

Region	Area (sq mile)	Population	People (sq mile)	% Urban
Western Siberia	978,700	12,251,000	14.7	
Kurgan Oblast	27,700	999,000	37.9	33
Tyumen Oblast	560,000	1,092,000	2.1	32
Khanty-Mansi N.O.	215,000	124,000	0.5	27
Yamal-Nenets N.O.	293,000	62,000	0.3	35
Omsk Oblast	54,700	1,645,000	30.6	43
Novosibirsk Oblast	69,600	2,299,000	33.4	55
Tomsk Oblast	127,000	747,000	6.2	47
Kemerovo Oblast	37,300	2,786,000	75.6	77
Altay Kray	102,400	2,683,000	26.8	33
Gorno-Altay A.O.	36,200	159,000	4.4	19
Northern Kazakhstan	563,200	5,824,000	11.6	
West Kazakhstan Kray				
Uralsk Oblast	59,000	381,000	6.5	30
Aktyubinsk Oblast (Northern[a])	62,000	401,000	3.4	44
Tselinnyy Kray	234,200	2,768,000	11.8	
Kustanay Oblast	77,000	711,000	9.3	27
North Kazakhstan Oblast	16,000	457,000	28.8	34
Kokchetav Oblast	30,800	493,000	16.1	25
Tselinograd Oblast	60,600	637,000	10.6	40
Pavlodar Oblast	49,800	455,000	9.3	27
Karaganda Oblast (Northern[a])	100,000	1,019,000	6.7	78
Semipalatinsk Oblast	70,000	520,000	7.5	47
East Kazakhstan Oblast	38,000	735,000	19.7	54
Total	1,541,000	18,075,000		

[a] Estimated areas of parts of Aktyubinsk and Karaganda Oblasts that are included in northern Kazakhstan. Population figures for these two oblasts are total population figures for the oblasts, since the excluded southern parts are only sparsely populated.

Western Siberia and Northern Kazakhstan

The deserts surrounding the Caspian, the Aral Sea, and Lake Balkhash give way in northern Kazakhstan and southwestern Siberia to landscapes that are influenced by a moister, cooler climate that has favored the growth of steppe grasses and the development of chernozem and chestnut soils. A homogeneity of climate, soils, and agricultural land use unites the northern tier of oblasts in Kazakhstan with the adjacent strip of land in southwestern Siberia to form a single geographical region. Recent urbanization and the construction of paralleling rail lines linking up with the Trans-Siberian Railroad have united the area still further. The combining in 1960 of the five northern oblasts of Kazakhstan into a new super region, Tselinnyy Kray, indicates that the Russians themselves consider this region to be something apart from the rest of Kazakhstan. Perhaps it is being groomed to be split off entirely from the Kazakh Republic and to be combined administratively with the adjacent part of Siberia under the jurisdiction of the Russian Republic. This northern area of Kazakhstan is peopled primarily by Russians, not Kazakhs* (Table 11–1).

---

* The formation of two more krays, West Kazakhstan and South Kazakhstan, in May 1962 somewhat weakens this argument. Purportedly Kazakhstan has been divided into krays purely for administrative convenience.

Table 11–1   Ethnic Groups in Tselinnyy Kray, in Per Cent of Total[a]

Year	Kazakhs	Russians	Ukrainians	Germans
1897	79.2	10.3	3.5	
1926	40.1	26.5	27.0	
1959	19.0	46.2	14.0	12.1

[a] *Source: Soviet Geography: Review and Translation,* April 1962, p. 37.
Note: Approximately 25 ethnic groups are represented in Tselinnyy Kray among peoples who have moved into the virgin lands from all parts of the Soviet Union.

Along with this core area of continuously populated land will be considered the vast expanse of western Siberia to the north and spottily settled central Kazakhstan to the south, because these regions do not logically fall within any other regions, and they do not warrant separate consideration. Thus western Siberia and the northern half of Kazakhstan will be considered as a single unit, even though in the Russian geographical literature the two are generally treated separately because of the political boundary. In partial deference to tradition, the eastern boundary of the region shall be arbitrarily set as the western boundary of Krasnoyarsk Kray just west of the Yenisey River, although the obvious topographic break occurs within Krasnoyarsk Kray east of the river. The Altay Mountains in the southeast are a part of the general mountain belt that continues through eastern Siberia and the Far East all the way to the Pacific. But in all Russian texts these mountains are considered an integral part of western Siberia, and so they will be treated here. The economy of the all-important Kuznetsk Basin within their flanks at present is much more oriented toward the west than the east, so inclusion of this area with the west makes sense.

In its entirety, western Siberia and northern Kazakhstan is an area of 1½ million square miles that contains a population of less than 20 million, much of which is rural. Only the heavy mining areas of Kemerovo Oblast in Siberia and Karaganda Oblast in Kazakhstan are predominantly urban.

Figure 11-1   Western Siberia and Northern Kazakhstan.

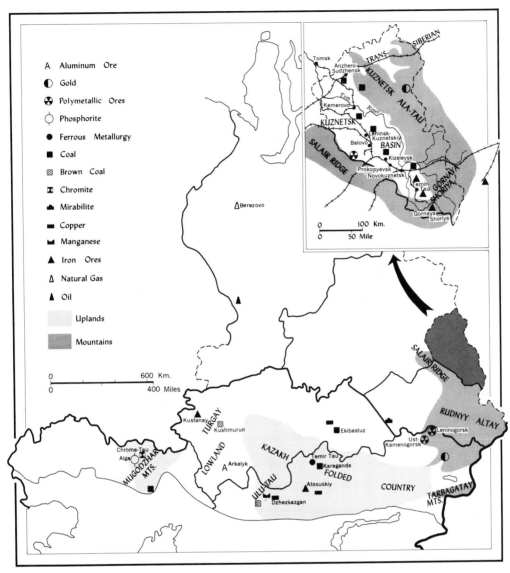

A Aluminum Ore
◑ Gold
⊛ Polymetallic Ores
⬡ Phosphorite
● Ferrous Metallurgy
■ Coal
▨ Brown Coal
⊠ Chromite
⬛ Mirabilite
▬ Copper
⋈ Manganese
▲ Iron Ores
△ Natural Gas
▲ Oil

Uplands
Mountains

Figure 11-2 Landforms and minerals.

The Physical Landscape

Topography The landforms of the northern half of Kazakhstan consist in the east and the west of broad rolling uplands, the stumps of old, worn-down mountains that are divided in the middle by a synclinal lowland that opens up to the north onto the broad plain of western Siberia.

The upland in the west is the Mugodzhar Mountains, a southern extension of the Urals, whose ranges fan out in northern Aktyubinsk Oblast at elevations of around 2000 feet. In eastern Kazakhstan north of Lake Balkhash and the Betpak-Dala lies a much more extensive upland known as the Kazakh Folded Country. This also is an old, worn-down mountain area which at present consists of low, short ranges of Paleozoic sedimentary formations and many separate hill groups of granite, syenite, porphyry, etc. The ranges in the central portion of the area are oriented primarily northwest-southeast and reach their highest elevation at 4800 feet. The general elevation of the area is considerably lower, however, and the relief everywhere is subdued. The Ulu-Tau, a separate segment of the upland at its western extremity, reach elevations of 3700 feet.

Between these two uplands, north of the Aral Sea, lies a synclinal lowland variously known as the Turgay Vale or Turgay Tableland. This northern extension of the Turanian Lowland takes its name from the Turgay River, which flows the length of it to end in the south in a playa lake bed. It is primarily a stripped sedimentary plain. Remnants of resistant higher layers of rock cap steep-sided mesas and buttes that rise 300 to 600 feet above the general elevation of the sandy plain. Hence, the term "Tableland." Elongated depressions between the mesas are filled by sand, clay, and salts washed in by small, intermittent streams. The Ishim and Tobol Rivers head in the northern portion of the lowland and flow northward into the broad plain of western Siberia where they join the Irtysh, which eventually delivers its water to the mighty Ob.

Western Siberia between the Ural Mountains and the Yenisey River is a featureless, low-lying plain that has been washed by the waters of the Arctic Ocean, even since the glacial period. Its surface materials are unconsolidated sediments, and the drainage is exceedingly poor. The entire region is drained by the Ob River northward into the Arctic. In the spring the headwaters of the river thaw before the downstream section to the north, causing large ice jams and wide-scale flooding to occur in the downstream portion. The main channel of the lower Ob at these times may reach a width of 20 to 30 miles, with literally hundreds of miles on either side being flooded to some degree. Large sections of the plain are constantly waterlogged. Standing water occurs over broad regions such as the Vasyugánye

Swamp in the south between the Irtysh and Ob Rivers. The southernmost portion of the plain in southwestern Siberia and northern Kazakhstan is dotted by numerous lakes and intermittently dry lake beds that are remnants of a once extensive proglacial lake. Some of these remnant lakes are becoming salty.

The southeastern corner of western Siberia and northern Kazakhstan is truly mountainous. On the eastern end of the Kazakh Folded Country north of the Dzhungarian Gate rise the Tarbagatay Mountains. These mountains descend on the north to the basin of Lake Zaysan, through which drains the Irtysh River. Northeast of the Irtysh rise the Altay Mountains, a series of ranges oriented northwest-southeast, which extend into China and the Mongolian Peoples Republic. The Altay culminate at 14,600 feet on the Kazakh-Siberian border where they are known as the Rudnyy Altay, or "Ore Altay." Two prongs of the Altay Mountains extend northwestward to surround the Kuznetsk Basin. The Salair Ridge on the west forms a low drainage divide between the Ob Valley to the west and the Tom River to the east, which runs the full length of the Kuznetsk Basin. The eastern prong, known as the Kuznetsk Ala-Tau, separates the Kuznetsk Basin on the west from the Minusinsk Basin and the Yenisey River on the east.

Climate, Vegetation and Soils Western Siberia and northern Kazakhstan is a region of long, hard winters and short, cool summers with only modest amounts of precipitation. Being extremely continental in location, the area is dependent for precipitation on cyclonic storms from the North Atlantic, and these storms have traveled over much land before they reach the region east of the Urals. In winter particularly the storms are ineffectual, because the great Siberian High dominates the area and shunts them off to the northeast around the northern end of the Urals where they die along the Arctic fringes of western Siberia. The storms that come into Middle Asia from the Mediterranean during the winter find the northeasterly path blocked by the Siberian High and die against the slopes of the Middle Asian mountains. Thus in the wintertime meager precipitation falls and temperatures hover around 0°F. Even in the southern portion of the region, at Semipalatinsk, January temperatures average only 3° above zero, and throughout much of western Siberia January temperatures average below zero. Such winter temperatures correspond to those in central Canada. Snow lies on the ground approximately 180 days of the year in northern Kazakhstan and more than 250 days along the Arctic fringe of western Siberia.

During the summer, a broad, shallow low-pressure area lies over much of interior Asia. Thus it is a bit easier for Atlantic air to penetrate the region at this time. Cyclonic storms are weaker and less frequent than they are during the winter, however, so they still do not affect the area appreciably. Local convection owing to surface heating at this time of year causes precipitation through thunderstorm activity and produces a decided summer maximum of precipitation over the entire region.

Annual precipitation decreases from between 15 and 20 inches in the lower Ob Basin to only 6 to 8 inches in central Kazakhstan. In addition, the longer, warmer summers in the south increase evaporation losses, so that the effects of diminished precipitation are magnified. Coolness and shortness of the growing season limits agriculture primarily to the zone south of 57° latitude. As one moves southward, the increasing length and warmth of the summers increase agricultural possibilities but the diminishing moisture decreases them. Hence optimum conditions for agriculture do not exist anywhere; one simply must choose as happy a median as is possible between cold and drought. This median lies along the boundary between Siberia and Kazakhstan in a strip of land 200 to 300 miles wide, which in general straddles the 55th parallel.

This zone of optimum climate is also a zone of rich chernozem and chestnut soils which have developed under a steppe grass vegetation. This zone is the eastern extension of the so-called "Black Earth Belt" which starts as a wide belt in the western Ukraine and continues east-northeastward in a narrowing belt across the middle Volga and the southern Urals. To the north of this belt lies the unbroken northern coniferous forest, the taiga, which gives way to the tundra north of the Arctic Circle. Much of this forest and tundra land is swampy and the soils are badly leached, acidic podzols. The northern third of the west Siberian Lowland is underlain by permafrost, which further hampers drainage.

In the foregoing area the change from grassland steppes in the south to the taiga of the north is so rapid that the northern limit of agriculture is not subject to much movement. No belt of mixed forests occurs between the steppes and the taiga as it does in European Russia. In southern Siberia the southern limit of the coniferous forest faces the open steppes broken only here and there by clumps of birch and aspen in sheltered valleys. South of the Black Earth Belt the grasses thin and the soils become coarser, and sometimes saline as the steppes give way to the semidesert in central Kazakhstan.

Hydrology The Ob River system drains practically all the area under discussion. The Irtysh and its two main tributaries, the Ishim and the Tobol, drain Tselinnyy Kray northward through western Siberia to the Arctic via the lower Ob. Short streams heading in the Kazakh Folded Country flow outward in all directions to end in salty lakes and playa lake beds, their entire volumes consumed by evaporation. The Turgay River flows southward through the Turgay Lowland and also ends in a salt flat. In the extreme west, the Emba and Ural Rivers flow through portions of Aktyubinsk and Uralsk Oblasts to empty into the Caspian.

Of these streams, only the Irtysh, fed by

its mountain headwaters in China and by large Lake Zaysan, maintains a steady flow through the summer. The other streams are freshets in spring when the snow and ground are thawing, but they have very low water in late summer. Hence the possibilities of irrigation and navigation are strictly limited. In the Kazakh Folded Country the only river of significance is the Nura, which during its short course of only about 100 miles flows through the heavily industrialized area at Karaganda. A reservoir has been constructed on the Nura to supply the domestic, mining, and industrial needs of Karaganda.

Several construction works are under way on the Irtysh River system to produce hydroelectricity and to improve navigation. In 1953 the completion of the Ust-Kamenogorsk Dam, built in a narrow gorge, raised the water level 40 meters and backed up the water about 80 kilometers to create the so-called "Small Irtysh Sea." Upstream from Ust-Kamenogorsk, near the mouth of the Bukhtarma River, the Bukhtarma Dam is now being completed. One of the highest dams in the Soviet Union, it has raised the water level 67 meters and backed water up the Irtysh 600 kilometers to create the Large Irtysh Sea, which engulfed Lake Zaysan and raised its water level 6 meters. The reservoir has a surface area of 5000 square kilometers and holds more water than the Tsimlyansk, Rybinsk, Uglich, Moscow, and Dnieproges reservoirs combined. The power plant has an ultimate capacity of 525,000 kilowatts. Navigation is made possible by a lock of four chambers. Construction of a third dam is planned on the Irtysh downstream from Ust-Kamenogorsk.

Construction was to start in 1961 on the Irtysh-Karaganda Canal to supply water to the water-deficient areas of growing industry in central Kazakhstan. The canal will lead off water from the Irtysh 30 kilometers south of Pavlodar, will run 175 kilometers due west past the coal-mining center of Ekibastuz and the future copper mines of Bozshakul, and then will turn southwest to follow the Shiderty River upstream to Karaganda. The total length of the Canal will be 500 kilometers. Twenty-three pumping stations will raise the water to an elevation of 520 meters at the divide between the headwaters of the Shiderty and the Karaganda area. The canal will be 40 meters wide at the top and 4 to 7 meters deep. Scheduled for completion in 1965, it will, in addition to supplying water to industrial and mining areas, allow the irrigation of 37,000 hectares of land which are to be cultivated to supply vegetables, potatoes, and fruit to the developing urban market.

A series of hydroelectric plants are planned for the Ob River. The first, which is now nearly completed, is the Novosibirsk plant with a capacity of 400,000 kilowatts. Its reservoir, the Ob Sea, is about 240 kilometers long and in places is 20 kilometers wide. The Kamen plant, 240 kilometers upstream from Novosibirsk, will raise water level 25 meters and produce a reservoir that will stretch upstream 70 kilometers above the city of Barnaul. The reservoir, with a surface area of 4500 square kilometers, will be one of the largest in the country. It will provide irrigation for more than 2 million hectares of dry land in the Kulunda Steppe and neighboring Kazakhstan. Also, it will prevent the annual spring flooding in the Ob Valley. The power plant is to have a capacity of 630,000 kilowatts.

A huge dam, the Nizhne-Ob, has been projected for construction near the Arctic Circle about 10 miles from the city of Salekhard on the lower Ob. As proposed, a long, low dam would raise the water level upstream as far as the junction with the Irtysh and produce an enormous reservoir 90,000 square kilometers in area with a capacity equal to three times the annual flow of the entire Ob River system. No construction date has been set. Whether or not this is a feasible or logical project remains to be seen.

In western Kazakhstan construction was begun in 1957 on the large Ural-Kushum irrigation network. An abandoned bed of

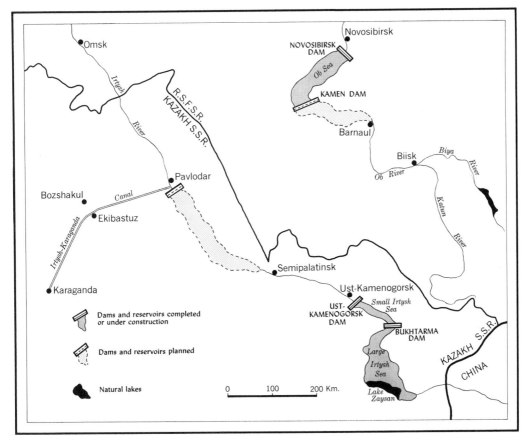

Figure 11-3   Construction projects on the Irtysh and Ob rivers.

the Kushum River, tributary to the Ural River, is being widened to serve as the central canal for the system. It will carry a stream of water 50 meters wide and 5 meters deep. When completed, the system will allow for the irrigation of considerable territory in western Kazakhstan.

Agriculture

The zone of chernozem and chestnut soils 300 to 400 kilometers wide in northern Kazakhstan and southwestern Siberia has a cool, subhumid to semiarid climate that is ideal for the growing of spring wheat, and this is the principal crop in the area. Barley also is grown extensively, and there are scattered fields of sunflowers and hemp. Hay crops and corn for silage form the basis for considerable livestock feeding. Along the northern fringes of the agricultural zone where the soils become acidic and the drainage poor, flax growing and dairying are of prime importance. Towns along the Trans-Siberian Railroad, which runs the length of this strip, reflect the agricultural economy with their grain elevators, flour mills, creameries, and cheese factories. Such features dotting the landscape give the area an appearance of a combination of Wisconsin and North Dakota. Sugar beets have been introduced into the area, particularly into the most southern portion around Barnaul, and sugar processing plants have been added to the urban scene.

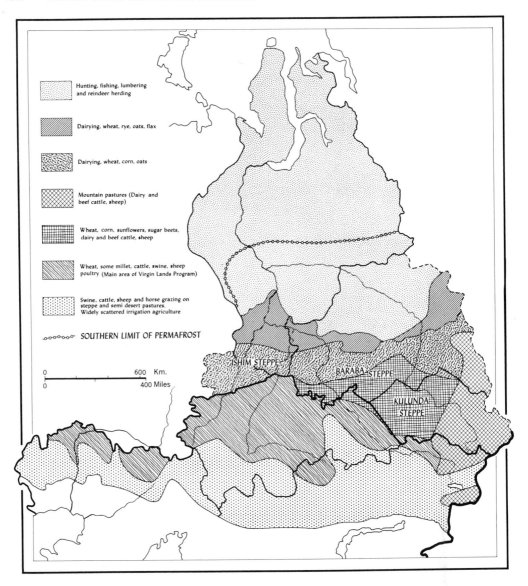

Figure 11-4   Land use in Western Siberia and Northern Kazakhstan.   Adapted from Atlas selskogo khozyaystva, SSSR.

The steppe lands of southwestern Siberia are usually divided into three parts which are given traditional regional names, although these parts do not vary from one another enough to warrant much subdivision.   West of the Irtysh River the area is known as the Ishim Steppe after the Ishim River which drains the region. Between the Irtysh and the Ob Rivers, between the large cities of Omsk and Novosibirsk, lies the Baraba Steppe, and in the southeast, nestled within the western slopes of the Altay Mountains, centered on the city of Barnaul, lies the rich Kulunda Steppe.   The Kulunda Steppe lies farthest south and has the best soils and the mildest climate of the three regions, and it is here that Ukrainian immigrants have introduced the growing of sugar beets.

Grain growing has been pushing steadily southward into the dry grazing lands of Kazakhstan under the virgin lands program initiated in 1954. Spring wheat now is being grown on 100 million acres of newly broken steppe lands which receive no more than 8 to 16 inches of precipitation per year. This virgin-lands area of northern Kazakhstan and adjacent western Siberia, extending westward across the southern Urals to the middle Volga, has displaced the Ukraine and Central Black Earth Region as the chief wheat-producing area of the Soviet Union. The expansion of wheat into this area has allowed the more richly endowed areas of the Ukraine and Central Black Earth Region to be taken out of wheat and to be put into heavier producing crops such as corn.

Wheat growing in the virgin lands is on a grand scale, gambling with the weather. Low yields per acre are compensated for by planting millions and millions of acres. The Soviets recognize that inevitable crop failures will be experienced perhaps half of the time in this region due to drought, but over a period of years they figure that the endeavor is worth the effort. Also, some agroclimatologists have pointed out that climatically the new wheat areas in the virgin lands complement the old wheat areas in the Ukraine. Rarely does drought occur in both places the same year; in fact, when one area is dry, the other appears to have above normal precipitation. Thus the virgin-lands program has been justified on the aspect of insurance that somewhere in the Soviet Union there will be a good wheat crop every year. On the other hand, some agricultural specialists fear that a huge dust bowl is being created. Nevertheless large state farms that have been carved out of the open steppe now have an air of permanency about them.

At first, young single people were recruited to work on these virgin lands, and they lived in tents and in other temporary dwellings. Most of these "Komsomols," Young Communist League members, have in one

way or another, found their way back to more civilized areas, however, and the virgin lands today are being built up with permanent dwellings in big rural villages peopled by families. There is a constant striving to make the economy of these areas more well rounded than simply wheat growing, so there is a great drive to recruit people to develop animal husbandry, dairying, poultry raising, vegetable and fruit growing, etc. An example of one of many letters appearing in daily newspapers appealing for volunteers to come to the virgin lands follows. It has been extracted from *Komsomolskaya Pravda,* the Young Communist League newspaper, dated February 4, 1959, and is entitled, "COME TO US, GIRLS.—The Virgin Lands Await Young Enthusiasts." Akmolinsk Province, Kazakhstan—Dear friends.

"In the fall of 1958 young men and women from all the fraternal republics came to Kazakhstan. They saw how the virgin steppe has been transformed by the will of the Party and how much wheat the new Young Communist League Lands are producing.

"The highly fertile virgin lands must give even more bounteously of their riches in the new seven-year period.

"Girls are working gloriously along with the men on the virgin lands. They have taken the initial adversities in stride; like everyone else, they have slept in tents on which the rain was pouring down and have

Figure 11-5   A crew of men inspecting a wheat field in the virgin lands of Kazakhstan.   Photograph by the author.

struggled fearlessly through snowstorms. Together with the men they have made adobe huts, built the first houses, plowed the virgin land, and sown, raised, and harvested grain.

"The names of the patriotic young women who left comfortable homes in order to develop the virgin steppe with their own hands, shunning no kind of work, and—all obstacles notwithstanding—to bring cleanliness, comfort, and order even to earth adobes and tents are pronounced with profound respect in the virgin-land regions. Among those who have been awarded orders and medals are tractor drivers, tractor-drawn implement operators, and the glorious brigade housekeepers who also do the combine operators' laundry and prepare borshch for our wonderful fellows.

"The other day the collective of the Zhanyspaisky State Farm nominated Masha Petukhova, a young tractor driver of the third brigade, as its candidate for deputy to the Republic Supreme Soviet. She had lived in Moscow and had worked as a radio operator at Vnukovo Airport. On the virgin lands, she became an implement operator, finished a course in tractor driving, and is now a wonderful equipment operator and an authoritative and respected person.

"Marina Pashkova was among the first to settle on the Young Communist League State Farm. Implement operator, tractor driver, then truck driver—as you read this letter, Y.C.L. member Marina Pashkova is probably driving her truck over snow-covered steppes and making her way through snowdrifts to deliver food and mail on schedule. Maria Shchurova is a mason, plasterer and stove tender—in other words, a jack-of-all-trades—on the Victory State Farm. People listen to Maria and learn from her, and she deserves the Merit Badge she has been awarded.

"Hundreds of patriotic young women, who have grown up on the virgin lands and passed through a unique school of life there, have been accepted into the ranks of the Communist Party. Quite a number of young men and women have also found per- sonal happiness on the virgin lands. Durable and solid families have been established there and children have been born.

"Our new settlements are growing and virgin-land farms are developing rapidly, but it is becoming more and more apparent that there are still very few girls here. There are brigades without a single girl; there are whole state farms where you can say 'one, two' and you will have counted all the girls. The livestock sectors need dairymaids and calf, pig, and poultry tenders. Tens of millions of chickens, geese, and ducks could be raised on the virgin lands; it is only a matter of girls to tend them, but they cannot be found in broad daylight with a torch.

"We need literate girls with initiative, who can master several trades. We still have few children's institutions and almost no laundries and tailoring shops. Once the Young Communist League girls marry they are obliged to become housewives and to waste precious time cooking, washing, sewing, and milking cows. We want to improve living conditions, trade, and public catering, but it cannot be done here without the solicitous hands of girls.

"Dear friends. You well understand that the present and the future of the new farms depends on the strengthening of the cadres of young people. Permanent women workers are very much needed here. And what is the situation now? Each year tens of thousands of wonderful fellows arrive here from the equipment operators' schools and from military service, but—and this is no secret—many of them are forced to leave because they cannot establish families here.

"Girls represent a great force on the virgin lands. The presence in a brigade of intelligent and glorious girls who deserve real respect noticeably affects cultural behavior and labor productivity. Brigade life thus becomes richer and brighter and acquires more content. Incidentally, when young women came here at the end of last summer to help with the harvest, many fellows began to wash more thoroughly, shave more often, and keep a closer watch on their appearance.

The very presence of girls ennobles the life of the distant steppe brigades.

"We are telling you about this frankly, and we hope that you will understand us correctly. Loyalty, candor, and maidenly pride are esteemed on the virgin lands.

"In the name of the girls of the Order of Lenin virgin-land state and collective farms of Akmolinsk Province, we address to you, dear friends, an ardent appeal to come to the Y.C.L. virgin lands, one of the militant sectors of communist construction. Here you will receive help in acquiring a specialty. You will meet solicitous friends, male and female, and work on the virgin lands will become the finest school of life. The virgin lands await enthusiastic, patriotic young women!

"We do not want to offend anyone, but we must say frankly that namby-pambies and adventure-seekers had better stay at home. The virgin lands need enthusiasts who will come here to advance our agriculture and animal husbandry, to build extensively. We wish to say to parents, and especially to mothers, that they should not interfere and should not be afraid to let their daughters go to the virgin lands. Believe us, dear mammas, here they will come to know the real, the great joy of labor.

"Dear friends! Last year the 13th Y.C.L. Congress called on girls to go to the virgin-land regions, to help make homes on the Y.C.L. lands. Now, on the threshold of the new seven-year period, your help is especially needed. Come, dear friends, to do great deeds; come here, best of all, for the spring of the seven-year plan.

(Signed) "In the name of the girls of the virgin-land state farms and collective farms of Akmolinsk Province: Raisa Fedorova, cook for the fourth brigade at the Samara State Grain Farm and auditor of a course in tractor driving; Tamara Moiseyeva, poultry tender at the Akmolinsk State Grain Farm; Galina Kravchenko, plasterer at the Victory State Grain Farm; etc."

One can deduce from such letters that life on these state farms still is in its pioneering

stage! Nevertheless, between 1953 and 1956 the area sown to wheat in Kazakhstan expanded from 4,638,000 hectares to 18,-318,000 hectares.

Mineral Resources and Metallurgical Industries

Northern Kazakhstan and western Siberia are especially richly endowed with mineral resources, particularly coal and ferrous and nonferrous metals. Already significant industrialization has developed because of these minerals, and discovery and development continue at a rapid rate.

Coal Two of the major coal fields of the Soviet Union, as well as other minor coal fields, are located in this area. The Kuznetsk Coal Basin, located along the Tom River, between two northwestern prongs of the Altay Mountains in western Siberia, is now the second producing coal basin in the Soviet Union, after the Donets Basin in the Ukraine. In 1959 it produced 15.7 per cent of all the country's coal, as compared to 36.5 per cent in the Donets Basin, 12.2 per cent in the Urals, and 9.3 per cent in the Moscow Basin. It produced about 30 per cent of the country's coking coal. Its reserves are much larger and somewhat higher in quality than are those of the Donets Basin. In the Soviet Union, its reserves are surpassed only by those of the Tunguskan and Lena coal fields in eastern Siberia, neither of which has a significant production. The Kemerovo part of the field has forty working seams, ranging from 2 to 50 meters thick, with an aggregate thickness of 70 meters. About 85 per cent of the coal produced at present is produced by shaft mines in steeply pitching seams in the southern part of the basin. Farther north the seams are thinner, more nearly horizontal, closer to the surface, and can be exploited by open-pit mines.

Shipments of coal from the Kuznetsk Basin travel farther than they do from any other coal basin in the country. In 1955,

42 per cent of the coal produced in the Kuznetsk Basin was used in western Siberia, 37.8 per cent was shipped to the Urals, 7.8 per cent was shipped to the Central Industrial Region, 6.7 per cent to the Volga region, and 5.5 per cent to Kazakhstan and Middle Asia.

The Kuznetsk Basin has been operative on a limited scale for more than a century, but it underwent a major expansion in the early 1930's with the establishment of the Magnitogorsk-Kuznetsk Combine, which project established steel mills both at the iron mines of Magnitogorsk in the southern Urals and at the coal mines of the Kuznetsk Basin. This allowed for coal to move westward on the Trans-Siberian Railroad and iron ore to move eastward, so that empty railroad cars would not be returned in one direction. Under this impetus, the Kuznetsk Basin soon became the second most important producing coal basin in the Soviet Union.

The Kuznetsk Basin still supplies most of the coal to the industries of the fuel-impoverished Urals, in spite of the inroads of Karaganda coal from Kazakhstan, which is only a little more than half as far away from the Urals as is the Kuznetsk Basin. During the early postwar years there were definite statements made by the Russians to the effect that Karaganda would soon replace Kuznetsk as the coal supplier of the Urals and the Volga Bend area. However, production at Karaganda has lagged, and as yet no reduction in the absolute amount of Kuznetsk coal reaching the Urals has been effected. Most recently, statements have been incorporated into the present seven-year plan and future plans to the effect that the Kuznetsk Basin will continue to be the main supplier of coal to the Urals. If this is true, the expansion of coal production in the Kuznetsk Basin should proceed at an uninterrupted rate.

Also, as people continue to move into Siberia and as industries continue to grow, the demand for steel will continue to rise so that the steel plants in the Kuznetsk Basin will demand more and more of the local coal. Since the establishment of the Magnitogorsk-Kuznetsk Combine, considerable quantities of iron ore have been discovered in the mountains bounding the Kuznetsk Basin on the south and in the Minusinsk Basin to the east, so that now the steel mills of the Kuznetsk Basin are almost wholly supplied with iron ore from local sources. Thus the area has both the raw materials and the market potentialities for an independent heavy industry growth.

The Karaganda coal fields in the central part of the Kazakh Folded Country rival the Donets and Pechora Basins in quantity of reserves. More than twenty working seams ranging in thickness from 1 to 8.5 meters lie in nearly horizontal positions at depths between 50 and 300 meters. Most of the coal is produced by shaft mines.

The Karaganda coals are hampered by ash contents of more than 22 per cent, which limits their usage in the steel industry. It has been found that in the blast furnaces of Magnitogorsk no more than 40 per cent of the coal mix can be made up of Karaganda coals. This explains why coal from the Kuznetsk Basin continues to move in large quantities to the Urals and to Middle Asia, even though it must travel almost twice as far as the Karaganda coal.

In 1959, Karaganda, with 4.8 per cent of the nation's coal production, ranked sixth among the coal-producing areas of the country. Of the Karaganda coal, 44.5 per cent went to the Urals, 40.1 per cent to Kazakhstan and Middle Asia, 10.6 per cent to the Volga region, 3.5 per cent to the Central Industrial Region, and 1.3 per cent to other regions.

Since World War II a new coal deposit in the Kazakh Folded Country has been opened at Ekibastuz about 75 miles southwest of Pavlodar. It is located in a small synclinal basin 25 kilometers long by 9 kilometers wide. At the edges of the syncline the coal outcrops at the surface, but in the middle it reaches depths of 350 to 400 meters below the surface. Four continuous seams of complex structure have a total thickness of up to 160 meters. The coals, with 34 to 45 per cent ash content, are hard to clean and are used mainly in large power stations at Omsk and Pavlodar and in the Urals. One large open-pit mine is in operation, and two more are under construction. Ekibastuz now is producing about one fourth as much coal as Karaganda.

Other coal fields in the region are the Kushmurun brown coal field in the Turgay Lowland in Kustanay Oblast, the Mamyt deposit in Aktyubinsk Oblast, and the western part of the elongated Kansk-Achinsk deposits in the eastern part of Kemerovo Oblast. Five big open-pit mines are scheduled to be built during the seven-year plan in the Kushmurun deposits to supply low-grade coal to power stations in the Urals and Kazakhstan.

Iron Ore and Alloys Until recently, northern Kazakhstan and western Siberia appeared to be one of the iron-poor regions of the country. When the Urals-Kuznetsk Combine was begun in the early 1930's, all the iron ore that was used in the Kuznetsk steel mills was shipped in from Magnitogorsk. Now the area appears to be one of the richest regions of iron ore in the country. By 1965, Kazakhstan alone is scheduled to provide 11.6 per cent of the total dressed ore output of the U.S.S.R. The iron and steel plants of the Kuznetsk Basin are now supplied with iron ore almost entirely from the iron mines in the Gornaya Shoriya area along the southern rim of the basin and in the vicinity of Abakan in the Minusinsk Basin to the east. A recently completed railroad between Novokuznetsk and Abakan has allowed for the opening of these eastern ores for use in the Kuznetsk Basin, and expansion in the future can utilize iron deposits in the Khakass A.O. in the mountains of southern Krasnoyarsk Kray.

Besides the large, full-cycle iron and steel plant operating at Novokuznetsk (Stalinsk) in the Kuznetsk Basin, there is a smaller iron and steel plant at Guryevsk in the Basin and there are steel mills at Novosibirsk northwest of the Basin. A second large iron and steel plant is now under construction 19 miles northwest of Novokuznetsk. Known simply as the "Second West Siberian Plant," it is to have a capacity on the same order of magnitude as the plant at Magnitogorsk, hence, a larger capacity than the present plant at Novokuznetsk.

Southwest of Karaganda the Atasuskiy iron ore deposit has been developed to supply the iron and steel plant being constructed at the new steel town of Temir-Tau just northeast of Karaganda. Begun in 1956, the Temir-Tau plant when completed is to have a capacity approximately equal to that at Magnitogorsk. The Atasuskiy iron ores, with only 30 to 65 per cent iron content, are limited in quantity and cannot fully supply a plant as large as the one under construction. Iron ore for the plant will be brought in more and more from large deposits in Kustanay Oblast.

It has been reported that during the last decade thirty-eight different deposits of iron ore have been discovered in the Turgay Lowlands of Kustanay Oblast. Most of this is low-grade ore, but it is near the surface, and large beneficiating plants are being constructed at several deposits to facilitate their use. These deposits aggregate one of the largest reserves of iron ore in the country. They are to be used in the iron and steel plants of Karaganda and Novotroitsk, the new steel center in the Orsk-Khalilovo area in the southern Urals. New iron and steel plants have been proposed at Pavlodar and Barnaul to use Kustanay ores hauled by returning railroad cars that have taken coal from the Kuznetsk Basin to the Urals and European Russia. Coal will be supplied by the Kuznetsk Basin.

Eventually Kustanay ores may also be shipped to the Kuznetsk Basin and the Central Urals. The steel plants of the Central Urals also are to be supplied with iron ore from other large low-grade deposits recently discovered in western Siberia and on the eastern slopes of the Urals adjacent to the

Turgay ores. Large beneficiating plants are under construction in these areas to supply concentrated ore to the iron and steel plants at Magnitogorsk, Chelyabinsk, and Nizhniy Tagil.

Manganese ore is obtained locally in both the Karaganda and Kuznetsk areas. Although these deposits are in no way comparable in size to those at Nikopol, they have a much lower phosphorus content and are of better quality than either the Nikopol or Chiatura manganese ores.

Nickel and chrome deposits have been discovered in the Mugodzhar Mountains adjacent to the Orsk-Khalilovo area in the southern Urals. They are being used in the new steel plant at Novotroitsk to produce high-grade nickel-chrome steels.

Nonferrous Metals Before ferrous metallurgy was developed in northern Kazakhstan and western Siberia, the Kazakh Folded Country and the Altay Mountains were already known for their production of nonferrous metals. This production is being greatly expanded with the continued discovery of deposits of ores. So far, copper, lead, and zinc have been the important minerals, but aluminum has recently joined the group.

It is now estimated that Kazakhstan possesses roughly half of the reserves of copper, lead, and zinc in the Soviet Union. Copper is found mainly in three large deposits, the newly discovered Dzhezkazgan deposit in the western part of the Kazakh Folded Country, which reportedly is the second largest deposit in the world, the Rudnyy Altay deposits near Leninogorsk, and the Balkhash deposits mentioned in Chapter 10 as belonging to southern Kazakhstan. It is anticipated that Kazakhstan will take over first place from the Urals in copper production as soon as the new smelters at Karsakpay, near Dzhezkazgan, become fully operative.

Lead and zinc deposits are found mainly in two areas in association with one another: the Rudnyy Altay around Leninogorsk and

in the Tyan Shans near Chimkent, as was mentioned in Chapter 10. Other scattered deposits exist in southern Kazakhstan. In northern Kazakhstan a primary lead smelter has been operating at Leninogorsk for years, and a zinc smelter, utilizing hydroelectric power from the Irtysh River, is located in Ust-Kamenogorsk. Zinc also is found in the Salair Ridge west of the Kuznetsk Basin in Siberia, and a smelting plant, utilizing cheap thermal electric power, was established early at the city of Belovo in the Kuznetsk Basin.

The aluminum industry is expanding into Kazakhstan and western Siberia as new bauxite and alunite deposits are being opened in northern and southern Kazakhstan. The most promising deposit seems to be the Arkalyk bauxite in the Turgay Lowland, which apparently rivals the Krasnaya-Shapochka deposits in the Urals. Ore from Arkalyk is to supply new alumina-aluminum plants in the Kuzbass and at Pavlodar. Electricity will be supplied to the Pavlodar plant from thermal generators using Ekibastuz coal and from hydro generators in the Bukhtarma Dam.

Other Minerals Tin has been reported along the upper Irtysh River in eastern Kazakhstan, and deposits of tungsten and molybdenum have been reported north of Lake Balkhash and in the Rudnyy Altay. Some magnesium salts exist in the dry lake beds of northern Kazakhstan and southwestern Siberia. Some silver and gold exist in the complex ores of the Rudnyy Altay, and there are considerable potentialities for petroleum and natural gas in the west Siberian lowland. In June 1960 the first commercial oil well in Siberia was reported at the eastern foot of the Urals about 220 miles north of the city of Tyumen. The Soviets have made mention of experimental wells in Tomsk Oblast. What appears to be a fairly large gas deposit is being opened at Berezovo on the lower Ob River, and a pipeline is being constructed from there to Sverdlovsk in the Urals.

Settlement and Economic Development

When Yermak led his small band of Cossacks across the Urals in 1583 to capture the Tatar town of Sibir, the vast area lying between the Urals and the Pacific was essentially unoccupied except for a few thousand widely scattered so-called Paleo-Asiatics who busied themselves with reindeer herding, hunting, and fishing. Thus the Russians met very little resistance in their eastward sweep to the Pacific, which took place in the short span of approximately 50 years. The original Russian adventurers went into the area primarily in quest of furs, and the first establishments of towns were nothing more than forts and trading posts to facilitate the collection of furs from native hunters. During the seventeenth and eighteenth centuries, however, many of these fur-trading

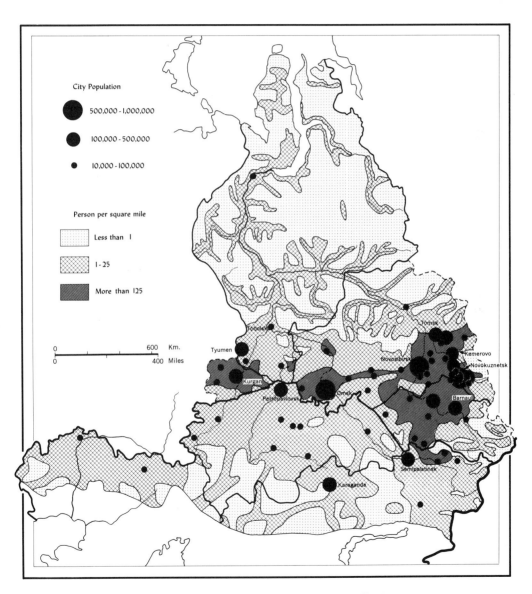

Figure 11-6   Population densities and city sizes.   After Cherdantsev.

centers in western Siberia grew into centers for agricultural settlement, and many new villages were established to accommodate the influx of Russian farmers. By the end of the nineteenth century southwestern Siberia and northern Kazakhstan presented the aspect of a continuously settled area with a population that was predominantly rural. Today the area is still predominantly rural, with the exception of Kemerovo and Novosibirsk Oblasts, and the recent influx of farmers under the virgin- and idle-lands program has temporarily prolonged the rural aspects of the region. Cities have developed and are growing rapidly, however, and new bases for industry are constantly being established.

The coming of the Trans-Siberian Railroad in the 1890's connected the elongated string of settlements with the more populous west, and initiated urbanization. Wherever the railroad crossed a major river a new town was established to handle the commerce. These river-rail towns grew with the railroad and soon surpassed the old regional centers that lay off the main rail line. Flour milling, textiles, and lumbering industries soon developed in the new towns. Later metallurgical industries became predominant as mining developed in the Kuznetsk Basin and in northern Kazakhstan, and rail lines, hooking up with the Trans-Siberian Railroad, spread out both north and south.

The Trans-Siberian Railroad between the Urals and the Kuznetsk Basin is no longer a single line. Paralleling branches cross the Urals at Sverdlovsk, Chelyabinsk, and Magnitogorsk. The line from Magnitogorsk crosses northern Kazakhstan eastsoutheastward straight to Karaganda to provide a direct line for coal transport from Karaganda to the southern Urals. North-south main lines and many spur lines link together the entire area. Oil is being piped into Omsk, Novosibirsk, and Pavlodar from the Bashkir Republic west of the Urals to provide the bases for chemical and other industries.

The main industries of the area are the metallurgical industries, based on local mining; machine-building industries to serve local agriculture, industry, and the railroad; textiles to utilize wool produced locally and cotton shipped in on the Turk-Sib Railroad from Middle Asia to satisfy local markets; food industries to mill the flour, process the meat and dairy products, and refine the sugar of the local farms; and, now, chemical industries, utilizing oil from Bashkiria to supply needed synthetics and plastics. Perhaps the major aspects of industry can be covered best in a discussion of the major cities of the region.

Cities

Novosibirsk Chief among the new rail-river towns, and now largest in all of Siberia, is Novosibirsk, at the important rail crossing of the Ob River. In 1959 Novosibirsk had a population of 886,000, making it eighth largest in the U.S.S.R. The industries of Novosibirsk are varied, and their importance is shared by that of commerce. It acts as the metropolis for the whole of western Siberia, and it is the regional center for the heavily industrialized Kuznetsk Basin, although the city itself is not located within the basin. Novosibirsk has often been called the "Chicago of Siberia." Diversified machine construction and metal working are the primary industries in Novosibirsk, but there are also important heavy metallurgical industries, chemical industries, and food industries.

Omsk The second largest city in Siberia might be called the sister city of Novosibirsk, since it sits on the same plain in a similar location on a terrace along the right bank of a stream where it is crossed by the Trans-Siberian Railroad. Novosibirsk occupies the rail crossing of the Ob River; Omsk the rail crossing of the Irtysh. Omsk, with a 1959 population of 581,000, is one of the most rapidly growing cities in all of Siberia. Like Novosibirsk, Omsk owes its origin to its strategic location on major transport lines within a rich agricultural plain, but also like Novosibirsk, Omsk long since has outgrown its function as the trading center of an agricultural region and has become a great industrial city. At present the industries of Omsk are concentrated approximately one half on machine construction and metal working, one fourth on chemicals, and one fourth on food industries. Omsk is destined to become the primary oil-refining and chemical center of Siberia, utilizing oil brought in by five pipelines from the Volga-Urals oil fields.

Karaganda Third in size, with a population of 397,000, is the new city of Karaganda, sitting in the important coal mining area in the Kazakh Folded Country. Karaganda is the chief center of heavy industry of Kazakhstan, and since its founding in 1926 it has been the most rapidly growing city of the Republic. Although the coal mining and the steel production have not proceeded as rapidly as had been hoped, Karaganda is destined to continue its growth and to dominate the heavy industry scene in Kazakhstan. A small steel plant with a capacity of 250,000 tons has operated in Karaganda since 1945. In July 1960 the first blast furnace of an integrated iron and steel plant finally opened. It is scheduled for full operation in 1964, with a steel capacity of 3,500,000 tons. This new blast furnace is located in the suburban city of Temir Tau, or "Iron Mountain," north of Karaganda. It receives its coal from the local mines and iron ore from Atasuskiy to the southwest. Later it will receive much greater amounts of iron ore from the Rudnyy mines in Kustanay Oblast. Karaganda lies in a somewhat barren landscape on the southern edge of the virgin lands. It gets its water supply from the small Nura River, which flows northwestward through the Kazakh Folded Country. The Nura is not much of a stream, but its water is to be supplemented eventually by the Irtysh-Karaganda Canal.

Cities of the Kuznetsk Basin Fourth in size now is Novokuznetsk, the main steel center of the Kuznetsk Basin, which grew from nothing in 1930 to 377,000 in 1959. Known as Stalinsk from 1932 to 1961, the city was founded as a new steel center during the first five-year plan across the Tom River from the old town of Kuznetsk. It soon engulfed the old town.

At present about one third of the industry of Novokuznetsk is concentrated on heavy metallurgy. Its other industries are chemicals, based on coking gases, machine construction and metal working, and light metallurgy.

The Kuznetsk Basin now has the greatest concentration of large cities in any area east of the Urals. Prokopyevsk, just northwest of Novokuznetsk, is concentrated on metal working and chemicals and has grown rapidly to a population of 282,000 in 1959. Farther northwest is Kemerovo, the oblast center for the Kuznetsk Basin, with a population of 273,000. Kemerovo originally was the largest city in the Kuznetsk Basin, but it has not been growing as rapidly as have Novokuznetsk and Prokopyevsk. Kemerovo is primarily a coal-mining town, and its industries are heavily concentrated on chemicals from the coking industry. It also has machine construction and metal working, as well as construction-material industries.

Four other cities, each with more than 100,000 population, lie in the Kuznetsk Basin. These are Leninsk-Kuznetskiy, with a population of 132,000, Kiselevsk, with a population of 130,000, Anzhero-Sudzhensk, with a population of 116,000, and Belovo, with a population of 107,000. These are all coal-mining towns that usually have some metal working and chemical industries as well as construction-material industries, food industries, etc. Belovo is known particularly for its zinc-processing plant. Anzhero-Sudzhensk lies on the main line of the Trans-Siberian Railroad between Novosibirsk and Krasnoyarsk, whereas the other cities lie on a branch line to the south; hence, part of its growth has been derived from its favorable location with respect to transport lines. One other smaller city in the Kuznetsk Basin that might be mentioned is Guryevsk which has the most intense concentration of iron and steel industries of any town in the Basin. Practically all its workers are engaged in the steel mills.

Cities of the Kulunda Steppe Fifth in size in western Siberia and northern Kazakhstan is Barnaul, population 305,000, the commercial and governmental center of Altay Kray in the rich farm lands of the Kulunda Steppe. Like Omsk and Novosibirsk, Barnaul has outgrown its function as the center of a rich agricultural region and is rapidly becoming an industrial city. It sits at the junction of the South Siberian Railroad coming in from the southwest from Pavlodar and Tselinograd, and the northern extension of the Turk-Sib Railroad coming in from the south from Semipalatinsk. The railroads join at Barnaul on the left bank of the Ob River, and a single rail line crosses the river and continues eastward to the Kuznetsk Basin. Barnaul long has been an important center for cotton textiles, utilizing raw cotton shipped in from Middle Asia over the Turk-Sib Railroad to supply cheap cotton goods to the markets in southwestern Siberia. It now has a major synthetic fiber factory. It also has machine building, woodworking, and food industries.

Two other significant cities in the Kulunda Steppe are Biysk, with a population of 146,-000, and Rubtsovsk, with a population of 111,000. They both are regional centers of rich farming districts. Rubtsovsk is known particularly for its manufacture of agricultural machinery.

Regional Centers of the Farming Belt of Northern Kazakhstan and Southwestern Siberia Seven cities in the rich farm lands of northern Kazakhstan and southwestern Siberia have populations between 85,000 and 155,000. In order of size they are Semipalatinsk, Kurgan, Petropavlovsk, Tselinograd, Aktyubinsk, Pavlodar, and Kustanay.

They serve the region as rail centers, grain storage centers, food processing centers, etc. All are administrative centers of their respective oblasts. Many have agricultural machine-building industries; Kurgan and Tselinograd particularly are important in this respect. Pavlodar is being developed into an industrial city with new oil refineries to refine petroleum from Ufa and a new alumina-aluminum plant to convert the bauxite from Arkalyk 640 miles to the southwest.

Until 1961 Tselinograd was named Akmolinsk. It is the administrative seat of the newly constituted Tselinnyy Kray in the virgin lands of northern Kazakhstan. The word "tselina" means "virgin soil." "Akmolinsk" meant "white tomb," a term that was considered inappropriate for this thriving area.

Old Towns of Western Siberia The old university town of Tomsk, located near the mouth of the Tom River north of the Trans-Siberian Railroad, is eighth in size in western Siberia and northern Kazakhstan, with a population of 249,000. It is one of the older towns in Siberia, having been founded in 1604, and together with Tobolsk and Tyumen farther west, it dominated urban life in Siberia for a couple of centuries. But when the Trans-Siberian Railroad was laid south of all these cities during 1892–1904, new towns established at major river crossings such as Omsk and Novosibirsk rapidly outgrew the older cities. Tomsk sits on a rail spur about 75 miles north of the Trans-Siberian Railroad. It has diversified industries with some concentration on machine building and wood working. It is the site of the first university in Siberia and long has been known as the cultural center of southwestern Siberia.

Tyumen, the oldest city in Siberia, was founded in 1585 on the site of the old Tatar city of Sibir, which had been captured 2 years earlier by Yermak and his band. Tyumen is near the mouth of the Tura River

Figure 11-7   A rayon factory in Barnaul.   Novosti Press.

where it joins the Tobol at the western head of navigation on the Ob-Irtysh River system. Although the major rivers of Siberia flow northward, it was their east-west flowing portions that were important during the early days of eastward penetration into Siberia, so the fact that Tyumen occupied the westernmost point of navigation made it a very strategically located city. Later it was the eastern terminus of the old Perm to Tyumen Railroad, and as such served as the main entrepot into Siberia until it was replaced by Chelyabinsk when the Trans-Siberian Railroad was established to the south. With the building of the northern branch of the Trans-Siberian Railroad from Sverdlovsk to Omsk, Tyumen gained a position on a major rail line. It has never regained its earlier importance, however, and its main function at present is as an important river-rail transfer point for lumber and grain. Its industries are concentrated on machine building, woodworking, and chemicals. In 1959 Tyumen was tenth in size in western Siberia and northern Kazakhstan with a population of 150,000.

Tobolsk, sitting at the mouth of the Tobol River where it joins the Irtysh, was once a mighty fur collecting city and until 1824 served as the administrative center of western Siberia. Now it is by-passed by the railroad, without even a spur line to serve it, and serves only as a river port and lumbering center of local significance.

Cities of the Rudnyy Altay The mining and smelting towns of Ust-Kamenogorsk and Leninogorsk in the Rudnyy Altay already have been mentioned in conjunction with the production of lead, zinc, copper, and associated metals. In 1959 Ust-Kamenogorsk

had a population of 150,000 and Leninogorsk had a population of 67,000.

Reading List

Durgin, Frank A., Jr., "The Virgin Lands Programme 1954–1960," *Soviet Studies*, 1962, pp. 255–280.

Holzman, Franklyn D., "Soviet Ural-Kuznetsk Combine: A Study in Investment Criteria and Industrialization Policies," *The Quarterly Journal of Economics*, August 1957, pp. 368–405.

Jackson, W. A. Douglas, "The Virgin and Idle Lands of Western Siberia and Northern Kazakhstan: A Geographical Appraisal," *Geographical Review*, January 1956, pp. 1–19.

—— "The Virgin and Idle Lands Program Reappraised," *Annals of the Association of American Geographers*, March 1962, pp. 69–79.

Eastern Siberia and the Far East

	Area (sq mile)	Population	People (sq mile)	% Urban
Eastern Siberia	2,208,500	6,960,000	2.7	
Krasnoyarsk Kray	327,000	2,615,000	2.9	50
Khakass A.O.	24,200	411,000	17.4	54
Evenki N.O.	291,000	10,000	0.03	20
Taymyr N.O.	336,000	33,000	0.10	60
Tuva A.O.	66,500	172,000	2.6	29
Irkutsk Oblast	300,000	1,976,000	6.7	62
Ust-Orda Buryat N.O.	8,400	133,000	16.1	15
Buryat A.S.S.R.	137,000	673,000	4.9	41
Chita Oblast	168,000	1,036,000	6.2	58
Aga Buryat N.O.	8,100	49,000	6.2	58
Yakut A.S.S.R.	1,210,000	488,000	0.5	49
Far East	1,215,900	4,347,000	3.6	
Amur Oblast	141,500	718,000	5.2	66
Khabarovsk Kray	322,000	1,142,000	3.6	74
Jewish A.O.	14,100	163,000	11.7	72
Maritime Kray	66,400	1,381,000	21.6	67
Magadan Oblast	468,000	236,000	0.5	81
Chukchi N.O.	288,667	47,000	0.3	56
Kamchatka Oblast	184,000	221,000	1.3	64
Koryak N.O.	118,333	28,000	0.3	22
Sakhalin Oblast	34,000	649,000	19.4	75
Total	3,424,400	11,307,000		

12

Eastern Siberia and the Far East

The belt of continuously settled land in northern Kazakhstan and southwestern Siberia ends abruptly against the northwestern spurs of the Altay Mountains surrounding the Kuznetsk Basin, and thus ends the continuously populated area of the Soviet Union. In the remaining 2000 miles to the Pacific, mountains break the string of settlements along the Trans-Siberian Railroad into isolated pockets of population located in steppe-like intermountain basins. Wherever the topography and climate are such that agriculture and urban development are possible, some settlement has taken place, but the development has been nothing like that in southwestern Siberia where a broad open plain has provided a continuous strip of rich soil and tolerable climate for both agricultural and urban settlement.

The vast expanse of territory east of the Kuznetsk Basin is known as eastern Siberia and the Soviet Far East. This region contains an area of more than 3,400,000 square miles, is larger than the United States of America, and comprises almost 45 per cent of the total area of the Soviet Union. Yet, it contains only some 11 million people, so that culturally and economically it is no more significant to the country than are many of the much smaller regions already considered. Hence it does not warrant division into several regions, even though the area is great, the

topography is varied, and culturally the southern strip is much different from the empty wastes of the rest of the region.

The western boundary of eastern Siberia is set conveniently along the western boundary of Krasnoyarsk Kray, although this falls a short distance west of the Yenisey River and includes within the area a narrow strip of the West Siberian Lowland. The boundary between eastern Siberia and the Far East is defined by the Soviets as the drainage divide between the Arctic and the Pacific. This is modified somewhat to fit the boundaries of the political units in the area. Thus, the political breakdown of eastern Siberia and the Far East is as is shown on the summary page at the beginning of the chapter. In general these political units are quite large, and, as was the case in western Siberia, many of them are elongated north-south, with a rather populous fringe in the south being connected to a long expanse of relatively empty land stretching toward the Arctic. This is particularily true of Krasnoyarsk Kray, which stretches from the southern borders of the country to the Arctic shores. Thus, as was done with western Siberia, discussion will focus on the south, but at the same time it will be kept in mind that a much larger expanse of land is attached to the north, about which there is little to say at present.

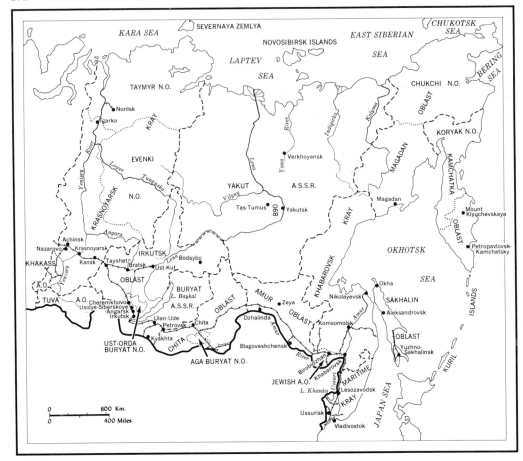

Figure 12-1   Eastern Siberia and the Far East.

Climate, Vegetation, and Soil

Although a major landform break occurs between east and west along the Yenisey River, the east-west zones of climate, vegetation, and soil that were distinguished in western Siberia and northeastern Europe continue unbroken to the Pacific. What generalizations were made about climate in the West Siberian Lowland can be emphasized in eastern Siberia and the Soviet Far East. In winter the Siberian High Pressure Cell, usually centered south of Lake Baykal, occupies the entire region and rules out any possibility of intrusion of maritime air. Cyclonic storms from the Baltic and the Mediterranean are shunted off to the north and to the south to die either along the Arctic Coast or the Middle Asian mountains, far from even the western extremities of the region under consideration. The northwest winds blowing out of the eastern side of the Siberian High across the Pacific coast consistently prevent the entrance of maritime air from the Pacific even along the very coastal sections of the Far East. Hence the winters are clear, calm, and cold. Verkhoyansk, in the upper Yana River Valley east of the Lena, has long been known as the "cold pole" of the world. January temperatures here average —56°F, and temperatures as low as —90°F have been recorded. To the east, in the valley of the Indigirka River, Oymyakon has recorded an even lower minimum temperature of —96°F.

Winter temperatures naturally increase toward the south, but even along the southern border of eastern Siberia Chita averages —14°F in January. This compares to central Canada. Even in the most southerly part of Maritime Kray along the Pacific Coast, Vladivostok averages only 6°F in January. At similar latitudes on the eastern coast of the United States, Boston averages 27°F in January. Hence, in winter, the Pacific coast of the Soviet Far East is much more continental in character than is the east coast of the United States. The explanation is that the consistency of the Siberian High causes the continental polar air of Siberia to be completely dominant even over the coast of the country in wintertime. January temperatures in Vladivostok are more similar to those in Winnipeg, Canada than they are to anything along the eastern coast of North America.

Since eastern Siberia and the Far East are dominated in winter by high atmospheric pressure, precipitation is at a minimum. Most of the area receives less than 4 inches of precipitation between November and March, and much of it receives less than 2 inches. This may mean between 2 and 4 feet of snow, which, when accumulated and drifted throughout the winter makes the precipitation appear heavier than it really is.

During the summer the area is covered by a broad, shallow low-pressure atmospheric system, which allows some penetration of air into the region. The cyclonic storms from the North Atlantic are less frequent and less intense during this period of the year, however, and they do not affect the region much more than do the storms in the wintertime. Nevertheless between April and October the weak cyclonic activity, coupled with local convective activity, produces between 4 and 12 inches of precipitation over much of the region. With the cool temperatures that prevail, this moisture is enough to make the climate humid.

During middle and late summer the Pacific monsoon sets in with some force in the Soviet Far East and penetrates up the Amur Valley occasionally as far as Lake Baykal. Maritime Kray particularly is affected; the Pacific slopes of the Sikhote-Alin receive upward of 40 inches of rainfall. During this time the maritime air modifies the weather along a narrow strip of coast as far north as the northern shore of the Sea of Okhotsk and Kamchatka Peninsula. Cold ocean currents flowing southward along the Asian coasts of the Okhotsk and Japan Seas, coupled with the sea breezes in summer, maintain very cool temperatures along the immediate coast and produce thick persistent fogs similar to those in the San Francisco Bay area across the Pacific during the same time of year. During the months of June and July, some of the Asian Coast experiences more than 20 days of dense fog. This is the case also on parts of Sakhalin Island and Kamchatka.

The same locational factors that make for very cold temperatures in the wintertime in interior Siberia make for relatively warm temperatures for this latitude in the summertime. Stagnant air in interior valleys, which during the winter experiences extreme temperature inversions and cold surface temperatures, during the summer experiences rapid increases in surface temperatures due to local radiational exchanges of heat in the absence of advection. Verkhoyansk, which in January averages 56°F below zero, in July averages 60°F above zero. There have been daytime temperatures in July of nearly 100°F; hence, the absolute range is nearly 200 degrees. Eastern Siberia thus has the questionable distinction of having the greatest temperature ranges on earth. In one of the settled basins in southern Siberia, Chita averages 66°F in July. This is comparable to northern Michigan in the United States.

The Pacific coast of the Soviet Far East in the summertime is influenced more by maritime air than is the Atlantic Coast of the United States. During the winter Vladivostok averages much colder than similar latitudes along the eastern coast of North America because of its dominance by continental air, and during the summer it also averages considerably cooler than comparable latitudes along the East Coast of North America because of the marine influence. In August, the warmest month, Vladivostok averages 69°F. At a comparable latitude, Boston, Massachusetts in July averages 72°F.

The subarctic climatic zone and the taiga vegetation zone expand in width in eastern Siberia and the Far East to engulf most of the area between the Arctic and the mountains along the southern border. The steppe lands, which are so important to the economy of southwestern Siberia and northern Kazakhstan are pinched out between the forest and the southern mountains east of the Kuznetsk Basin, except for isolated mountain basins that occur along the Trans-Siberian Railroad. The arctic fringes of the area, as well as higher elevations throughout the mountainous portions of the region, particularly in the mountains east of the Lena River, lie beyond the tree line and bear only a poor tundra vegetation. Much of the tundra and the taiga are underlain by permafrost, even as far south as Outer Mongolia. This induces a forest predominantly of larch, instead of pine and fir as is typical of western Siberia. The larch spreads its shallow root system over the permafrost and can survive in the thin layer of top soil that thaws during the summer. The podzol and tundra soils that prevail throughout the region are universally poor and drainage is a major problem. The percolation of water from the thawed top soil is largely prevented by the underlying permafrost.

The lowlands of the southern portion of the Soviet Far East that are affected by the monsoons are something apart from the rest of the area. The climate is humid continental with cool summers, the vegetation is predominantly a broad-leaf deciduous forest, and the soils, though still podzolic, in general are better than they are throughout much of the region. This area, together with the steppe basins along the Trans-Siberian Railroad, contains the better soils, the milder climate, and the greater agricultural development of eastern Siberia and the Far East.

Geology and Topography

Although the climate, vegetation, and soil zones stretch unbroken from the Urals to the Pacific, east of the Yenisey, and again east of the Lena River, definite geological and topographic breaks divide Siberia into three distinct regions. The first, the West Siberian Lowland, has already been discussed in Chapter 11.

Central Siberian Uplands The second region, between the Yenisey and the Lena Rivers, variously known as the Central Siberian Uplands, the Tunguskan Plateau, the Anabar Shield, etc., is a roughly dissected upland of complex rock structure which here and there rises into subdued mountains. The area is highest in its northwestern portion where the Putoran Mountains rise to elevations of more than 6000 feet above sea level. Elevations are generally below 3000 feet, but the relief is considerable, some of the streams having cut almost canyon-like valleys below the surface of the upland. Much of this extensive area of land represents a geologically stable block of complex crystalline rocks that has resisted tectonic movement as younger mountains have been built to the south and east. Extensive sections of the upland are overlain by more recent sedimentary materials, and in places large lava flows that have emitted from recent fault lines reach thicknesses of more than 1000 feet.

Different sections of the upland are known by different names which correspond to the names of the main rivers flowing through them. Thus in the southeast are the Patom Plateau, the Vitim Plateau, and the Aldan Plateau, all named after rivers that are tributaries to the Lena. In the southwest is the Tunguskan Plateau, named after the

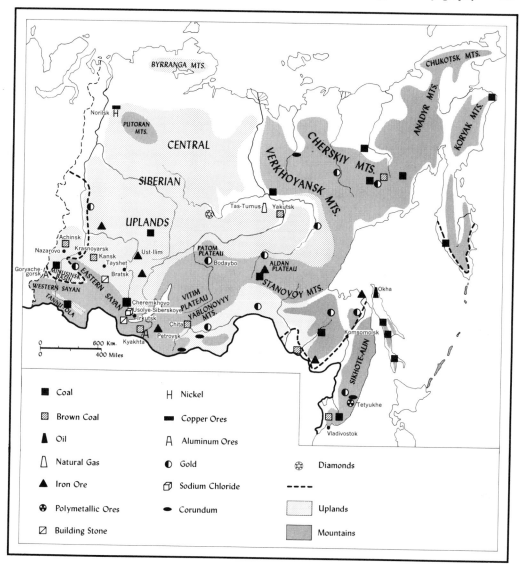

Figure 12-2   Landforms and minerals.

three main right bank tributaries of the Yenisey, the Lower Tunguska, the Stony Tunguska, and the Upper Tunguska, which drains the large Lake Baykal and is also known as the Angara River. Other parts of the upland have other regional names.

The natural environment of the Central Siberian Uplands is so harsh that there has been little development in the area. Only along the broad flood plain of the Lena River where it is joined by its two main tributaries, the Aldan and the Vilyuy, has agriculture been attempted. The settlement of Yakutsk in the Lena-Aldan-Vilyuy Lowland is famous for its Arctic agriculture, and it is by far the largest agricultural settlement this far poleward in the world.

East of the Lena   East of the Lena River the landscape changes from one of low uplands to one of mountains and river valleys. The Verkhoyansk, Cherskiy, and Kolyma ranges, with elevations in the vicinity of 10,000 feet, are separated by the valleys of the Yana, Indigirka, and Kolyma Rivers, which flow northward into the Arctic. The Anadyr Range, on the Chukotsk Peninsula in the easternmost part of the country, and the Koryak Range, to the south where the Kamchatka Peninsula joins the mainland, reach elevations of more than 6000 feet. Having contained mountain glaciers during the Pleistocene and lying well above the tree line at present, all these mountains exhibit definite alpine features.

Kamchatka and the Kurils The Kamchatka Peninsula is a mountainous piece of land which belongs more to the volcanic island arcs of the Pacific than to the more subdued and older mountains of the mainland. It is essentially a double line of volcanic peaks, many of which are active. The highest of these, Mount Klyuchevskaya, with an elevation of more than 15,000 feet, is one of the great symmetrical volcanic cones of the world. The volcanoes of Kamchatka spew out dust and ashes so continuously that in places the snow is covered to a depth great enough to prevent the use of sleds. The Russians speak of these places as "nonslip" areas.

The Kamchatkan Peninsula is so remote from the main centers of population in Russia that in the minds of Russian schoolboys it has become associated with the back seats of the school room. At the beginning of each school term there is some juggling of position among the more ornery boys to see who is going to get to sit in "Kamchatka."

The volcanic peaks of Kamchatka continue southwestward in an arc of small islands, the Kurils, which join Kamchatka and Hokkaido with an underwater ridge to complete the encirclement of the Sea of Okhotsk. Since World War II the Kurils and the southern half of Sakhalin Island

have reverted from the Japanese to the Russians, and the Sea of Okhotsk has become a Russian sea.

The Southern Mountains and Basins South of the Central Siberian Uplands and the mountains and valleys of the northeast, along the southern borders of the Soviet Union all the way from the Kuznetsk Basin to the Pacific, are rugged mountain ranges of varying ages and orientations, broken here and there by basins and valleys. In the west, the Minusinsk Basin along the upper Yenisey is bordered on the south and the northeast respectively by the Western and Eastern Sayans. The Sayans are fairly old mountains with intermediate altitudes similar to those of the Altay in the west, which separate the Minusinsk Basin from the Kuznetsk Basin. The Western Sayans, which are oriented nearly west-east, separate the Minusinsk Basin to the north from the Tuva Autonomous Oblast to the south along the upper Yenisey. Tannu Tuva joined the Soviet Union in 1944 and was made an autonomous oblast directly responsible to the Russian Republic. It is the only autonomous oblast in the country that is directly responsible to a Union Republic.

The Eastern Sayans are oriented northwest-southeast between the Yenisey River on the west and its main right-bank tributary, the Angara River, on the east and north. They reach their highest elevation at approximately 11,500 feet, and then continue eastward to Lake Baykal in a lower series of generally north-south oriented ranges lying between the tributaries of the Angara River. As Lake Baykal is approached, the mountains take on a fault block form.

Lake Baykal lies in a fault graben and is bounded by exceedingly steep slopes on all sides. The precipitous cliffs of the deeply dissected mountain spurs around the south end of the lake delayed the completion of the Trans-Siberian Railroad for more than 10 years. During this period, trains were ferried across the lake in summer and tracks were laid across the ice in winter. Finally, the line was completed around the southern end, clinging to the sheer cliff faces and utilizing more than fifty tunnels and intervening high trestles.

Approximately 1 mile deep, Lake Baykal is credited with having the greatest volume of water of any lake in the world. It is drained from the southwestern corner by the Angara River through the Yenisey to the Arctic. Hence the water in the lake is fresh. The lake freezes over from December to May, but the water flowing down the Angara has such a steep gradient and high speed that the river itself does not freeze. The Lena River heads very near the lake on the western side, but, as is so often true with fault grabens, the highest land lies along the immediate rim of the lake, and thus the Lena does not tap the lake. The Selenga River, coming into the southeastern side of the lake from the Mongolian Peoples Republic, is the main stream flowing into the lake.

Around Lake Baykal the mountains and basins become exceedingly complex; it is laborious to separate one from another and to attach names individually. Generally the regional name assigned to the area lying between ˝the Yenisey and Lake Baykal is simply Prebaykalye, and to the area lying to the east of Lake Baykal and extending to the eastern edge of Chita Oblast as Transbaykalya. Thus, Lake Baykal, in the minds of the Russians, is a land mark by which the territories around it are designated, either as those lying on the near side of the lake, that is, nearest to populated parts of Russia, or those on the far side of the lake.

East of Lake Baykal the Yablonovyy Range, oriented southwest-northeast, separates the basin around Ulan-Ude in the Buryat A.S.S.R. on the west from the basin surrounding Chita on the east. Other mountains continue northeastward between the tributaries of the Amur River to the south and the Lena River to the north, and form the drainage divide that separates eastern

Siberia from the Far East. South of these ranges, the Argun River flows northeastward out of the Mongolian Peoples Republic to form the boundary between the Soviet Union and Manchuria for a distance of about 400 miles before it is joined by the Shilka in Chita Oblast to form the Amur. The Amur continues along the border of Manchuria for another 600 miles before it is joined by the Ussuri at Khabarovsk, where it turns abruptly northward to empty into the Tatar Strait near the northern end of Sakhalin Island.

A continuous strip of lowland follows the Amur all the way to the Pacific. This lowland is constricted everywhere, but it widens somewhat wherever a tributary comes in from the north to join the Amur. Three broader segments of the plain stand out in their development. One is the Zeya-Bureya Lowland around the city of Blagoveshchensk where the Zeya and Bureya Rivers come in from the northeast to join the Amur. The second is the Jewish Autonomous Oblast, nestled in the southward bend of the river where the small Bira and Bidzhan Rivers come in from the north to join the Amur. The capital city of the oblast, Birobidzhan, takes its name from these two small streams. The third and largest and most significant lowland is the Ussuri-Khanka Lowland in Maritime Kray where the Ussuri River flows northward to join the Amur at Khabarovsk. The large Lake Khanka occupies part of this lowland. Although this lowland continues northeastward along the lower Amur to Nikolayevsk at its mouth, the segment north of Khabarovsk, except for the city of Komsomolsk, is sparsely settled forest land. East of the Ussuri-Khanka Lowland lie the low, heavily forested Sikhote-Alin Mountains.

Across the Tatar Strait, mountains rise once again to form the long island of Sakhalin. A double range of low mountains, rising to heights of approximately 6000 feet, is split down the middle by a valley that runs the length of the island. The cool, moist, foggy climate has fostered the growth of fairly good stands of forest, except in the low, marshy northwestern part of the island, which is tundra.

Agriculture

The Minusinsk Basin, the Tuva A.O., the Irkutsk Basin along the Angara west of Lake Baykal, the basin of the Buryat A.S.S.R., and the basin around Chita are all steppe basins with subhumid and semiarid climates that have been conducive to a good grass growth and a development of chernozem and chestnut soils that are quite adaptable to cultivation. Many of the areas are still being used as extensive grazing lands for sheep and beef cattle; native herders carry on life much as they did before the Soviet Era. The Russians are eager to plow up these grazing lands and plant them to wheat and, in some cases, to sugar beets, but so far the conversion from grazing to cultivation has been slow. The Russians would also like to settle the seminomadic herders and make sedentary farmers out of them. The last strongholds

of native life are in the Tuva A.O. and the Buryat A.S.S.R. No doubt, as Russian settlement progresses in these areas, they also will change from a predominantly pastoral economy to a predominantly agricultural one.

East of Chita Oblast, the moister lowlands of the lower Amur River valley, with their monsoonal influences, afford possibilities for a variety of agricultural crops. Drainage is the big problem in these areas, but paradoxically supplementary irrigation may be necessary for some crops in spring and early summer. The rainfall regime in summer is almost exactly wrong, since the monsoon flow of air from the Pacific is not really at its peak until midsummer. Spring and early summer may be positively dry when moisture is most needed for the rapid growth period of the crops, and late summer and fall may be very wet when the crops are being harvested. Nevertheless, the Zeya-Bureya Lowland, the Jewish A.O., and the Ussuri-Khanka Lowland hold the most promise for agriculture in eastern Siberia and the Far East.

The Ussuri-Khanka Lowland in particular

Figure 12-3   Sheep being driven to mountain pastures in the Buryat A.S.S.R. east of Lake Baykal.   Novosti Press.

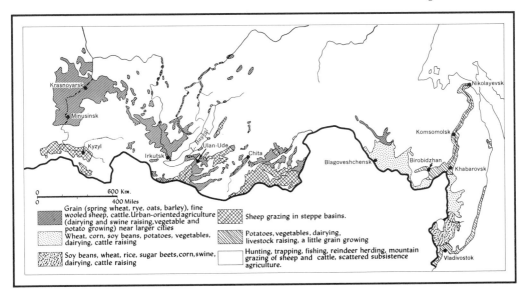

Figure 12-4   Land use in eastern Siberia and the Far East.   Adapted from Atlas selskogo khozyaystva SSSR.

has been adapted to a variety of crops. Russian and Ukranian farmers from the west have met up with Chinese and Korean farmers from the south. Thus the settlement in the Ussuri-Khanka Lowland is a mixture of western and oriental, and so is the crop complex. Wheat, sugar beets, potatoes, and a great variety of fruits, vegetables, and melons mix with such oriental crops as rice, soy beans, millet, and grain sorghums. This is the primary soy bean growing region of the Soviet Union. Chinese and Korean farmers have even developed some terrace agriculture with paddy fields. The majority of the people in the area are Russians and Ukrainians, however; many of the towns, with bungalows of whitewashed adobe walls and blue shuttered windows, appear to have come straight from the Ukraine. The transplanted Ukrainian farmers claim that even the dust is Ukrainian!

Other than these major areas, scattered agricultural settlements have been established along many sheltered river valleys of middle and northern Siberia, the Far East, Sakhalin Island, and Kamchatka. These agricultural settlements in general have been made in conjunction with mining, lumbering, fishing, or hunting enterprises to support the people of the local areas. They thus are limited in size and produce a few hardy grains and vegetables under very restricted environmental conditions. Among these settlements the most noted is Yakutsk in the Lena-Aldan-Vilyuy Lowland where the Russians over a period of many years have developed strains of wheat, barley, and rye that in some cases mature within 60 days after planting. Most of the strains of these grains that have been introduced into the Fairbanks area of Alaska have come from Yakutsk. These grains do not bear heavily, but transportation being what it is in Siberia, the cost of bringing food into the scattered settlements of the area from better farming lands would no doubt be excessive. Because of low productivity, subsistence farming permits only a low standard of living. During the three centuries or more that Yakutsk has existed, little change in the pioneer outlook of the area has taken place. The buildings of Yakutsk are of rough-hewn logs, and the streets are mud.

With all the effort that has been expended

for the development of agriculture, the area east of Lake Baykal still is only about one third self-sufficient in foodstuffs. The rest must be shipped long distances from the west.

Resources and Industries

From a glance at the figures on urbanization on the summary table at the beginning of this chapter, it is quite obvious that the Soviet Far East, and to some extent eastern Siberia also, has been settled primarily for reasons other than agricultural. In these remote areas of sparse population the cities stand out as conspicuous nodes of settlement separated by wide expanses of almost unoccupied virgin territory. The resources that have induced and sustained this nodal form of settlement are minerals, timber, and fish. Industry based on these resources, coupled with the functions of transport and trade, explain the existence of most of the cities.

As might be expected in an area as large and geologically varied as Siberia and the Soviet Far East, there is potential for a great variety of mineral resources. Geological surveys are still inadequate, but better estimates of the quantity and quality of old deposits are being made and new minerals are constantly being discovered.

The Mineral Fuels The most important mineral in Siberia and the Far East today is coal, and it may well retain this position in the future for the reserves are large. Some 70 per cent of the total coal reserves of the Soviet Union lie in this area. Coal has already been the basis for some industrial growth, and it promises to be the basis for a considerable expansion of future industries. In 1959 the East Siberian coal fields produced 7.2 per cent of the Soviet Union's coal, which puts them in fifth place among the producing coal fields of the country. The Far Eastern fields produced 4.1 per cent of the total U.S.S.R. coal. About two-thirds of the coal produced in eastern Siberia came from the Cheremkhovo deposit near Irkutsk. The coal in this deposit lies in flat seams 1 to 8 meters in thickness, and more than half of it is mined by open-pit methods. Since they are not of good coking quality, these coals are used for chemical processing, as fuel for large power stations, and on the railroad.

Other important coal-producing basins in eastern Siberia are the Kansk-Achinsk, the Minusinsk, and those in the Buryat A.S.S.R. The Kansk-Achinsk coal field forms a wide band running parallel and adjacent to the Trans-Siberian Railroad for a distance of more than 700 kilometers in Krasnoyarsk Kray and eastern Kemerovo Oblast. Thirty almost flat seams lie at depths of no more than 200 meters. Brown coals predominate except in one deposit which contains hard coal. Forty per cent of the country's brown coal deposits are located in this field. Open-pit mines are being developed to produce low-grade coals for local heating and power industries.

The Minusinsk coal field contains smaller deposits of higher-grade coals that are mined by shaft methods. The Minusinsk coal is used primarily for power production.

In the Buryat A.S.S.R. and in Chita Oblast deposits of brown coal are being used to power local industry and on local sections of the Trans-Siberian Railroad.

In the Far East, important producing coal fields are the Bureya coal field, situated in the upper reaches of the Bureya River 300 kilometers north of the Trans-Siberian Railroad, and scattered coal fields in Maritime Kray and on Sakhalin Island. The Bureya coal is used locally for industry, power generation, and the railroad. Much of the coal is of coking quality and may become important in the Amurstal iron and steel industry to be established in the city of Komsomolsk. The Sakhalin coals are largely hard coals of coking quality, but at present they are used only for local heating, power generation, and steamships.

These producing fields along the southern

margins of eastern Siberia and the Far East represent only a minor portion of the total coal reserves of the region. Over 90 per cent of the reserves lie in the huge deposits of the Tunguskan, Yakutsk, and Lena fields to the north. Much of these large coal reserves are high-grade coking coals, but they probably will not be intensively utilized in the foreseeable future since they are removed from the population of the region. None of these deposits is now producing enough coal to warrant formation of a kombinat to administer the mining. The most promising among them for immediate development are the south Yakutsk coal fields which may lie far enough south to be used to supplement the Bureya coal in the Far Eastern iron and steel industries that are to be established.

Besides coal, there are some deposits of oil and gas in the area. The oil fields of northern Sakhalin have been supplying about 1 per cent of the Soviet Union's oil for the last 40 years, and it appears that they will continue to do so. These oil fields were developed in the 1920's largely by the Japanese on leased land after the Russo-Japanese War of 1905 had given the Japanese the southern half of the island. After the Japanese had leased the oil rights of much of the area around the city of Okha in the north and had developed wells there, the Russians developed what was left of their area. Now, of course, the Soviets control the entire operation, as well as the entire island of Sakhalin. A pipeline has been laid from the city of Okha across the Tatar Strait to Nikolayevsk at the mouth of the Amur River and up the Amur to Komsomolsk and Khabarovsk where oil refineries have been built. The Sakhalin oil serves most of the needs of the Soviet Far East.

Mention has been made in the past of the possibilities of oil in the Lena-Vilyuy Lowland and along certain segments of the alluvial coast of the Arctic. Apparently no large reserves of oil have yet been discovered in these areas, however, and eastern Siberia is to be served with oil largely by pipeline from the Volga-Ural oil fields 2,000 miles to the west. Two pipelines are being laid from Ufa to Irkutsk, and refineries are being built in Krasnoyarsk and Irkutsk.

Apparently, a significant deposit of natural gas has been discovered in the Lena-Vilyuy Lowland at Tas-Tumus northwest of Yakutsk. The seven-year plan calls for a pipeline to be laid from Tas-Tumus to Yakutsk to utilize this deposit.

Water Power The large volume of water in the rivers of eastern Siberia coupled with the steep gradients in their mountain headwaters give the region the highest water power potential of any area in the Soviet Union. Together, eastern Siberia and the Far East are accredited with 55 per cent of the water power potential of the U.S.S.R. The Yenisey-Angara River system alone has a hydroelectric potential of at least 30 million kilowatts. The outlet for Lake Baykal, the Yenisey, has the largest and steadiest flow of any river in the country.

The Irkutsk plant on the Angara, was completed in 1958 with a capacity of 660,-000 kilowatts. An earthen dam 2363 meters long backed up the water 70 kilometers to Lake Baykal. Downstream on the Angara, the Bratsk plant, which had been under construction for a number of years, began limited operation in October 1961. A concrete dam 127 meters high will create the Bratsk Sea more than 500 kilometers long reaching upstream to the Irkutsk Dam. The reservoir with a capacity of 180 billion cubic meters of water will store more water than all the reservoirs on the Volga River combined. The ultimate capacity of the power plant is to be in the vicinity of 4,500,000 kilowatts. The annual output of the power plant will be considerably greater than that of Kuybyshev and Volgograd together, since the flow of the Angara is very consistent throughout the year. The Bratsk and Irkutsk Reservoirs will make it possible for ships to sail from Lake Baykal down the Yenisey to the Arctic Ocean. Two other large plants, the Ust-Ilimsk and the Boguchanskaya, each with capacities of three to four million

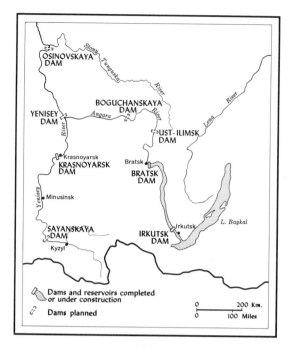

Figure 12-5   Construction projects on the Yenisey and Angara rivers.

kilowatts, are scheduled to be constructed on the Angara downstream from Bratsk.

On the Yenisey itself, construction was begun on the Krasnoyarsk plant in 1955. The dam, over 100 meters high, is being constructed about 35 kilometers above the city of Krasnoyarsk where the river is squeezed within a gorge 800 meters wide. The dam will raise the water 100 meters and back it up 300 to 400 kilometers, thus creating one of the largest reservoirs in the world. The ultimate capacity of the power plant is to be in the neighborhood of 4 million kilowatts. Elevators are to be used to raise and lower ships over the dam.

The so-called Yenisey plant is planned for construction downstream from Krasnoyarsk with a power capacity of 6 million kilowatts. A high dam will raise the water to a level that might allow for the long-cherished plan of Soviet engineers to join tributaries of the Yenisey and the Ob Rivers. Two other major hydroelectric plants on the Yenisey are planned for construction in the near

future. They are the Osinovskaya plant, not far from the mouth of the Stony Tunguska, and the Sayanskaya plant, in the upper reaches of the river. Long-range plans call for the building of at least eleven plants on the Yenisey-Angara River system which will have a combined electrical capacity of up to 30 million kilowatts.

A grand scheme has been drawn up for controlling the floods and at the same time exploiting the water power resources of the Amur River system. As many as 70 power stations of various sizes and capacities have been proposed for the Amur River and its tributaries. Two plants of immediate importance, since they would bring under control the waters of the unpredictable Amur, are the Zeya plant, to be constructed about 6 kilometers above the city of Zeya on the Zeya River, and the Dzhalindskaya plant, to be built near the town of Dzhalinda about 700 kilometers above Blagoveshchensk on the Amur River. As planned, the Dzhalindskaya plant will have a dam 80 meters high, which will help in eliminating the floods on the Amur due to the summer monsoons. The Zeya plant calls for a dam 100 meters high. The power station at each dam would have a capacity in the neighborhood of 1,000,000 kilowatts. The Chinese part of the project to control the Amur provides for the construction of ten hydroelectric plants on the Sungari River, one plant of which already is operative.

The large power plants of the Angara-Yenisey system will provide abundant electric power for aluminum and synthetic plants in the cities of Krasnoyarsk and Irkutsk and at intervening locations now under construction. Also they will greatly enhance the electrification of the Trans-Siberian Railroad, which now has been accomplished all the way from Moscow to Irkutsk. The electrification of the Trans-Siberian Railroad will increase the freight-carrying capacity of the most densely traveled railroad in the world and will eliminate a large portion of the previous coal movement on the railroad, one third of which was for the consumption of the steam engines themselves.

If all the hydroelectric plants now planned for the Yenisey-Angara system are completed, there will be a great surplus of electric power in the area. One Soviet planner has calculated that to utilize fully the electricity produced by the Bratsk hydroelectric plant by the methods in which electricity is now being used in the area, 3,120,000 workers would have to be moved into the area. Obviously, such a transposition of people would be very expensive in terms of housing and other services, which is why large power-consuming industries, such as aluminum reduction plants, are planned. The same planner points out that even by utilizing much of the electricity produced by the Bratsk plant in large aluminum plants at Krasnoyarsk and Irkutsk, 28,000 workers would have to be settled in the area. With construction projects lagging as they are, the settlement of even this number of workers appears to be a Herculean task. Thus we

might suspect that many of the planned construction projects will be a long time in materializing. For the time being, much of the electricity produced at Bratsk may be transmitted more than 1,000 miles to the west to be utilized in the Pavlodar aluminum plant now under construction in northeastern Kazakhstan. Transmission of electricity over such long distances, however, would result in much loss of power along the line.

Iron and Steel At present there are only two small steel plants east of Lake Baykal. These are located at Petrovsk, just east of the lake and at Komsomolsk on the lower Amur River. Both of the steel plants depend on imported pig iron from the west, but it is hoped that eventually full-cycle plants can be established here utilizing iron ore deposits in eastern Siberia and the Far East. Adequate coal to operate such plants exists in the Bureya, south Yakutsk, and Sakhalin fields. The present Komsomolsk steel plant, with a capacity of 300,000 tons, supplies only 35 to 40 per cent of the present regional needs, and the steel consumption of the Far East is expected to rise shortly to seven or eight million tons.

The location of a so-called "third metallurgical base" in the Kazakhstan-Siberian-Far Eastern area has been under discussion since World War II. Actually the term is rather meaningless since it implies a series of widely scattered locations of iron and steel plants, some in Kazakhstan, some in Siberia, and some in the Soviet Far East. Construction of the first important plant of this series appears now to be scheduled for the small town of Tayshet, a railroad junction about 250 miles east of Krasnoyarsk. This small settlement was decided on after much debate because of its strategic position among several deposits of iron ore and coal at the major fork of the railroad where the Trans-Siberian turns southeast towards Irkutsk and the Tayshet-Lena rail line heads northeastward to Ust-Kut. The Tayshet plant is scheduled to be completed during the present seven-year plan with the first output of pig iron scheduled for 1965. Its iron ore base will be the Angara-Ilimsk deposit east of Tayshet near the junction of the Ilim and Angara Rivers. At first the Kuznetsk Basin will have to supply the coke and coal, but later local coal can be used. Immediately following the construction of the Tayshet plant, a new major plant is planned to be constructed at Krasnoyarsk utilizing the same iron and coal deposits.

Farther east, plans are being made for the construction of an iron and steel plant in the Aldan area in southern Yakutia, where rich deposits of iron ore and coking coal have been found in some abundance and in close proximity to one another. Realization of these plans appears to lie in the very distant future. One Soviet planner has pointed out that before steel plants can be constructed in this empty area, people, houses, transport facilities, food supplies, etc. must be established.

Other Minerals Besides fuels and iron, a variety of other minerals are found in small amounts scattered about eastern Siberia and the Far East. Although no single deposit is of national significance, it is recognized that surveying has been far from sufficient in this region, and that many minerals might exist in a large area of complex crystalline rocks such as this is.

One of the major mining areas that has been developed under the Soviets is at Norilsk on the lower Yenisey where large deposits of copper and nickel have laid the basis for the development of a boom town.

Tin and some lead and zinc have been mined for years in Chita Oblast and around Tetyukhe in Maritime Kray. More recently, tin, in conjunction with tungsten, has been discovered in the far northeastern corner of the country in the Chukotsk Peninsula, and a refining plant reportedly is under construction in this area to process the two metals.

Gold is scattered widely throughout eastern Siberia and the Far East, the richest fields occurring in the Vitim and Aldan Plateaus south of the Lena River. The small city of Bodaybo in the Vitim Plateau is the central outfitting city for the gold workers. Also, important gold mines have been established in far off Magadan Oblast about 200 miles inland from the northern shore of the Sea of Okhotsk. Huge dredges as high as a three-story house have been shipped in and assembled on the middle Yenisey and are working the gravels of that stream for placer gold. As far as can be determined, the Soviet Union is second only to South Africa in gold production, and most of the gold comes from eastern Siberia and the Far East.

One of the big developments in mining and industry that is now taking place in eastern Siberia is in the production of aluminum. Nephelite ore has been discovered at Goryachegorsk about 200 miles southwest of Krasnoyarsk, and sillimanite ore has been found near Kyakhta southeast of Lake Baykal. Both ores are usable for the production of aluminum. An alumina plant with a capacity of 800,000 tons per year, the largest in the Soviet Union, has been constructed at Achinsk on the Trans-Siberian Railroad about 110 miles west of Krasnoyarsk to process the nephelite from Goryachegorsk and to supply alumina to the large aluminum plants now being completed at Krasnoyarsk and Irkutsk.

The Krasnoyarsk aluminum plant, which reportedly is the largest in the world, spreads over an area of 172 hectares of land and has a capacity of 400,000 tons. This compares with a 335,000-ton capacity at the Alcan plant at Arvida, Quebec, which before was rated as the largest in the world. The Krasnoyarsk plant will obtain electric power from the huge 4,000,000-kilowatt hydroelectric station now under construction on the Yenisey River near Krasnoyarsk. Also it will obtain some power from the 1,200,-000-kilowatt coal-fueled thermal station at Nazarovo south of Achinsk. The Krasnoyarsk aluminum plant was to be in operation in 1960; however, it seems that construction has lagged, and no opening date has been announced yet.

The Irkutsk aluminum plant began operation in 1961 utilizing power from the new 660,000-kilowatt hydroelectric station at Irkutsk on the Angara River. The capacity of the plant has been reported to be in the vicinity of 300,000 tons. It is not clear from Soviet sources whether the Irkutsk plant has an alumina department nor how much of its supply comes from the Kyakhta sillimanite concentrate and how much from the Achinsk alumina plant.

In December 1961 it was reported that construction had begun on a large aluminum plant at the town of Anzeb in the vicinity of Bratsk.

Perhaps the most exciting development in the mining industry in Siberia recently has been the opening up of newly discovered diamond deposits which are scattered widely through the western portion of the Central Siberian Upland. The Russians state simply that "these deposits are in no way inferior to those in South Africa." A sizable diamond production would greatly facilitate the machine tool industry in the Soviet Union, since diamonds are needed in all sorts of cutting instruments.

Forests Roughly half of the forest reserves of the U.S.S.R. lie in eastern Siberia and the Far East. The eastern forests in general are not of the best quality, and as long as better forests are available nearer to the markets of European Russia and west-

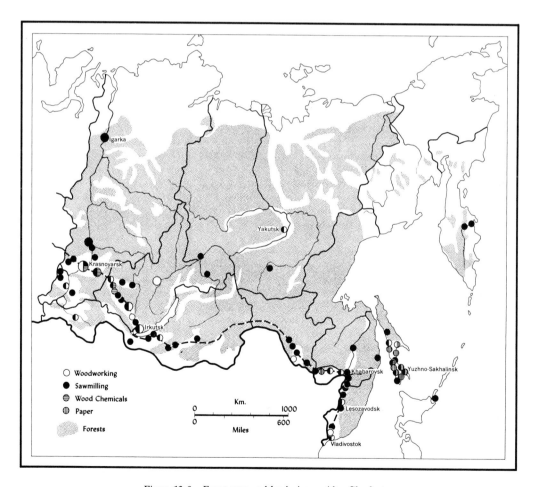

Figure 12-6   Forest cover and lumbering.   After Cherdantsev.

ern Europe a great expansion of lumbering cannot be expected in this area. Eastern Siberia and the Far East normally produce about one sixth of the sawn lumber in the Soviet Union and enough paper to serve the needs of the local area.

The sawmilling industry in eastern Siberia and the Far East is sufficient to serve all local needs, and some lumber is sent down the major streams in summer to be shipped westward via the Northern Sea Route to foreign markets in western Europe. All the major towns along the Trans-Siberian Railroad engage in some sawmilling, and some major centers exist off the railroad along the primary streams. Igarka is just such a sawmilling center established on the lower

Yenisey, to ship lumber via the Northern Sea Route to foreign markets.

A string of smaller sawmilling towns exist in the Ussuri-Khanka Lowland in Maritime Kray, located wherever the railroad between Khabarovsk and Vladivostok crosses tributaries of the Ussuri River flowing down the western slopes of the Sikhote-Alin Mountains. The prime forests of Maritime Kray are found on the slopes of the Sikhote-Alin, and timber is floated down the streams to the west. The largest of these sawmilling towns, located where the railroad crosses the Ussuri River itself, is called Lesozavodsk, or "sawmill."

Lumbering is one of the major industries on Sakhalin Island, particularly in the better

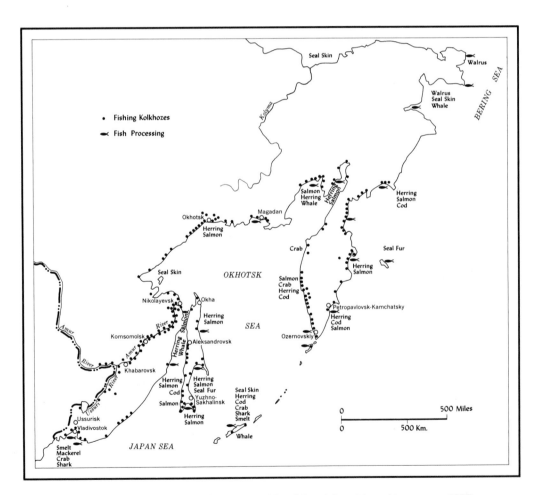

Figure 12-7   Fishing in Far Eastern waters.   Adapted from Atlas selskogo khozyaystva SSSR.

forested southern part of the island. Many pulp and paper factories are located in the towns of southern Sakhalin, particularly in the largest city, Yuzhno-Sakhalinsk, or "South Sakhalin."

Fish Since World War II the total fish catch in the Soviet Union has increased steadily, and the geographical distribution has changed until at present the seas of the Far East yield 30 per cent of the total catch. Together with 2.6 per cent of the total catch contributed by Siberian rivers and lakes, this area becomes the most important fishing ground in the Soviet Union. The main centers of the fishing industry are along the shores of Maritime Kray, especially around Peter the Great Bay in the vicinity of Vladivostok, the southern part of Khabarovsk Kray, particularly around the mouth of the Amur River, and Kamchatka Peninsula and Sakhalin Island.

The Sea of Okhotsk, or "hunters sea," is one of the richest fishing grounds of the country. It is especially known for its salmon, which are caught mainly in either the lower Amur River, as the fish enter for their annual spawning, or the Gulf of Penzhina next to Kamchatka. The Gulf of Penzhina, with an average difference of 45 feet between high and low water, has some of the greatest tides in the world. According to the Russians the salmon are so large and so numerous in this area that in shoal water during low tides sea gulls stand on the backs of the salmon and peck at them. The fisheries of Kamchatka account for about 60 per cent of the salmon catch in the U.S.S.R. Another product, one that is world renowned, is the Kamchatka crab, which the Russians claim reach the size of a washtub! The waters surrounding Kamchatka supply a large percentage of the world's crabs.

Far Eastern waters also are rich in sea animals: whales, walruses, and seals. Whaling ships based in Vladivostok range to the Bering Straits, 3000 miles to the northeast. Seal rookeries are maintained on the Commander Islands. Although minor fishing ports exist in many places along the coast of the mainland, the peninsula of Kamchatka, and the island of Sakhalin, larger ocean-going fleets all are based in Vladivostok.

Before World War II a large part of the fishing in the Sea of Okhotsk was done by the Japanese who then controlled the southern half of Sakhalin and the Kuril Islands. Now that the Soviet Union controls all these islands, it considers the Sea of Okhotsk to be its own territorial waters, and the Japanese have had difficulty negotiating fishing rights with the Russians.

Cities

As in western Siberia, the largest cities in eastern Siberia and the Far East lie in the south where the Trans-Siberian Railroad crosses the major rivers.

Krasnoyarsk Krasnoyarsk, located at the point where the Trans-Siberian crosses the Yenisey, is the largest city, wtih a population of 412,000. The city serves important transport functions, is the seat of government for huge Krasnoyarsk Kray, and has a variety of industries, chief among which are the machine-building industries, metal working, lumbering, woodworking and paper-milling, textiles, and food industries. Recent innovations to the industries of Krasnoyarsk are an oil refinery and associated chemical plants, a synthetic rubber factory, and a large aluminum plant, which is to utilize electricity from the large hydroelectric plant being constructed on the nearby Yenisey.

Irkutsk Second in size in eastern Siberia and the Far East is Irkutsk at the mouth of the Irkut River on the upper Angara near Lake Baykal, which in 1959 had a population of 366,000. Irkutsk serves as the metropolis of the rapidly industrializing region west of Lake Baykal. Situated on the Angara River in the midst of the Cheremkhovo coal fields, Irkutsk has become very

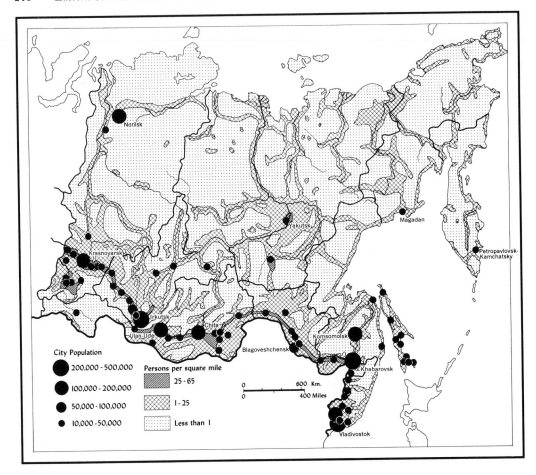

Figure 12-8   Population densities and city sizes.   After Cherdantsev.

rich in supplies of energy both from coal and from hydroelectric power generated by the huge dams being constructed on the Angara. Also, oil pipelines are being laid all the way from the Volga-Urals oil fields and an oil refinery is being constructed in Irkutsk. The industries in Irkutsk at present are primarily machine and metal-working industries, lumbering and woodworking industries, food industries, and other diversified industries. A new aluminum plant has been opened in Irkutsk, and with the development of oil refining in the city some growth of the chemical industries might be expected. Other cities of note in the vicinity are Angarsk, with a population of 134,000, Cheremkhovo, with a population of 123,-

000, and Usolye-Siberskoye, so named from the salt deposits in the region. These cities utilize the coal of the Cheremkhovo fields and the local salt deposits to produce chemicals. Metalworking and machine building also are important. Angarsk is a new city established at the site of the hydroelectric plant and dam forming the Irkutsk Reservoir.

Khabarovsk   Third in size is Khabarovsk at the junction of the Ussuri and Amur Rivers. With a population of 323,000, Khabarovsk is the metropolis of the Far East. It serves as the governmental seat of extensive Khabarovsk Kray and occupies a strategic position on the rail and water transport systems where the Trans-Siberian Railroad leaves the Amur River to run southward through the Ussuri-Khanka Lowland to Vladivostok. Its varied industries are concentrated somewhat on machine building and metal working, oil refining, chemicals, and lumbering and woodworking. It also has some textile and food industries to serve the Far Eastern markets.

Vladivostok Vladivostok, "Ruler of the East," with a population of 291,000 is the major seaport on the Pacific. Sitting on a knobby granite peninsula at the head of Golden Horn Bay, an arm of Peter the Great Bay, its physical setting and shipping functions have been likened to those of San Francisco. Although topograpically the setting of Vladivostok can be likened to San Francisco, climatically the two are quite different. As has been pointed out before, average January temperatures in Vladivostok plunge to 6°F above zero, whereas in

San Francisco they are well above freezing throughout the winter. Snow lies on the ground in Vladivostok almost 100 days out of the year, and Peter the Great Bay is greatly hampered by ice during much of the winter. Vladivostok owes its growth primarily to its function as the main port on the Pacific serving all fishing and commercial vessels. Its industries are varied with some concentration on machine building, woodworking, and food industries. The food industries are dominated by fish canning and fish processing of many types.

A number of smaller towns lie along the railroad between Vladivostok and Khabarovsk, chief among which is Ussurisk, the old town of Voroshilov, with a population of 104,000. These towns serve as trading centers for the fertile farming area and as sawmilling centers for timber floated down the streams from the Sikhote-Alin Mountains to the east. Ussurisk looks much like a Ukrainian town with its whitewashed adobe

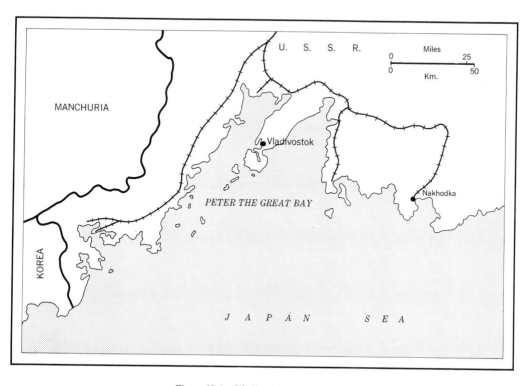

Figure 12-9   Vladivostok and its environs.

cottages with thatched roofs and blue painted shutters.

Komsomolsk The fifth city in size is Komsomolsk-on-Amur with a population of 177,000. Komsomolsk is a new city founded in 1932 in the forests along the lower Amur to serve as a primary steel center for the Far East. So far, it has only a steel plant, and must ship in pig iron and scrap metal for steel production. It is hoped that in the future coal from the Bureya fields to the west and iron ore from Maritime Kray can be utilized to produce pig iron at Komsomolsk. As its name implies, it is a Young Communist League city, and was constructed primarily by young volunteers. It is one of those strange zionistic endeavors staged now and then by the Soviets to excite the imaginations of certain groups of people, but it does not make much sense economically. If a primary steel industry was really needed in the Far East it might better have been placed in the large city of Khabarovsk. Nevertheless, no matter how artificial the setting, under the Soviet system of induced settlement new cities grow rapidly, and Komsomolsk now is third in size in the Far East. Besides its steel industry it has machine and metal-working industries and chemical industries. The chemical industries are based largely on the by-product gases from the oil refinery set up in the city to refine oil brought in by pipeline from northern Sakhalin.

Ulan-Ude and Chita Sixth and seventh in size respectively are Ulan-Ude, with a population of 175,000, and Chita, with a population of 172,000. These two cities are situated in similar mountain basins east of Lake Baykal and are governmental centers of their respective regions. Ulan-Ude is the capital of the Buryat A.S.S.R., and Chita is the governmental center of Chita Oblast. Commercial and governmental functions are foremost in both cities, but some diversified industries have developed in machine building, woodworking, food industries, etc. The cities also serve important rail service func-

tions on the Trans-Siberian Railroad; Ulan-Ude has the main locomotive repair shops between the Urals and the Pacific.

Norilsk Norilsk, in the far north near the mouth of the Yenisey River, is a boom town in the wilderness and owes its growth to the copper and nickel mining and smelting that is carried on there. In 1959 Norilsk had grown to a city of 109,000, making it eighth in size in eastern Siberia and the Far East.

Blagoveshchensk and Birobidzhan Blagoveshchensk, with a population of 95,000, is the regional center of the Zeya-Bureya Lowland. It lies along the Amur River at the end of a rail spur leading southward from the Trans-Siberian Railroad. Its industries are concentrated on machine building, woodworking, and food industries. Once it was the largest Russian city on the Amur, but it has stagnated since the Trans-Siberian Railroad by-passed it. Just east of Blagoveshchensk is Birobidzhan, the capital of the Jewish Autonomous Oblast, with a population of 41,000. The Jewish A.O. has not developed as the Soviets had envisioned it would; Jews have not moved into the area in great numbers, and those that have moved in from the west have not taken up farming as they were supposed to have done. Rather, they set up the same tailoring shops that they had been running in western Russia, Belorussia, and the Ukraine. Thus, in spite of its world reknown, Birobidzhan has remained a minor city in size. It has some woodworking and food processing, but it is probably best known for its tailor shops whose products serve much of the clothing needs of the Soviet Far East.

Cities on Sakhalin Island Yuzhno-Sakhalinsk, near the southern end of Sakhalin Island, with a population of 86,000 is the largest city in Sakhalin Oblast, which includes the Kuril Islands. Other towns of significance on Sakhalin are Aleksandrovsk, along the middle of the west coast, and Okha, the center of the oil fields in the north. A single highway connects the towns along the west coast, but tides daily inundate the shore and in places cover the highway. Local newspapers publish the times of day during which the highway will be covered by water. Much of the local transportation is by boat.

Petropavlovsk and Magadan Petropavlovsk-Kamchatsky, also with a population of 86,000, is the chief city and governmental seat of Kamchatka Oblast. It serves as an important port and fish processing center. On the coast of the mainland to the northwest is Magadan, with a population of 62,-000, which serves as the center of large Magadan Oblast and as the port and regional center for the Kolyma gold fields to the north.

Yakutsk Yakutsk, on the middle Lena, with a population of 74,000, is another important regional center. It serves as the political and commercial center of the Yakut A.S.S.R., the largest single political unit in the Soviet Union except for the Russian Republic itself, within which it lies. The Yakut A.S.S.R. is even larger than the very extensive Kazakh Republic. Its total population is small, however, and the economy is very limited. The agricultural area within the immediate vicinity of Yakutsk has already been mentioned.

Kansk Kansk, on the Trans-Siberian Railroad midway between Krasnoyarsk and Tayshet, has a population of 74,000. It is an important textile center for both cotton and woolen textiles. Situated in the important Kansk-Achinsk coal fields, it no doubt will profit from the general industrial development of the Tayshet-Krasnoyarsk area.

Transportation

The lifeline of Siberia and the Far East is the Trans-Siberian Railroad. Since construction began in 1892, a number of branch lines and paralleling lines have been laid along certain sections, and the entire line has been doubletracked. It still serves only the southern part of the region, however, and millions of square miles of territory are without adequate transportation facilities. Nevertheless, the railroad, supplemented by the major streams, is the main supplier of Siberia and the Far East. Goods for northern Siberia usually are moved into Siberia by rail and then floated downstream to the north. All this must take place during the summer since the streams are frozen at least half the year.

Much fanfare has been made about the

Figure 12-10   The Lenin *atomic icebreaker convoying ships through the Vilkitski Strait between the Kara and Laptev Seas on the Northern Sea Route.   Novosti Press.*

Northern Sea Route, which during 2 or 3 months of summer is kept open from Murmansk on the Kola Peninsula across the Barents, Kara, Laptev, East Siberian, and Chukotsk Seas, and through the Bering Strait into the Pacific. The Northern Sea Route has bases along the Arctic coast near the mouths of the major streams for transshipment between ocean-going vessels and river boats. But the shortness of the navigation season, coupled with the fact that supplies going into Siberia must be shipped upstream rather than down, has rendered the Northern Sea Route of little economic significance to Siberia and the Far East. Its significance lies more in its potential strategic value during wartime, and even that is questionable because of the hazards to navigation. Convoys of ships must be accompanied by ice breakers and aided by airplanes and helicopters, which spot the courses from aloft, a costly and slow operation.

The Trans-Siberian Railroad originally hooked up with the Chinese Eastern Railway across northern Manchuria, which came under the strong influence of the Russians after the Boxer Rebellion. This provided a direct route to Vladivostok. After the Russo-Japanese War of 1905, when Manchuria was taken over by the Japanese, the Russians were forced to extend the Trans-Siberian Railroad on Soviet territory north of the Amur River all the way to Khabarovsk and then south to Vladivostok. Since that time, until World War II, the Soviets intended to build a second line, the so-called "BAM," leading off from Tayshet east of Krasnoyarsk, going north of Lake Baykal, and staying considerably north of the southern boundary, because they feared the disruptive possibilities of the Japanese in Manchuria. This rail line was never built because the Soviets never got around to it. Since World War II, with the removal of the Japanese from Manchuria and with the supposedly friendly Communist regime in China, the Soviets apparently have felt no need for building this second line. There have been plans formulated recently, however, to extend the line from Tayshet to Yakutsk and on to Magadan to better serve the remote areas of the northeast. This projected railroad is known as the BAM-Chulman-Aldan Railroad.

Other branch lines leading off the Trans-Siberian Railroad, such as the Achinsk-Abalakovo Railroad are being constructed to facilitate mining and industrial development. Service on the Trans-Siberian itself is being improved through electrification and automatic signaling.

Reading List

Thiel, Erich, *The Soviet Far East,* Praeger, 1957, 388 pp.

PART TWO

Topical Analysis of Cultural and Economic Phenomena

IN THE PRECEDING CHAPTERS the geography of the U.S.S.R. was covered region by region. Within each region all geographical phenomena were considered in the spatial and functional relations to one another. This was necessary to become familiar with locations, to understand the interplays among phenomena, and to depict distinctive regions as functioning entities.

Now it is necessary to tie the regions together, to consider separate phenomena across the entire country, and to place each region in its correct perspective with regard to each set of phenomena. The geographical aspects of population, agriculture, industry, transport, trade, and foreign relations are taken up in turn. Analyses of their evolution through time and distribution in space are presented. For each phenomenon the significance of separate regions within the U.S.S.R. are noted, and the U.S.S.R. as a whole is considered in context with the rest of the world.

13

Population, Nationalities, and Labor Force

In many respects the greatest resource of any country is its population. The strength and potential of a given population depends not only on total number, but to a large degree on the cultural attainments of that population, the social organization, and the distribution with respect to age and sex. The Soviets took an all-Union census on January 15, 1959, so it is now possible to make some precise statements about the population of the U.S.S.R. and to compare it with populations of other leading countries of the world. This is the first census that has been taken since 1939 and the most complete census since 1926.

Population Dynamics

The 1959 census counted 209 million people, which makes the Soviet Union the third most populous nation on earth. The birth rate was 25 per 1000 of the population per year, and the death rate was 7.6 per 1000. By comparison, in 1959 the United States population was 176 million, the birth rate 24.1, and the death rate 9.4. Both countries exhibit relatively high birth rates and some of the lowest death rates in the world. The death rate in the U.S.S.R. is slightly lower than that of the United States because of a younger age distribution. Death

rates for comparable age groups in the two countries are slightly lower in the United States than in the U.S.S.R. The infant mortality rate in the Soviet Union is at least one third greater than it is in the United States. The present growth rates of the populations of both countries are between 1.5 and 1.7 per cent per year, which would double the populations in approximately 35 to 40 years. Neither the U.S.S.R. nor the United States has a high birth rate compared to some of the underdeveloped countries of Latin America, Asia, and Africa, but their birth rates are nearly twice those of countries of western Europe, and they have much lower death rates than any of the countries with higher birth rates.

The demographic response of both the communist society of the U.S.S.R. and the capitalist society of the United States to industrial-urban development has been the same—lower mortality and fertility. Since 1920 the birth rate in the U.S.S.R. has dropped from 45 per thousand to 25 per thousand and the death rate has dropped from between 20 and 30 per thousand to 7.6 per thousand. At the same time the life expectancy has risen sharply from about 45 years to 68 years in 1959. This compares to an age expectancy of about 72 years in the United States at the present time. (One Soviet wit has said that life really is no longer under the Soviet regime than it was in the Russian empire; it just seems that way!) The drastically reduced death rate in the Soviet Union has been due to a commendable improvement in general sanitary and medical conditions throughout the country and the control of communicable diseases which often reached epidemic proportions in the past. The Soviet Union now has more doctors per 10,000 people than does the United States.

The American image of the fertile Russian peasant woman with a big family is largely a misconception. Fertility has steadily decreased in the Soviet Union since the Revolution with increasing industrialization and urbanization and the increasingly large use of Soviet women in the labor force. And it is no higher in the countryside than in the cities. Among the high fertility age group, approximately one third less babies are born per thousand women in the Soviet Union than in the United States, and this disparity is not due primarily to the deficit of men in this age group; even before World War II the trend was quite noticeable. The number of large families has been on the decline since the beginning of the five-year plans; in 1940 the annual number of fifth or higher order births in families was something over 200,000 in the Soviet Union whereas in the United States it was 350,000.

Elements of birth control are taught along with general hygiene in factory and farm health dispensaries, and contraceptives have been sold and advocated since before the Revolution. Abortions have been made legal and free of cost, as long as they are certified by a medical worker as having been performed under safe and sanitary conditions. Sterilization is legal for health and other reasons. During the period of experimental community living and free love, according to Hegelian and Marxian concepts, in the early 1930's in some of the larger cities the abortion rate rose to double the birth rate. Hence there are strong elements in the social structure that work to restrict population growth in spite of an economic

structure that tends to penalize unmarried people and couples without children and a system of awards to mothers with large families. The Order of Mother Heroine with a scroll from the praesidium of the Supreme Soviet of the U.S.S.R. goes to women who have had ten children.

Birth rates vary drastically from one part of the Soviet Union to another, with the highest birth rates in the Middle East (Caucasus, Kazakhstan, and Middle Asia) and the lowest birth rates in western European Russia. Azerbaydzhan shows the greatest natural increase of all the republics (32.6 per thousand per year) with a birth rate of 39.6 and a death rate of 7.0. Estonia has the lowest increase (5.8) with a birth rate of 16.9 and a death rate of 11.1. In the Baltic Republics a family rarely consists of more than two children, and there are many unmarried middle-aged people. In contrast, the birth rate is fairly consistent throughout the United States. As the Middle Asians and Caucasians become more industrialized and urbanized no doubt the high birth rates in these areas will drop drastically, thereby radically lowering the growth rate of the total population of the U.S.S.R.

The Last 50 Years of Population Development Calamity has been endemic in the U.S.S.R. Not a single generation of the Soviet people, except those who are under 12 years of age, has escaped the repercussions of war, revolution, forced labor, or famine. These misfortunes have left many scars on the Russian population. In 1913 the population of Tsarist Russia was 160 million. In 1959 the population of the Soviet Union was 209 million within the same boundaries. This represents an increase of only 30 per cent in 46 years. In contrast, the population of the United States increased about 80 per cent, growing from 97 million in 1913 to 176 million in 1959.

It has been estimated that since 1913 population losses in the U.S.S.R. from war, civil strife, and famine, together with birth deficits and modest emigration, amounted to a stag-

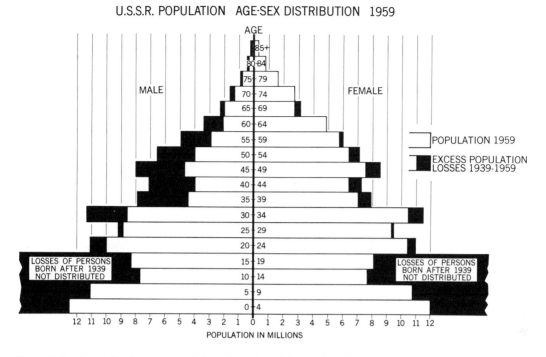

U.S.S.R. POPULATION AGE-SEX DISTRIBUTION 1959

Figure 13-1   Age-sex distributions of population and population deficits in the U.S.S.R., 1959.   Courtesy of Michael K. Roof and Population Index.

gering total of between 70 and 80 million people.   Losses from World War I and subsequent revolution, civil wars, and famine have been assessed at more than 25 million, losses during 1931 to 1933 due to collectivization of agriculture with its attendant famine have been estimated at over 5 million, and losses associated directly or indirectly with World War II have been placed at 45 million.   During the same period the United States profited from a heavy immigration and high birth rates induced by wars on foreign soils.   The World War II population losses in the United States amounted to about 300,000, almost exclusively military.   The 40 to 50 million population deficit caused by World War II in the Soviet Union (the number approximately equal to the total population of France today), includes 25 to 30 million excess deaths brought about by military and other war related causes and a deficit of approximately 15 million births during the period.

Age-Sex Structure   The excessive population losses have had unbalancing effects on the sex ratio and on almost every age group of the population.   There is a large deficit of young people, particularly in the ages between 10 and 19, and there is a great disparity between the sexes in ages over 32. In ages over 32 women outnumber men by 20 million; there are only 375 males for every 625 females (Table 13–1).   The U.S.S.R. probably has the largest proportion of widows of any country of the world. Most of these widows live in rural areas where women comprise 57 per cent of the agricultural labor force on collective farms. The deficit of young people has probably worked to an advantage in the growth of the economy in the past, for the bulk of the population was in the productive ages from 20 to 50, and it was not necessary to allot a large proportion of the national product to the upbringing of children.   But this deficit is now beginning to take its toll

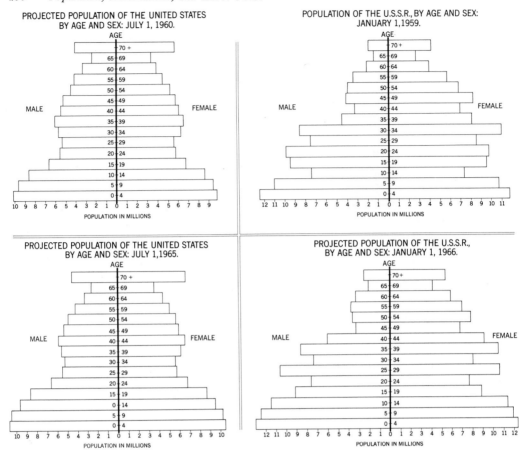

Figure 13-2   Age-sex distributions of present and projected populations in the U.S.S.R. and the U.S.A.   Data from Comparisons of the United States and Soviet Economies, *Washington, 1959, p. 71.   Note the abnormal characteristics of the Soviet population as compared to that of the United States.   The population pyramid for the Soviet Union shows a great deficit of teenagers and a preponderance of women in older age groups.   Although the pyramid will tend to assume a more normal shape as time goes on, the scars of previous catastrophes will not be totally erased by 1966.*

in the form of reduced numbers entering the labor force, slower growth rates in school enrollments, and lower reproductive rates among the ages from 20 to 34. The number of people that enter the years of high fertility, 20 to 34, will be constricted until 1975.

Labor Force The legal age for entering the labor force in the U.S.S.R. is 16. The new census data indicate that the average annual number of youths reaching 16 in the period 1951 to 1955 was 4,100,000. These were born during the peak fertility years of 1934 to 1938. In the period 1956 to 1959 (survivors of 1939 to 1942 births) the figure

declined by 10 per cent, during the one year of 1960, the 16-year-olds numbered only about 1,700,000, or less than the 1951 to 1955 average by nearly 60 per cent. According to the census groupings, the average annual number reaching 16 in the period 1961 to 1964 will be 3,100,000, considerably above the level of 1960 but still far below the 1951 to 1955 level. Probably not until 1966 will the average annual number of entrants into the labor force exceed the average of 1951 to 1955 (Table 13–2).

The economic significance of these irregularities in the population structure has caused modifications in the Soviet manpower policies

Table 13–1	*Males per 100 Females by*	
Age Groups—U.S.A. and U.S.S.R.[a]		

Males per 100 Females

Age	U.S.S.R. 1959	United States 1960
All ages	82	98
Up to 4 years	105	104
5 to 9 years	104	104
10 to 14 years	104	104
15 to 19 years	104	103
20 to 24 years	104	102
25 to 29 years	91	99
30 to 34 years	80	97
35 to 39 years	60	96
40 to 44 years	50	96
45 to 49 years	53	95
50 to 54 years	62	96
55 to 59 years	64	94
60 to 64 years	60	91
65 to 69 years	58	88
70 years and over	51	79

[a] *Source: Comparisons of United States and Soviet Economies*, Part I, p. 66.

Table 13–2   *Estimated Population of the U.S.S.R., 16 to 59 Years of Age: 1956–1966*[a] *(in Thousands)*

Year	Population 16 to 59 Years	Population Change during Preceding Year
1956	121,923	—
1957	124,094	2171
1958	126,090	1996
1959	127,709	1619
1960	128,813	1104
1961	129,083	270
1962	129,144	61
1963	129,386	242
1964	130,298	912
1965	131,914	1616
1966	133,342	1428

[a] *Source: Comparisons of United States and Soviet Economies*, Part I, p. 38.

that will act to minimize full-time educational opportunities and to maximize labor force participation. Whereas in the United States enrollment rates in higher education are

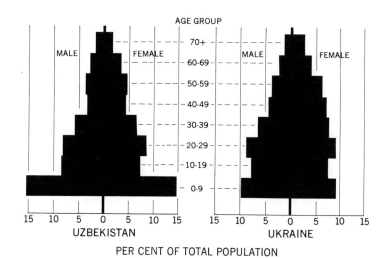

Figure 13-3   *Age-sex distributions of the populations in the Ukraine and in Uzbekistan. Courtesy of Michael K. Roof and* Population Bulletin. *The age-sex structure of the population varies from one part of the Soviet Union to another. Uzbekistan did not suffer the wartime losses that the Ukraine did and it has a much higher birth rate.*

mounting rapidly, in the U.S.S.R. the policy, at least for the short run, is to prevent expansion of higher education. The old Soviet system of 7 years compulsory schooling has been changed to require 8 years of schooling for all children. There will be 3 additional years of noncompulsory secondary education which students may complete either as evening or correspondence students in "schools for working and rural youth" or as full-time students of the new vocational schools which are to be substituted for the old general schools. Students in schools for working and rural youth will be full-time members of the labor force subject to the limitations put on their hours of work because of age. Students in vocational schools will work 2 days a week in local enterprises or school workshops if training facilities of local industry are inadequate. The graduate of the 8-year schools will also be able to complete his secondary education by enrolling in a tekhnikum. In their final year (third of fourth), full-time tekhnikum students will be required to work a regular 46 hour week in their chosen trade or speciality. Preference in gaining admission to schools of higher education will be given to students that have completed their secondary education with a good comparative standing, and who have accumulated 2 years of work experience. They also must have the support of the Komsomol, trade union, party, and management representative, all of whom have a hand in selecting candidates. The strong polytechnic emphasis and the combination of work and study in the new program are devices for directly infusing manpower into the labor force as well as remedies for qualitative deficiencies in the present school system.

The male population age 20 to 34 is often regarded as the backbone of a country's military manpower capability. The U.S.S.R. census data indicate that the peak of military capability in the postwar period, purely from the point of view of human effectives, was reached in 1960 to 1961, when, significantly enough, major reductions of the armed forces

were announced. In the future the male population age 20 to 34 will decline continuously, reaching a level of 11 per cent below the 1961 peak by approximately 1968. Thereafter a modest increase can be expected, but the 1961 peak will not be reached even by 1975.

The predominance of women over men in the upper age brackets has imparted a peculiar sex structure to the labor force even in industries in which women workers usually are not found in other parts of the world. A large percentage of the work in such heavy industries as mining, lumbering, and construction is done by women (Table 13–3).

Table 13–3 Per Cent of Labor Force Composed of Women, by Sector of the Economy, 1957[a]

Industry Group	U.S.S.R.	United States
Manufacturing	45	26
Construction	31	3
Agriculture	59	19
Transportation and communication	32	18
Trade and supply	65	39
Government and administration	51	27

[a] *Source: Comparisons of United States and Soviet Economies*, Part I, p. 40.

The typical road repair crew in the Soviet Union is composed of two men in the cab of a truck taking turns doing the driving while three or four women in the back shovel out hot tar and gravel into the pot holes of the road. Approximately 53 per cent of the labor force in the Soviet Union are women. This compares to around 32 per cent in the United States, which itself has experienced somewhat of a revolution in the employment of women during and since World War II. Women workers are particularly dominant on collective farms and in certain professions such as the medical profession.

So far the Soviets have used their manpower rather wastefully, often utilizing an abundance of human labor to economize on capital expenditure. But now the fact has become quite clear to them that the age-sex structure of their population is such that the labor force in the very near future will be severely strained. Thus they are beginning to look for unused portions of the population and for more efficient uses of the present labor force. Probably the greatest waste of manpower always has been and still is on the farms (Table 13–4). In 1959 almost

Table 13–4 U.S.S.R. Labor Productivity as Per Cent of U.S.A.[a]

Branch of Economy

Industry	50
Construction	59
Transportation	33
Agriculture	20–25

[a] *Source: Comparisons of United States and Soviet Economies,* Part I, p. 35.

39 per cent of the U.S.S.R.'s total labor force was engaged in agriculture. In 1960 less than 9 per cent of the United States smaller labor force was so employed, and this much smaller group of farmers produced approximately 60 per cent more agricultural produce. Obviously much could be done to make the agricultural operation more efficient and thus release millions of rural people to the urban labor force.

A rural to urban migration has been going on at a rather rapid rate throughout the Soviet period, but half of the population still lives on farms. The inability to supply adequate urban housing is probably the greatest deterrent to a more rapid movement into the cities. To fulfill the goals of the current seven-year plan the Soviets must erect urban housing equivalent to that built during all previous plan periods, an amount

equal to 60 per cent of the 1958 housing inventory. It must also be remembered that the Soviet population is a polyglot population which includes segments that probably could not be adapted to urban factory life because of illiteracy, alien attitudes, or deeply ingrained modes of living. This applies primarily to the peripheral nationality groups. The Soviets are still reluctant to recruit Caucasian and Middle Asian labor in areas inhabited by Russians.

Nationalities

The 1959 census identified 108 distinct nationality groups by name and listed others totalling 17,000 people. These peoples stem from a long history of migrations and assimilations from all directions across the Eurasian Plain. From time immemorial wave after wave of nomadic peoples swept out of central and eastern Asia westward across the southern plain into eastern and central Europe, there to mingle with existent populations, often to lose their respective identities, and to impart new characteristics to the indigenous peoples. It is impossible to unravel fully the past of most of these groups, but strong physical and cultural differences still remain.

Slavs The Slavs emerged during the first few centuries of the Christian era in the region between the Carpathians and the Baltic. They suffered successive invasions from Turkic and Mongolian peoples from the east and fought a constant struggle against the Germans and Scandinavians in the northwest. In their flight northward before the Tatar invasion in the thirteenth century they came into contact with ancient settlers of northeastern Europe, the Finno-Ugrians. Thus as the Slavs emerged and became distinguished into separated groups— Great Russians, Ukrainians and Belorussians —they displayed admixtures of mingling groups—Tatars, Finns, Germans, and western Slavs—the Poles and Slavonic-Baltic peoples.

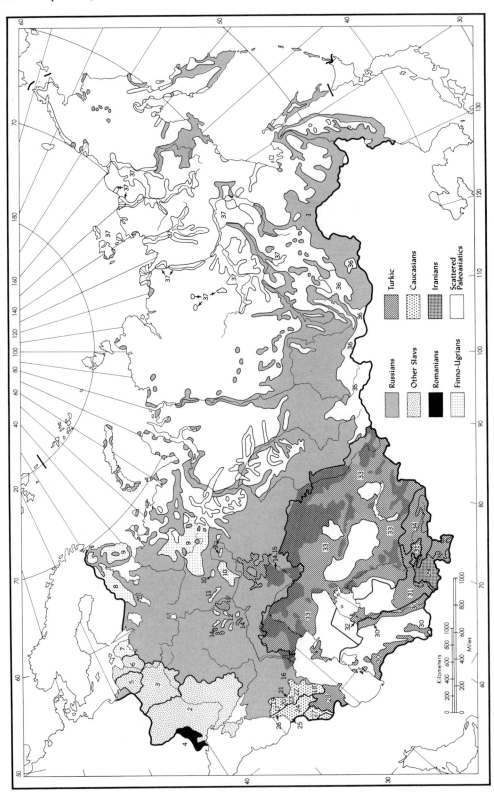

Figure 13-4 See opposite page for discriptive legend.

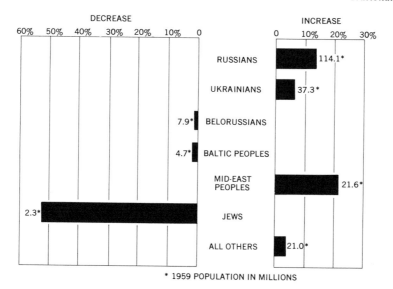

DECREASE INCREASE

60% 50% 40% 30% 20% 10% 0   0 10% 20% 30%

RUSSIANS 114.1*

UKRAINIANS 37.3*

7.9* BELORUSSIANS

4.7* BALTIC PEOPLES

MID-EAST PEOPLES 21.6*

2.3* JEWS

ALL OTHERS 21.0*

* 1959 POPULATION IN MILLIONS

Figure 13-5 Changes in populations of leading nationality groups. Courtesy of Michael K. Roof and Population Bulletin. *The rate of increase varies drastically among nationality groups. The Jews suffered great losses during World War II.*

In the Soviet Union today the Russians make up 55 per cent of the population and their percentage of the total population is slowly increasing. Together with the other two large Slavic groups, the Ukrainians and Belorussians, they make up 76 per cent of the total U.S.S.R. population. They dominate much of the European Plain and all of Siberia and are predominant in many of the cities and new farming areas of Kazakhstan and Middle Asia.

Turkic Groups The Turkic groups are the next most populous in the Soviet Union and comprise a number of important and populous political units: the Tatar, Bashkir, and Chuvash A.S.S.R.'s in the Volga-Urals area, the Uzbek, Kazakh, Kirgiz, and Turkmen S.S.R.'s in Middle Asia, and the Azerbaydzhan S.S.R. in Transcaucasia. Lesser

groups in the Caucasus also are of Turkic origin as are the Yakuts in eastern Siberia and the Khakass and Tuvinians in southern Siberia. All these Turkic groups originated in Central Asia and are strongly Moslem in religion. The Azerbaydzhanis migrated to the Caucasus around the southern end of the Caspian Sea and on the way absorbed many Persian influences into their culture.

Caucasians The so-called Caucasians have a very old histroy of location in the Transcaucasian region. The Georgians, or Gruzians, and Armenians are the most numerous, but there are many small groups in isolated valleys among the mountains. The Armenians apparently are related to the old Tadzhik population of Iran. They have occupied the volcanic plateau straddling the border between the Soviet Union, Turkey,

Figure 13-4 Ethnic Groups of the U.S.S.R. Adapted from Atlas selskogo khozyaystva SSSR. *The central locations of major nationalities other than Russians are shown on the map by numbers as follows:*

2. Ukrainians, 3. Belorussians, 4. Moldavians, 5. Lithuanians, 6. Latvians, 7. Estonians, 8. Karelians, 9. Komi, 10. Udmurts, 11. Mari, 12. Mordovians, 13. Chuvash, 14. Tatars, 15. Bashkirs, 16. Kalmyks, 17. Karachay, 18. Dagestani Groups, 19 Adyge, 20. Balkars, 21. Kabardinians, 22. Chechen-Ingush, 23. Osetians, 24. Georgians, 25. Adzhars, 26. Abkhaz, 27. Armenians, 28. Azerbaydzhanis, 29. Tadzhiks, 30. Turkmen, 31. Uzbeks, 32. Karakalpaks, 33. Kazakhs, 34. Kirgiz, 35. Tuvinians, 36. Buryats, 37. Yakuts, 38. Jews.

Table 13–5   Ethnic Groups of the U.S.S.R.: Their Populations and Locations, 1959[a]

1. Groups historically associated with European Russia (30):

Russians—114,588,000

Russian S.F.S.R.	97,845,000	Georgian S.S.R.	438,000
Ukrainian S.S.R.	7,400,000	Moldavian S.S.R.	293,000
Kazakh S.S.R.	4,014,000	Tadzhik S.S.R.	263,000
Uzbek S.S.R.	1,101,000	Turkmen S.S.R.	263,000
Belorussian S.S.R.	729,000	Estonian S.S.R.	260,000
Kirgiz S.S.R.	624,000	Lithuanian S.S.R.	231,000
Latvian S.S.R.	556,000	Armenian S.S.R.	56,000
Azerbaydzhan S.S.R.	515,000		

Ukrainians—36,981,000

Ukrainian S.S.R.	31,853,000	Georgian S.S.R.	52,000
Russian S.F.S.R.	3,377,000	Latvian S.S.R.	29,000
Kazakh S.S.R.	762,000	Tadzhik S.S.R.	27,000
Moldavian S.S.R.	421,000	Turkmen S.S.R.	21,000
Belorussian S.S.R.	150,000	Lithuanian S.S.R.	18,000
Kirgiz S.S.R.	137,000	Estonian S.S.R.	16,000
Uzbek S.S.R.	88,000		

Belorussians—7,829,000

Belorussian S.S.R.	6,444,000	Latvian S.S.R.	61,000
Russian S.F.S.R.	845,000	Lithuanian S.S.R.	30,000
Ukrainian S.S.R.	291,000	Estonian S.S.R.	11,000
Kazakh S.S.R.	108,000		

Tatars—4,969,000

Russian S.F.S.R.	4,077,000	Tadzhik S.S.R.	57,000
Uzbek S.S.R.	445,000	Kirgiz S.S.R.	56,000
Kazakh S.S.R.	192,000	Turkmen S.S.R.	30,000

Lithuanians—2,326,000

Lithuanian S.S.R.	2,151,000	Latvian S.S.R.	32,000
Russian S.F.S.R.	109,000		

Jews—2,268,000

Russian S.F.S.R.	875,000	Georgian S.S.R.	52,000
Ukrainian S.S.R.	840,000	Latvian S.S.R.	37,000
Belorussian S.S.R.	150,000	Lithuanian S.S.R.	25,000
Moldavian S.S.R.	95,000	Estonian S.S.R.	5,000
Uzbek S.S.R.	94,000		

Moldavians—2,214,000

Moldavian S.S.R.	1,887,000	Russian S.F.S.R.	64,000
Ukrainian S.S.R.	239,000		

Germans—1,619,000

Russian S.F.S.R.	820,000	Tadzhik S.S.R.	33,000
Kazakh S.S.R.	700,000	Uzbek S.S.R.	18,000
Kirgiz S.S.R.	40,000		

Chuvash—1,470,000

Russian S.F.S.R.	1,436,000

Latvians—1,400,000

Latvian S.S.R.	1,298,000	Russian S.F.S.R.	75,000

Table 13–5   Ethnic Groups of the U.S.S.R.: Their Populations and Locations, 1959[a]
(*Continued*)

Poles—1,380,000

Belorussian S.S.R.	539,000	Russian S.F.S.R.	118,000
Ukrainian S.S.R.	363,000	Latvian S.S.R.	60,000
Lithuanian S.S.R.	230,000	Kazakh S.S.R.	53,000

Mordovians—1,285,000

Russian S.F.S.R.	1,211,000

Bashkirs—983,000

Russian S.F.S.R.	948,000

Estonians—969,000

Estonian S.S.R.	873,000	Russian S.F.S.R.	79,000

Udmurts—623,000

Russian S.F.S.R.	613,000

Mari—504,000

Russian S.F.S.R.	498,000

Komi and Komi-Permyak—431,000

Russian S.F.S.R.	426,000

Bulgarians—324,000

Ukrainian S.S.R.	219,000	Moldavian S.S.R.	62,000

Greeks—310,000

Ukrainian S.S.R.	104,000	Russian S.F.S.R.	47,000
Georgian S.S.R.	73,000		

Karelians—167,000

Russian S.F.S.R.	164,000

Hungarians—155,000

Ukrainian S.S.R.	149,000

Gypsies—132,000

Russian S.F.S.R.	72,000

Gagauz—124,000

Moldavian S.S.R.	96,000

Rumanians—106,000

Ukrainian S.S.R.	101,000

Kalmyks—106,000

Russian S.F.S.R.	101,000

Finns—93,000

Russian S.F.S.R.	72,000	Estonian S.S.R.	17,000

Veps—16,000
Karaites—5900
Saamy (Lapps)—1800
Izhora—1100

Table 13–5   Ethnic Groups of the U.S.S.R.: Their Populations and Locations, 1959[a] (*Continued*)

2. Groups historically associated with the Caucasus (27):

Azerbaydzhanis—2,929,000
Azerbaydzhan S.S.R.	2,481,000	Armenian S.S.R.	108,000
Georgian S.S.R.	157,000	Russian S.F.S.R.	71,000

Armenians—2,787,000
Armenian S.S.R.	1,552,000	Russian S.F.S.R.	256,000
Georgian S.S.R.	443,000	Turkmen S.S.R.	20,000
Azerbaydzhan S.S.R.	442,000		

Georgians—2,650,000
Georgian S.S.R.	2,558,000	Russian S.F.S.R.	58,000

Dagestan ethnic groups—945,000
Russian S.F.S.R.	795,000

Avars—268,000
Lezgins—223,000
Azerbaydzhan S.S.R.	98,000

Dargins—158,000
Kumyks—135,000
Lak—64,000
Nogai—41,000
Tabasaran—35,000
Agul—8000
Rutul—7000
Tsakhur—6000

Chechen—418,000
Russian S.F.S.R.	261,000	Kirgiz S.S.R.	25,000

Rest mainly in Kazakh S.S.R.

Osetians—410,000
Russian S.F.S.R.	248,000	Georgian S.S.R.	141,000

Kabardians—204,000
Russian S.F.S.R.	201,000

Ingush—106,000
Russian S.F.S.R.	56,000

Karachay—81,000
Russian S.F.S.R.	71,000

Adyge—80,000
Russian S.F.S.R.	79,000

Abkhaz—74,000
Georgian S.S.R.	71,000

Kurds—59,000
Armenian S.S.R.	26,000	Georgian S.S.R.	16,000

Balkars—42,000
Russian S.F.S.R.	35,000

Table 13–5　Ethnic Groups of the U.S.S.R.: Their Populations and Locations, 1959[a]
(Continued)

Cherkess—30,000
Aissor—22,000
Abaza—20,000
Tats—11,000
Udins—3700

3. Groups historically associated with Siberia and the Far East (27):

Koreans—314,000			
Uzbek S.S.R.	139,000	Russian S.F.S.R.	91,000
Kazakh S.S.R.	74,000		
Buryats—253,000			
Russian S.F.S.R.	252,000		
Yakuts—236,000			
Russian S.F.S.R.	235,000		
Tuvinians—100,000			
Russian S.F.S.R.	100,000		
Khakass—57,000			
Russian S.F.S.R.	56,000		

Altaians (Oirots)—45,000
All in Russian S.F.S.R.

Nentsy (Samoyeds)—25,000　　Nivkhi (Gilyaks)—4000
Evenki (Tungus)—24,000　　Ulchi—2000
Khanty (Ostyaks)—19,000　　Udege (Ude)—1400
Shors—15,000　　Eskimos—1100
Chukchi—12,000　　Itelmen (Kamchadals)—1100
Eveny (Lamuts)—9000　　Ket (Yenisey Ostyaks)—1000
Nanai (Golds)—8000　　Orochi—800
Koryaks—6300　　Nganasan (Tavghi)—700
Mansi (Voguls)—6000　　Tofalar—600
Selkups (Ostyak-Samoyeds)—4000　　Yukagir—400
　　Aleuts—400

4. Groups historically associated with Middle Asia (8):

Uzbeks—6,004,000			
Uzbek S.S.R.	5,026,000	Kazakh S.S.R.	137,000
Tadzhik S.S.R.	454,000	Turkmen S.S.R.	125,000
Kirgiz S.S.R.	219,000		
Kazakhs—3,581,000			
Kazakh S.S.R.	2,755,000	Turkmen S.S.R.	70,000
Russian S.F.S.R.	383,000	Kirgiz S.S.R.	20,000
Uzbek S.S.R.	335,000	Tadzhik S.S.R.	13,000
Tadzhiks—1,397,000			
Tadzhik S.S.R.	1,051,000	Kirgiz S.S.R.	15,000
Uzbek S.S.R.	312,000		

Table 13–5   Ethnic Groups of the U.S.S.R.: Their Populations and Locations, 1959ᵃ (Continued)

Turkmen—1,004,000			
Turkmen S.S.R.	924,000	Uzbek	57,000
Kirgiz—974,000			
Kirgiz S.S.R.	837,000	Tadzhik S.S.R.	26,000
Uzbek S.S.R.	92,000		
Kara-Kalpaks—173,000			
Uzbek S.S.R.	168,000		
Uygurs—95,000			
Kazakh S.S.R.	60,000	Kirgiz S.S.R.	14,000
Dungans (Chinese Moslems)—21,000			
Kazakh S.S.R.	10,000		

5. Minor groups historically associated with foreign countries (16):

Turks—35,000	Yugoslavs—5000
Chinese—26,000	Spaniards—2400
Czechs—25,000	Afghans—1900
Iranians—21,000	Mongols—1800
Slovaks—14,700	Italians—1200
Arabs—8000	French—1000
Beluchi—7800	Japanese—1000
Albanians—5000	Vietnamese—800

ᵃ *Source: Soviet Geography: Review and Translation*, March 1960, pp. 71–75 and September 1961, pp. 69–70.
Note: Population totals for republics vary somewhat from subsequent figures in *Narodnoe khozyaystvo*.

and Iran for more than 2000 years. During the period 1926 to 1959 some 100,000 Armenians immigrated into the U.S.S.R. from France, England, and the United States in the hopes of at last establishing a political state in their national territory. Only about half of the Armenians in the Soviet Union today are located within the territorial limits of the republic bearing their name; other major concentrations are in the neighboring republics of Georgia and Azerbaydzhan. They are also scattered rather widely in the Russian republic.

Finno-Ugrian Groups   It is thought that the Finno-Ugrian peoples originated in the Altay Mountains of southwestern Siberia and early migrated to Scandinavia and adjacent parts of the Baltic area. Later they were forced to migrate southeastward again where many of them settled in the region between the Volga and the Urals. They now comprise the Estonian S.S.R. and Karelian A.S.S.R. in the northwest, the Komi A.S.S.R. in northeastern Europe, and the Mordovian, Udmurt, and Mari A.S.S.R.'s in the middle Volga-Ural region.

Other Peoples   The Latvians and Lithuanians belong to the so-called Slavonic-Baltic groups of peoples. They are closely related to the Slavs to the south but display some of the features of other Baltic peoples to the north. In Middle Asia the Tadzhiks are related to the Iranians. And in the southwestern part of the country, the Moldavians are of Romanian stock.

Jews, Germans, and Poles exist in considerable numbers in the Soviet Union, but are scattered throughout various regions.

Table 13–6   Numbers of People by Nationality by Union Republic, 1959ᵃ

	Number of People	Per Cent of Total		Number of People	Per Cent of Total
R.S.F.S.R.	117,534,000	100.0	Belorussia S.S.R.	8,055,000	100.0
Russian	97,864,000	83.3	Belorussian	6,532,000	81.1
Tatar	4,075,000	3.5	Russian	659,000	8.2
Ukrainian	3,359,000	2.9	Pole	539,000	6.7
Chuvash	1,436,000	1.2	Jew	150,000	1.9
Mordovian	1,211,000	1.0	Ukrainian	133,000	1.7
Bashkir	954,000	0.8			
Jew	875,000	0.7	Uzbek S.S.R.	8,106,000	100.0
Belorussian	844,000	0.7	Uzbek	5,038,000	62.2
German	820,000	0.7	Russian	1,091,000	13.5
Dagestan Peoples	797,000	0.7	Tatar	445,000	5.5
Udmurt	616,000	0.5	Kazakh	335,000	4.1
Mari	498,000	0.4	Tadzhik	311,000	3.8
Komi and Komi-			Kara-Kalpak	168,000	2.1
Permyak	426,000	0.36	Korean	138,000	1.7
Kazakh	382,000	0.3	Jew	94,000	1.2
Armenian	256,000	0.2	Kirgiz	93,000	1.1
Buryat	252,000	0.2	Ukrainian	88,000	1.1
Osetian	248,000	0.2	Turkmen	55,000	0.7
Yakut	236,000	0.2			
Kabardinian	201,000	0.2	Kazakh S.S.R.	9,310,000	100.0
Karelian	164,000	0.1	Kazakh	2,795,000	30.0
Peoples of the North	126,000	0.1	Russian	3,974,000	42.7
Pole	118,000	0.1	Ukrainian	762,000	8.2
Kalmyk	101,000	0.09	Tatar	192,000	2.1
Tuvinian	100,000	0.08	Uzbek	137,000	1.5
Korean	91,000	0.08	Belorussian	107,000	1.2
Adyge	79,000	0.07	Korean	74,000	0.8
Gypsy	72,000	0.06	Uygur	60,000	0.6
Finn	72,000	0.06	Pole	53,000	0.6
Azerbaydzhanian	71,000	0.06	Dungan	10,000	0.1
Moldavian	62,000	0.05			
Georgian	58,000	0.05	Georgia S.S.R.	4,044,000	100.0
Khakass	56,000	0.05	Georgian	2,601,000	64.3
Greek	47,000	0.04	Armenian	443,000	11.0
Altay	45,000	0.04	Russian	408,000	10.1
			Azerbaydzhanian	154,000	3.8
Ukraine S.S.R.	41,869,000	100.0	Osetian	141,000	3.5
Ukrainian	32,158,000	76.8	Greek	73,000	1.8
Russian	7,091,000	16.9	Abkhazian	63,000	1.6
Jew	840,000	2.0	Ukrainian	52,000	1.3
Pole	363,000	0.9	Jew	52,000	1.3
Belorussian	291,000	0.7	Kurd	16,000	0.4
Moldavian	242,000	0.6			
Bulgarian	219,000	0.5	Azerbaydzhan S.S.R.	3,698,000	100.0
Hungarian	149,000	0.4	Azerbaydzhanian	2,494,000	67.5
Greek	104,000	0.2	Russian	501,000	13.6
Rumanian	101,000	0.2	Armenian	442,000	12.0
			Lezghian	98,000	2.7

Table 13-6   Numbers of People by Nationality by Union Republic, 1959[a] (Continued)

	Number of People	Per Cent of Total		Number of People	Per Cent of Total
Lithuania S.S.R.	2,711,000	100.0	Tadzhik	15,000	0.7
Lithuanian	2,151,000	79.3	Uygur	14,000	0.7
Russian	231,000	8.5			
Pole	230,000	8.5	Tadzhik S.S.R.	1,980,000	100.0
Belorussian	30,000	1.1	Tadzhik	1,051,000	53.1
Jew	25,000	0.9	Uzbek	454,000	23.0
Ukrainian	18,000	0.7	Russian	263,000	13.3
			Tatar	57,000	2.9
Moldavia S.S.R.	2,885,000	100.0	Ukrainian	27,000	1.4
Moldavian	1,887,000	65.4	Kirgiz	26,000	1.3
Ukrainian	421,000	14.6	Kazakh	13,000	0.6
Russian	293,000	10.2			
Gagauz	96,000	3.3	Armenia S.S.R.	1,763,000	100.0
Jew	95,000	3.3	Armenian	1,552,000	88.0
Bulgarian	62,000	2.1	Azerbaydzhanian	108,000	6.1
			Russian	56,000	3.2
Latvia S.S.R.	2,093,000	100.0	Kurd	26,000	1.5
Latvian	1,298,000	62.0			
Russian	556,000	26.6	Turkmen S.S.R.	1,516,000	100.0
Belorussian	62,000	2.9	Turkmen	924,000	60.9
Pole	60,000	2.9	Russian	263,000	17.3
Jew	37,000	1.7	Uzbek	125,000	8.3
Lithuanian	32,000	1.5	Kazakh	70,000	4.6
Ukrainian	29,000	1.4	Tatar	30,000	2.0
			Ukrainian	21,000	1.4
			Armenian	20,000	1.3
Kirgiz S.S.R.	2,066,000	100.0			
Kirgiz	837,000	40.5	Estonia S.S.R.	1,197,000	100.0
Russian	624,000	30.2	Estonian	893,000	74.6
Uzbek	219,000	10.6	Russian	240,000	20.1
Ukrainian	137,000	6.6	Finn	17,000	1.4
Tatar	56,000	2.7	Ukrainian	16,000	1.3
Kazakh	20,000	1.0	Belorussian	11,000	0.9
			Jew	5,000	0.5

[a] *Source: Narodnoe khozyaystvo SSSR v 1960 godu,* pp. 17–20.

Before the Revolution the Jews were relegated to the so-called "pale of settlement" in Belorussia and the western Ukraine, but under the Soviet regime they have been allowed to migrate to other parts of the country. In 1934 the Jewish A.O. was created in the Far East, but only about 50,000 Jews have migrated to that region. The Jewish population in the Soviet Union might have reached 5 million early in World War II when many of them fled eastward before the German armies. But later the policy of total extermination in the German-held territory of the Soviet Union drastically reduced their numbers until at present they total less than half that figure. Most of them are still in the western part of the country, but a significant number migrated to Soviet

Middle Asia during the war, and many of them stayed there.

The Germans at times have been freely invited into Russia to serve as technicians in various branches of the economy. This was particularly true during the reign of Catherine the Great. Consequently they became rather numerous in some of the larger cities and they also established wealthy agricultural colonies in some of the better agricultural regions. In general they maintained their racial identities and their ties with Germany. Before World War II the greatest concentration was in the Middle Volga area where a Volga German A.S.S.R. had been created. They also existed in considerable numbers in the Black Sea Steppes of the Ukraine. During the war the Volga German Republic was abrogated, and the Germans were moved eastward into Siberia and Middle Asia. Many of the Black Sea Germans evacuated westward with the retreating German army in 1943.

In Siberia and the Far East exist some Mongol and Paleo-Asiatic groups. The largest Mongol group is in the Buryat A.S.S.R. Some of the old Asiatic groups apparently are related to the American Indians and the Eskimos.

Population Distribution and Location Change

Population Distribution The population is distributed very unevenly throughout the Soviet Union. The European Plain, which comprises less than one sixth of the total territory of the country, contains 65 per cent of the population, despite the movement eastward since the Revolution. Within the European Plain the population is concentrated in the western and central portions where the possibilities for agriculture are most favorable. The population thins out very rapidly north of latitude 58 degrees where the climate becomes too cool and the soils too poor for agriculture, and it thins again east of the Sea of Azov where the climate becomes too dry. East of the Urals, much of Siberia and the Far East, except for a narrow strip along the southern margin, are practically devoid of population.

The continuously populated area of the Soviet Union may be described as a wedge with its broad base at the western border of the country which extends eastward in an ever narrowing belt across the middle Volga Valley and southern Ural Mountains into western Siberia. It stretches eastward as a belt about 200 or 300 miles wide along either side of the Trans-Siberian Railroad to the Altay Mountains, after which it continues to the Pacific as isolated spots of settlement in intermontaine basins.

This wedge of population corresponds very closely in areal extent to the region of mixed forest and steppe vegetation with associated black and chestnut soils, a fact which reflects the influence of agricultural potentialities on original settlement. The nodes of concentrated population within this wedge are in the heavily industrialized areas: the Central Industrial Region, the eastern Ukraine, and the Urals; or in the areas of most favorable agricultural conditions, such as in the western Ukraine and Moldavia. In portions of this western region, the rural population density is more than 150 people per square mile.

Two important areas of outlying population are the Caucasus and portions of Middle Asia. Here again it is the agricultural potentialities that have induced the settlement. The summers are long and hot, and, in Transcaucasia, the winters are mild so that crops exotic to the rest of the Soviet Union may be grown. An abundance of irrigation water from the surrounding mountains has made possible ever-expanding areas of intensive agriculture. Hence rural populations in these areas have become quite high. In portions of the Fergana Valley in Uzbekistan the rural population density is as high as 350 people per square mile. But these two areas are islands of population separated from the main population wedge to the north by deserts and mountains.

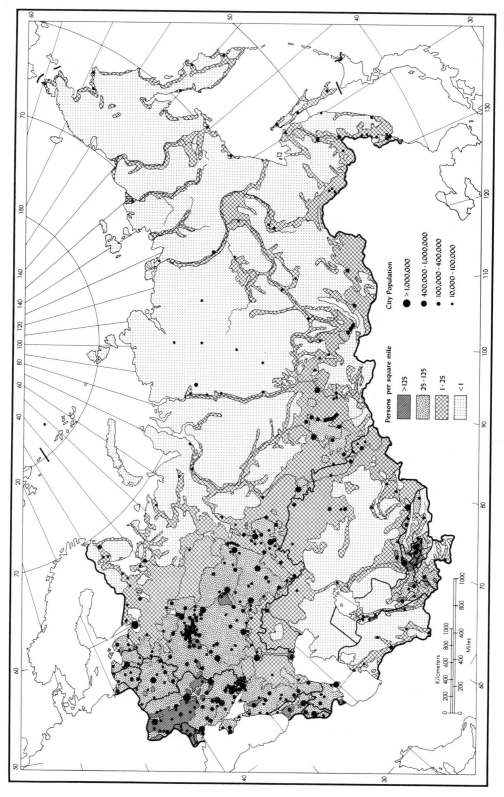

Figure 13-6   Population densities and cities of the U.S.S.R.   From Atlas selskogo khozyaystva SSSR.

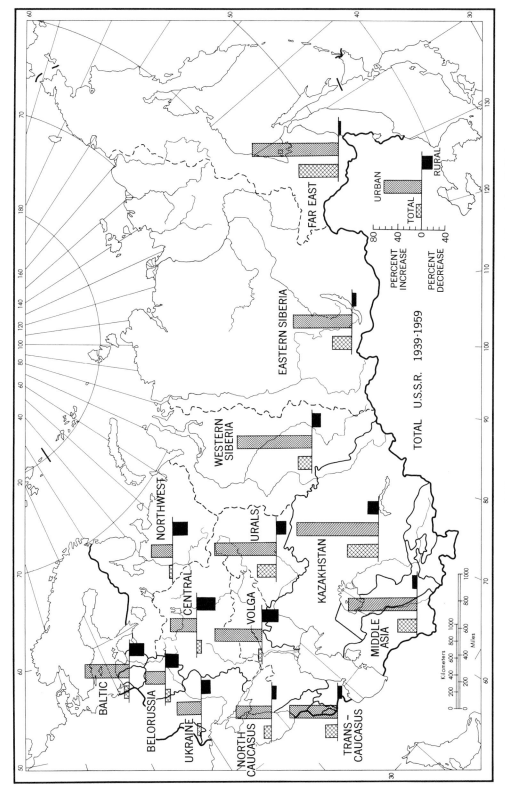

Figure 13-7 Population Changes by Regions in the U.S.S.R. Courtesy of Michael K. Roof and Population Bulletin.

Locational Changes Soviet policy has favored a shift of population eastward and a large rural to urban migration. Although certain economic and cultural factors have worked against an eastward movement, the German invasion in World War II largely produced the territorial shift in population that Soviet policy had not been able to accomplish.

If the 20,000,000 people gained by the wartime annexation of the western provinces of the Ukraine, Belorussia, Moldavia, Lithuania, Latvia, and Estonia are subtracted from the intercensal (1939 to 1959) increase in population of 38,000,000, the natural increase during the 20-year period within the present boundaries of the U.S.S.R. was 18,000,000 people. This figure corresponds almost precisely to the population gain in the eastern regions (Urals and eastward). The population west of the Urals and north of the Caucasus has remained almost exactly the same; in 1939 the population of this part of the country was listed as 135,530,000 people and in 1959 it was listed as 135,669,000.

The loss of life and the destruction of property in the west during the war was very severe. The Belorussian Republic in particular lost almost one tenth of its population. On the other hand, the Urals increased their population during the period 1939–1959 by 32 per cent, western Siberia increased by 24 per cent, eastern Siberia by 34 per cent, Kazakhstan by 53 per cent, Middle Asia by 30 per cent, and the Far East by 70 per cent. During the 20-year period, the share of the East in the total population of the country rose from 29 per cent to 35 per cent.

The area bounded by Leningrad-Kirov-Kharkov-Lvov-Leningrad contained 70 per cent of Russia's population a century ago, 50 per cent in 1940, and 40 per cent in 1959. This "old Russia" supplied population first to the southeastern Ukraine, North Caucasus, and Middle Volga steppes, then to the southwest Siberian agricultural lands, and later to the Urals and central Siberia. The Uralo-Baykal industrial area grew largely from migration from old Russia. This new region, which contained only 5 per cent of the country's population a century ago, contained 12 per cent in 1940 and 15 per cent in 1959.

Old Russia lost seven million people from 1940 to 1955. Within the area only the Central Industrial Region, Latvia, and Estonia have gained population. The area completely surrounding the Central Industrial Region (Central Black Earth Region, Volga-Vyatka region, Valday region, Belorussia, the western Ukraine, Lithuania, and Kaliningrad Oblast) has suffered a loss of more than 10 per cent of its population due to intense out-migration. This has occurred in areas that were not occupied by the Germans during World War II as well as in areas that were.

During the years 1955–1959 a total population increment in the U.S.S.R. approximately equal to that which occurred during the years 1940–1955 has been far more evenly distributed across the country. During this period natural growth has been the dominant factor in each region. Only the Valday area and western Belorussia show a decline. A decrease in the Tyan Shans during this period has been coincident with increases in the north Caspian and north Caucasian areas. This reflects the restoration of the Chechen, Ingush, and Kalmyks to their homelands. Migration into the Subarctic, Middle Volga, and Kazakh and Middle Asian industrial areas continues, but flows to eastern Siberia and the Far East are no longer evident.

Although in some of the eastern areas both the urban and the rural population has increased, the urban population has increased much more rapidly. In Kazakhstan and in Armenia the urban population rose by 141 per cent during the 20-year period, in the Kirgiz Republic it rose by 156 per cent, and in the Tadzhik Republic by 159 per cent. For comparison, in the Ukraine the rise in urban population was 41 per cent and in Belorussia 33 per cent. As a result of the more rapid urban population growth in the East, its share in the total urban population of the U.S.S.R. rose from 29 per cent in 1939 to 36 per cent in 1959. This corresponds precisely to the total eastward population shift, and illustrates the fact that the urban-rural ratio for the total eastern part of the country is similar to that for the total western part of the country. In other words, in comparison to its total population, the eastern part of the country at present is just as urbanized as the west.

The urban percentage varies drastically, however, from one individual oblast or kray to another; from 92 per cent in Murmansk Oblast within the Russian Republic to 13 per cent in Kashka-Darya Oblast within the Uzbek Republic. The urban percentage depends on a number of factors. It may appear very high in low-population density regions where a few large mining towns have been established, and it may appear rather low in densely populated, high-quality farming areas in spite of the fact that these areas contain some good sized cities.

In spite of the rather impressive population growth in the east, the movement has not kept up with industrialization in the eastern areas, and a severe labor shortage exists in some regions, whereas in most of the older cities of European Russia there is still a labor surplus. Most citizens shun the more pioneer living conditions of the eastern regions, and so far wage differentials between east and west have not been great enough to entice many people eastward.

Russians and Ukrainians have made up the bulk of laborers recruited for new factories and farms even in other national areas, so Russians and Ukrainians often predominate in major industrial cities and newly opened state farms. Thus there has been a steady dissemination of the two largest nationality groups throughout the entire country. The number of Russians in the Urals and Siberia rose more than 30 per cent between 1939 and 1959, in the Far East by more than 70 per cent, and in Kazakhstan and Middle Asia by 30 to 40 per cent. Russians now outnumber Kazakhs in their own republic.

During the same period, Ukrainians in the Komi A.S.S.R. increased twelve times and on Sakhalin, Kamchatka, and in Yakutia three times.

Urbanization   Increased urbanization has come about in the Soviet Union both in the increase of numbers of cities and in the rapid growth of already established cities. The populations of many of the larger cities in the country have doubled or more during the 20-year period. And in spite of the policy to limit in-migration into Moscow, the city grew 20 per cent during the period 1939–1959. Some major cities show a population decrease from 1939–1959, but this is because the Soviets have designated certain of their suburbs as individual cities since 1939, and hence their populations are listed separately from the central city. This formation of new cities out of industrial suburbs is a constant process in the Soviet Union. Also, the formation of cities in mining areas or in strategic transportation areas to serve as primary industry centers for extensive surrounding areas has been a policy of the Soviet regime. Some large cities of the 300,000 class, such as Karaganda and Magnitogorsk, did not exist at all before 1925.

During the intercensus period from 1939 to 1959 the urban population of the Soviet Union increased from 60.4 million people to 99.8 million people, that is, by 39.4 million or 65 per cent. This increase in urban dwellers was brought about in three ways: first, a natural increase of births over deaths in the cities amounted to 8 million people; second, the change in classification of settlements from rural to urban added about 7 million people to the urban category; and third, the rural to urban migration accounted for between 24 and 25 million people. In connection with this migration to the cities, the rural population dropped from 130.3 million people to 109 million people, that is, by 21 million odd people. From 1917 to 1959 the urban portion of the total population rose from 15 per cent to 48 per cent.

Table 13–7   Populations of Soviet Cities in Order of Size, in Thousands[a]

City	Population January 15, 1939	1959	% of 1939	City	Population January 15, 1939	1959	% of 1939
Moscow	4,137	5,046	120	Tula	272	316	121
Leningrad	3,385	3,300	97	Krasnodar	193	313	162
excluding cities and				Magnitogorsk	146	311	213
urban-type settle-				Barnaul	148	305	216
ments under city				Astrakhan	254	296	116
Soviet	3,015	2,900	96	Gorlovka	181	293	161
Kiev	847	1,102	130	Vladivostok	206	291	137
Baku	775	968	125	Zhdanov	222	284	128
excluding urban-type				Izhevsk	176	285	161
settlements under city				Prokopyevsk	107	282	263
Soviet	571	643	111	Tallin	160	282	175
Gorky	644	942	146	Lugansk	215	275	128
Kharkov	833	934	112	Kemerovo	133	273	209
Tashkent	550	912	166	Orenburg	172	267	151
Novosibirsk	404	886	219	Kalinin	216	261	121
Kuybyshev	390	806	206	Archangel	251	256	102
Sverdlovsk	423	779	184	Penza	160	255	159
Donetsk (Stalino)	466	699	150	Kirov	144	252	175
Tbilisi	519	695	134	Tomsk	145	249	171
Chelyabinsk	273	689	252	Grozny	172	242	139
Odessa	602	667	111	Vilnyus	215	236	109
Dnepropetrovsk	527	660	125	Nikolayev	169	226	133
Kazan	398	647	162	Dushanbe (Stalinabad)	83	224	271
Perm	306	629	205	Murmansk	119	222	189
Rostov-on-Don	510	600	117	Frunze	93	220	234
Volgograd (Stalingrad)	445	592	133	Kishinev	112	216	191
Saratov	372	581	156	Kaunas	152	214	140
Omsk	289	581	201	Ryazan	95	214	224
Riga	348	580	170	Bryansk	174	207	118
Ufa	258	547	212	Ulyanovsk	98	206	209
Minsk	237	509	214	Kursk	120	205	169
Yerevan	204	509	250	Kaliningrad	—	204	—
Alma-Ata	222	456	206	Taganrog	189	202	107
Voronezh	344	448	132	Shakhty	135	196	145
Zaporozhye	282	435	154	Samarkand	136	196	143
Krasnoyarsk	190	412	215	Dneprodzerzhinsk	148	194	131
Lvov	340	411	121	Simferopol	143	186	132
Yaroslavl	309	407	132	Rybinsk	144	182	126
Karaganda	156	397	255	Kadiyevka	135	180	133
Krivoy Rog	189	388	204	Komsomolsk-on-Amur	71	177	250
Novokuznetsk (Stalinsk)	166	377	228	Orsk	66	176	265
Irkutsk	250	366	146	Ulan-Ude	126	175	138
Makeyevka	242	358	148	Chita	121	172	142
Nizhniy Tagil	160	339	212	Kostroma	121	172	141
Ivanovo	285	335	116	Tambov	106	172	160
Khabarovsk	207	323	155	Ashkhabad	127	170	134

Table 13–7 Populations of Soviet Cities in Order of Size, in Thousands^a (*Continued*)

City	Population January 15, 1939	1959	% of 1939	City	Population January 15, 1939	1959	% of 1939
Gomel	139	168	120	Kiselevsk	44	130	296
Ordzhonikidze				Andizhan	85	130	153
(North Osetian				Kutaisi	78	128	165
A.S.S.R.)	131	164	125	Kirovograd	100	128	127
Dzerzhinsk (Gorky O.)	103	164	158	Podolsk	72	124	171
Zlatoust	99	161	162	Cheremkhovo	56	123	220
Kopeysk	60	161	267	Namangan	80	123	154
Kherson	97	158	162	Mogilev	99	122	122
Lipetsk	67	157	234	Vinnitsa	93	122	130
Semipalatinsk	110	156	141	Makhachkala	87	119	137
Vladimir	67	154	230	Andzhero-Sudzhensk	69	116	168
Chimkent	74	153	205	Kirovabad (Azer-			
Orel	111	150	138	baydzhan S.S.R.)	99	116	117
Ust-Kamenogorsk	20	150	580	Kramatorsk	94	115	122
Tyumen	79	150	189	Babushkin (Moscow O.)	70	112	158
Sevastopol	114	148	130	Sterlitamak	39	111	287
Syzran	83	149	177	Armavir	84	111	133
Vitebsk	167	148	88	Rubtsovsk	38	111	294
Smolensk	157	147	93	Norilsk	14	109	778
Biysk	80	146	182	Leninakan	68	108	160
Chernovtsy	106	146	137	Orekhovo-Zuyevo	99	108	109
Kurgan	53	146	272	Novomoskovsk			
Poltava	128	143	110	(Stalinogorsk)	76	107	140
Kamensk-Uralsky	51	141	278	Belovo	45	107	247
Stavropol				Berezniki	51	106	207
(Stavropol Kray)	85	141	164	Serpukhov	91	106	116
Vologda	95	139	145	Zhitomir	95	106	110
Petrozavodsk	70	136	194	Kokand	85	105	124
Angarsk	—	134	—	Uralsk	67	104	156
Kaluga	89	134	149	Novoshakhtinsk	48	104	216
Leninsk-Kuznetskiy	83	132	160	Ussuriisk (Voroshilov)	72	104	144
Petropavlovsk (North				Akmolinsk	32	102	314
Kazakhstan O.)	92	131	143	Kolomna	75	100	133

^a *Source: Narodnoe khozyaystvo SSSR v 1960 godu,* pp. 52–56.

By comparison, in 1960, 63 per cent of the population of the United States was classified as urban. (Only about 35 per cent of the rural population in the United States are actually farm families, whereas in the U.S.S.R. 85 per cent are engaged in agriculture.) The Soviet Union has a greater number of cities with populations above 50,000 than the United States—299 in 1959 as compared with 232 in the United States in 1950. Of these, the U.S.S.R. had 25 with populations over 500,000, and the United States had 18.

"Border Purifications" Mass resettlements of certain groups of people have taken place from time to time for strategic reasons. As a consequence of World War II approximately 350,000 Black Sea Germans and 200,000 Baltic peoples fled westward with the retreating German armies. 1,800,000 Poles and Jews were expatriated to Poland, and 500,000 Ukrainians, Belorussians, and Lithuanians were moved into the Soviet Union. In general, incoming peoples were scattered throughout the Soviet Union, and empty areas left by expatriation in the west were filled up with Russians or Russified people from the local nationalities who had spent some time in the interior of the U.S.S.R.

The 1,500,000 Germans in Kaliningrad Oblast (formerly East Prussia) were largely expatriated, and 600,000 Russians were moved in. 370,000 Japanese (100 per cent) have been resettled from southern Sakhalin and the Kurils.

During the war the political identities of the Kalmyks, Chechen-Ingush, Balkars, Karachay, Volga Germans, and Crimean Tatars were abrogated and the people reportedly were moved eastward. After the death of Stalin in 1953, 30,000 Kalmyks, 200,000 Chechen-Ingush, and unknown numbers of Balkars and Karachay were allowed to return home, and their homelands were reinstated politically. Apparently only the Volga Germans and Crimean Tatars have not been returned and reinstated.

Border purifications took place along the Chinese frontier in the late 1930's. For the present at least, the uneasy alliance between the U.S.S.R. and China has allowed a relatively free settlement of peoples on either side of the border.

Reading List

Brackett, James W., "Population Dynamics in the U.S.S.R.," report of the Foreign Man-power Research Office, U.S. Bureau of Census.

Eason, W. W., "The Soviet Population Today," *Foreign Affairs,* July 1959, 598–606.

——, *Soviet Manpower: The Population and Labor Force of the U.S.S.R.,* PhD Dissertation, Columbia University, 1958.

Goldberg, B. Z., *The Jewish Problem in the Soviet Union, An Analysis and Solution,* Crown Publishers, New York, 1961, 374 pp.

Hrdlicka, Alex, *The Peoples of the Soviet Union,* Smithsonian Institution War Background Studies, Number 3, Washington, July 15, 1942, 29 pp.

Lamont, Corliss, *The Peoples of the Soviet Union,* Harcourt, Brace, and Company, New York, 1944, 214 pp.

Lorimer, Frank, *The Population of the Soviet Union: History and Prospects,* Geneva, League of Nations, 1946, 289 pp.

Kantner, John F., "The Population of the Soviet Union," *Comparisons of the United States and Soviet Economies,* Part I, U.S. Government Printing Office, Washington, 1959, 31–71.

Newth, J. A., "Some Trends in the Soviet Population, 1939 to 1956," *Soviet Studies,* January 1959, 252–278.

Podyachikh, P. G., *Naselenie SSSR,* Moscow, 1961, 190 pp. (in Russian)

Population Bulletin, Vol. XVII, No. 6, October 1961, Population Reference Bureau, Inc., Washington, D.C.

Roof, Michael, "Soviet Population Trends," *Eugenics Quarterly,* Vol. 8, No. 3, September 1961, 123–134.

Roof, Michael, and Leedy, Frederick, "Population Redistribution in the Soviet Union, 1939–1956," *Geographical Review,* Vol. 49, 1959, 208–221.

Schlesinger, Rudolf, *The Nationalities Problem and Soviet Administration,* Routledge and Kegan Paul, London, 1956, 299 pp.

Shimkin, Demitri, "Demographic Changes and Socio-Economic Forces within the Soviet Union, 1939–1959," in *Population Trends in Eastern Europe, the U.S.S.R., and Mainland China,* Milbank Memorial Fund, 1960, 224–262.

14

Agriculture

General Production Levels

The Soviet Union is one of the world's leading agricultural countries. It regularly possesses about one third of the world's wheat land and produces more than one fourth of the world's wheat supply. It produces nearly one half of the world's rye, one third of the world's sugar beets, three fourths of the world's flax, one half of the world's sunflowers, and one third of the world's potatoes. In all these crops, as well as in barley, it is the world's leading producer. The Soviets claim now to have surpassed the United States in butter and milk production, and they are bending every effort to surpass the United States in the production of meat and eggs. Yet there seems to be a chronic food shortage, and the agricultural crisis has been a perennial one. The Soviet Union with a sixth of the land area of the earth and less than one fifteenth of the earth's population has had a hard time feeding itself. Nearly seven times as many farmers in the Soviet Union cultivating about 50 per cent more land raise approximately 65 per cent as much agricultural produce as farmers in the United States do. This 65 per cent must feed 30 million more people than are in the United States.

Although the per capita caloric intake in the Soviet Union is approximately equal to that in the United States, the Soviets diet is poorly balanced. It is heavy on starches and low on meat, eggs, milk, fresh fruits and vegetables, and to some extent on vegetable oils and fats. And these ills will probably plague the Soviets for a number of years to come, despite the optimism of Premier Khrushchev. Soviet economists have told Khrushchev that the Soviet Union will not be able to surpass the United States in per capita livestock production before 1975. The 1958 meat production in the Soviet Union was no larger a percentage of the contemporary United States' meat production than was the 1913 production. In 1913 the Soviet Union produced 47.6 per cent as much meat as the United States, and in 1958 it produced 48 per cent as much. If we subtract the amount of milk used by calves, milk production in the Soviet Union in 1958 was only about 84 per cent that in the United States, whereas in 1913 it was 86.7 per cent. Soviet egg production is even less impressive. Tables 14–1 through 14–6 present some comparisons between the U.S.S.R. and the United States of basic agricultural resources, development, and production. Table 14–7 indicates the major agricultural goals of the seven year plan.

Total agricultural output in the Soviet Union has increased just enough to approximately maintain per capita output at the

Table 14–1   Agricultural Resources[a]

Item	Year	Unit	United States	Soviet Union	U.S.S.R. as % of U.S.A.
Population	Jan. 1959	million	173	209	121
Labor force	1959	million	69.4	106.4	153
Farm labor force	1959	million	7.4	48.3	653
Per cent farm force of total labor force	1959	per cent	10.7	45.4	—
Sown cropland	1960	million acres	329	501	152
Sown cropland per capita	1960	acres	1.8	2.3	128
Tractors on farms	1960	thousand	4,770	1,090	23
Motor trucks on farms	1960	thousand	3,110	776	25
Grain combines on farms	1960	thousand	1,065	526	49
Agricultural consumption of electricity	1959	billion kwh	26.9	8.4	31
Primary commercial fertilizer consumption, in terms available nutrients	1959	million tons	7.4	2.6	35

[a] *Source:* Bell, Richard E., "How Soviet Agriculture Compares With Ours," *Foreign Agriculture*, September 1961, p. 6.

levels of the late 1920's during the early 1950's. The per capita availability of grains in 1953 was approximately what it was in 1926. Potatoes, sugar, and cotton increased substantially, and there was a small improvement in eggs, but there were fewer vegetables, less meat and milk, less wool and flax fiber, and less sunflower seed, the major source of vegetable oil. Roughly speaking, the index of net agricultural output on a per capita basis was slightly lower in 1950 to 1953 than in 1928. The situation has improved significantly since 1953, however (Table 14–8).

During the period 1925–1958 the index of farm output for both the United States and the Soviet Union increased by roughly 58 per cent. This, while the United States was trying to curtail production! (The agricultural problems of the two countries are almost diametrically opposed. While the Soviet Union is straining to feed itself, the United States is trying to control production in order to avoid glutting the market.)

Table 14–2   Farm Sizes and Workers, U.S.S.R. and U.S.A., 1960[a]

Farm numbers 1960:	
All U.S. farms	3,700,000
Soviet collective farms	53,400
Soviet state farms	6,500
Farm size, average in 1960:	Acres
Land area per U.S. farm	302
Sown area per U.S. farm	89
Sown area per Soviet collective farm	6,785
Sown area per Soviet state farm	22,485
	Number
Workers per U.S. farm	1½
Households per Soviet collective farm	386
Workers per Soviet state farm	753

[a] *Source:* Bell, Richard E., "How Soviet Agriculture Compares With Ours," *Foreign Agriculture*, September 1961, p. 6.

Reasons for Production Lag   The natural environment over much of the country sets severe limits on agriculture; cold and drought limit cultivation to little more than 10 per cent of the total area. In general, where the area is humid the temperatures are cold, and where the temperatures are warm the area is dry. It is estimated that practically all of even the producing area needs climatic amelioration of one sort or another; three million square miles of the country require

Table 14–3   Crop Acreages[a]

Crop	Year	United States	Soviet Union	U.S.S.R. as % of U.S.A.
		1,000 Acres	1,000 Acres	%
Corn for grain	1960	71,443[b]	27,700[c]	39
Wheat	1960	51,859	148,500	286
Rye	1960	1,652	40,800	2,470
Oats	1960	26,554	35,800	135
Barley	1960	13,763	23,500	171
Grain sorghum	1960	15,444	(d)	—
Rice	1959	1,586	237	15
Cotton	1960	15,309	5,350	35
Soybeans for beans	1959	22,631	1,124	5
Sunflowers	1960	(d)	10,353	—
Peanuts grown alone	1960	1,542	(d)	—
Flaxseed	1959	2,932	4,571	156
Hemp	1959	(d)	877	—
Sugar beets	1960	957	7,500	784
Sugarcane, all	1960	342	—	—
Tobacco	1959	1,153	247	21
Makhorka	1959	—	128	—
Potatoes	1960	1,397	22,486	1,610
Sweet potatoes	1960	203	—	—
Vegetables	1959	3,482[e]	3,627	104
Citrus	1959	778[f]	(d)	—
Other fruits and berries	1959	1,796[f]	4,537[f]	253
Tree nuts	1959	250	—	—
Tea	1959	—	154	—

[a] *Source:* Bell, Richard E., "How Soviet Agriculture Compares With Ours," *Foreign Agriculture,* September 1961, p. 7.

[b] More than 9.2 million additional acres were harvested for other uses.

[c] Nearly 42 million additional acres were harvested for silage and fodder.

[d] Not available.

[e] Area of commercial crops of principal vegetables.

[f] Bearing acreage.

additional water, and one million square miles require drainage.

It is the in-between areas of climate—the subhumid and semiarid—that carry the bulk of the agriculture. Throughout these areas the soil is generally good. In fact the Soviet Union contains one of the largest areas of high-grade soil in the world. But even under the most favorable environmental conditions crop yields have always been low compared to much less favorably endowed areas, such as western Europe. Table 14–9 compares yields of some leading crops in the Soviet Union and in the United States.

Table 14–4   Crop Production[a]

Crop	Year	Unit	United States	Soviet Union	U.S.S.R. as % of U.S.A.
Corn for grain	1960	1,000 bushels	3,891,212	600,000[b]	15
Wheat	1960	"	1,350,339	1,700,000	126
Rye	1960	"	32,491	520,000	1,600
Oats	1960	"	1,150,774	850,000	74
Barley	1960	"	427,018	440,000	103
Grain sorghum	1960	"	637,673	(c)	—
Rice	1959	1,000 tons	2,720	157[d]	6
Cotton, lint	1960	1,000 bales	14,272	6,800	48
Cottonseed	1960	1,000 tons	10,353	3,265	32
Soybeans	1959	1,000 bushels	533,175	8,230	2
Sunflower seed	1960	1,000 tons	(c)	4,222[d]	—
Peanuts	1960	"	892	(c)	—
Flaxseed	1959	1,000 bushels	31,101	15,550[d]	50
Hempseed	1959	1,000 tons	(c)	34[d]	—
Sugar beets	1960	"	16,421	56,000	341
Sugar cane	1960	"	7,721	—	—
(Sugar production)	(1960–61)	(1,000 tons)	(5,259)[e]	(7,259)[f]	(138)
Tobacco	1959	1,000 pounds	1,960,373	251,328[d]	13
Makhorka	1959	"	—	165,347[d]	—
Fiber flax	1960	1,000 tons	(c)	470[d]	—
Hemp fiber	1959	"	(c)	133	—
Potatoes	1960	1,000 cwt.	257,435	1,851,889[d]	719
Sweet potatoes	1960	"	15,636	(c)	—
Vegetables	1959	1,000 tons	19,046[g]	16,285[d]	86
Citrus	1959	"	8,065	(c)	—
Other fruits and berries	1959	"	10,068	5,722[d,h]	32[i]
Tree nuts	1959	"	216	(c)	—
Tea	1959	"	—	161[d]	—
Hay, all	1959	"	113,650	88,674[d]	78

[a] *Source:* Bell, Richard E., "How Soviet Agriculture Compares With Ours," *Foreign Agriculture*, September 1961, p. 7.

[b] Including some corn harvested in the milk stage for silage.

[c] Not available.

[d] Official Soviet figure.

[e] Centrifugal sugar (raw value) of which 47% from continental beet, 12% continental cane, 21% Hawaiian cane, 20% Puerto Rican cane, and a small amount of cane from Virgin Islands of U.S.

[f] Centrifugal sugar (raw value), all beet.

[g] Total commercial production only.

[h] Includes citrus.

[i] Share U.S.S.R. total fruit, including citrus, and berries is of U.S. total fruit, including citrus and berries.

Table 14–5   Livestock Numbers[a]

Kind	Year[b]	United States	Soviet Union[c]	U.S.S.R. as % of U.S.A.
		Millions	Millions	Per cent
All cattle	1961	97.1	75.8	78
Cows[d]	1961	19.3[e]	34.8	180
Hogs	1961	55.3	58.6	106
Sheep	1961	32.9	132.9	404
Horses	1960	3.1	11.0	355
Poultry	1960	372.5[f]	530.4	142

[a] *Source:* Bell, Richard E., "How Soviet Agriculture Compares With Ours," *Foreign Agriculture*, September 1961, p. 7.
[b] Beginning of year.
[c] Official Soviet figures.
[d] Included in all cattle numbers.
[e] Two years old and for milk.
[f] Chickens and turkeys.

Table 14–7   Agricultural Goals for 1965[a]

Item	Output	% Increase over 1958
Total agricultural production		80
Grain	164–180 million tons	18–30
Raw cotton	57–61 " "	30–40
Sugar beets	76–84 " "	40–55
Vegetable oil seeds	5.5 " "	10
Flax fiber	580 thousand tons	31
Potatoes	147 million tons	71
Meat	16 " "	100
Milk	100–105 " "	70–80
Wool	548 thousand tons	70
Eggs	37 million tons	60

[a] *Source:* P. E. Doroshenko, *Selskoe khozyaystvo SSSR v 1959–1965 godakh*, pp. 7–8.

Table 14–6   Production of Livestock Commodities[a]

Commodity	Year	Unit	United States	Soviet Union	U.S.S.R. as % of U.S.A.
Beef and veal	1960	million pounds	15,833	5,261	33
Pork[b]	1960	"	11,630	6,253	54
Mutton, lamb, and goat meat	1960	"	768	2,035	265
Poultry meat	1959	"	6,301	1,612[c]	26
Horse meat	1959	"	(d)	430[c]	—
Lard	1960	"	2,568	1,170[e]	46
(Margarine and shortening)	(1959)	(million pounds)	(3,861)	(996)[c]	(26)
Tallow and grease	1960	million pounds	3,827	410	11
Milk (from cows)	1960	"	122,920	112,500	92
Butter	1960	"	1,479	1,870[c]	126
Eggs	1960	billions	61.4	26.4[c]	43
Wool (greasy basis)	1960	million pounds	300	776	259

[a] *Source:* Bell, Richard E., "How Soviet Agriculture Compares With Ours," *Foreign Agriculture*, September 1961, p. 7.
[b] Excluding lard and unrendered pork fat.
[c] Official Soviet figure.
[d] Not available.
[e] Includes unrendered pork fat in terms of lard; calculated from pork production.

Table 14–8   Per Capita Net Output of Major Agricultural Products, Soviet Union (Kilograms per Annum)[a]

	1926–1929	1950–1953	1955–1958
Grains	241.4	247.9	297.6
Potatoes	102.1	172.8	163.2
Vegetables	49.8	41.2	56.4
Sugar beets	52.0	118.0	187.5
Sunflower seeds	12.2	10.8	18.1
Milk	176.2	144.8	200.9
Meat	32.7	27.5	34.8
Eggs	64.2	68.0	95.1
Cotton	4.9	19.7	20.8
Wool	1.12	1.06	1.34
Flax fiber	1.86	1.18	2.09

[a] *Source: Comparisons of the United States and Soviet Economies*, Part I, p. 210.

Probably the greatest limitation to agricultural production is inefficient social organization. Not only are yields per acre low but also yields per farmer are very low. During the period 1928 to 1957, the increase of average production per farmer in the Soviet Union was 100 per cent, whereas in the United States it was 149 per cent. Khrushchev has indicated that the labor used per unit of output in the Soviet Union ranges from 160 per cent of the United States' level for cotton on state farms to 1630 per cent for production of hogs on collective farms (Table 14–10). In the Soviet Union excess labor has been used in lieu of capital expenditure; much hand labor is still used in many phases of agriculture. Plowing and sowing of grain are mechanized, but some harvesting and almost all of the drying and cleaning of grain are still done by hand. Almost all potato growing is done by hand, and much cotton picking is still done by hand. Only in the last decade have the Soviets been able to allot some extra time and money to the improvement of agriculture.

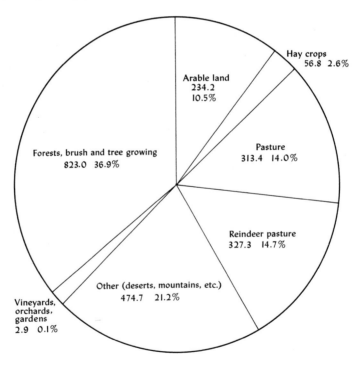

Figure 14-1   Land use in the U.S.S.R., 1957, in millions of hectares and in per cents of total. Note: *Unless otherwise specified, all information for maps and graphs in this chapter has been derived from* Atlas selskogo khozyaystva SSSR, *Moscow, 1960.*

Table 14–9 Yields per Acre[a]

Crop	Year	Unit per Acre	United States	Soviet Union	U.S.S.R. as % of U.S.A.
Corn for grain	1960	bushels	54.5	21.7	40
Wheat	1960	"	26.0	11.4	44
Rye	1960	"	19.7	12.7	64
Oats	1960	"	43.3	23.7	55
Barley	1960	"	31.0	18.7	60
Rice	1959	pounds	3,369	1,324	39
Cotton lint[b]	1960	"	448	610	136
Soybeans	1959	bushels	23.7	7.3	31
Flaxseed	1959	bushels	9.1	3.4	37
Sugar beets	1960	tons	17.2	7.5	44
Tobacco	1959	pounds	1,559	1,017	65
Potatoes	1960	cwt.	184.3	82.4	45

[a] *Source:* Bell, Richard E., "How Soviet Agriculture Cnmpares With Ours," *Foreign Agriculture*, September 1961, p. 6.

[b] All cotton in the U.S.S.R. is grown on irrigated land; only 25 to 30 per cent of all the United States harvested cotton acreage is irrigated, yet this irrigated acreage produces 40% of the cotton production.

So far the two most important factors for increasing agricultural production for human consumption have been the substitution of mechanical for animal power and the increase in the sown area. Although draft animals still are much more numerous in the U.S.S.R. than in the U.S.A., the decline in the number of horses in the U.S.S.R. has been sufficient to release enough feed to supply 60 per cent of the edible livestock increase from 1928 to 1958.

The expansion of cultivated land, often into hazardous climatic conditions, has been only a stopgap measure to realize instantaneous increases in foodstuffs to meet emergencies, and it must be backed up by great efforts everywhere to increase yields per acre in order to achieve long term goals. Most of the projected increase (80 per cent) in agricultural produce during the seven-year plan is to be achieved through significantly increased yields. With better farming and marketing methods the Soviets should be able to increase yields for most crops and supply needed foods and fibers to the urban areas. More mechanization, electrification, adequate fertilization, correct crop adaptations and rotations, good conservation measures, and adequate incentives for the farmers to work efficiently and harvest the crops at

Table 14–10 Labor Used Per Centner of Output, U.S.S.R. and United States[a]

Man-hours

	Collective Farms U.S.S.R. 1956–57	State Farms U.S.S.R. 1956–57	United States 1956
Grain	7.3	1.8	1.0
Potatoes	5.1	4.2	1.0
Sugar beets	3.1	2.1	.5
Cotton	42.8	29.8	18.8
Milk	14.7	9.9	4.7
Beef	112.0	52.0	7.9
Pork	103.0	43.0	6.3

[a] *Source: Comparisons of the United States and Soviet Economies*, Part I, p. 215.

the right times should bring about some very significant increases in agricultural production.

The ability to increase production when proper emphasis is placed on it has already been demonstrated to a certain extent in the production of industrial crops. Whereas during the period 1928 to 1957 livestock products increased 65 per cent and food crops increased 52 per cent, industrial crops increased 232 per cent. Their share in net agricultural output rose from 7.7 to 15.5 per cent whereas the portion of total sown area occupied by them declined from 7.7 to 6.1 per cent. A policy of self-sufficiency in such items as cotton and sugar has fostered the scientific growth of these crops whereas other crops have been left to traditional devices. Heavy fertilization, irrigation, and drainage have been the most important means for intensifying production. Also grand climatic amelioration schemes involving the construction of large reservoirs of water and the planting of thousands of miles of windbreaks are being experimented with in the drier, better soil regions of the country.

Since 1913 the irrigated area has been increased from approximately 4 million hectares to 11.1 million hectares, although apparently a significant fraction of this area is not being cropped currently. Saline soils plus labor shortages have forced some lands to lie idle in areas equipped with irrigation systems. The *Atlas of Agriculture of the Soviet Union* shows that in 1957, 7,210,000 hectares were under irrigation. At the same time nearly 6 million hectares were under drainage. At present, cultivable land is being expanded more rapidly by drainage than by irrigation. Although the chief irrigated areas are in the dry regions of Middle Asia, Kazakhstan, the Transcaucasus, and adjacent parts of the Russian Republic, major drainage projects are located in the Baltic Republics, northwestern R.S.F.S.R., northwestern Ukraine, and Belorussia. Some rather large-scale drainage projects were initiated along the shallow limans, or lagoons,

along the northern shore of the Black and Azov Seas in 1950.

All Soviet cotton is now irrigated, although as late as 1952 about 35 per cent of the cotton land was unirrigated in climatically unsuited areas. Cotton yields have approximately doubled since 1930. Although a large portion of the United States' sugar beet areas are irrigated, only minor areas in Middle Asia and Kazakhstan are under irrigation in the Soviet Union.

As long as marketing facilities are inadequate a certain degree of crisis is going to remain in the food supply of the country no matter what the production on the farms. Poor transportation is a prime factor in agricultural inefficiencies and in the structure of the agricultural economy. For instance, lack of all-weather farm-to-market roads largely has determined the development of the butter industry instead of a full development of the use of whole milk. Refrigeration equipment is very limited in the Soviet Union. Much of the meat slaughtered in state packing houses is immediately canned. Much of the fresh meat supply depends on the free markets though the sales of meat by private individuals make up only a small portion of total meat sales.

Improvements since 1953   There has been a clear improvement in agricultural production since 1953, especially in grain, sugar, sunflowers, milk, eggs, and flax fiber. The change in per capita meat availability has been rather modest, but an improvement has occurred. Some estimates place the 1953 to 1959 increase in overall agricultural production as high as 55 per cent and in grain production at 60 per cent. These increases have been associated with a large increase in sown area, a small increase in total labor input, a marked increase in machinery and equipment, and a substantial increase in the use of fertilizers. Between 1953 and 1957 commercial fertilizer production increased 60 per cent. The 1957 production was still only 40 per cent of that of the United States, but production in the

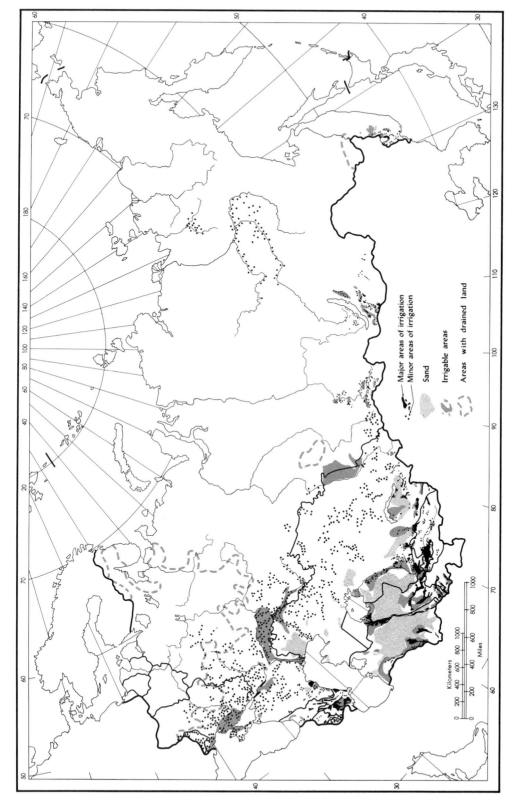

Figure 14-2 Irrigation and drainage in the U.S.S.R.

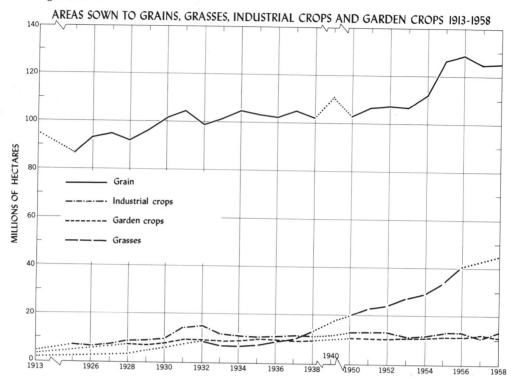

Figure 14-3　Areas sown to grains, grasses (annual, perennial, silage), industrial crops (sunflowers, sugar beets, cotton, flax), and garden crops (potatoes, vegetables, melons), 1913–1959.　Data from Comparisons of the United States and Soviet Economies, *pp. 228–230.　Areas sown to fodder crops (grasses) and grain have been increased rapidly since 1953 with the opening of the new lands, the heavy introduction of corn into the crop complex, and the emphasis on the improvement of animal products.*

U.S.S.R. is supposed to treble during the seven-year plan.

Between 1928 and 1958 the total sown area in the Soviet Union increased from 113 to approximately 195 million hectares or by 82 million hectares, a 73 per cent rise. Approximately 14 to 15 million hectares of the increase was due to the acquisition of new territories during and after World War II. Of the 68 million hectares of new land cultivated within the pre-World War II boundaries of the Soviet Union, nearly 40 million hectares have been opened up since 1953 in conjunction with the virgin lands program, an area equal to the total arable land of France, West Germany, and the United Kingdom combined!

Although all the virgin lands suffer from cool, short, droughty growing seasons that frequently become cold and rainy during the harvest, the total production of grain has been significantly increased by their cultivation. The Soviets are gambling against the weather and are making up for low yields per acre by cultivating millions of acres. Soviet climatologists have pointed out that frequently years of drought in the old grain-growing areas of European Russia and the Ukraine are years of excess moisture in the virgin lands, and vice versa. Thus, they say that the virgin lands program can be justified on an insurance basis, that somewhere in the country there will always be a decent crop.

Soviet economists have pointed out that to overtake the 1956 levels of per captia production of milk and meat in the United States the livestock feed supply will have to be doubled. Despite the large area of the Soviet Union, pasture resources are quite limited. To improve the feed supply, in 1955 it was announced that the corn area was to be expanded to 28 million hectares by 1960, an increase of about 24 million hectares. In 1960, 28.2 million hectares were planted, but this was reduced to 25.7 million hectares in 1961. Of the 1961 crop, 13.2 million hectares were harvested for dry grain and the rest was used for silage and green feed. The corn harvested as dry grain yielded about twice as much weight per unit area as other grains yield, but it must be remembered that corn has taken

over some of the best areas in the Soviet Union. Approximately three fourths of all corn harvested for grain is grown in the rich farming regions of the Ukraine, Moldavia, and the Kuban. One advantage of corn is that the seed requirement is much lower than that for any of the small grains, since only a few kernels of corn are planted in widely spaced hills.

The most significant contribution that corn has made to the feed supply has been not grain but silage and green feed. And here the contribution has been not so much the increase in total quantity of feed (land in hay and oats has consequently decreased) as

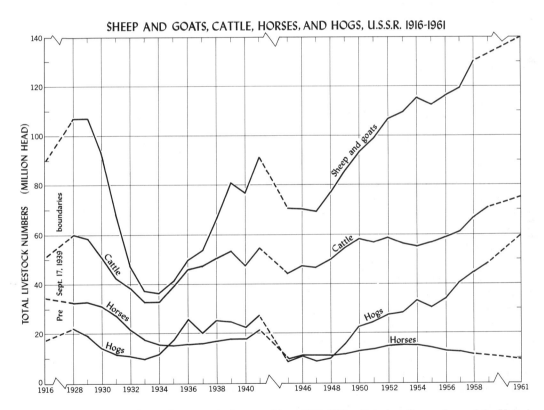

SHEEP AND GOATS, CATTLE, HORSES, AND HOGS, U.S.S.R. 1916-1961

Figure 14-4   Numbers of sheep and goats, cattle, horses, and hogs, 1916–1961.   Data from Comparisons of the United States and Soviet Economies, *p. 230, and* Soviet Geography: Review and Translation, *March 1962, p. 85.   Although data are lacking for the years 1913–1928, it is generally known that livestock suffered heavily after 1916 during the periods of Civil War and War Communism and then recovered during the New Economic Policy until in 1928 they were more numerous than they had been before the Revolution.   Livestock numbers plunged to a record low in 1933 and 1934 owing to unwarranted slaughtering during forced collectivization.   They recovered steadily up to the beginning of World War II, although there still was less livestock in 1941 than there had been in 1928.   All livestock suffered some during World War II, but recovered quickly after the war.   At present, hogs are increasing most rapidly, and the number of horses has gone into a decline as the farms become more and more mechanized.*

it has been the improvement in quality and a change in the seasonal distribution of the feed. Previously the diet of the dairy cows in the Soviet Union was primarily straw, chaff, and wild hay. An addition of silage to the diet has increased the butter fat production per cow by about 50 per cent. Also corn used as green feed supplements the diet during the late summer months when the pastures are drying up, and this maintains a high level of milk flow throughout the summer and into the fall months. Previously milk production dropped off drastically during the late summer months when green grass was no longer available, and once the milk flow had diminished little could be done to bring it up again by heavier feeding in the fall.

Economic and Social Organization

It is generally agreed that the lack of capital investments, the inflexible social order, and the disparity between prices and costs have been the chief restraints on Soviet agricultural performance. Overpopulation on the farms and net incomes of almost zero have stymied any incentive that the farmers might inherently have had for improving production. In the dialectical jargon of the Marxist, the farmers in the Soviet Union have been the exploited and the city dwellers the exploitors. This has even been stated as a basic principle by some Soviet economists. Stalin himself said that agriculture provides the Soviet state, bent on industrialization, with "something like a tribute." Until recently as much as possible was extracted from agriculture and as little as possible was put into it.

Agriculture, like the rest of the economy, was in a sorry state during the period of "War Communism" following the Revolution. A substantial recovery was made during the period of the New Economic Policy (NEP) in the 1920's, but then a collectivization drive was launched in 1929 to organize the peasantry to comply more

closely with communist doctrine and to insure adequate food procurements for the cities. With temporary retrenchments to meet emergencies, the socialization of agriculture has continued and increased in intensity down to the present time, until now practically no independent farmers remain.

The Socialized Sector   The socialization took two forms, and in each case minor degrees of private enterprise were allowed in order to appease the peasants and to assure them enough foodstuffs for their own sustenance. The two forms of farm organization are state farms or sovkhozes (state economy) and collective farms or kolkhozes (collective economy). In general the collective farms were organized in the better farming areas that were already densely settled by farmers. They greatly outnumber the state farms and in the past have produced the bulk of the agricultural produce. State farms largely were organized in outlying areas of sparse settlement or newly opened land where vested interests in the area were small or nonexistent.

The collective farmers work on their collective farms without wages and share the produce of the farm according to the number of work days they have put in. Workers on the state farms on the other hand are salaried workers working on state-owned land. The land of the collective farms ultimately belongs to the state also, but the collective farmers, many of whom originally held title to the land, hold a perpetual lease on the land. In general the collective farmers still are living in their villages of huts that they have always lived in, whereas on many of the state farms individual and multiple dwellings have been built for the workers. Often one collective farm will comprise several old villages, in which the peasants live, and new farm buildings which have been built at focal points about the farm. The buildings and facilities in one part of the farm may be concentrated on dairying, in another part on truck gardening, and so forth. Khrushchev's so-called "agrogorods," or agricultural cities composed of apartment houses for farmers, appear to be a long time in the future, building construction and demand being what it is in the cities.

The collective farms have been the most exploited part of the economy. State procurements of produce at practically no price, state purchases at not much better prices, and large payments in kind to the Machine Tractor Stations (MTS) for services rendered have left very little produce to divide among the peasants. It has been calculated that up until 1958 the average income on collective farms was equivalent to about $60 per year, and there was a great disparity between good and bad farms. Some collectives yielded their farmers practically nothing. Had it not been for foodstuffs and some cash income derived from their private plots, many collective farmers could not have existed at all. Workers on state farms at least had a guaranteed wage, and until recently enjoyed a considerably higher standard of living than collective farmers.

The Private Sector A minimal amount of private enterprise has persisted in agriculture in three forms: (1) the private plots of the collective farmers, (2) the private plots of employees and workers on collective and state farms and in some factories, and (3) individual farms. The third catagory has practically ceased to exist since 1950. Only about 14,000 hectares, or less than one hundredth of one per cent of the total cultivated land, is in uncollectivized farms in remote areas where settlement is so sparse and production so limited that it would not pay to collectivize.

Although the private plots of all collective farmers and workers and employees has amounted to only 5 per cent or less of the total sown area in the country, the production from these plots has represented a much larger fraction of total agricultural production, particularly livestock products, and the plots have been all-important to the sustenance of the collective farmers (Tables 14–11 and 14–12). Much more effort has been expended on these plots than on similar areas of the collectivized land and much higher yields have been attained (Table 14–13). Although there has been an effort

Table 14–11 Sown Areas, Total and Private Sector, 1950 and 1959 in Thousands of Hectares and Per Cents[a]

	1950	1959
Total	146,302	196,319
Private Sector	9,375 (6.41%)	7,238 (3.69%)
Private plots of collective farmers	5,904 (4.04%)	5,312 (2.71%)
Plots of workers and employees	1,563 (1.07%)	1,912 (0.97%)
Uncollectivized farms	1,908 (1.30%)	14 (0.01%)

[a] *Source:* J. A. Newth, "Soviet Agriculture: The Private Sector, 1950–1959," *Soviet Studies*, October 1961, p. 161.

Table 14–12 Output of Private Sector and Percentage of Total, 1950 and 1959[a]

	1950		1959	
Crop	1000 Tons	Per Cent of Total	1000 Tons	Per Cent of Total
Potatoes	65,248	73.6	54,959	63.5
Vegetables	4,068	43.5	6,774	45.9
Ripe maize	2,139	32.2	1,323	23.4
Roots (fodder)	2,761	33.9	2,141	20.5
Sunflowers	83	4.6	140	4.5
Rye	1,878	10.5	501	3.0
Millet	144	8.4	38	2.9
Barley	541	8.5	259	2.6
Pulses	183	8.9	29	1.5
Hay	1,142	1.8	892	1.1
Oats	363	2.8	39	0.3
Wheat	423	1.4	98	0.1

[a] *Source:* J. A. Newth, "Soviet Agriculture: The Private Sector, 1950–1959," *Soviet Studies*, October 1961, p. 167.

Table 14–13   Average Yields of Crops, 1950–59, Public and Private, in Centners per Hectare[a]

	Public	Private
Fully ripe maize	13.84	18.45
Potatoes	61.5	119.9
Vegetables	70.6	147.4

[a] *Source:* J. A. Newth, "Soviet Agriculture: The Private Sector, 1950–1959," *Soviet Studies*, October 1961, pp. 163–165.

to reduce these plots and eventually to eliminate them, there is no indication that their total elimination will come about in the near future; they are too much an integral part of the agricultural setup. Until collectivized production is greatly improved and the share of the collectivized product going to the individual farmer is greatly increased, the private plot can be expected to remain.

Most of these private plots are no more than a half acre or an acre per family, but with constant care a great deal of produce can be raised on that amount of land. The private plots are sown primarily to heavily producing food crops, potatoes, vegetables, and fruit, and to livestock feed, maize and fodder (Table 14–14). A certain amount

Table 14–14   Percentages of Private Plots of Collective Farmers under Various Crops, 1959[a]

Grain		23
Maize (fully ripe)	11	
Rye	5	
Barley	3	
Wheat	1	
Oats	1	
Industrial crops		2
Potatoes, vegetables, and fruit		68
Fodder		7

[a] *Source:* J. A. Newth, "Soviet Agriculture: The Private Sector, 1950–1959," *Soviet Studies*, October 1961, p. 162.

of cattle, hogs, and an unlimited number of poultry can be maintained by an individual household. In 1960 the private plots produced almost half the meat and milk of the country and almost all the eggs; in the past they had produced even larger percentages of the total (Table 14–15). In the 1940's

Table 14–15   Meat, Milk, and Egg Production[a]

	Total	Public	Private
Meat (dead weight, millions of tons)			
1947	2.5	0.9	1.6
1954	6.3	2.7	3.6
1960	8.7	5.1	3.6
Milk (millions of tons)			
1947	30.2	5.1	25.1
1954	38.2	13.5	24.7
1960	61.7	32.6	29.1
Eggs (billions)			
1947	4.9	0.4	4.5
1954	17.2	2.2	15.0
1960	27.4	5.3	22.1

[a] *Source:* J. A. Newth, "Soviet Agriculture: The Private Sector, 1950–1959—Animal Husbandry," *Soviet Studies*, April 1962, pp. 431–432.

the private sector held about half of the country's livestock. This has decreased to about 30 per cent, largely due to the urging by Khrushchev for the kolkhozniki to turn over their livestock to the kolkhozes (Table 14–16). Almost half the land devoted to potatoes, vegetables, and fruits is in these private plots (Table 14–17). Yields of potatoes and vegetables from the private plots are nearly twice as high as they are from the collectivized areas. In 1959 the private sector of agriculture produced 63.5 per cent of the potatoes of the country and 45.9 per cent of the vegetables. It had produced almost three fourths of the potatoes in 1950. Much of the introduction of corn for dry grain has been effected on the private plots; in 1959 the private sector produced almost one quarter of the ripe maize.

Table 14–16   Livestock Holdings (January 1), in Millions[a]

	Cows	Other Cattle	Pigs	Sheep	Goats	Horses
1947						
Total	23.0	24.0	8.7	57.7	11.6	10.9
Public	4.6	14.1	4.0	40.4	5.1	8.4
Private	18.4	9.9	4.7	17.3	6.5	2.5
1954						
Total	25.2	30.6	33.3	99.8	15.7	15.3
Public	10.1	22.0	17.8	84.8	4.2	14.8
Private	15.1	8.6	15.5	15.0	11.5	0.5
1961						
Total	34.8	41.0	58.7	133.0	7.3	9.9
Public	18.4	33.6	42.2	104.3	1.3	n.a.
Private	16.4	7.4	16.5	28.7	6.0	n.a.

[a] *Source:* J. A. Newth, "Soviet Agriculture: The Private Sector, 1950–1959—Animal Husbandry," *Soviet Studies*, April 1962, pp. 430–431.

Until 1954 sales on the free (Kolkhoz) markets in the cities exceeded the total cash income of collective farms. This has now been reduced to less than one third of the total farm income. A much smaller portion of the produce from private plots enters the retail trade than does produce from public lands. In 1959, 19 per cent of the crops and 23 per cent of the livestock products of the private sector were sold, whereas 59 per cent of the crops and 72 per cent of the livestock products of the public sector were sold (Table 14–18). It appears that a significant portion of the Soviet population is providing its own foodstuffs with only a minor interest in supplying the market. The output of private producers has increased substantially in recent years, and they are consuming the increase themselves. According to the 1959 census, nearly 10 million people (dependents of kolkhozniki and workers) were engaged in this activity. Add to this full-time workers and kolkhozniki who grew produce and reared livestock in their spare time, and the total number of persons involved must be very large.

Machine Tractor Stations Until 1958 the Machine Tractor Station was an integral part of the agricultural scene. Collective farms owned practically no agricultural

Table 14–17   Private Sector as Percentage of All Land Devoted to Particular Crops, 1959[a]

Potatoes	50
Vegetables	32
Fruit, etc.	9
Total of three groups	45

[a] *Source:* J. A. Newth, "Soviet Agriculture: The Private Sector, 1950–1959," *Soviet Studies*, October 1961, p. 163.

Table 14–18   Percentage of Public Sector in Total Commercial Production, 1953 and 1959[a]

	1953	1959
Total	80	85
Crops	86	89
Livestock	68	82

[a] *Source:* J. A. Newth, "Soviet Agriculture: The Private Sector, 1950–1959," *Soviet Studies*, October 1961, p. 170.

machinery and were totally dependent on Machine Tractor Stations for heavy field work. A typical Machine Tractor Station had a crew of tractor drivers, implement operators, mechanics, agronomists, and zootechnicians who did the field work, serviced the machinery, and advised on problems of agronomy and animal husbandry for four or five collective farms. Thus the economy of the collective farms was tied very closely to that of the Machine Tractor Station. A considerable proportion of the produce of each farm went to the Machine Tractor Station at the end of each harvest to pay for work done. Also the Machine Tractor Station was usually a focal point for governmental activities to disseminate information and propaganda in the rural areas. It was, thus, a governmental control point in the countryside.

The Machine Tractor Station gradually outlived its usefulness, and since 1958 most of them have been abolished and the machinery has been sold to the collective farms. The MTS has largely been replaced by the RTS, Repair and Technical Station, which maintains mechanics and agricultural technicians to serve the farm operations. The RTS appears to be on the way out also as more and more of the total operation is assumed by the collective farms themselves.

Agricultural Reforms under Khrushchev
Since the death of Stalin in 1953 a number of steps have been taken in the field of agriculture to increase total production and to improve the lot of the peasants. Khrushchev has a much greater knowledge of and greater interest in agriculture than Stalin ever had, and he has taken a much more realistic approach to agricultural problems than Stalin did. Also the general economy of the country has risen to a level now where some energy and capital can be diverted from industry to the improvement of agriculture. The first emphasis was placed on increasing farm output through any means in order to substantially increase the living standards of urban workers. Probably the

two most significant measures taken in this respect were the opening up of nearly 40 million hectares of virgin land in northern Kazakhstan and western Siberia, primarily for wheat growing, and the widespread introduction of corn into the crop complex throughout the country. The introduction of corn has provided a base for greatly increased livestock production.

In 1958 a series of administrative reforms were initiated to substantially improve the lot of the collective farmers and thereby increase their incentive to improve production. The most important reform of the institutional structure was the liquidation of the Machine Tractor Stations and the sale of the machines to the collective farms. This eliminated the situation of "two bosses on the land" and at the same time set the stage for more amalgamation of collective farms and some outright conversions of collective farms to state farms, a process which is part of the long term policy of the government. The MTS no longer served a needed political function in the countryside, and economically it had gotten to the point where it was a stumbling block to production improvement. Differences of opinion often arose between the collective farm management and the MTS personnel, and field work would not get done as it was supposed to be done or it would not get done at the proper time.

The sale of machinery to the collective farms allows them to control more fully their farming operations. The purchase of expensive machinery proved to be a financial burden on many collective farms, which brought about some combining of collective farms into larger units and in certain cases, where capital outlays by the national government were needed, a conversion of collective farms into state farms.

The other important reform was the reduction of the types of payment to the state to only one category of sales and the raising of prices for these sales to a reasonable level. This has greatly improved the lot of collective farmers, more than tripling their incomes between 1952 and 1956. In 1953 prices of livestock and poultry products were increased more than five and a half times, milk and butter two times, potatoes two and a half times, and vegetables by 25 to 40 per cent.

Long-Term Goals in Agricultural Organization The state farm has always been considered a superior organization to the collective farm, and the long-term goal is to convert all farmers into agricultural workers, similar to factory workers, working for wages on state-owned land. The collective farm was simply a compromise measure to meet expediencies, and it was considered transitory from the first. The fact that it has persisted this long is somewhat of a surprise. Now that the economy has improved and the peasants have been more adequately indoctrinated into the Soviet system, it might be expected that there will be a gradual likening of the two types of farms. The process has already been initiated by the sale of machinery to the collective farms which allows their operation to be much more similar to that of the state farms than it was previously. Also, some collective farms have now started to pay their farmers partially in cash. This again brings the collective operation nearer to the state farm.

The abolishment of the Machine Tractor Station, a state institution, was first looked on by some American analysts as a retreat from state control and a move toward a more collective economy. It can also be interpreted, however, as a move to gradually convert collective farms into state farms. In fact, some conversion took place along with the sale of machinery in areas where it was necessary for the national government to loan substantial sums of money to the collectives so they could buy equipment. Some wholesale conversions of collective to state farms also have taken place in the western part of the country where the collective economy had broken down during the German occupation and in the new lands of northern Kazakhstan and western Siberia.

In 1957 in northern Kazakhstan 833 collective farms were merged into 188 state farms. Some conversion of collective to state farms has also taken place in the irrigated cotton growing regions of Middle Asia in cases where the need for new capital investment by the state has been large.

Another recent development which has placed greater reliance on state farms is the designation of a number of state farms, first near Moscow and subsequently near other large cities, to specialize in growing potatoes and vegetables cheaply to lower their costs to city consumers. If these experiments prove successful, they will operate to the disadvantage of collectives which derive an important share of their incomes from selling these products at high prices on the free markets in the cities.

Apparently there is some justification for the conversion of collectives to state farms in that labor productivity generally has been higher on the state farms than on the collectives (Table 14–19). Also the government

Table 14–19 Share of Labor in Costs of Production on Collective and State Farms (Per Cent)[a]

	Collective Farms (1955)	State Farms (1956)
Grain	45.0	23.5
Beef	32.3	20.7
Pork	36.9	18.4
Milk	49.0	27.0

[a] *Source: Comparisons of the United States and Soviet Economies*, Part I, p. 262.

hopes eventually to lower prices on farm products to reduce the cost of living for urban consumers. Thus the recent increases in farm prices to kolkhozes may be reversed once these collective farms convert to state farms. In fact, there has been no significant increase in prices for agricultural produce since 1957.

Throughout the collectivization drive there has been a general trend to merge collective farms into fewer and larger farms. The number of collective farms reached a peak in 1935 with approximately 245,000. In 1940 this was reduced to 237,000. After a weak collectivization effort in the western regions newly annexed during the war, the number of collectives increased to 252,000 for a short period, but in 1950 within 1 year the number of collectives was reduced by more than half to 121,000. Since then there has been a continual drive for merger, until at the end of 1960 there were only 44,000 collective farms in the country. This brings the average size of the collective farm much nearer to that of the state farm. The average collective farm in 1960 contained nearly 3000 hectares of plow land and 400 households.

If agricultural production can be increased enough to bring about an abundance of food and other agricultural produce, we can look for a gradual elimination of the private plots. The Soviet regime hopes that through abundant production and gradual transition to all state-owned farms the private plots will simply become superfluous and farmers will no longer want to retain them. Such a situation appears to be at least 20 years in the future, but it is a goal to be kept in mind.

Crop and Livestock Distributions

General Pattern With few exceptions, the Soviet Union is humid north of a line starting at approximately the city of Lvov in the western Ukraine and extending east-northeastward in an irregular line to the vicinity of Ufa in the western Urals, from where it continues eastward in a nearly straight line at about 56° north latitude. And it is definitely dry south of a line which begins in the eastern part of the North Caucasus, swings northward around the Caspian Sea approximately through the cities of Volgograd and Uralsk, and then

extends eastward to the Chinese border in an irregular line which criss-crosses the parallel of 50° north latitude. Between these two lines exists a strip of land approximately 350 miles wide, extending from the western border of the country in the western Ukraine and Moldavia eastward to the Yenisey River in central Siberia, where the climate is transitional from humid to dry, the original vegetation was tall grasses, and the soils are of high fertility. This is the so-called chernozem or black-earth belt. It is within this belt of prime soils and subhumid to semiarid climate that much of the agriculture of the Soviet Union is found. Wheat, sugar beets, corn, sunflowers, and a great variety of other crops are grown here.

To the north of this belt the climate is humid and cool, the soils are of a podzol character, drainage is often poor, and the crops are primarily potatoes, flax, hardy grains, and vegetables South of the black-earth belt in the deserts of the Caspian Lowland and Middle Asia cultivation is limited to isolated patches of grain growing without irrigation wherever the precipitation is above normal for the region or to areas of intensive irrigated agriculture wherever water can be derived from the melting snows and glaciers in the high mountains. The chief crop throughout the irrigated areas of Soviet Middle Asia is cotton, but a great variety of fruits and vegetables are grown as well as considerable quantities of alfalfa, grain, and sugar beets. In Transcaucasia, the crop complexes are split between east and west, with the dry eastern portion of the region resembling the deserts of Middle Asia with their irrigated fields of cotton and alfalfa and the humid west being an area of subtropical crops such as citrus, tea, and tobacco.

Agriculture in eastern Siberia is almost absent except for patches of cultivation in the steppe-like mountain basins along the southern fringes of the region on either side of the Trans-Siberian Railroad. These mountain basins still are utilized primarily for sheep and cattle grazing, but some wheat is grown. The cultivated acreage increases again as one approaches Amur Oblast and Maritime Kray in the Soviet Far East where the summer monsoon from the Pacific provides favorable conditions for a variety of crops. Western and Oriental types of agriculture meet here to produce a complex of wheat, sugar beets, sunflowers, soy beans, rice, and a variety of fruits, vegetables, and melons.

It must be realized that various crops often are competing with one another for their optimum soil and climatic conditions in the same areas, and hence a choice has to be made as to which crop is going to be grown in the area that is most conducive to its growth and which crop will have to take second best as far as its growth environment is concerned. For instance, grains largely have been pushed out of the irrigated areas of Middle Asia in favor of cotton, which yields more value per acre and which cannot be grown in other regions of the country, as grains can be. Within the last decade probably the greatest competition between crops has been taking place in the prime agricultural areas of the Ukraine, the Central Black Earth Region, and the Kuban District in the North Caucasus. Here the introduction of corn as a heavily producing grain and fodder crop for livestock and, to some extent, sugar beets, have displaced much wheat, which in turn has had to move to drier and drier regions. Thus the opening of the virgin lands in northern Kazakhstan and southwestern Siberia partially has been due to the introduction of corn into the better farming areas of the European Plain. Heavy yields of wheat in the Ukraine and European Russia have been sacrificed for the growing of corn in that area, and to compensate for the reduction of wheat production in this area, the Soviets have resorted to extensive cultivation of this crop in a less favorably endowed area with reduced production per acre. Hence a grain such as wheat is often found growing in an area not optimal for it.

In general it can be said that the policies that largely determine the relative distributions of crops in the Soviet Union are as follows: (1) a more heavily yielding crop will displace a less yielding crop in areas that have favorable growth conditions for both; (2) a specialty crop such as cotton or citrus that has very restricted tolerances for climate and soil conditions will displace other crops with wider tolerances in areas of its optimum growth conditions, even though its value yields per acre may be no higher than those of the other crops; (3) the desire for national and regional autarchy in most types of production has induced the experimentation and commercial growth of a variety of crops that might more economically be imported from another country or another part of the U.S.S.R. Examples are the rather extensive cultivation over a considerable number of years of kok-sagyz and other rubber-producing plants, even though the effort never proved to be very successful; the present great push to produce corn for grain and silage in practically all regions of the country in spite of unfavorable climatic and soil conditions in many regions; and the dispersal of sugar beet production into many outlying regions of the country, some of which do not have favorable environments for sugar beets.

Since 1953 the Soviets have launched a drive to overtake the United States in per capita production of meat, milk, butter, and eggs. This means that a large number of livestock and poultry of all types have been introduced into all regions of the country, and in many cases regions that previously had concentrated primarily on a cash grain crop now have adopted a more rounded agricultural economy with livestock as the main source of cash income. The livestock economy of the country has at the same time been changed from one of extensive seminomadic herding of cattle and sheep to one of a more sedentary raising of cattle, sheep, hogs, and poultry fed primarily on fodder and grain within feedlots in the main grain-growing areas. The dairy industry, for instance, has shifted considerably from western

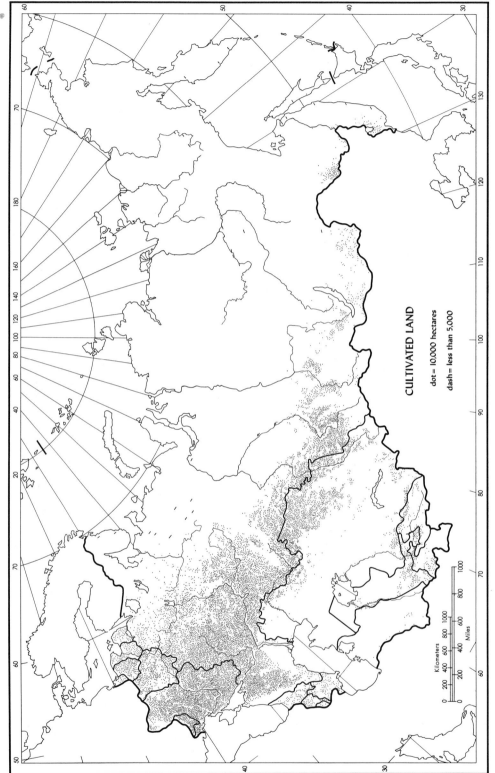

Figure 14-5 Cultivated land in the U.S.S.R.

Russia to the Ukraine. With these generalizations in mind, we can better understand the distribution of crops and animals shown on maps 14–6 through 14–25 adapted from the *Atlas of Agriculture of the U.S.S.R.* which was published in Moscow in 1960.

Distributions of Individual Crops The greatest concentration of all grain growing is in the southern part of the European Plain where the level of production is the highest. But wheat growing is no longer concentrated in this area. It has constantly been pushed

Table 14–20   Regional Variations in Cost of Production on Collective Farms, 1953–55 (U.S.S.R. Average = 100)[a]

Region	Grain	Pota-toes	Vege-tables and Cucur-bits	Sugar Beet	Sun-flower	Cot-ton	Fiber Flax	Beef	Pork	Milk	Wool	Eggs
R.S.F.S.R.	100	102	106	111	101		88	112	122	109	127	99
North	276	137	128				112	152	136	128	271	159
Northwest	229	145	122				98	140	134	113	243	105
Central nonblack soil	195	91	106	220			93	167	175	133	239	157
Central black soil	98	98	102	111	106			129	158	116	148	107
Volga	100	116	101	329	146			102	114	105	125	114
North Caucasus	69	155	90	64	81			91	93	93	105	65
Urals	95	118	137	171	210			117	122	114	153	118
West Siberia	70	92	144	205	222			87	90	86	112	97
East Siberia	76	115	156	549	280			88	88	94	103	145
Far East	78	240	148	156	487			106	114	100	165	134
Belorussian S.S.R.	274	94	130	271			107	156	133	137	160	195
Ukrainian S.S.R.	87	93	89	95	105	144		94	76	92	95	98
Moldavian S.S.R.	89	283	91	90	109	563		80	67	82	70	101
Kazakh S.S.R.	72	230	131	115	195	108		65	84	73	68	160
Uzbek S.S.R.	153	233	93			101		90	34	97	39	122
Turkmen S.S.R.	158	879	130			116		66		76	30	103
Tadzhik S.S.R.	194	277	109			98		88		90	62	131
Kirgiz S.S.R.	105	236	153	103		121		95	100	93	75	119
Azerbaydzhan S.S.R.	133	200	108			75		153	58	124	93	129
Georgian S.S.R.	154	209	149	92	217			138	143	127	83	183
Armenian S.S.R.	165	147	76	133		87		69	78	70	76	120
Lithuanian S.S.R.	265	93	202	175			76	95	105	90	112	87
Latvian S.S.R.	193	72	125	140			109	70	59	62	125	80
Estonian S.S.R.	208	72	88	244			82	81	58	70	165	84

[a] *Source: Comparisons of the United States and Soviet Economies,* Part I, p. 259.

By comparing crop and livestock distributions on these maps with the data on regional variations in cost of production presented in Table 14–20 we can judge whether or not a crop is being raised in the areas most favorable for its growth.

eastward as corn has been introduced into the Ukraine and the North Caucasus. The greatest concentration of wheat growing is now in northern Kazakhstan and southwestern Siberia, and most of this is spring wheat because the winters generally are too severe for winter wheat. Throughout much of this eastern area spring wheat occupies over half of the cultivated area, whereas back in the Ukraine and the North Caucasus wheat occupies no more than 20 to 40 per cent of the sown area. Most of the wheat raised on the European Plain is winter wheat, because it is possible to raise winter wheat there, and because winter wheat yields more heavily and has a higher quality than spring wheat. Both winter and spring wheat are scattered throughout the moister areas of the foothill belt of Middle Asia.

Corn is grown most heavily in the Ukraine and the Kuban District where in many cases it occupies more than 30 per cent of the sown area. Much of the corn in these areas is grown for grain, although much is grown for fodder and silage, whereas farther north in a rather wide belt in European Russia and extending into Siberia, most of the corn is grown for silage for dairy cattle. Corn produces most heavily in the central and western Ukraine and in the Kuban District in Krasnodar Kray. Hence, corn is grown mainly in the areas with the most favorable environmental conditions. Actually, optimum environmental conditions for corn do not exist in the Soviet Union, which is why corn was not grown extensively until Khrushchev decreed that it would be. In the humid north the summers are too short and cool, and the south with its longer, warmer summers is too dry. There simply does not exist an area with long, hot, humid summers which are ideal for corn growing.

The small hardy grains in general are grown north of the wheat and corn in areas not optimal for their growth. Rye and oats are grown extensively on the European Plain and are concentrated in the central portions around the Central Industrial Region, the Central Black Earth Region, and Volga Bend area. Barley is grown throughout much of the sown area of the Soviet Union with some concentration in the Ukraine and the Kuban where it occupies from 10 to 15 per cent of the sown area.

Potatoes are the staple food of European Russia and also serve as a base for industrial alcohol. They are grown very extensively throughout European Russia, the Ukraine, and the western republics where they often occupy up to 20 per cent of the sown area. They also are scattered widely throughout all the other agricultural areas of the Soviet Union. Potatoes are suited to cool, moist climate and acidic soil environment, so they are concentrated in the areas having optimum growth conditions.

Buckwheat is a staple food throughout European Russia, the Ukraine, and Belorussia, and it is grown extensively among the other crops in these areas where it occupies up to 8 per cent of the sown area.

Rice is the basic food of Soviet Middle Asia, and to some extent of the Caucasus. It is grown in considerable quantities in the more swampy areas of the irrigated regions along the streams of Middle Asia, Transcaucasia, and the Kuban. Particular concentrations of rice growing exist in the Kuban delta, the middle Kura River Valley, the Lenkoran Lowland, the middle Syr-Darya, the Tashkent region, the Fergana Basin, and the lower Amu-Darya. Rice also is grown in the Maritime Province of the Far East around the shores of Lake Khanka.

Sunflowers, which are the main source of vegetable oil in the Soviet Union, are grown most extensively in the drier parts of the western Ukraine and adjacent Moldavia, the eastern Ukraine, and the Kuban. They produce most heavily under these hot, dry conditions, and hence are located in their optimum areas for growth. Throughout much of this region they occupy from 10 to 15 per cent of the sown area. They are also scattered rather extensively east of the middle Volga and into the drier parts of southwestern Siberia and northern Kazakhstan.

Sugar beets are a very important crop in the Soviet Union. With their desire to become self-sufficient in all lines of production, the Soviets have greatly expanded the production of sugar beets to supply themselves with sugar, since there are no areas in the Soviet Union in which it is possible to grow

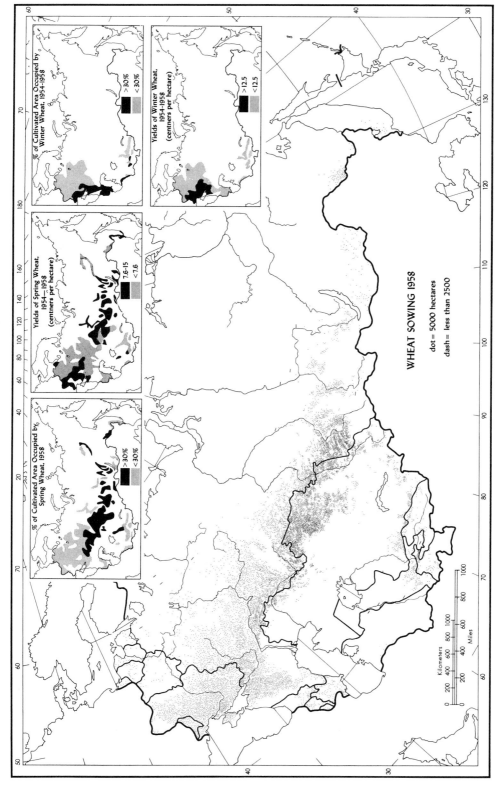

Figure 14-6 Wheat sowing.

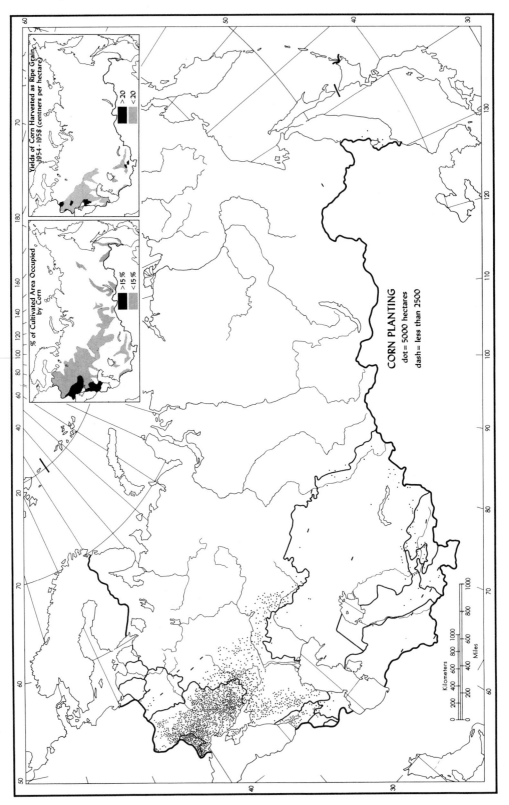

CORN PLANTING
dot= 5000 hectares
dash= less than 2500

Yields of Corn Harvested as Ripe Grain, 1954 - 1958 (centners per hectare)

> 20
< 20

% of Cultivated Area Occupied by Corn

>15 %
<15 %

Figure 14-7a   Corn harvested in ripe or wax stage.

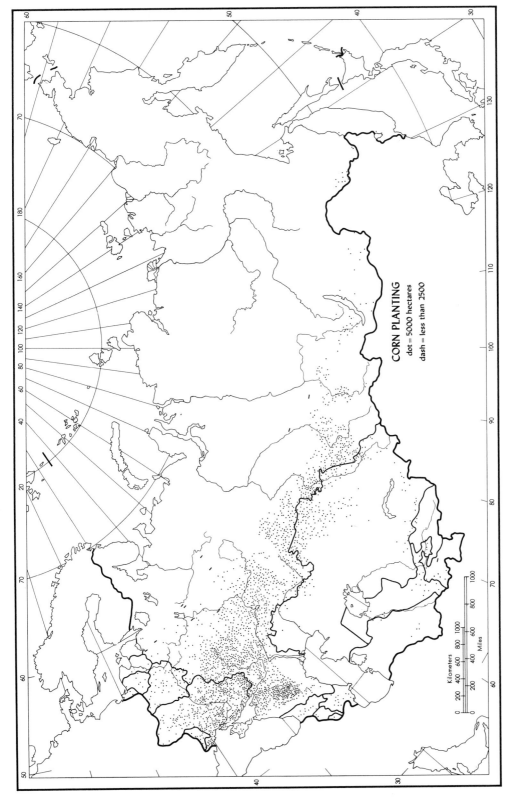

CORN PLANTING
dot = 5000 hectares
dash = less than 2500

Figure 14-7b Corn used for silage and green fodder.

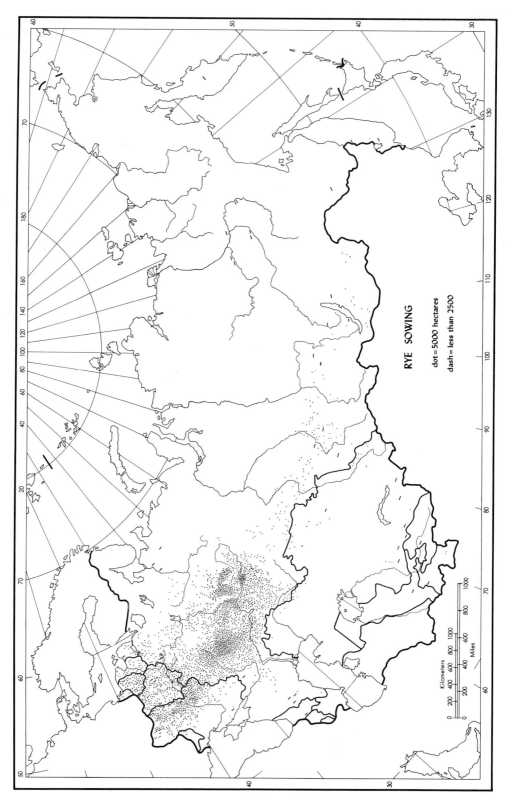

Figure 14-8   Rye sowing.

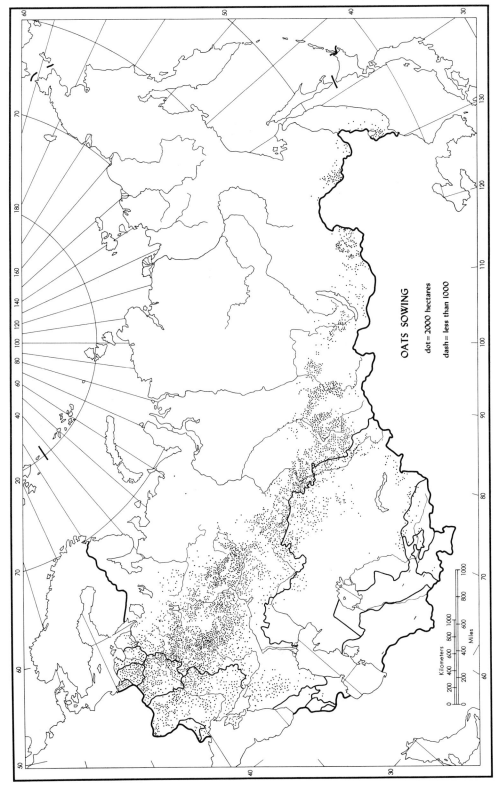

OATS SOWING

dot = 2000 hectares

dash = less than 1000

Figure 14-9 Oats sowing.

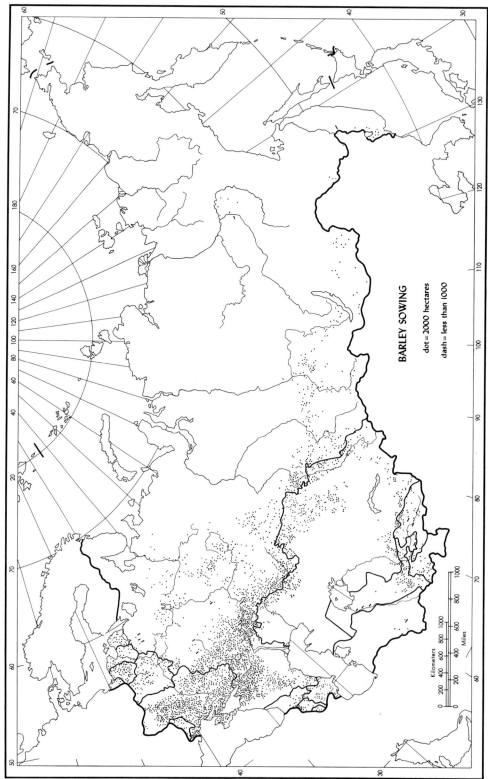

Figure 14-10   Barley sowing.

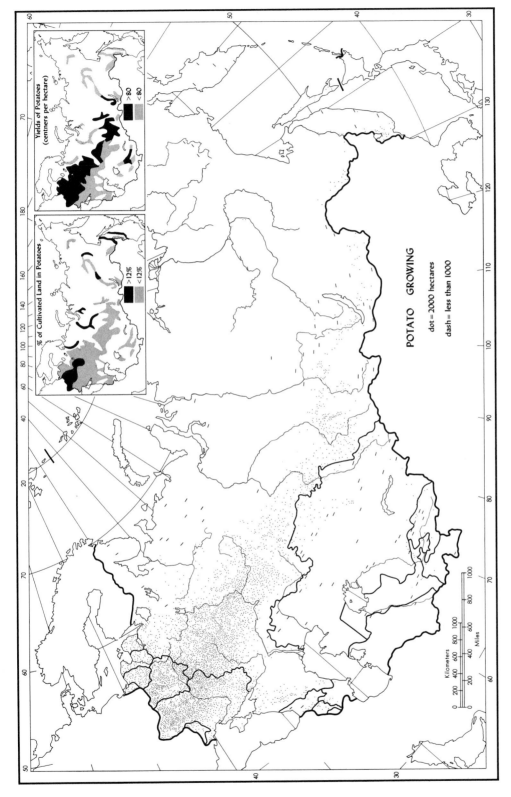

POTATO GROWING

dot = 2000 hectares

dash = less than 1000

% of Cultivated Land in Potatoes

>12%
<12%

Yields of Potatoes
(centners per hectare)

>80
<80

Figure 14-11   Potato growing.

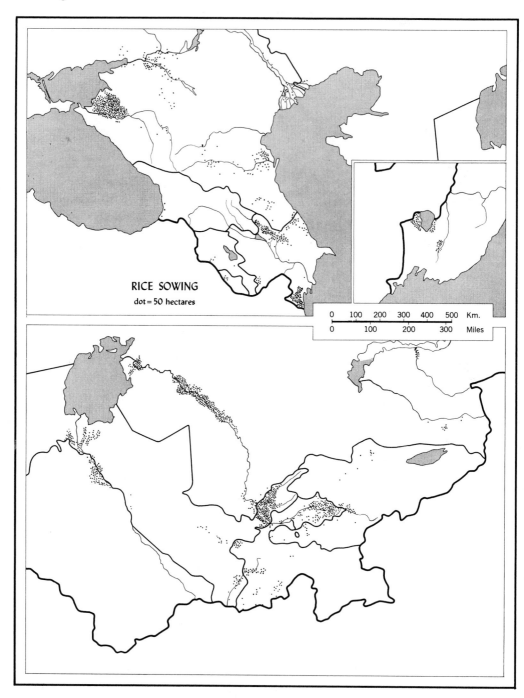

Figure 14-12   Rice sowing.

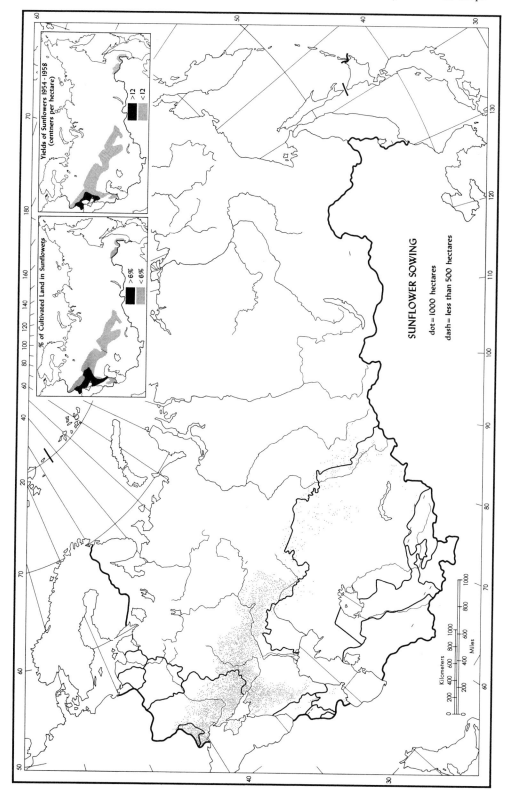

Figure 14-13   Sunflower sowing.

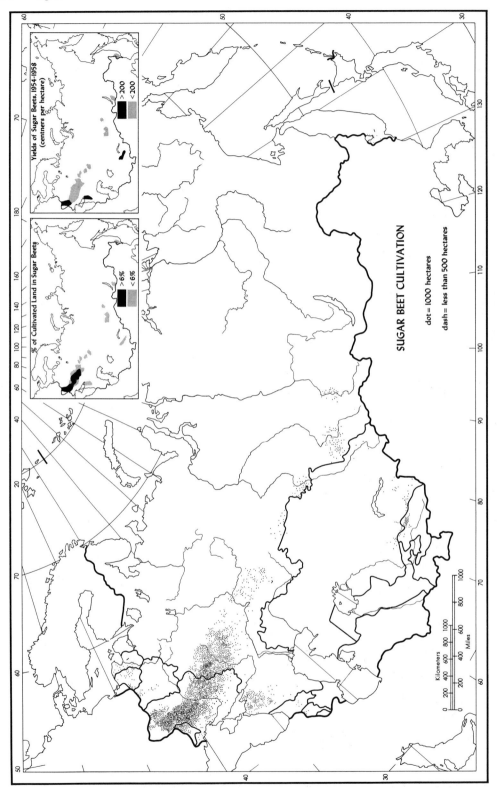

Figure 14-14 Sugar beet cultivation.

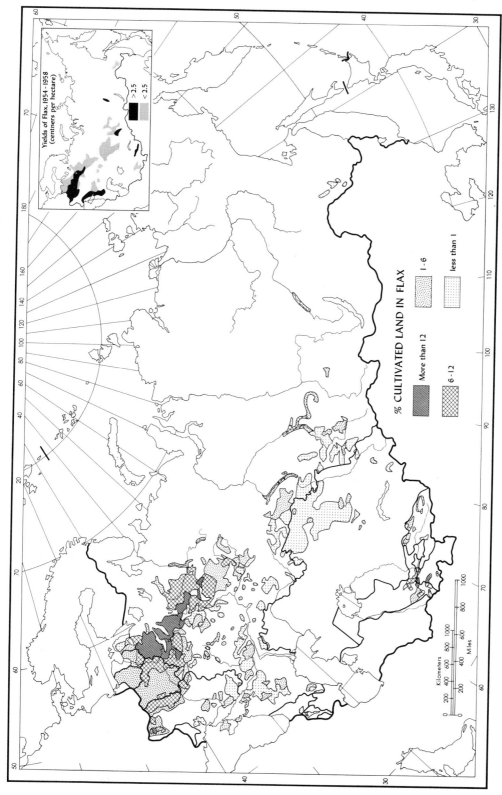

% CULTIVATED LAND IN FLAX

More than 12

6-12

1-6

less than 1

Yields of Flax, 1954-1958
(centners per hectare)

> 2.5

< 2.5

Figure 14-15 Flax sowing.

sugar cane. The Soviet Union raises over 40 per cent of the world's sugar beets. The traditional sugar-beet belt lies in the western Ukraine and northern Moldavia and extends northeastward into the oblasts of Kursk, Belgorod, and Voronezh in the Central Black Earth Region. The greatest concentration of beets is southwest of Kiev where in places they occupy over 12 per cent of the cultivated area. In an effort to make separate regions self-sufficient in sugar, the Soviets have dispersed the growing of beets to other parts of the Union, such as the Kuban in the North Caucasus, Belorussia, Lithuania, and Latvia in the European West, the Chu Valley and Taldy-Kurgan areas in Middle Asia, the Kulunda Steppe in southwestern Siberia, and in Maritime Kray in the Far East, as well as in some other scattered spots in southern Siberia, the Urals, the Volga Bend area, and Transcaucasia. Although natural conditions are almost ideal for sugar-beet raising in the western Ukraine and in the Kuban, the highest yields per acre have been obtained in the irrigated areas of Middle Asia, where the Soviets claim to have attained the highest yield in the world.

Soy beans might well be adapted to extensive areas of warm and semiarid Russia, where they would compete with sunflowers, wheat, and corn, and this might be some solution of the need for vegetable oils in the country. They have been introduced in significant amounts only in the Far East, however, particularly in the Khanka-Ussuri Lowland and the Zeya-Bureya Lowland. Other beans and peas for human consumption are raised extensively, with concentrations in the western Ukraine and Moldavia and in the eastern part of the Central Black Earth Region and the Volga Bend area.

Flax is a traditional crop of Russia; the Soviet Union produces about 78 per cent of the world's supply. It is admirably suited to the cool, moist, poorly drained northern part of the European Plain where it is grown extensively in conjunction with potato growing and dairying. It reaches its greatest concentration northwest of Moscow where it occupies about 12 per cent of the sown area. Fiber flax yields most heavily in this region and southwestward in Belorussia and the northern Ukraine. Flax for linseed oil is raised in scattered areas of the dry south, along the lower Don and North Caucasus and in the steppes of northern Kazakhstan and southwestern Siberia, as well as in scattered regions of the eastern Ukraine and Middle Asia.

The other important fiber crop, cotton, is grown exclusively in the irrigated areas of Middle Asia and Transcaucasia. It is most concentrated in the Fergana Basin, the Tashkent region, the Zeravshan Valley, and the lower Amu-Darya. It produces most heavily in the Fergana Basin, southwestern Tadzhikistan, and the Tedzhen Oasis. Since the late 1920's cotton output has increased by five or six times until now it is approximately one half of the output of the United States. The sown area has more than doubled and yields have approximately doubled.

Mulberry trees grown along the canal systems of most of the irrigated areas of Middle Asia and Transcaucasia provide the basis for the silk industry in those areas.

Some kenaf and jute are grown in a few areas of irrigation in Middle Asia and the Transcaucasus. The largest area is near Tashkent. A considerable acreage of hemp, raised primarily for its oilseed, is raised in the central Ukraine, the Central Black Earth Region, and the area west of the Volga Bend.

Truck gardens and orchards are widely distributed throughout the warmer parts of the Soviet Union, particularly in the Ukraine and Moldavia, in the Caucasus, and in Middle Asia. The amount and quality of production still are not nearly what is to be desired, and marketing facilities are very primitive. Grapes are one of the major fruit crops; they are used both for eating and for wine making. The major grape-growing region in the country is in Moldavia and adjacent parts of the Ukraine

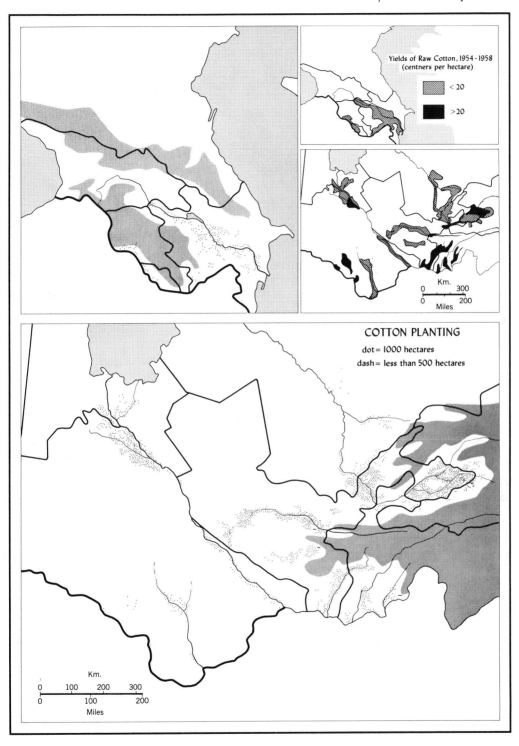

Figure 14-16   Cotton planting.

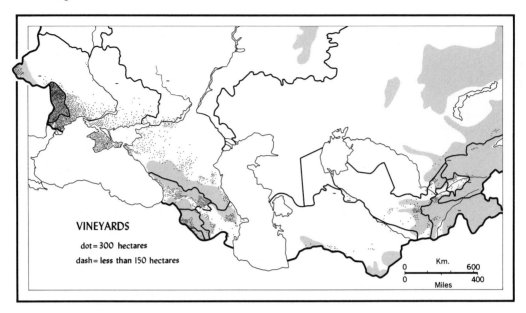

Figure 14-17   Vineyards.

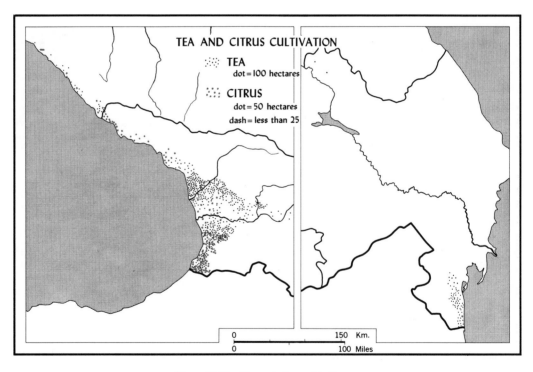

Figure 14-18   Tea and citrus cultivation.

including the Crimean Peninsula. Moldavia might be called the Champagne of the Soviet Union. Grape growing also is well developed in Transcaucasia and in the irrigated areas of Middle Asia. Such table fruits as apples, peaches, pears, plums, cherries, apricots, etc. are grown widely throughout the Union wherever it is possible. The growing of citrus fruits is limited to the Colchis Lowland in Georgia, particularly in the foothills around Batumi, and to a very small area in the Lenkoran Lowland. Tea growing is limited to the same two areas.

Fodder Crops With the increased emphasis on livestock raising, the expansion of the acreages of forage and silage crops has become very necessary. These needs are satisfied mostly by clover, alfalfa, and green corn. Clover and alfalfa make good rotation crops for grain, both being legumes, and they have largely replaced the fallowing phase of the rotation cycle of earlier days. This provides a greatly increased amount of forage for livestock, and also is better for the soil than fallowing. In general clover is raised in the more humid parts of the agricultural area whereas alfalfa is raised in the drier south. Alfalfa is highly tolerant of saline soil conditions and hence is ideal in semiarid and arid regions. Alfalfa is raised in the irrigated areas in rotation with cotton, not only to restore nitrogen to the soil but also to remove excessive salts which tend to accumulate under prolonged irrigation.

Livestock The country's livestock are concentrated in the better farming areas, particularly in the Ukraine and adjacent regions. Cattle and swine especially are concentrated in these areas; sheep and goats are scattered more widely with some concentrations in Moldavia, the Caucasus, and the Middle Asian mountains. The production of wool is especially important in the Caucasus and in the mountains and deserts of Middle Asia. In 1959 cattle made up 52 per cent, by weight, of all the livestock in the U.S.S.R., sheep and goats accounted for 19 per cent, swine for 18 per cent, and horses for 11 per cent, so the concentration of sheep and goats in the mountains of the Caucasus and Middle Asia does not significantly affect the distribution of total livestock. With the recent large increase in swine production, which is taking place primarily in the same regions as the major beef and dairy cattle raising, concentrations of total livestock remain in the better farming areas. Although the northern areas, such as Vologda Oblast, have become known as the dairy regions of the Soviet Union, more milk and butter are now produced in the grain-growing regions farther south. Dairying occupies a larger part of the total farming economy in the north than it does in the south. Throughout much of the northern part of European Russia, milk cows make up more than 60 per cent of the cattle population. This reflects the much greater emphasis on milk than on beef at present. In fact, much of the beef of the Soviet Union is derived from dairy stock rather than from beef stock. Veal is one of the chief entrees found in Soviet restaurants, indicating the great number of bull calves of dairy stock which are sold for meat soon after birth.

Poultry raising is also being greatly expanded in the Soviet Union, for, like swine, poultry are scavengers and can be raised on table scraps and other waste materials. Poultry are scattered throughout all the farming regions of the country but are heavily concentrated in the Ukraine and the adjoining areas of Moldavia and the Kuban. A small, separate region of concentration surrounds the Moscow area. Most of the poultry are kept on private plots by individual farmers.

Although the age of the tractor supposedly arrived in Russia early in the Soviet period, many draft animals are still kept on the farms. Horses are raised extensively throughout European Russia and the steppe lands of northern Kazakhstan and southwestern Siberia as well as in the Caucasus

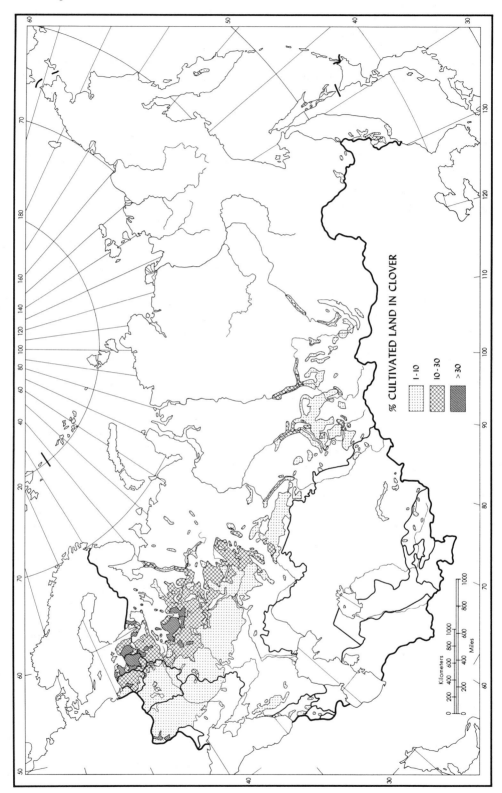

Figure 14-19   Per cent of cultivated land in clover.

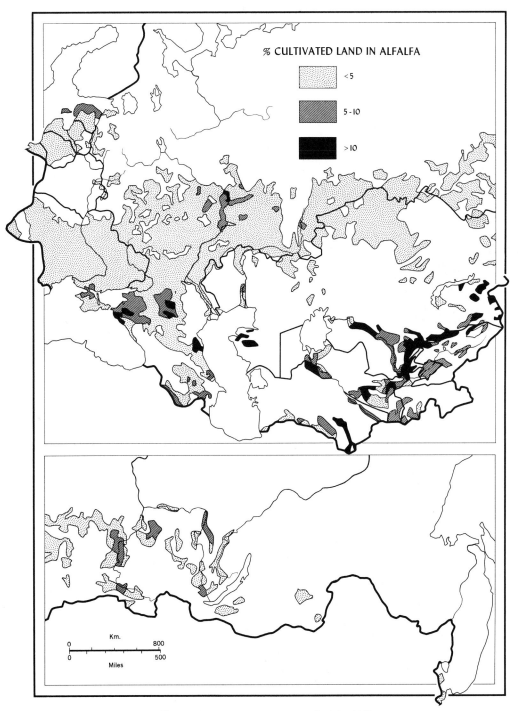

Figure 14-20   Per cent of cultivated land in alfalfa.

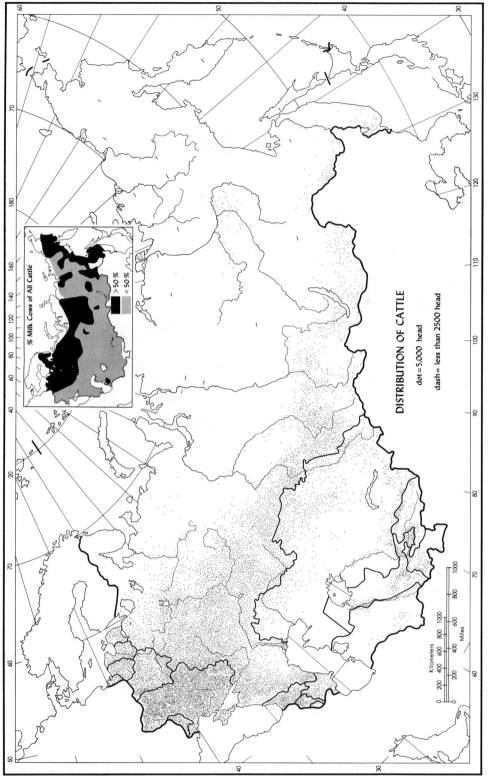

DISTRIBUTION OF CATTLE

dot = 5,000 head

dash = less than 2500 head

% Milk Cows of All Cattle

> 50 %

< 50 %

Figure 14-21 Distribution of cattle.

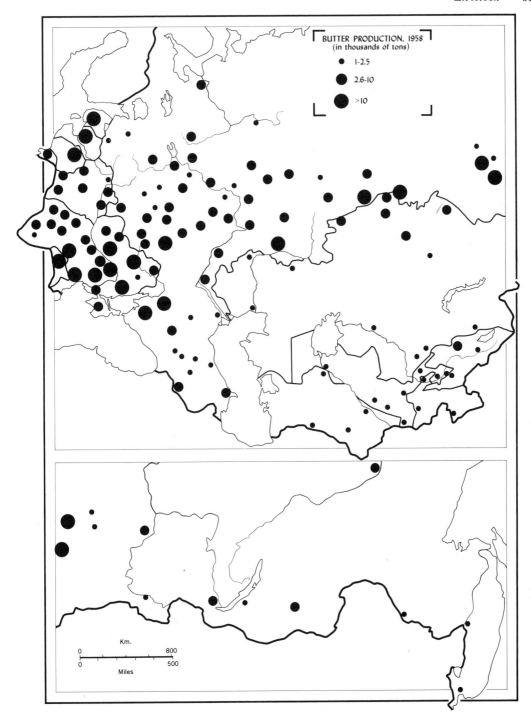

Figure 14-22   Butter production, 1958.

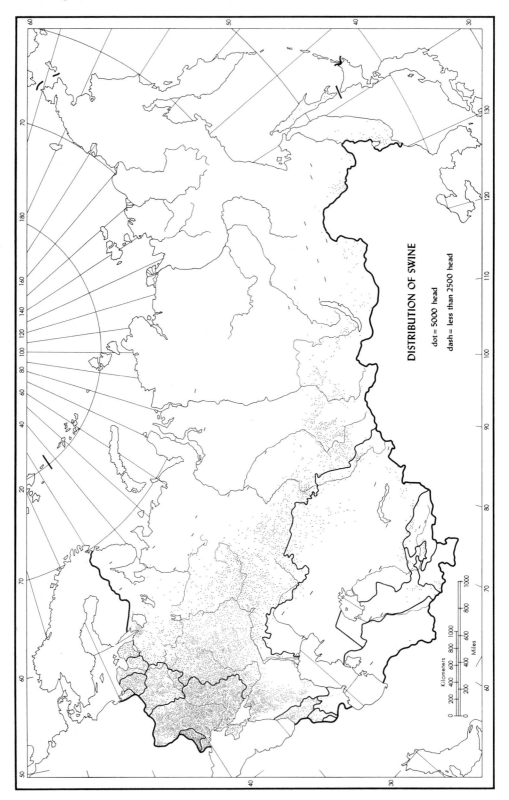

Figure 14-23   Distribution of swine.

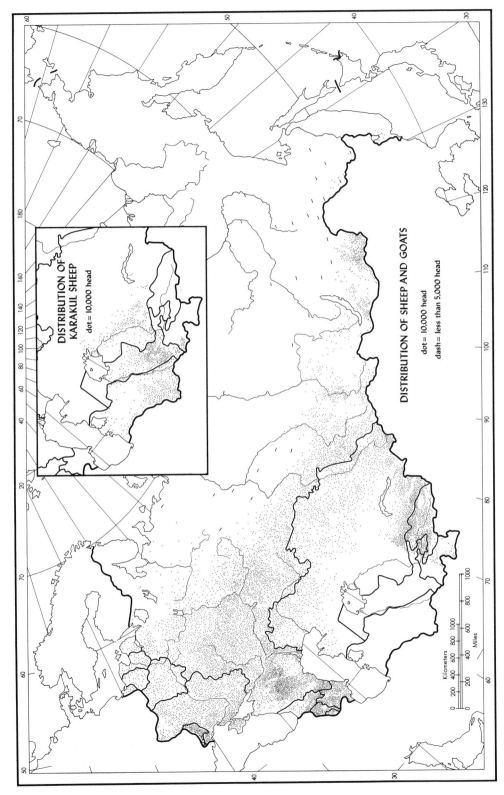

DISTRIBUTION OF SHEEP AND GOATS

dot = 10,000 head
dash = less than 5,000 head

DISTRIBUTION OF
KARAKUL SHEEP

dot = 10,000 head

Kilometers

Miles

Figure 14-24 Distribution of sheep and goats and karakul sheep.

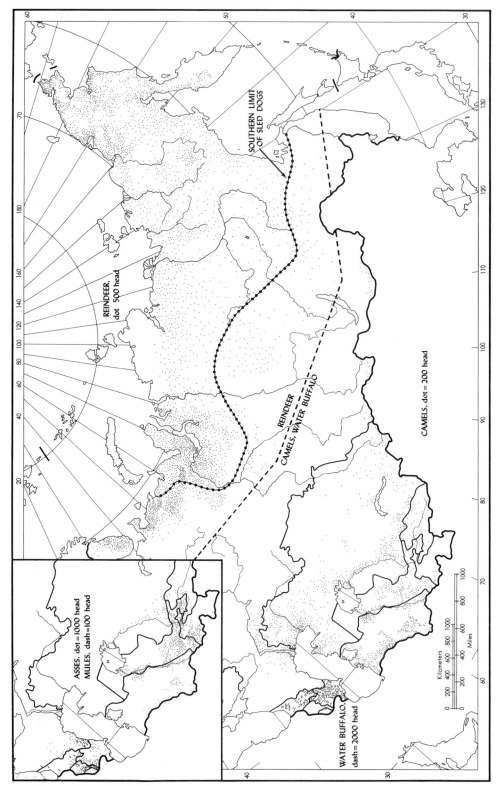

Figure 14-25   Distributions of camels, asses, mules, water buffalo, reindeer, and sled dogs.

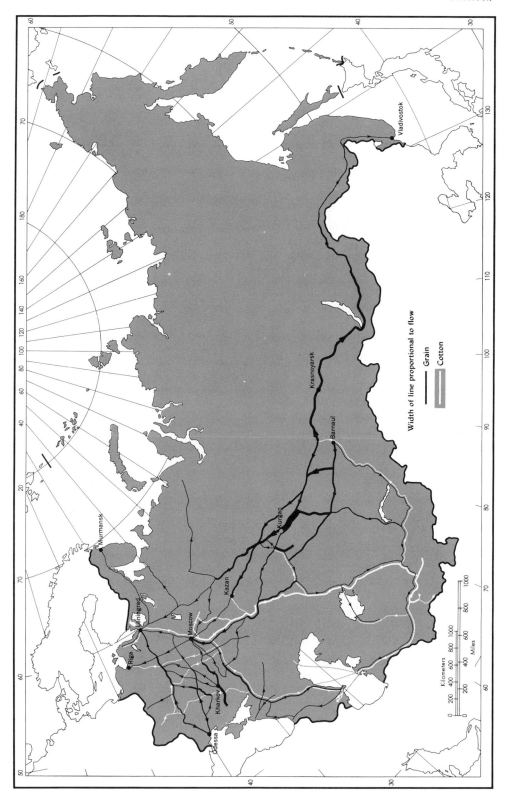

Figure 14-26 Movements of grain and cotton.

and Middle Asia. Also, some oxen are still used. Bulls not slaughtered for veal are castrated and put to work at the age of 10 months, and cows are often worked after they are no longer useful for milk. The large Siemmenphal and Holstein breeds are admirably suited for tri-purpose duty: milk, meat, and work. Asses and mules are used extensively in the Ukraine, the Caucasus, and Middle Asia. The principal means for conveying produce to market in Middle Asia is the donkey standing no more than 3 feet or so in height pulling a cart whose wheels are considerably greater in diameter than the height of the donkey. The camel is widely distributed as a beast of burden throughout the deserts of Middle Asia, in the North Caspian Lowland, and in the dry Kura River Valley of Transcaucasia. Water buffalo are used in the moister areas of Transcaucasia, and reindeer are used extensively in the north both for draft animals and for meat.

Interchanges of Agricultural Products

The fact that there are some sharp crop differentiations from one part of the country to another necessitates considerable movements of produce from growing to consuming areas. Grain flows northward from the Ukraine and the North Caucasus to the central and northwestern parts of European Russia, and heavy grain flows move out of southwestern Siberia and northern Kazakhstan westward to the Urals and European Russia, eastward along the Trans-Siberian Railroad to eastern Siberia and the Far East, and southward into Middle Asia. A heavy cotton flow moves northwestward from Middle Asia to the Central Industrial Region and a lighter flow moves from Transcaucasia to the center. Flax moves generally northeastward from the flax-growing areas of the European West, the Central Black Earth Region, and the Ukraine to the Central Industrial Region and other processing centers of European Russia. Minor flows of these products, as well as flows of livestock products and vegetable oil products,

move from producing areas to outlying areas of consumption.

Reading List

Atlas selskogo khozyaystva S.S.S.R. (Atlas of Agriculture of the U.S.S.R.), Moscow, 1960, 308 pp. (in Russian).

Bell, Richard E., "How Soviet Agriculture Compares with Ours," *Foreign Agriculture,* September 1961, 6–7.

Belov, Fedor, *The History of a Soviet Collective Farm,* Praeger, 1955, 237 pp.

Doroshenko, P. E., *Selskoe khozyaystvo S.S.S.R. v 1959–1965 godakh,* Moscow, 1959, 176 pp. (in Russian).

Hoeffding, O., and Nimitz, N., *Soviet National Income and Product,* Rand Corporation, ASTIA No AD213477, April 6, 1959, 218 pp.

Jasny, Naum, *The Socialized Agriculture of the U.S.S.R.; Plans and Performance,* Stanford University Press, Stanford, 1949, 837 pp.

Johnson, D. Gale, and Kahan, Arcadius, "Soviet Agriculture: Structure and Growth," Nimitz, Nancy, "Soviet Agricultural Prices and Costs," and Volin, Lazar, "Agricultural Policy of the Soviet Union," in *Comparisons of the United States and Soviet Economies,* Part I, United States Government Printing Office, Washington, 1959, 201–318.

Kalvoda, Joseph, "Soviet Agricultural Reform and the Future of Collective Farms," *The Russian Review,* October 1960, 384–395.

Kucherov, Samuel, "The Future of the Soviet Collective Farm," *American Slavic and East European Review,* April 1960, 180–201.

Laird, Roy D., "Soviet Goals for 1965 and the Problems of Agriculture," *Slavic Review,* October 1961, 454–464.

Newth, J. A., "Soviet Agriculture: The Private Sector, 1950–1959," *Soviet Studies,* October 1961, 160–171 and April 1962, 414–432.

Nove, Alec, "Soviet Agriculture Marks Time," *Foreign Affairs,* July 1962, 576–594.

Report of the Institute of International Education Seminar on Agriculture in the Soviet Union, April 28–29, 1960, Chicago, Illinois, 67 pp.

Schlesinger, Rudolf, "The New Structure of Soviet Agriculture," *Soviet Studies,* January 1959, 228–251.

United States Department of Agriculture, *Livestock in the Soviet Union,* 1961, 84 pp.

Volin, Lazar, "The Russian Peasant: From Emancipation to Kolkhoz," in Cyril E. Black, *The Transformation of Russian Society,* Harvard University Press, Cambridge, 1960, 292–311.

——, "Soviet Agriculture; A Continuing Problem," *Current History,* November 1961, 286–291.

——, *A Survey of Soviet Russian Agriculture,* United States Department of Agriculture Monograph 5, 1951.

15

Industry

Since the beginning of the five-year plans in 1929 the Soviets have been pouring the bulk of their capital expenditures into the development of industry. As a result, today the Soviet Union is second only to the United States in industrial output. Between 1913 and 1960 Soviet industrial production multiplied between six and seven times. Its volume in 1960 was estimated by Western observers to be somewhere between 25 and 40 per cent that of the United States. The Soviets claim that it was 50 per cent that of the United States. During the seven-year plan total industrial production is scheduled to increase by approximately 80 per cent, production goods by 85 to 88 per cent, and consumer goods by 62 to 65 per cent. The Soviets hope to equal the production of the United States in certain of the basic industries by 1972.

Industry and construction now account for about as much of the national income in the U.S.S.R. as they do in the United States (Table 15–1). The national income of the U.S.S.R., however, is only about one fourth that of the United States, and the value added by industry is roughly one quarter that of the United States. More people are engaged in industry in the Soviet Union than in the United States; hence labor productivity in the Soviet Union is very low (Table 15–2). Soviet inefficiency is particularly

flagrant in the wood and fuel industries (Table 15–3).

Table 15–1   *National Income by Sector of Origin, U.S.S.R. and the United States, 1955[a]*

Sector	U.S.S.R. Per Cent of Total	U.S.A. Per Cent of Total
Industry and construction	36.6	40.7
Agriculture	27.1	4.6
Transportation and communications	5.0	6.5
Services and trade	31.3	48.2
National income	100.0	100.0

[a] *Source: Comparisons of United States and Soviet Economies*, Part II, p. 383.

Light industry in the Soviet Union makes up only about 30 per cent of the total industrial production, whereas in the developed countries of the West it makes up about 70 per cent of the total. In terms of capital outlay, labor force, and production the Soviets have concentrated on the development of heavy industries at the expense of light industries. Such a policy makes sense if one country is bent on surpassing all other countries, but in the mean time it is rather

Table 15–2 Relative Value Added and Labor Productivity of Industry: Soviet Union as a Percentage of United States, 1955[a]

	1955
Value added of industry	22.7
Persons engaged	109.6
Man-hours	129.2
Value added per person engaged	20.7
Value added per manhour	17.6
Value added per head of population	19.1

[a] *Source: Comparisons of the United States and Soviet Economies*, Part I, 1959, p. 113.

hard on the consumer. It has been estimated that although total industrial output in the Soviet Union between 1913 and 1955 multiplied five or six times, the output of machinery and equipment multiplied about 16 times, that of intermediate industrial products about 9 times, and consumer goods only 3 times.

Table 15–3 Distribution of Persons Engaged by Major Industrial Groups: Soviet Union and United States[a]

	Per Cent	
	U.S.S.R. 1955	U.S.A. 1953
Ferrous and nonferrous metals	6.0	7.6
Fuel	8.0	5.3
Electricity	1.6	2.2
Chemicals	3.3	5.9
Wood construction materials	15.3	6.6
Mineral construction materials	6.2	4.2
Machinery and allied products	32.4	41.5
Machinery and equipment	—	(27.6)
Metal products	—	(13.9)
Food and allied products	9.5	8.8
Textiles and allied products	17.7	17.9
Total	100.0	—

[a] *Source: Comparisons of the United States and Soviet Economies*, Part I, p. 114.

The average annual growth rate from 1913 to 1955 for industry as a whole was 4.2 per cent, for machinery and equipment 6.8 per cent, for intermediate and industrial products 5.5 per cent, and for consumer goods 2.6 per cent. Some of this growth is attributable to the territorial expansion that took place during and after World War II. It has been estimated that the acquired territory added about 11 per cent to industrial output. Thus the annual growth rate for all industry has to be reduced from 4.2 per cent to 3.9 per cent to eliminate the effects of territorial expansion. This growth rate compares to one of 5.3 per cent per year during the last 40 years of the Tsarist period.

This fact has led several observers to the conclusion that Russia would be farther ahead now had the Soviet system never been initiated; they say that the growth rate that has been achieved has been done so not because of the Soviet system, as the Soviets boast, but in spite of it. At the time of the Revolution, Russia was not an altogether undeveloped country, it was undergoing a faltering industrial revolution which began about 1880. Thus the Soviets have had a considerable base on which to build, unlike many of the underdeveloped countries of today. But it is useless to speculate on what might have been; the Revolution did occur and the Soviets are solidly in control.

One should not average industrial growth rates throughout the entire Soviet period because it was so broken up by wars—the two World Wars, the Revolution, and at least two periods of civil war. The measurable Soviet output dropped by 80 per cent between 1913 and 1920, and the 1913 level was not recovered until 1927 or 1928. From 1928 to 1937 all civilian industrial production in the Soviet Union increased at an annual rate of about 10.9 per cent, the production of intermediate products rose at about 15 per cent per year, machinery at about 26.3 per cent, and consumer goods at about 5.5 per cent. Since 1950 the overall growth rate has been about 8 per cent per year.

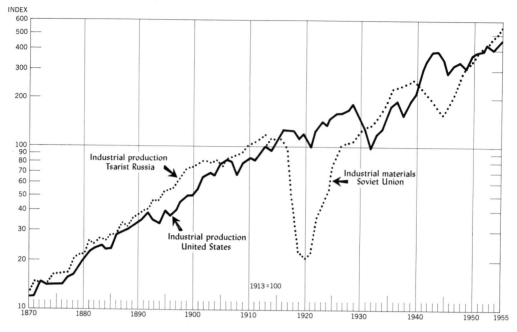

Figure 15-1   Indexes of Industrial Production: Tsarist Russia, U.S.S.R., and U.S.A., 1870–1955.   Data have been plotted on semilogarithmic coordinates to illustrate relative rates of growth.   From Comparisons of the United States and Soviet Economies, *p. 98.*

It should be realized that during these periods of rapid growth the rates have been no higher than they have been in other countries undergoing rapid industrialization. The rate of increase in industrial production in the Soviet Union still is limited only by physical ability to produce and not by market considerations, as is the case in most developed countries where supply and demand are critically balanced. In the United States during the 1950's the annual growth rate has fluctuated between 0.5 per cent and about 5 per cent, depending upon general economic conditions.

The industry that is found in the Soviet Union today is largely a product of the Soviets themselves; indeed it is largely a product of construction after World War II, since so much of the prewar buildup was destroyed by the Germans. At the time of the Revolution some 70 per cent of the industrial production of Russia was concentrated in the European part of the country. The Central Industrial Region accounted for

more than 80 per cent of the textile industry, and the Ukraine and adjacent parts of the Donets Basin in the Russian Republic accounted for over 90 per cent of the coal production, almost all the iron ore production, and nearly 75 per cent of the pig iron production. The machine-building industries almost entirely were located in the European part of Russia.

Although it was the intent of the Soviets to disperse industry into underdeveloped peripheral areas, and although some new industrial enterprises were built in such areas as the Urals, Siberia, the Far East, and Middle Asia, the fact was that the relative distribution of industry remained very little changed up until World War II. Economic realities induced conservatism into ideological policies for rapid widespread change. According to Soviet doctrine the economy should develop according to the following precepts: (1) there should be a rapid industrialization, (2) the economic activity should be distributed as evenly as possible through-

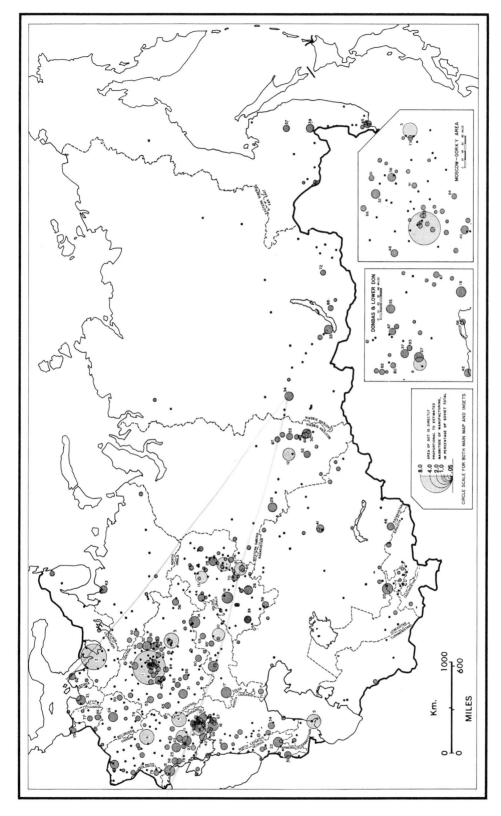

Figure 15-2   See following page for descriptive legend.

Figure 15-2   Industrial outputs of cities in the U.S.S.R.   A list of the 93 foremost industrial cities with their percentages of total U.S.S.R. production follows.   Numbers correspond to those on map.   1. Moscow, 8.20; 2. Leningrad, 4.90; 3. Gorky, 1.65; 4. Kharkov, 1.65; 5. Baku, 1.60; 6. Kiev, 1.60; 7. Sverdlovsk, 1.45; 8. Donetsk, 1.30; 9. Chelyabinsk, 1.25; 10. Kuybyshev, 1.25; 11. Dnepropetrovsk, 1.10; 12. Novosibirsk, 1.10; 13. Perm, 1.10; 14. Kazan, 0.95; 15. Odessa, 0.95; 16. Ufa, 0.95; 17. Volgograd, 0.90; 18. Rostov, 0.85; 19. Saratov, 0.80; 20. Tashkent, 0.80; 21. Riga, 0.75; 22. Tbilisi, 0.75; 23. Zaporozhye, 0.75; 24. Minsk, 0.70; 25. Krivoy Rog, 0.65; 26. Magnitogorsk, 0.65; 27. Makeyevka, 0.65; 28. Nizhniy Tagil, 0.65; 29. Omsk, 0.65; 30. Novokuznetsk, 0.65; 31. Voronezh, 0.65; 32. Yaroslavl, 0.65; 33. Irkutsk, 0.60; 34. Krasnoyarsk, 0.60; 35. Lugansk, 0.60; 36. Lvov, 0.60; 37. Gorlovka, 0.55; 38. Ivanovo, 0.55; 39. Khabarovsk, 0.55; 40. Tula, 0.55; 41. Karaganda, 0.50; 42. Zhdanov, 0.50; 43. Archangel, 0.45; 44. Izhevsk, 0.45; 45. Vladivostok, 0.45; 46. Alma-Ata, 0.40; 47. Kadiyevka, 0.40; 48. Kalinin, 0.40; 49. Krasnodar, 0.40; 50. Orenburg, 0.40; 51. Yerevan, 0.40; 52. Barnaul, 0.35; 53. Bryansk, 0.35; 54. Grozny, 0.35; 55. Kemerovo, 0.35; 56. Kirov, 0.35; 57. Komsomolsk, 0.35; 58. Nikolayev, 0.35; 59. Orsk, 0.35; 60. Penza, 0.35; 61. Prokopyevsk, 0.35; 62. Tallin, 0.35; 63. Dneprodzerzhinsk, 0.30; 64. Kopeysk, 0.30; 65. Kursk, 0.30; 66. Rybinsk, 0.30; 67. Shakhty, 0.30; 68. Taganrog, 0.30; 69. Ulyanovsk, 0.30; 70. Zlatoust, 0.30; 71. Astrakhan, 0.25; 72. Chita, 0.25; 73. Dzerzhinsk, 0.25; 74. Gomel, 0.25; 75. Kaliningrad, 0.25; 76. Kamensk-Uralskiy, 0.25; 77. Kaunas, 0.25; 78. Kherson, 0.25; 79. Kishinev, 0.25; 80. Konstantinovka, 0.25; 81. Kostroma, 0.25; 82. Kramatorsk, 0.25; 83. Lipetsk, 0.25; 84. Ryazan, 0.25; 85. Syzran, 0.25; 86. Tambov, 0.25; 87. Tomsk, 0.25; 88. Ulan-Ude, 0.25; 89. Vilnyus, 0.25; 90. Vitebsk, 0.25; 91. Vladimir, 0.25; 92. Vologda, 0.25; 93. Yenakievo, 0.25. From Lonsdale, Richard E. and Thompson, John H., "A Map of the U.S.S.R.'s Manufacturing," Economic Geography *January 1960, facing p. 36.*

out the country, (3) the economy should stimulate the development of backward nationalities and areas, (4) production should take place close to raw materials and markets, in order to minimize transport, and (5) specialized production should be promoted in regions that possess uniquely favorable conditions for such development, in terms of either natural resources, transport facilities, skilled labor, or historic precedence. In practice, it was found that some of these objectives are largely mutually exclusive. Shortage of capital and emphasis on speed of industrialization have led to the construction of giant industrial enterprises in old centers of production, at the expense of industrial dispersal. Also, it became apparent that if major developments were to take place in the East, the requirements of massive construction projects, movements of people, and urban housing and facilities would have to be met initially by the industries of the West. Thus the industrial capacities of the old centers had to be strengthened before large-scale development could be attempted in outlying areas. During the late 1930's considerations of national defense and strategic security under the imminent threat of war induced abnormalities into the economy which further delayed the "eastward movement."

Within 3 months after the German attack in June 1941, more than 1360 major industrial enterprises, mainly of military significance, were moved from European Russia and the Ukraine into the eastern regions of the country. About 455 enterprises were relocated in the Urals, 210 were moved to western Siberia, and 250 to Middle Asia and Kazakhstan. Before the Germans were finally repulsed, they had occupied and largely devastated an area that before the war had housed 40 per cent of the total population of the Soviet Union and had produced 62 per cent of the coal, 68 per cent of the pig iron, 58 per cent of the steel, and 60 per cent of the aluminum. During this time the eastern regions experienced a rapid growth, and the Urals eventually produced 40 per cent of all the war industrial materials. Between 1940 and 1943 the output of industrial production in western Siberia increased 3.4 times. These hastily relocated industries remained in the eastern areas after the war, and new industries were added to them. Table 15–4 shows the distribution of industry by region in 1955.

In 1960 the eastern part of the country, with four fifths the total territory and three fourths the total fuel and raw material resources, still possessed only one third of the population and one fourth of the industrial production of the country. However, it appears that as a result of World War II

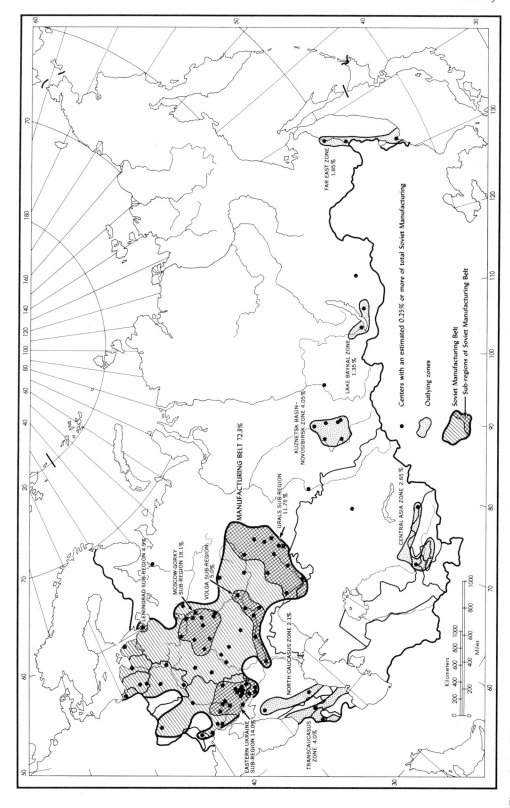

Figure 15-3 The manufacturing belt of the U.S.S.R. From Lonsdale, Richard E. and Thompson, John H., "A Map of the U.S.S.R.'s Manufacturing," Economic Geography, January 1960, p. 42.

the West has suffered a permanent setback in its relative position among Soviet regions, and the East, including the Urals, has been gaining in its per cent of total production. The seven year plan says that in 1965 the Urals, Siberia, the Far East, Kazakhstan, and Middle Asia will account for more than 40 per cent of the national capital investment and will produce 44 per cent of the pig iron, 48 per cent of the steel, 50 per cent of the coal, 30 per cent of the oil, 46 per cent of the electric power, and more than 45 per cent of the lumber.

Table 15–4   Distribution of Industry by Region, U.S.S.R., 1955 (in Per Cents)[a]

R.S.F.S.R.	63.8
European North	1.9
European West	6.2
Center	18.8
Volga	5.4
North Caucasus	5.0
Urals	13.8
Siberia and Far East	12.7
Ukrainian S.S.R.	20.2
Belorussian S.S.R.	1.6
Baltic Republics	2.0
Transcaucasia	5.6
Middle Asia	3.0
Kazakh S.S.R.	3.4
Moldavian S.S.R.	0.4

[a] *Source:* Cherdantsev, G. N., and others, *Ekonomicheskaya geografiya SSSR: obshchiy obzor*, Moscow, 1958, p. 95.

The most rapid industrial growth in the country is taking place in the Volga-Urals area (Kuybyshev Oblast and the Tatar and Bashkir A.S.S.R.'s) and Novosibirsk Oblast in southwestern Siberia. These regions got their initial impetus as a result of World War II, but their high growth rates have continued since the war. Between 1950 and 1956, while the production of the U.S.S.R. as a whole roughly doubled, Kuybyshev Oblast and the Bashkir A.S.S.R. increased their industrial output by about 2.5 times, and

the Tatar A.S.S.R. and Novosibirsk Oblast increased theirs by about 2.25 times. The increases in capital investment, labor force, and railroad freight traffic in these regions have been correspondingly high.

The "Volga Bend" is rapidly becoming a focal point in the Soviet Union strategically located between the three most industrialized areas—the Central Industrial Region, the Ukraine, and the Urals—on major rail and water transportation routes. It is no longer merely a crossroads for goods moved from one region to another; it is generating its own freight traffic. In most analyses of differential regional industrial growth in the Soviet Union the division is unfortunately made between East and West, and the Urals are lumped with the East. Such a two-fold division splits the Volga-Urals down the middle and obscures the fact that its core area is the most rapidly developing part of the country, developing at a considerably higher rate than the much vaunted Siberian, Far Eastern, and Middle Asian areas. Since World War II the Far East seems to have lost much of its tendency for rapid industrialization that it displayed in the late 1930's.

The Mineral Fuels

The mineral fuels are still the primary bases for industry. The Soviet Union, having the second largest industrial output in the world, naturally has great demands for fuel. The Soviet Union now uses more coal than the United States, nearly half as much oil, and about one eighth as much natural gas. Fortunately for the Soviets the U.S.S.R. contains large reserves of all three of these items. The Soviets now claim to have more than half the total geological reserves of coal on earth. In 1958 it was estimated that the U.S.S.R. had 11 per cent of the oil reserves of the world. And in 1959 the natural gas reserves of the U.S.S.R. were estimated to be more than one eighth those of the United States and slightly larger than those of Canada. This puts the Soviet Union first in the world in terms of coal reserves, fifth in terms of oil reserves, and second in gas reserves. Since large areas of the Soviet Union are still inadequately explored, reserves there may be considerably greater than are now stated. It has been estimated on the basis of suitable sedimentary structures that the U.S.S.R. should eventually produce about 68 per cent more oil than the United States. The discovery of natural gas in the Soviet Union has only just begun; it was not until 1955 that the Soviets started a serious drive for the increased production and use of natural gas.

So far coal is still the primary fuel in the Soviet Union. In 1940 it accounted for more than 70 per cent of all mineral fuel consumption and oil and gas accounted for only 24 per cent. The official policy from 1940 to 1957 was to limit the production of oil and gas and to concentrate on coal production. In 1950 the share of coal in total fuel production had risen to 73 per cent and that of oil and gas had dropped to less than 20 per cent. But in 1957 a new fifteen-year plan for fuels was launched which completely reversed the policy. By 1972 coal is to account for only about 30 per cent of total fuel production and oil and gas are to rise to more than 60 per cent. Such a fuel ratio will be much more nearly like that of the United States at the present time, a fuel ratio that one might expect to be geared to a highly industrialized economy. During the seven-year plan natural gas production is to increase 5.6 times, crude oil is to increase more than two times, and coal production is to increase only about 20 per cent. The output of natural gas that is planned for 1965 is equal in thermal effect to the total coal production of the Donets, Moscow, and Pechora Coal Basins in 1958.

The change in policy has been brought about by economic considerations which only recently have begun to play a major role in Soviet planning. It has been found that for the U.S.S.R. as a whole the cost of

Table 15–5   Expected Percentage Changes in the Structure of Energy Fuels (Not Counting Coking Coal), 1955 to 1965[a]

Fuel	1955	1965
Coal	72.9	49.2
Oil fuel	10.9	17.8
Gas	2.6	24.8
Peat	5.1	3.6
Oil shale	0.8	1.1
Firewood	7.7	3.5

[a] *Source:* Lydolph, Paul E., and Shabad, Theodore, "The Oil and Gas Industries in the U.S.S.R.," *Annals of the Association of American Geographers,* December 1960, p. 474.

production of oil is one fourth that of coal in equivalent heat units. Oil also presents a two-fold advantage in transport considerations: (1) pipelines will relieve the heavily overburdened railroads, and (2) the conversion of railroad locomotives to Diesel and electric traction will greatly reduce the need for long coal hauls and will increase the efficiency and power of the locomotives. By 1965 electric and Diesel locomotives are expected to handle 87 per cent of all rail traffic, as compared with 26 per cent in 1958. Oil and gas are to play a greater role in the fuel consumption of thermal-electric stations, in steel furnaces, and in cement kilns. Natural gas is to become the second most important energy fuel by 1965. Also the development of oil and gas industries will provide a broad base for the badly needed development of all aspects of the chemical industry. And lastly, adequate development of the oil and gas industries will make the Soviet Union more defensively viable.

The Coal Industry   The Soviet Union has enough coal reserves to last about 20,000 years at the present rate of consumption. Although three fourths of these reserves lie in eastern Siberia and the Far East, deposits are scattered widely throughout the Soviet Union. Since transportation is a major part

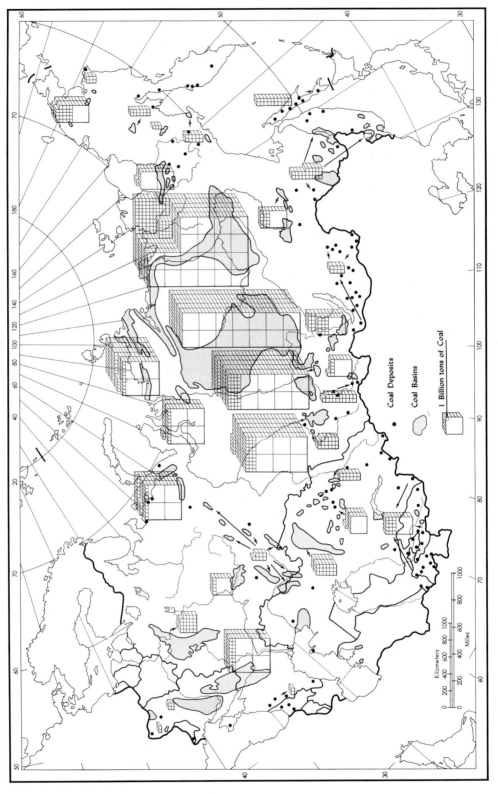

Figure 15-4   Coal resources of the U.S.S.R.   From Hodgkins, Jordan A., Soviet Power: Energy Resources, Production and Potential, 1961.   By permission of Prentice-Hall, Inc.

of the cost to consumers, development has taken place as near as possible to markets, and the most productive fields are not necessarily those that are richest in deposits. The most productive fields are the Donets, the Kuznetsk, the Urals, the Moscow, the eastern Siberian fields, and Karaganda. In 1960 the Donets Basin still produced 37 per cent of the country's coal and more than half of the country's coking coal. Although by percentage this is a reduction from pre-Soviet days when the Donets Basin produced almost all of Russia's coal, its absolute production is higher than it ever was, and

Table 15–6 Mineable Reserves of Coal by Regions[a]

Traditionally Established Regions	Per Cent of Mineable Reserves
European Russia	6.52
Caucasia	0.01
Urals	0.09
Kazakhstan	1.58
Middle Asia	0.49
Arctic and Subarctic Siberia	60.52
South Siberian Belt	27.61
Transbaykal	0.09
Sakhalin	0.21
Far East	0.50
North East	2.38
Totals	100.00

[a] *Source:* Hodgkins, Jordan A., *Soviet Power*, p. 28.

it is still by far the most important producing field in the country. And apparently it is to remain so; the 1965 plan calls for the Donbass to produce 37 per cent of the country's coal, exactly the same percentage that it produced in 1960. The order of rank of the producing coal basins has remained the same throughout the Soviet period and apparently is to remain the same in the foreseeable future. Thus the heavy producers have been and will remain the Donets, Kuznetsk, Urals, Moscow, Cheremkhovo, and Karaganda Basins. Of these, only the

Donets, Kuznetsk, and Karaganda fields produce coal of coking quality; the Karaganda coals are hampered by high ash content and must be mixed with higher grade coals for

Table 15–7 Proven Coal Reserves by Basins as of January 1956 (in Billions of Metric Tons)[a]

Basins and Deposits

European Part of the U.S.S.R.	74.91
Donets Basin	57.16
Ukraine S.S.R.	49.00
Rostov Oblast, R.S.F.S.R.	8.16
Lvov-Volyn coal bearing region	1.65
Dnieper basin	3.05
Moscow basin	8.89
Pechora basin	4.10
Caucasus	0.56
Tkibuli deposits	0.29
Tkvarcheli deposits	0.07
Urals	5.00
Kizel basin	0.61
South Urals basin	1.56
Chelyabinsk basin	1.37
Western and Eastern Siberia (Southern Part)[b]	114.49
Kuznetsk basin	0.07
Kansk-Achinsk basin	35.00
Minusinsk basin	2.31
Irkutsk basin	5.17
Eastern Siberia (Northern Part)[b]	4.11
Transbaykal, Far East, Sakhalin	8.74
Bureya basin	1.63
Sakhalin deposits	2.01
Kazakhstan	28.99
Karaganda basin	10.30
Ekibastuz deposit	9.11
Middle Asia	3.55
Angren deposits	1.52

[a] *Source:* Hodgkins, Jordan A., *Soviet Power*, pp. 158–162.
[b] Siberia contains large unproven reserves of coal.

heavy metallurgical use. Thus much of the coking coal for the country is produced by two basins, the Donets and the Kuznetsk, and long hauls are required to serve the

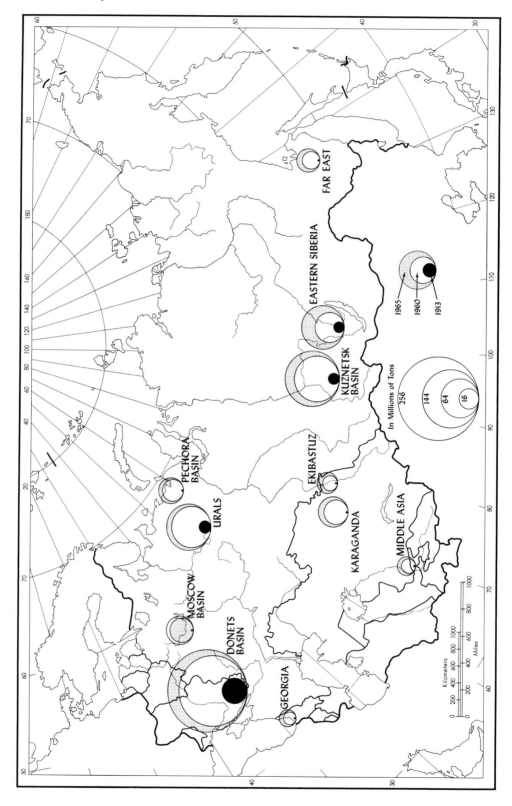

Figure 15-5 Coal production by basins: 1913, 1960, and 1965 plan. Production in the Moscow Basin is to decrease from 1960 to 1965. Data from Narodnoe khozyaystvo SSSR v 1960 godu, p. 265 and Hodgkins, Soviet Power, p. 58.

needs of many consuming areas. The Pechora Basin in the northeastern corner of European Russia produces good coking coal, but because of its remote location it serves only the needs of the European North and Northwest.

All this movement of coal puts a tremendous burden on the railroads, which transports more than 90 per cent of the coal moved. Coal and coke constitute 22 per cent of all railroad freight traffic. Fourteen million tons of coal mined east of the Urals

Table 15–8 Coal Production by Basin or Region, 1913–1965 (in Millions of Tons)[a]

	1913	1940	1955	1960	1965 plan
U.S.S.R.	29	166	391	513	700 (approx.)
Donets	25	94	141	188	258
Kuznetsk	1	22	59	84	118
Ural	1	12	47	62	67
Moscow	—	10	39	43	41
Eastern Siberia	1	9	27	37	64
Karaganda	—	6	25	26	57[b]
Far East	—	7	17	22	29
Pechora	—	—	14	18	22
Middle Asia	—	2	6	8	13
Ekibastuz	—	—	2	6	
Georgia	—	—	3	3	4

[a] *Sources: Narodnoe khozyaystvo v 1960 godu*, p. 256, and Hodgkins, Jordan A., *Soviet Power*, p. 58.
[b] Includes both Karaganda and Ekibastuz.

The big coal consumers are the eastern Ukraine, the Urals, and the Central Industrial Region. Of these only the Ukraine produces all its own coal needs. Although the Urals fields, particularly the Kizel field, supply more than half the coal needs of the Urals, coking coal must be imported from Kuznetsk and Karaganda. The Central Industrial Region derives half its coal locally from the Moscow Basin, but all this coal is low grade and suitable only for electrical generation and heating. Higher-grade coals must be brought in from Donets, Kuznetsk, Kizel, and Karaganda. The Donets Basin supplies the bulk of the imported coal for the Central Industrial Region.

Table 15–9 Coal Production, Mining, and Ash Content by Basin, 1955[a]

	Per Cent of Total Production	Per Cent Open-Pit Mining	Per Cent Ash Content
U.S.S.R.	100.0	19.0	—
Donbass	35.9	0.0	14.5
Ukraine	29.7	0.0	14.6
Rostov Oblast	6.2	0.0	14.0
Moscow Basin	10.4	0.0	29.4
Kuznetsk	15.0	10.0	10.5
Karaganda	7.1	31.1	21.0
Pechora	3.8	0.0	19.2
Urals	12.4	50.5	24.8
Kizel	2.9	0.0	24.7
Chelyabinsk Oblast	4.7	36.9	28.3
Sverdlovsk Oblast	4.3	93.6	20.9
Middle Asia	1.7	33.5	14.1
Eastern Siberia	6.2	47.0	15.3
Far East	4.3	44.4	15.5
Maritime Kray	1.4	0.0	22.4
Sakhalin	1.0	16.3	14.2
Other	1.9	93.5	10.6
Georgia	0.7	0.0	30.3

[a] *Source:* Sudoplatov, A., *Coal Industry of the U.S.S.R.*, Moscow, 1959, pp. 50–53.

are transported annually to the European part of the country. It is hoped that this can be eliminated by the greater production of hydroelectricity in European Russia, by the development of the gas industry which in the future is to supply much of the fuel needs of the Central Industrial Region, and by increasing coal output in the European part of the country. Also it is planned to

Table 15–10   Regional Distribution of Soviet Coal Consumption, 1955 (in Metric Tons)[a]

Consuming Region and Source of Coal	Tons of Coal Consumed	Per Cent of Total Consumption
The South		
Local production		
Donets Basin	82,716,201	
Ukrainian Brown Coal	8,694,400	
Total consumption	91,410,601	24.28
The Urals		
Local production	44,081,538	
Imported coal		
Kuznetsk Basin	21,382,331	
Karaganda Basin	11,926,022	
Total consumption	77,389,891	20.55
Central Region		
Local production		
Moscow Basin	39,301,500	
Imported coal		
Donets Basin	30,057,703	
Kuznetsk Basin	4,415,547	
Kizel Basin	2,413,577	
Karaganda Basin	943,785	
Total consumption	77,132,112	20.49
Western Siberia (Southern Section)		
Local production	23,717,313	
Imported coal		
Karaganda Basin	329,788	
Total consumption	24,047,101	6.39
Eastern Siberia		
Local production	23,173,300	
Total consumption	23,173,300	6.15
Far East		
Local production	16,057,100	
Total consumption	16,057,100	4.26
The Northwest		
No local production		
Imported coal		
Donets Basin	2,706,682	
Pechora Basin	11,888,856	
Total consumption	14,595,538	3.88
Kazakhstan		
Local production	10,424,545	
Imported coal		
Kuznetsk Basin	2,681,166	
Total consumption	13,105,711	3.48

Table 15–10   Regional Distribution of Soviet Coal Consumption, 1955 (in Metric Tons)[a] (Continued)

Consuming Region and Source of Coal	Tons of Coal Consumed	Per Cent of Total Consumption
Volga Region		
No local production		
Imported coal		
Donets Basin	4,614,892	
Kuznetsk Basin	3,810,600	
Karaganda Basin	2,858,169	
Kizel Basin	52,900	
Total consumption	11,336,561	3.01
The Northern Caucasus		
Donets coal only	9,608,721	
Total consumption	9,608,721	2.55
Middle Asia		
Local production	6,333,100	
Imported coal		
Kuznetsk Basin	435,335	
Karaganda Basin	329,788	
Total consumption	7,098,223	1.89
The West		
No local production		
Imported coal		
Donets Basin	4,208,890	
Total consumption	4,208,890	1.12
Transcaucasia		
Local production	2,706,200	
Imported coal		
Donets coal	1,353,341	
Total consumption	4,059,541	1.08
The North		
Local production	2,264,544	
Total consumption	2,264,544	0.60
Coal exported from regions indicated—consuming region unknown		
Donets Basin	13,535	
Kuznetsk Basin	84,805	
Kizel Basin	308,000	
Total exported	406,338	0.11
Coal production and consumption unaccounted for	616,096	0.16
	376,498,700	100.00

[a] *Source:* Hodgkins, Jordan A., *Soviet Power*, pp. 62–63.

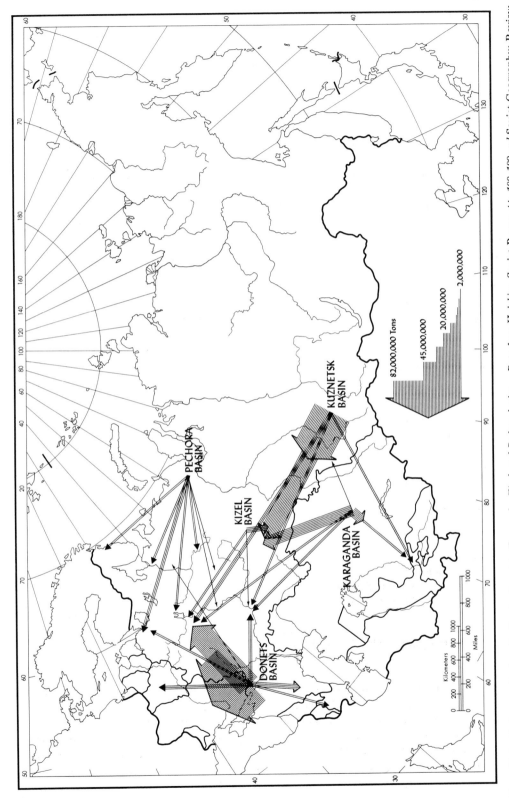

Figure 15-6   Coal movements from the Donets, Kuznetsk, Karaganda, Kizel, and Pechora basins.   Data from Hodgkins, Soviet Power, pp. 188–189 and Soviet Geography: Review and Translation, March 1960, pp. 9–20.

limit the building of heavy fuel consuming industries in the European part of the U.S.S.R. and in the Urals.

Coal used by railroad locomotives is another burden on the railroads, since the coal has to be hauled as it is used. The railroads have always been one of the greatest users of coal; until 1957 they accounted for more than 20 per cent of coal consumption in the country. Since then, with conversion from steam engines to Diesel and electric, coal consumption has been reduced. By 1965 it is planned that the railroads will consume no more than 1.2 per cent of the country's coal production. In 1958 the greatest coal consumers were thermal electric stations which used almost one third of the country's coal production and which generated about three fourths of the country's electricity.

imately 33 per cent below that of the Donbass coal, primarily because of thicker seams of coal in the east which in some cases lie nearer to the surface so that open-pit mining can be utilized. On the average the coal seams in the Kuznetsk Basin are six times as thick as those in the Donbass. Large open-pit mines are being introduced wherever possible, since productivity in open pits is four to six times higher and costs are 3.5 times lower than in shaft mines. Mines can be brought into production four to six times faster by open-pit methods. Some of the better fields, however, are not adaptable to open-pit mining because of the depth of the seams. All mining in the Donets Basin is done by shaft mining. The per cent of coal mined by open-pit methods jumped rapidly after the war from around 4 per cent in 1940 to around 20 per cent in 1958.

Table 15–11   Coal Consumers[a]

Consuming Branch of the Economy	Per Cent of Total		
	1954	1958	1965 (Plan)
Railroad transport	22.96	17.3	1.2
Ferrous metallurgy			
(Power and coke-chemical)	21.38	—	—
Including coke burned	(15.00)	15.5	21.1
Electrostations	18.53	32.8	41.1
Machine building	6.02	—	—
Coal industry	4.69	—	—
Domestic uses	—	13.1	18.3
Other industries and agriculture	—	21.3	18.3
All other branches of the economy	26.42	—	—
Total	100.0	100.0	100.0

[a] *Source:* Hodgkins, Jordan A., *Soviet Power*, p. 41.

Coal mining in the east is more economical than it is in the west. The capital expenditure per ton increase of coal output in eastern Siberia on the average is about 40 per cent and in the Kuzbass about 67 per cent of that in the Donbass. The production cost per ton of Kuzbass coal is approx-

Since that time it has remained at about 20 per cent.

Underground gasification of coal had its inception in 1935 in the Moscow and Donets Coal Basins. The German invasion interrupted this development, but underground gasification plants have been built at other

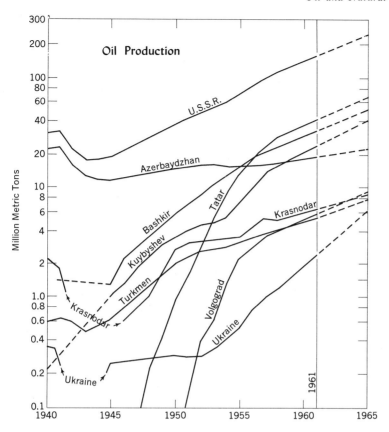

Figure 15-7 Oil production by regions in the U.S.S.R., 1940–1965. After Lydolph and Shabad.

coal fields as well as in the Moscow and Donets fields since the war. Apparently this method of coal utilization has met with some success in supplying gas to thermal electric stations; however, this type of utilization is only a minor part of the total coal consumption of the country. The seven-year plan indicates that gas generated by combustion of coal undergound will comprise only 0.5 per cent of the fuel balance of the country.

Oil and Natural Gas One of the most spectacular and significant recent developments in industry in the Soviet Union is the rapid expansion of the oil and natural gas industries. Russia and the Soviet Union has always been a major oil producer, and at the turn of the century it was the leading

producer in the world. But during the 1930's the industry had not expanded as rapidly as most other industries, and the German invasion during World War II caused an absolute decline in production. Since 1945, and particularly since 1953, production has rapidly increased. In 1960 the Soviet Union produced 148 million metric tons of crude petroleum and 45 billion cubic meters of natural gas; this compared to 348 million metric tons of oil and 362 billion cubic meters of natural gas produced by the United States. The 1972 goals for the U.S.S.R. are 350–400 million metric tons of petroleum and 270–320 billion cubic meters of natural gas.

A major geographical shift has occurred in the primary producing areas of oil. Whereas in 1940 the Caucasus produced 87 per cent of the country's oil, in 1960 the new Volga-Urals fields produced 70 per cent, and their share is to increase to 73 per cent in 1965. At the same time there has been almost an exact reversal in the proved reserves of the two regions; in 1940 the Caucasus were credited with 80 per cent of the country's reserves and the Volga-Urals fields were credited with 16 per cent; in 1955 the Caucasus were credited with 15 per cent and the Volga-Urals with 81 per cent.

The Baku fields, the traditional leaders of Russian production, were surpassed in production first by the Bashkir fields in 1954, then by the Tatar fields in 1956, and by Kuybyshev Oblast in 1959. Thus, three separate political regions within the Volga-Urals fields—the Bashkir A.S.S.R., the Tatar

A.S.S.R., and Kuybyshev Oblast—individually have surpassed the Baku production. And a fourth region in the Volga-Urals area, Volgograd Oblast, is to become the fifth most important producing region in the country, after Baku, by 1965. The Tatar A.S.S.R. is the leading producer in the country at present and is to remain so in the future, with the Bashkir A.S.S.R. and Kuybyshev Oblast close behind.

The Baku fields suffered an absolute decline during World War II, but since that time production has been slowly rising, largely by deeper drilling and drilling in the water of the Caspian offshore, and production is to continue to rise slowly until it recovers its 1941 level. The old North Caucasian oil fields and the minor producers of the Turkmen, Kazakh, and Uzbek Repub-

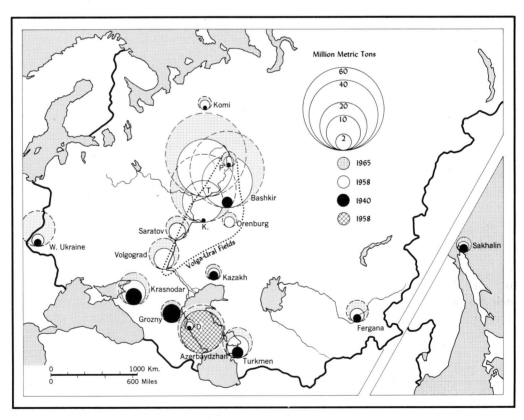

Figure 15-8   Oil production by regions in the U.S.S.R., 1940, 1958, 1965 plan.   After Lydolph and Shabad.   The 1940 production of Azerbaydzhan was almost identical with its planned production for 1965 and more than it was in 1958.   D = Dagestan, K = Kuybyshev, T = Tatar, P = Perm.

lics and Sakhalin Island maintain small constant percentages of the country's total oil production. Production in the newly acquired fields of the western Ukraine is rising rapidly and is so nearly equal that of Krasnodar Kray and the Turkmen S.S.R. by 1965. There has been much prospecting in the other broad sedimentary basins of the U.S.S.R., particularly in western Siberia, but so far no outstanding deposits have been discovered. In 1960 the Soviets reported the first oil well in Siberia along the eastern foot of the Urals about 220 miles north of Tyumen. But the country's oil production more and more is being concentrated in the Volga-Urals area, and it appears that it will remain there.

Table 15–12   Per Capita Consumption of Petroleum Products, in United States Gallons, 1958[a]

Country or Area	1958
United States	793
Canada	688
Scandinavia	406
United Kingdom and Ireland	214
Other Western Europe	133
Austria, Greece, Yugoslavia	47
U.S.S.R.	182

[a] *Source:* Lydolph, Paul E., and Shabad, Theodore, "The Oil and Gas Industries in the U.S.S.R.," *Annals of the Association of American Geographers,* December 1960, p. 475.

Per capita consumption of petroleum products in the Soviet Union is only about one fourth that in the United States and Canada, about half that of Scandinavia, and somewhat greater than that of much of western Europe. With production in the U.S.S.R. scheduled to quadruple by 1972, per capita consumption may approximate that of the United States, unless petroleum exports from the Soviet Union continue to rise sharply. The pattern of consumption is somewhat different from what it is in the United States. Industry, transport, agriculture, and the armed forces consume almost all the petroleum products produced in the U.S.S.R.; private individuals consume perhaps 2 per cent of the production. There are great regional discrepancies in types of fuel consumption in the U.S.S.R. The fuel-deficient, heavy-industry areas of the Central Industrial Region and the Urals are to rely much more heavily on oil products than are the sparsely settled, coal-rich areas of Asiatic U.S.S.R.

The shift of oil production from Baku to the Volga-Urals has brought about a rapid change in the mode of transport of petroleum products. No longer is the Caspian-Volga waterway the primary carrier of petroleum products; in fact some reversal of flow has occurred on this waterway, since refining capacity has not kept up with production in the new Volga-Urals fields. Some crude oil is shipped south down the river to the Baku refineries and then the refined products are shipped north again. But pipelines are being built east and west from the Volga-Urals to carry petroleum to the far reaches of the country, and new refineries are being built primarily in consuming centers. During the seven-year plan more than 30 thousand kilometers of oil pipeline are to be constructed. This will nearly triple the length of pipeline in the country, and the movement of oil by pipe is to increase 460 per cent.

Five pipelines are being built eastward from the Volga-Urals fields to Omsk in western Siberia, which is to become the major refining center in Siberia. Two of these lines will continue on to new refineries in Krasnoyarsk and Irkutsk. Other lines lead westward from the Volga-Urals fields to the Central Industrial Region, the Central Black Earth Region, Belorussia, and on to the satellite countries of eastern Europe. Older pipelines exist in the south between the fields in the eastern Caucasus and refineries on the Black Sea coast.

The production and consumption of large

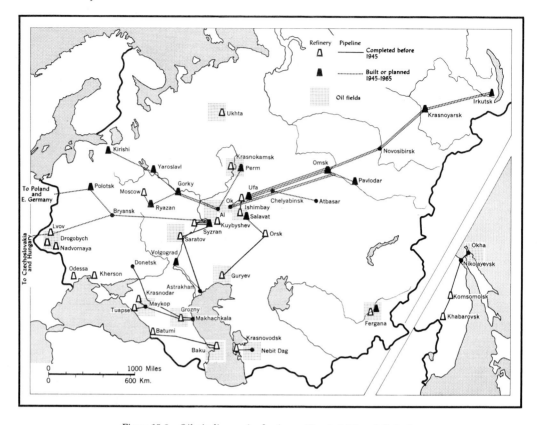

Figure 15-9   Oil pipelines and refineries.   After Lydolph and Shabad.

quantities of natural gas in the Soviet Union is a much more recent development than is the oil industry. Only since 1955 has there been a significant production of natural gas. Until this time gas was not recognized as one of the primary fuels; much of the by-product gases of oil production were flared off at the fields, and the Soviets were largely unaware of the great deposits of natural gas that existed in their country. During the last 7 or 8 years all this has changed. Large deposits of natural gas have been discovered in Stavropol and Krasnodar Krays in the North Caucasus, in Transcaucasia near Baku, in the eastern and western Ukraine, and in the Middle Asian desert near Bukhara. Other deposits exist in the Volga-Urals area, in the Komi A.S.S.R. in north-eastern European Russia, and in the Lena-Vilyuy Lowland in eastern Siberia. Produc-

tion from these fields is to increase approx-imately eight times during the seven-year plan.

On January 1, 1959 the natural gas re-serves of the Soviet Union were estimated at 930 billion cubic meters. This figure compares with 1958 reserves of around 7140 billion cubic meters in the United States and 857 billion cubic meters in Canada. The Soviets expect to increase their gas reserves to 3411 billion cubic meters by the end of 1965 while extracting 559 billion cubic meters of gas during the seven-year period. Extensive sedimentary basins conducive to gas deposits exist in the Soviet Union, so such an increase in reserves might be quite possible.

The major regions of gas production are to be the fields of the North Caucasus, Transcaucasia, the Ukraine, and Middle

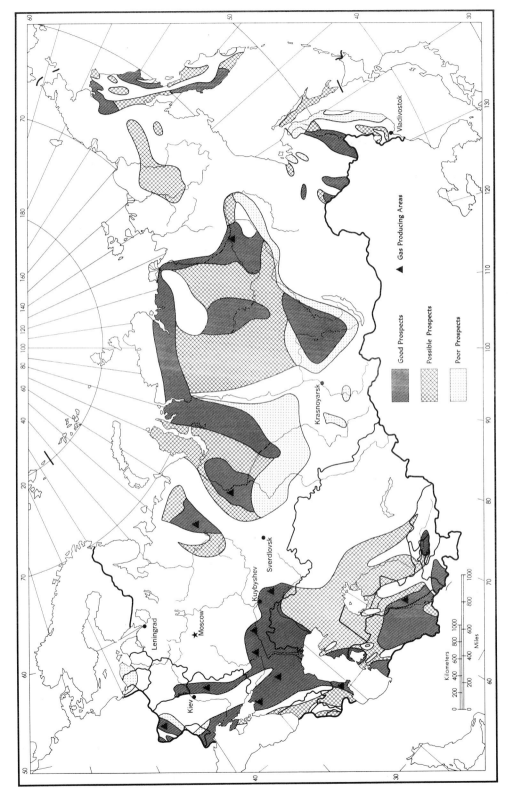

Figure 15-10   Prospective Gas Bearing Regions of the U.S.S.R.   After Lydolph and Shabad.

Asia and older producing fields at Saratov on the middle Volga. The development of the fields is entirely dependent on the construction of pipelines to consuming areas. At the beginning of 1958 there was a total of, 9500 kilometers of pipelines in the U.S.S.R., and during 1958 approximately

for the needs of industry and power generation, gas lines are being built primarily from producing fields to major industrial areas. Two pipelines have been completed from the Stavropol fields in the North Caucasus through the heavy industry area of the eastern Ukraine northward to Moscow.

Table 15–13   Natural Gas Proved Reserves and Planned Increases 1959 to 1965 (in Billion Cubic Meters)[a]

	Reserves January 1, 1959	Planned Increase 1959–1965	Planned Production 1959–1965	Expected Reserves January 1, 1966
Total U.S.S.R.	930	3040	559	3411
R.S.F.S.R.	550	1325	306	1569
Kuybyshev Oblast	8	25	51	28
Saratov Oblast	52	185	52	185
Volgograd Oblast	68	200	37	230
Astrakhan Oblast	8	50	18	56
Orenburg Oblast	5	80	12	73
Komi A.S.S.R.	13	70	10	83
Krasnodar Kray	130	260	76	314
Stavropol Kray	230	150	108	272
Chechen-Ingush A.S.S.R.	2	—	—	2
Siberia (Berezovo and Tas-Tumus)	21	300	4	317
Sakhalin	2	5	1	6
Ukraine S.S.R.	200	550	159	591
Azerbaydzhan S.S.R.	80	250	50	280
Uzbek S.S.R.	100	620	40	680
Turkmen S.S.R.	8	150	2	156
Kirgiz S.S.R.	2	35	2	35
Tadzhik S.S.R.	—	10	—	10
Kazakh S.S.R.	—	100	—	100

[a] *Source:* Lydolph, Paul E., and Shabad, Theodore, "The Oil and Gas Industries in the U.S.S.R.," *Annals of the Association of American Geographers*, December 1960, p. 473.

30 billion cubic meters of gas were transported. During the seven-year plan forty main pipelines totaling 26 thousand kilometers are to be built. Together with branch lines and with oil pipelines to be built, this means a total of over 60 thousand kilometers of pipe to be laid within 7 years, or approximately 3 kilometers every working hour!

Since 80 per cent of the gas is to be used

A third line is under construction, and one of the lines is being extended from Moscow to Leningrad. The new Shebelinka gas fields in the eastern Ukraine are conveniently located with respect to these lines and can be hooked in directly with them. Older lines transport gas from the Dashava fields in the western Ukraine eastward to Kiev and Moscow and from Saratov on the middle Volga northwestward to Moscow. Other

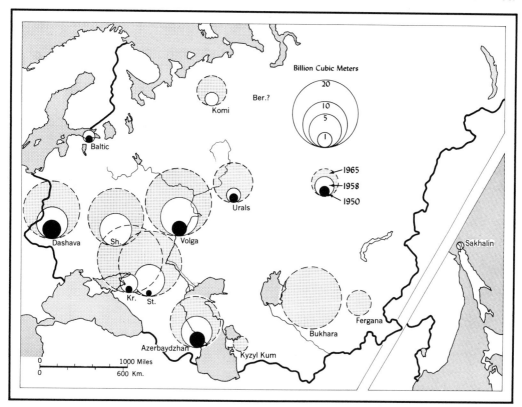

Figure 15-11   Gas production by regions in the U.S.S.R., 1950, 1958, 1965 plan.   After Lydolph and Shabad.   Sh. = Shebelinka, Kr. = Krasnodar, St. = Stavropol, Ber. = Berezovo.   There are indications that the Berezovo fields have been given a low priority and might not be developed before 1965.   For the Baltic area and for Sakhalin, neither of which has a significant production of natural gas, 1965 plan data indicate that production of gas from shale and from petroleum development will remain essentially the same as in 1958.   Komi production in 1958 was approximately the same as in 1950, and the two years are shown on the map by only one circle.   The Emba oil fields produce about 0.1 billion cubic meters of gas annually, which is too small an amount to be represented on the map.   A potential gas-producing area, which is not shown on the map, is Tas-Tumus, near the confluence of the Vilyuy and Lena rivers.

lines are being built northward from Dashava to serve the Belorussian and Baltic Republics.   In Transcaucasia a pipeline has been completed from the new Karadag fields near Baku up the Kura River valley to Tbilisi and Yerevan.   Two lines more than 2000 kilometers in length are being constructed from the Gazli fields near Bukhara north to Chelyabinsk and Sverdlovsk in the Urals. Another line is being built eastward from Gazli to serve the cities along the northern slope of the Tyan Shans and in the Fergana Valley.   Numerous shorter lines will service other areas.

By 1965 natural gas is to make up 25 per cent of the fuel consumption of the European U.S.S.R. and 28 per cent of the Urals. It is to be supplied to 500 cities serving roughly half of the urban population.   In Uzbekistan the share of natural gas in the fuel balance is to rise from 3.3 per cent in 1958 to 60 per cent in 1965.

Shale   The mining of oil shale has persisted in the Soviet Union in spite of the growth of the oil and gas industries and the fact that the production of oil from shale is much more expensive than it is from

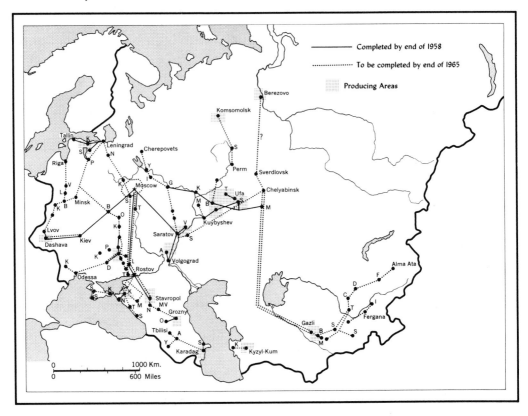

Figure 15-12   Gas pipelines in the U.S.S.R.   After Lydolph and Shabad.

petroleum. In 1958 shale accounted for 0.8 per cent of the energy consumed in the U.S.S.R., and it is planned that in 1965 it will supply 1.1 per cent. Although the resources of oil shale in the Soviet Union are nowhere near as great as they are in the United States, significant reserves exist in Estonia and adjacent parts of the Russian Republic, in the middle Volga area, in northeastern Europe, in the northeastern Siberian platform west of the Lena River, and in Kazakhstan east and northeast of Lake Balkash. The northeast Siberian area contains more than 70 per cent of the geological reserves, but the oil content of the Baltic reserves is higher, and since 1956 only the Baltic and middle Volga areas have been producing. In 1959 the Baltic region produced 86 per cent of the country's oil shale, and the area around Syzran and Kuybyshev produced about 14 per cent.

The Volga region has the longest continuous record of shale production in the U.S.S.R.; production began here in the late 1920's. By 1932 both the Baltic and the Volga regions were in production with the major share centered in the Volga area. With the acquisition of Estonia during World War II there was a large expansion in the shale industry in the Baltic area. Apparently the Baltic is the only region that engages in complex refining operations; it seems that all the shale in the Volga area is burned in power generating stations.

Although the Baltic shales yield about 60 gallons of oil per ton, the highest in the world, shale is still considered a local fuel because of its low-energy content per unit of weight, and it is not shipped over extensive distances. Its production is most important to the Estonian Republic, where it generated 86 per cent of the electricity in

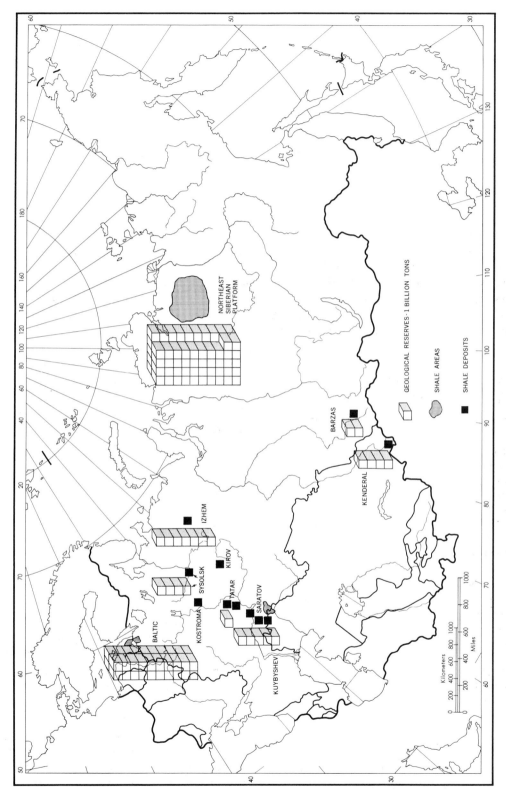

Figure 15-13   Geological reserves of shale.   After Hodgkins, Jordan A., Soviet Power: Energy Resources, Production, and Potential, 1961.   By permission of Prentice-Hall, Inc.

1955, and to the Leningrad area to the east. Pipelines were completed in 1948 from the gasification plant in Kokhtla-Yarve to Leningrad and Tallin.

Electric Power

The U.S.S.R. has 12 per cent of the world's water-power potential, the greatest potential possessed by any country except the Republic of the Congo. These resources are sufficient to generate annually more than twice as much as all the electric power generated in the world in 1957. However, it is not feasible to realize all this energy. Four fifths of the potential is located in comparatively undeveloped Asiatic territory and half of the remaining one fifth is in the Caucasus (Table 15–14). Inaccessibility and remoteness from industrial centers pre-clude the development of much of this resource, although some large hydroelectric plants are being built in fairly remote areas to supply large electric-consuming industries such as aluminum, magnesium, nitrate, and synthetic rubber.

In spite of all that has been written about hydro power plants, their share in Soviet output of electric power still is only about 17 per cent, and it appears that it will remain so. During the seven-year plan concentration is to be on the construction of thermal power plants with generating capacities of about 1.2 million kilowatts, which can be built in half the time needed for water power plants with similar capacities. In the long run water power plants may produce cheaper power, but the goals of the seven-year plan cannot be met by long-term construction projects. Khrushchev says that the main element in the struggle to catch up with the United States is the time element. Hence, many proposed hydro projects are being delayed until sometime after the seven-year plan. During the seven-year plan only 17 per cent of the investment capital for the electric power industry will be allocated to hydroelectric projects, as compared to 48 per cent for the years 1952 to 1958.

Thermal power plants are not much in the news because they are all of similar construction and they do not involve natural phenomena such as rivers and mountains which are integral parts of particular regions. Nevertheless, the building of thermal power plants has been going on all the time all over the country, primarily in the heavily industrialized areas near sources of fuel. With the great expansion of the oil and natural gas industries, many thermal power plants are being converted from coal to natural gas and by-product gases of oil refining. This allows for more flexibility of power plant location, since fluid fuels can be piped anywhere. Another innovation in the generation of thermal electricity is underground gasification of coal whereby coal is burned underground without mining, and the gases given off are used to generate the steam to

Table 15–14   Water Power Potential of Major Rivers in the U.S.S.R.[a]

River	Million Kilowatts
Lena	18.4
Yenisey	18.2
Angara	9.9
Amur	6.4
Indigirka	6.2
Volga	6.2
Naryn	5.9
Pyandzh	5.8
Ob	5.7
Amu-Darya	3.8
Irtysh	3.2
Syr-Darya	2.0
Kura	2.0
Zeya	1.9
Bureya	1.7
Dnieper	1.7
Pechora	1.6
Kama	1.5
Sulai	1.2
Rioni	1.0

[a] *Sources:* Petrov, Victor, *Geography of the Soviet Union: Electric Power*, p. 4 and *Soviet Geography: Review and Translation*, June 1960, p. 38.

turn the turbines in thermal electric plants. Underground gasification of coal is now utilized in several different parts of the country, particularly in some of the large brown-coal deposits near large concentrations of industry, such as the Moscow basin.

vides the basis for the new workers' settlements. Navigation, irrigation, and recreational facilities may be important adjuncts of the electrical function. Some of the larger reservoirs may even alter the climate significantly along their shores. Thus there

Table 15–15 Data on Selected Water Construction Projects

Dam	Height in Meters	Length in Meters	Reservoir Area in Square Kilometers	Power Capacity in Kilowatts	Date Completed
Dnieper River					
Dnieproges	50	700		650,000	1932[a]
Kakhovka	20			300,000	1956
Volga River					
Kuybyshev	80	4400	6500	2,100,000	1956
Volgograd	48	6000	3500	2,300,000	1960
Irtysh River					
Bukhtarma	90		5000	525,000	After 1960
Ob River					
Novosibirsk	25		4500	400,000	After 1960
Kamen				630,000	Proposed
Angara River					
Irkutsk		2363		660,000	1958
Bratsk	100		5000	3,600,000	After 1960
Yenisey River					
Krasnoyarsk	100			4,000,000	Construction begun 1956. Completion sometime after 1962.
Yenisey	139			6,000,000	Proposed
Zeya River					
Zeya	100			900,000	Proposed
Amur River					
Dzhalindskaya	80			1,000,000	Proposed

[a] Destroyed during World War II and reconstructed in 1947.
Data are from scattered Soviet sources.

Water-power projects often have significance to the regions in which they are located other than those of power generation. The construction of large dams to create large reservoirs on rivers completely alters the natural settings of the surrounding areas and often necessitates the moving of old villages out of the reservoir areas, and pro-

is some reason for the attention that some of these projects have received which may seem excessive judged from their power outputs alone. Such mighty rivers as the Volga and the Dnieper in Europe have been completely altered into stairways of huge reservoirs. And high dams on rivers such as the Angara, Yenisey, Ob, and Irtysh in

Asia have transformed the aspects and economies of these remote areas. Table 15-15 lists significant data on some of the most important water construction projects.

According to the long-range economic development plan now being drafted, Soviet electric generation capacities are expected to rise from 53 million kilowatts in 1958 to 121 million in 1965, 190 million in 1970, 300 million in 1975, and 480 million in 1980. Power production is scheduled to increase from 292 billion kilowatt hours in 1960 to about 2,500 billion in 1980. By comparison, the United States in 1960 produced 841 billion kilowatt hours. Among power consumers in the Soviet Union the share of industry is expected to drop from 69 per cent in 1950 to 60 per cent in 1980 whereas the share of agriculture and home uses will rise from 13.8 to 23 per cent. The power output share of the eastern regions (Urals, Siberia, Kazakhstan, and Middle Asia) is expected to rise from 19.5 per cent in 1958 to 44 per cent in 1980.

Ferrous Metallurgy

Historical Development Ferrous metallurgy in Russia originated around Tula in the early part of the seventeenth century when the smelting of small deposits of local iron ore was begun with the utilization of charcoal from the surrounding forests. During the reign of Peter the Great in the first part of the eighteenth century a considerably greater development of ferrous metallurgy took place in the Urals where rich deposits of iron ore were opened up and the smelting again was done with charcoal from the local forests. The Urals quickly became the main metallurgical base of Russia and remained so for nearly two centuries until they were surpassed by the eastern Ukraine with the technological shift in iron smelting from charcoal to coke.

For a time the Urals were the foremost metallurgical area in the world. In 1767 the Urals produced 56,000 tons of pig iron,

which was twice as much as was then produced in England. Russia even exported iron to England at this time. But during the early part of the nineteenth century when western Europe underwent the Industrial Revolution Russia lost the lead in iron production. In 1860 England produced 3,980,000 tons of pig iron, France produced 967,000 and Russia produced only 336,000.

During the 1860's construction of metallurgical plants began in the eastern Ukraine to utilize the rich coal deposits in the Donets Basin and the rich iron ore deposits of Krivoy Rog west of the Dnieper. By 1900 the Ukraine had replaced the Urals as the main metallurgical base of Russia. In 1913 the Ukraine produced 75 per cent of the iron ore of the country, 69 per cent of the pig iron, and 57 per cent of the steel, while the Urals produced only about 21 per cent of both pig iron and steel.

A revitalization of the steel industry in the Urals was begun late in the first five-year plan with the opening of the iron ore mines at Magnitogorsk and the establishment of the Urals-Kuznetsk Combine in 1932. With relocation of plants from the west during World War II the steel industry in the Urals took a great spurt forward. By 1956 the Urals were producing nearly 36 per cent of the country's pig iron and 36 per cent of its crude steel. According to the seven-year plan by 1965 the Urals will roughly have matched the pig iron and steel production of the Ukraine.

The Soviet Iron and Steel Industry Compared to Other Producers Since World War II the production of iron and steel in the Soviet Union has been increasing at more than 10 per cent per year. At the same time in the United States and most west European countries production has been rising unsteadily and faltering with general economic conditions. By 1960 iron ore production in the U.S.S.R. had reached 106 million metric tons, which was somewhat greater than the production in the United States. The United States imports a good deal of iron ore, however, whereas the Soviet Union is entirely self-sufficient. Therefore the production of pig iron and steel in the United States is still considerably higher than it is in the Soviet Union. In 1960 steel production in the Soviet Union was approximately 70 per cent that of the United States. By 1965 the Soviets hope to equal the steel production of the United States, assuming that production in the United States does not increase.

Table 15–16   Production of Iron Ore, Pig Iron, and Crude Steel in Leading Countries, 1960 (Millions of Tons)[a]

	Iron Ore[b]	Pig Iron	Crude Steel
U.S.A.	48.0	62.3	90.1
U.S.S.R.			
1960	61.8	46.8	65.3
1965 plan	150–160[c]	65–70	86–91
France	21.7	14.3	17.3
West Germany	4.6	25.9	34.1
United Kingdom	4.7	16.0	24.7
Mainland China	—	27.5	18.5
Japan	1.6	12.3	22.1

[a] *Sources: United Nations Statistical Yearbook* and *Soviet Handbook, 1959–1965.*
[b] Iron content.
[c] Crude ore.

Present Distribution of the Iron and Steel Industry in the Soviet Union   The two big regions of pig iron and crude steel production in the Soviet Union are the eastern Ukraine, with adjacent parts of Rostov Oblast in the Russian Republic, and the Urals. These two regions account for about 84 per cent of the country's pig iron production and 76 per cent of its crude steel. The eastern Ukraine contains large quantities of all the ingredients necessary for steel production: iron ore, coking coal, manganese, and limestone for fluxing. Production in the Urals is based primarily on rich iron ore

deposits, and coal must be shipped in from Kuznetsk and Karaganda.

Krivoy Rog in the Ukraine is the largest deposit of iron ore in the country, and although reserves of high-grade ore have been seriously depleted, vast untapped reserves of low-grade ore suitable for concentration still exist. Large ore concentrators are being built in the Krivoy Rog region, and the area is to remain the chief producer of iron ore in the country. In 1956 the Ukraine was credited with having about 38 per cent of the proved reserves of iron of the Soviet Union. These reserves include the low-grade ores on the Kerch Peninsula as well as those at Krivoy Rog. A number of separate deposits of iron ore in the Urals are credited with totaling over 15 per cent of the country's reserves.

The large integrated iron and steel centers in the Ukraine include Donetsk (Stalino), Makeyevka, and others in the Donets Basin; Zaporozhye, Dnepropetrovsk, and Dneprodzerzhinsk in the Dnieper Bend, an expanding plant at Krivoy Rog itself, and a large plant at Zhdanov on the north shore of the Sea of Azov. The Zhdanov plant depends in part on Kerch iron ore. Of the three large integrated iron and steel plants in the Urals, Magnitogorsk and Chelyabinsk are to be supplied with iron ore from the newly developed Rudny mines in nearby Kustanay Oblast of northwestern Kazakhstan as local ores in the Urals run out, whereas Nizhniy Tagil will rely more and more on the new Kachkanar mine in the Urals.

Two other important iron- and steel-producing centers are the Kuznetsk Basin in western Siberia and a cluster of minor plants in the European Center. The large integrated iron and steel plant at Novokuznetsk (Stalinsk) was developed in the early 1930's in conjunction with the Urals-Kuznetsk Combine to utilize the rich coal deposits of the Kuznetsk Basin and iron ore brought by coal cars returning from the Urals. It is now almost a self-contained plant obtaining both coal and iron ore locally. Iron ore is mined in the spurs of the Altay Moun-

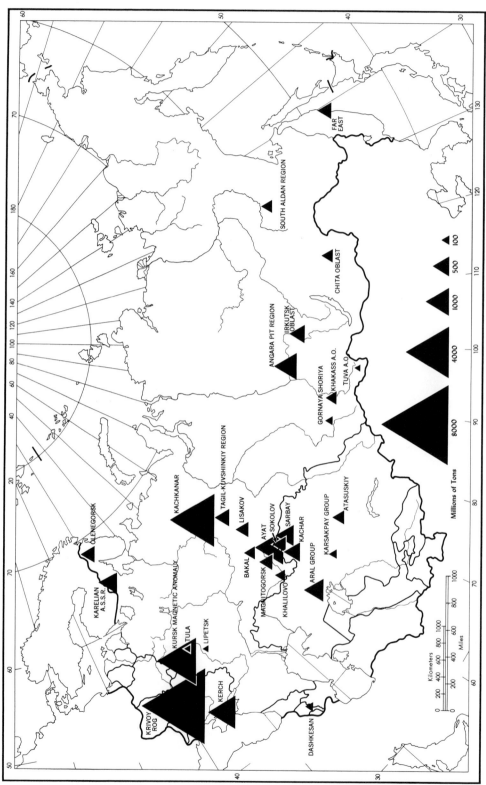

Figure 15-14   Iron ore deposits in the U.S.S.R.   Data from Cherdantsev.

Table 15–17   Production of Iron Ore by Regions, for Selected Years (in Millions of Tons)[a]

	1913	1940	1955	1959	1960	1965
U.S.S.R.	9.2	29.9	71.9	94.4	106.0	150–160
R.S.F.S.R.	2.3	9.7	30.9	36.5	40.4	?
Northwest	—	—	0.4	?	?	?
Center	0.6	1.1	1.8	?	?	?
Urals	1.8	8.1	25.0	?	?	?
Magnitogorsk			12.2			
West Siberia	—	0.5	3.6	?	?	?
Ukraine	6.9	20.2	40.0	53.5	59.1	79.7
Krivoy Rog			37.2			
Kazakhstan	—	—	0.2	3.2	5.8	30.0
Azerbaydzhan	—	—	0.8	1.2	?	?

[a] *Sources: Promyshlennost SSSR*, Moscow, 1957, p. 116, *SSSR v tsifrakh*, 1959, *Soviet Geography: Review and Translation*, March 1962, p. 82, and *Zhelezorudnaya baza chernoy metallurgii SSSR*, Moscow, 1957.

Table 15–18   Production of Pig Iron, Crude Steel, and Rolled Steel by Regions, 1940 and 1956[a]

	Pig Iron				Crude Steel				Rolled Steel			
	1940		1956		1940		1956		1940		1956	
Region	Million Tons	Per Cent of Total	Million Tons	Per Cent of Total	Million Tons	Per Cent of Total	Million Tons	Per Cent of Total	Million Tons	Per Cent of Total	Million Tons	Per Cent of Total
U.S.S.R.	14.9	100	35.8	100	18.3	100	48.6	100	13.1	100	37.8	100
North	—	—	0.7	2.0	—	—	—	—	—	—	—	—
Northwest	—	—	—	—	0.6	3.3	0.9	1.8	0.5	3.8	0.9	2.4
Center	1.0	6.7	1.9	5.3	1.5	8.2	2.7	5.6	0.9	6.9	1.6	4.2
Volga	—	—	—	—	0.9	4.9	1.7	3.5	0.6	4.6	1.0	2.7
Ukraine and North Caucasus	9.7	65.1	17.2	48.0	9.4	51.4	19.3	39.7	6.9	52.6	15.4	40.7
West	—	—	—	—	—	—	0.1	0.2	—	—	0.1	0.3
Urals	2.7	18.1	12.8	35.7	3.9	21.3	17.5	36.0	2.8	21.4	13.4	35.4
West Siberia	1.5	10.1	2.6	7.3	1.9	10.4	4.1	8.5	1.4	10.7	3.8	10.0
East Siberia	—	—	—	—	0.1	0.5	0.4	0.8	—	—	0.3	0.8
Far East	—	—	—	—	—	—	0.3	0.6	—	—	0.2	0.5
Kazakhstan and Middle Asia	—	—	—	—	—	—	0.5	1.0	—	—	0.4	1.1
Transcaucasia	—	—	0.6	1.7	—	—	1.1	2.3	—	—	0.7	1.9

[a] *Source:* Livshits, R. S., *Razmeshchenie chernoy metallurgii SSSR*, Moscow, 1958, p. 214.

tains to the south and southeast of the Kuznetsk Basin. The iron and steel industry of the European Center is oriented toward markets. None of the plants are integrated iron and steel plants. The two plants pro-ducing pig iron are at Tula and Lipetsk, both of which are old plants that have been revitalized since World War II and that apparently are being groomed to undergo much greater expansion in the near future

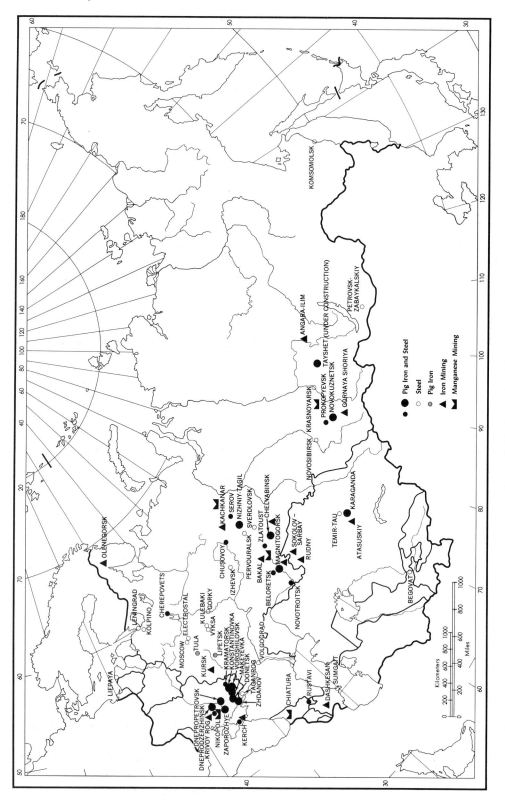

Figure 15-15 Iron and steel industry.

with the opening up of the Kursk Magnetic Anomoly to the southwest. The Kursk Magnetic Anomoly is credited with having 10 per cent of the country's iron-ore reserves. The steel plants of Moscow, Gorky, and other minor centers in the Central Industrial Region must import pig iron from the Ukraine and from the Tula and Lipetsk plants. All the iron and steel plants of the Center must import coal from the Donets Basin.

Reservoir, imports coal all the way from Vorkuta in the European northeast and iron ore from Olenegorsk on the Kola Peninsula to provide iron and steel to the Leningrad and Central Industrial areas. Rustavi in Transcaucasia is a new small iron and steel city established specifically to serve the needs of Transcaucasia. It utilizes local iron ores from Dashkesan in the Azerbaydzhan Republic and coal from the Colchis Lowland in Georgia. Begovat is to Middle Asia what

Table 15–19 *Production of Pig Iron, Crude Steel, and Rolled Steel by Union Republic, 1960 and 1965 Plan (in Millions of Tons)*[a]

	Pig Iron		Crude Steel		Rolled Steel	
	1960	1965	1960	1965	1960	1965
U.S.S.R.	46.8	65–70	65.3	86–91	51.0	
R.S.F.S.R.	21.6	35	36.6	51	28.0	
Ukraine S.S.R.	24.2	30	26.2	36	21.1	24.2
Kazakh S.S.R.	0.3		0.3	4.6	0.3	
Georgian S.S.R.	0.7		1.1		0.8	
Belorussian S.S.R.	—		0.1		—	
Uzbek S.S.R.	—		0.3		0.2	
Azerbaydzhan S.S.R.	—		0.6		0.4	
Latvian S.S.R.	—		0.1		0.1	

[a] *Sources: Narodnoe khozyaystvo SSSR v 1960 godu, SSSR v tsifrakh v 1959 godu,* and *Current Digest of the Soviet Press,* April 1, 1959.

Besides these four major regions, there is some pig-iron production in the European north and in Transcaucasia and some steel production in the Volga Valley, the European northwest, the European west, Transcaucasia, Kazakhstan and Middle Asia, eastern Siberia, and the Far East. Only two of these areas have integrated iron and steel plants—Cherepovets in the European north and Rustavi in Transcaucasia. The rest produce only steel, either from pig iron that is shipped in or from scrap metal. A new large integrated iron and steel plant is now being initiated at Karaganda in Central Kazakhstan. All these plants except Karaganda are primarily market oriented. Cherepovets, on the north shore of the Rybinsk

Rustavi is to Transcaucasia, but Begovat has no local supplies of either iron or coal. It mixes some local coals with Karaganda and Kuznetsk coal to produce steel either from pig iron shipped in from Karaganda or Kuznetsk or from scrap metal. East of Lake Baykal two minor steel centers, Petrovsk-Zabaykalskiy and Komsomolsk, import pig iron all the way from the Kuznetsk Basin to produce steel for eastern Siberia and the Far East.

In 1955, 52 per cent of all Ukrainian iron and steel shipments terminated within the Ukraine. The rest went to all parts of the Union with the heaviest traffic going to Moscow and the Volga region. The Urals consumed 42 per cent of their iron and steel production, and the rest was shipped primarily to the Center, the Volga, the Caucasus, and the Ukraine. Western Siberia consumed about 35 per cent of its iron and steel production, and the rest was shipped mainly to the Urals and eastern Siberia. Kuznetsk pig iron is shipped all the way to the Far East, and Kuznetsk iron and steel joins with iron and steel from the Urals at Perm to be shipped westward to the Center and Leningrad. The Center consumes 52 per cent of the iron and steel that it produces and ships the rest to the Ukraine, the West, the Northwest, the Urals, the Far East, and the Caucasus. There is a good deal of interchange of products between the major producing areas, indicating some differentiation of specialization among areas.

Recent Developments and Plans for the Future Probably the most significant recent development for the future of the iron and steel industry of the Soviet Union is the discovery of huge deposits of low-grade iron ores in northern Kazakhstan and western Siberia along the eastern foot of the Ural Mountains. It has been reported that thirty-eight different deposits of iron ore have been discovered in the Turgay Lowlands in Kustanay Oblast in Kazakhstan. Beneficiating plants have been built and production has been started at Sokolovsko-Sarbayskoe and Lisakovskoe. In the Urals the large Kachkanar deposit has been opened west of Serov. Its ore contains only 16 to 18 per cent iron, but large beneficiating plants make utilization possible. All these ores in the vicinity of the Urals have been discovered just as it appeared that supplies for the large industrial plants in the southern Urals were running out. As a result, the iron and steel plant at Magnitogorsk is being doubled in capacity, to about 12 million tons per year, and the large iron and steel plant at Karaganda is being completed with a similar capacity. These capacities compare to those of around 8 million tons at Gary, Indiana and 6 million at Sparrows Point, Maryland.

The new Karaganda plant is one of three large integrated plants to be built in the Asian part of the Soviet Union to establish a so-called "third metallurgical base." The other two plants are a second plant at Novokuznetsk in the Kuznetsk Basin, the so-called "West Siberian Plant," and a plant at the railroad junction of Tayshet east of Krasnoyarsk. These large steel enterprises are to utilize iron ore resources in central and northwestern Kazakhstan, in the Altay Mountains, and in the Angara-Ilim area near the junction of the Angara and Ilim rivers in eastern Siberia.

The other important development now taking place is the opening up of the Kursk Magnetic Anomoly, which is advantageously located between the heavy industry of the Ukraine and that of the Central Industrial Region. This opening will revitalize the iron and steel industries of the cities of Tula and Lipetsk.

Ferroalloys The Soviet Union is well supplied with most of the ferroalloys, particularly the most important of them, manganese. Both of the world's largest deposits of manganese lie in the Soviet Union, one at Nikopol on the Dnieper in the Ukraine, and the other at Chiatura in the Colchis Lowland of Georgia. These two deposits alone account for about two thirds of the world's production. In 1955 out of the U.S.S.R.'s manganese production of 4.7 million metric tons, Chiatura produced 2.8 million metric tons and Nikopol 1.7 million. Lesser amounts were mined in the Urals, Siberia, and Kazakhstan. During the seven-year plan Nikopol is supposed to surpass the production of Chiatura and become the world's leading producer of manganese with an output of about 4 million metric tons per year. The Nikopol deposits apparently are two or three times as large as those at Chiatura.

Nickel and chromium are scattered up and down the Urals, with some of the most significant deposits having only recently been discovered in the southern Urals in the Orsk-Khalilovo area. Besides the production in

Table 15–20   Iron Ore Reserves, U.S.S.R., as of January 1, 1956, Proved and Probable Reserves $(A + B + C_1)^a$

Region	Type of Ore	Per Cent Iron	Millions of Tons
U.S.S.R.			29,984
Ukraine			10,585
Krivoy Rog	Rich ore	53–64	1,592
Krivoy Rog	Iron quartzites	30–36	6,549
Kerch	Brown iron ore	37–40	1,658
Kazakhstan			6,008
Eastern Urals			4,919
Ayat Basin	Brown iron ore	37	1,755
Sokolov Deposit	Magnetite	47	382
Sarbay Deposit	Magnetite	46	597
Kachar Deposit	Magnetite	45–50	460
Atasuyskiy	Magnetite and Hematite	55	247
Aral Group	Brown iron ore	35–41	687
Karsakpay Group	Iron quartzites	34–40	128
Urals			5,746
Kachkanar	Titanomagnetite	15–17	3,900
Tagil-Kuvshinkiy Region	Magnetite and Titanomagnetite	17–39	511
Bakal	Siderite and brown	29–47	208
Khalilovo	Iron and Chrome ores	32–39	245
Magnitogorsk	Magnetite	50–54	300
Center			2,969
Tula	Brown iron ore	—	66
Lipetsk	Brown iron ore	—	36
Kursk Magnetic Anomaly	Rich ore	53–57	634
Kursk Magnetic Anomaly	Iron quartzites	32–33	2,228
Eastern Siberia			2,100
Khakass A.O.	Magnetite	34–47	229
Angara-Pit Region	Hematite	40	1,034
Tuva A.O.	Hematite	32	49
Irkutsk Oblast	Magnetite	33–53	476
South Aldan Region	Magnetite	46–58	183
Chita Oblast	Brown ore and Siderite	43	229
Murmansk Oblast			897
Olenegorsk	Iron quartzites	32.5	336
Karelian A.S.S.R.		28–34	790
Far East	Magnetite and quartzites	30–60	351
Western Siberia	Magnetite	32–50	265
Azerbaydzhan (Dashkesan)	Magnetite	37–45	86

^{a} *Source:* Cherdantsev, G. N., and others, *Ekonomicheskaya geografiya SSSR: obshchiy obzor*, Moscow, 1958, pp. 278–279.

the Urals, nickel is produced on the Kola Peninsula and at Norilsk along the lower Yenisey. The Soviet Union annually is the second most important producer of nickel in the world, after Canada, producing about one sixth of the world's nickel.

Titanium also is scattered rather widely in the Urals. The largest deposit of molybdenum in the country is in the North Caucasus in the Kabardino-Balkar A.S.S.R. Lesser deposits of molybdenum, as well as deposits of tungsten, are scattered through the mountains of Middle Asia, southern Siberia, and the Far East. Recently impressive deposits of tungsten and molybdenum have been discovered in Kazakhstan primarily in the Tyan Shans, north of Lake Balkhash, and in the Rudny Altai. Important deposits of tungsten also exist in the Urals. The Soviet Union is regularly the third largest producer of tungsten in the world after China and the United States, producing about one ninth of the world's supply.

Nonferrous Metallurgy

Soviet data on the production of nonferrous metals are the most conspicuous ommission in the handbooks of statistics released since 1956. For some reason the Soviets have not reported many data on total productions for various nonferrous metals and they have not reported any data on regional distributions of production. Enough information has been . gleaned from scattered sources, however, to make some generalizations.

It appears that the Soviet Union is well situated in virtually all nonferrous metals needed by a modern industrial economy. These metals are located primarily in old crystalline rock areas in Kazakhstan, the Urals, and the Kola Peninsula and in pockets among the younger more rugged mountains of the Caucasus, Middle Asia, western Siberia, the Transbaykal area and Maritime Kray in the Far East. So far the Urals have been outstanding in their production of non-

ferrous metals, but Kazakhstan seems to have the potential to be the prime producer of many of these metals, and the Urals are becoming more important for the production of iron. In general, the nonferrous ores in Kazakhstan are found in the Mugodzhar Mountains in the northwest, the Kazakh Folded Country in the center, the Rudnyy Altay in the east, and in the Tyan Shans in the south. Most recently, important bauxite ores have been discovered in the Turgay Lowland in north central Kazakhstan.

Copper   According to Soviet sources the U.S.S.R. now has more known reserves of copper than any other country in the world. Kazakhstan possesses more than half of the country's reserves, Middle Asia about one sixth, the Urals one sixth, and Transcaucasia about one tenth. Until World War II the Urals produced most of the copper of the country, but since then large new deposits have been opened up in Kazakhstan which have catapulted that area into first place. The three major deposits in Kazakhstan are at Kounrad on the northern shore of Lake Balkash and near Leninogorsk in the Rudnyy Altay—both of which have been producing copper for quite a long time—and at Dzhezkazgan on the western fringe of the Kazakh Folded Country which has been opened up recently and is said to be the second largest deposit of copper in the world.

Copper deposits are scattered up and down the Urals with concentrations in Sverdlovsk, Chelyabinsk, and Orenburg Oblasts and in the Bashkir A.S.S.R. Recently a major deposit of copper pyrite was discovered near the town of Gay in the Orsk-Khalilovo region in the southern Urals. Deposits here are reputed to be even richer than those at Dzhezkazgan. Mining operations are under way, and the area is to be fully operative within the seven-year plan period.

Besides Kazakhstan and the Urals, large-scale copper mining and smelting is carried on near Alaverdi in Armenia and at Almalyk in the Uzbek Republic. Two other large copper reserves lie in the Arctic, at Monche-

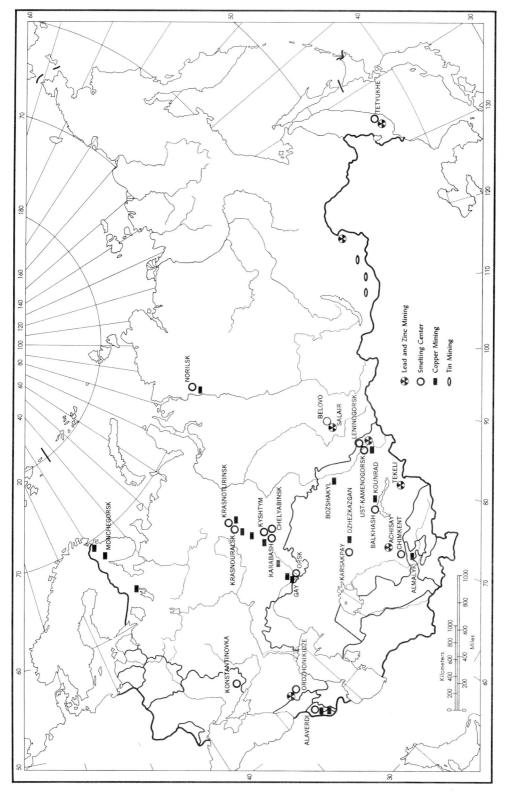

Figure 15-16 Copper, lead, zinc, and tin mining and smelting.

gorsk on the Kola Peninsula and at Norilsk in northern Siberia on the Lower Yenisey.

Lead and Zinc Lead and zinc are often found in the same ore, commonly in association with other metals such as gold, silver, and copper. The Soviet Union appears to be well supplied with lead and zinc. It is regularly the second producer of lead in the world after the United States producing about one eighth of the world's supply, and second after the United States in the production of zinc with about one tenth of the world's production.

The Kazakh Republic apparently contains about one half the lead and zinc deposits of the Soviet Union. These deposits occur primarily in the Altay region around Leninogorsk and in the Tyan Shans in the vicinity of Chimkent. Other important producing centers are in the vicinity of Ordzhonikidze in the Osetian A.S.S.R. in the Northern Caucasus and at Tetyukhe in the Sikhote-Alin Mountains in Maritime Kray in the Far East. Primary lead-producing plants in the Soviet Union are at Chimkent, which reportedly is the largest smelter in all of Eurasia, at Leninogorsk, at Ordzhonikidze, and at Tetyukhe.

Zinc is produced in all these areas and also in the Urals and in the Salair Ridge west of the Kuznetsk Basin. The zinc ore of the Urals is found in combination with copper, but at all other places it is found in combination with lead. Whereas the lead smelters are located near the ore, zinc processing is concentrated in regions of abundant cheap electric power. The first zinc plant was established in Ordzhonikidze to utilize hydroelectric power produced by dams on headwaters of the Terek River. It has been reported that before World War II Ordzhonikidze produced about 37 per cent of the zinc in the U.S.S.R. Then two plants were established at Konstantinovka in the Donets Basin and at Belovo in the Kuznetsk Basin to utilize cheap thermal electric power in these coal basins. Later, plants were constructed at Chelyabinsk, utilizing electric power generated by steam using the low-grade lignite, and at Ust-Kamenogorsk in the Rudnyy Altay, utilizing hydroelectric power.

Aluminum The large-scale production and use of aluminum is a relatively recent development in the Soviet Union. Before World War II its use was limited and imports supplied much of what was needed. During and since the war production in the Soviet Union has probably jumped at least twenty times until now the Soviet Union apparently is the third largest producer in the world after the United States and Canada, producing about one sixth of the world's supply. The recent expansion of production has been accompanied by the surveying and opening up of many new deposits of various aluminum ores; bauxite, alunite, nephelite, and sillimanite.

Aluminum production started in the Soviet Union in 1932 at Volkov east of Leningrad to utilize bauxite mined nearby at Boksitogorsk and hydroelectricity produced by the new power plant on the Volkov River. Shortly thereafter another aluminum plant was established at the Dnieper Dam, and alumina, an intermediate product, was shipped from Boksitogorsk to the Dnieper for final processing. The production of aluminum is a two-stage process, the first of which usually is carried on near the mines where the ore is smelted into alumina. The reduction process from alumina to aluminum requires large amounts of electricity and usually is done near large and cheap sources of electricity. The intermediate product, alumina, is often shipped over considerable distances to areas of abundant electricity and to markets for conversion into the final product, aluminum.

The plants at Volkov and Zaporozhye largely were destroyed during World War II, and the deposits of bauxite at Boksitogorsk were rapidly running out anyway. Since the war, both plants have been reconstructed and enlarged, and the bauxite of Boksitogorsk is supplemented about 80 per cent by nephelite from the Kola Peninsula.

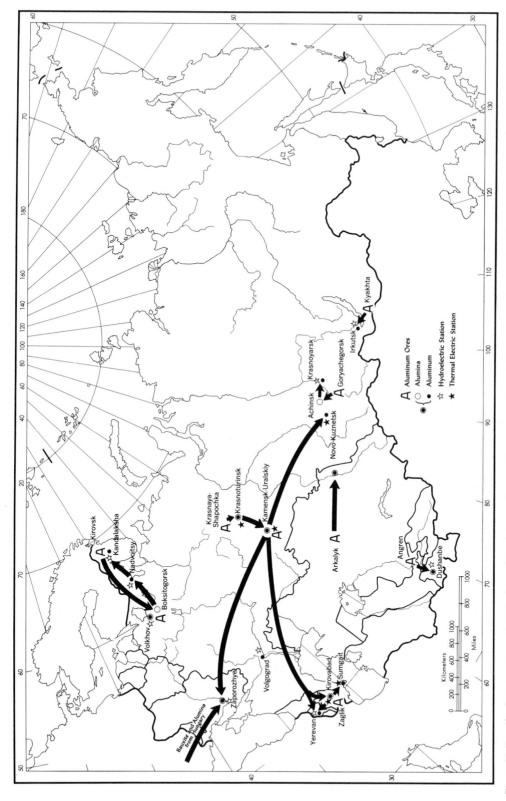

Figure 15-17   Aluminum resources and production.   Compiled from Shabad, Theodore, The Soviet Aluminum Industry, American Metal Market, New York, October 1958, and other scattered sources.

The nephelite is a by-product of apatite ores mined at Kirovsk which originally was dumped on the waste heaps.

In the meantime operations in the Urals eclipsed those at Volkov and Zaporozhye. Bauxite ores were discovered in a number of places in the Urals, but the chief deposit was the so-called Krasnaya-Shapochka group north of Serov. Large smelting plants were built at Kamensk-Uralskiy and Krasnoturinsk. Both alumina and aluminum are produced at Kamensk-Uralskiy, utilizing electricity produced by a thermal power plant using low-grade Chelyabinsk coal, but some of the alumina produced there is shipped to Transcaucasia to be transformed to aluminum using cheap hydroelectric power of the Sevan-Zanga Cascade at Yerevan and thermal electricity at Sumgait. Apparently the Urals produce about 80 per cent of the country's alumina and 40 per cent of its aluminum.

Recently alunite deposits have been opened up at Zaglik south of Kirovabad in the Kura River Valley of Transcaucasia and an alumina plant has been constructed at Kirovabad. Apparently some of the alumina is transformed to aluminum at Kirovabad and some is shipped to Yerevan and Sumgait for conversion.

Two new plants in the Kola Peninsula and the Karelian areas started operations about 1955. These are the Kandalaksha and Nadvoitsy plants which utilize nephelite from Kirovsk and bauxite from Boksitogorsk. Abundant hydroelectricity has dictated the locations of these plants. Three dams across the Niva River provide electricity to Kandalaksha. Aluminum is also being produced in a large plant at Volgograd, which apparently utilizes alumina from the Urals and abundant hydroelectricity from the Volgograd Dam.

The geographical distribution of the aluminum industry is rapidly changing as new ores are being exploited in Kazakhstan, Middle Asia, and Siberia. The most promising of these ores seem to be the Turgay bauxite near Arkalyk in northern Kazakhstan and the Goryachegorsk nephelite in the Yenisey region. Other ores exist in northern Kazakhstan, in southern Kazakhstan, and in Transbaykalia. The Turgay and Goryachegorsk deposits are to supply an aluminum plant built in the Kuznetsk Basin in 1943 as well as new plants that are being built in the Kuzbas and in the cities of Pavlodar, Krasnoyarsk, and Irkutsk.

Tin Although no recent information has been released on the tin production of the Soviet Union, it has been known for some time that tin has been produced in certain parts of eastern Siberia, the Far East, and northeastern Kazakhstan. These deposits still do not supply the demands of the Soviet Union, and considerable amounts of tin must be imported from China and southeast Asia.

Chemical Industries

During the seven-year plan the greatest increase in capital investment in all industries will be in the chemical industries. This is in response to a serious lag in this important sector of industry that has existed thus far in the Soviet Union. A rapid expansion of this field is needed not only to supply the needs of other industries but also to partially solve the demand for more and better consumer products made out of plastics and synthetics which are so common in Western markets.

The Soviets do not publish statistics directly on most of their chemical industries; but it would be difficult to assess the total chemical production and to compare it with that of other countries anyway, because the raw materials, processes, and products are so varied. The major categories of finished products are mineral fertilizers, synthetic rubber, artificial and synthetic fibers, plastics, paints and dyes, soaps and detergents, insecticides and weed killers, pharmaceuticals, and various products for use in industries, such as chemicals for use in oil refining and metallurgy. The chief intermediate substances for the production of these products are sulfuric acid, nitric acid, hydrochloric acid, ammonia, soda ash, caustic soda, chemical pulp, and various polymers. The basic raw materials for these intermediate products are natural gas and oil by-product gases, petroleum, coal tars and gases, sulfur and pyrites, phosphorite and apatites, potassium salts, sodium chloride and sodium sulfate, wood waste, and various vegetable products, such as potato and grain alcohol.

Some idea of the relative world position of the U.S.S.R. in chemicals can be gained from a comparison of productions of the intermediate products by leading countries for which data are available. Of these intermediate products perhaps the most important to the entire chemical complex is sulfuric acid. Large quantities are used in the production of rayon; in the metallurgical processing of copper, cobalt, nickel, platinum, and silver; in the production of galvanizing elements; in the production of oil products; in the processing of starches and sugar; in the production of dyes; in the tanning of hides; and in many other uses.

In the production of sulfuric acid the Soviet Union is a poor second to the United States and is only slightly ahead of Japan and the main western European countries. It annually produces approximately one third as much sulfuric acid as the United States. In 1960 the Soviet Union produced 5,391,000 metric tons, as compared to 16,223,000 in the United States.

Soda is the second most important chemical material. Calcined soda, or soda ash, is used in the production of a great array of chemical products and also in the production of soap, glass, textiles, leather, paper, and many other things. Caustic soda is used in the production of such things as artificial fibers and organic dyes. In the production of soda ash the relative position of the U.S.S.R. is much the same as it is in the case of sulfuric acid, and in caustic soda the U.S.S.R. is even less impressive. In the chemical applications of pulp the U.S.S.R. with its great supply of wood lags behind Canada and Sweden and is only slightly ahead of Finland.

So far much of the plastic and synthetic materials, including synthetic rubber, that has been produced in the Soviet Union has been produced from ethyl alcohol derived from potatoes, grain, and molasses. Such practice is a serious drain on an already short food supply and it also provides an inadequate base for chemical products. According to Soviet statements, the U.S.S.R. is now sixth in the world in the production of plastics. In the production of synthetic fibers, the Soviet Union is a step behind the United States in technology; the Soviet Union now is increasing the production of rayon and acetate rapidly, whereas in the United States such production has passed its peak and has given way to the technologically more advanced production of synthetic fibers from various polymers.

During the seven-year plan the Soviets hope to effect a major shift away from the use of edible products for the production of industrial alcohol to the use of natural and by-product gases. During this period the overall chemical production is approximately to triple, and the manufacture of artificial fibers is to increase three or four times, of synthetic fibers twelve or thirteen times, of plastics and synthetic resins more than six times, and of synthetic rubber 3.4 times.

Chemical production is so complex and so interrelated with other industries that it is impossible to determine accurately distributions of separate items. It is particularly difficult to separate out the production of modern-type synthetics and plastics based on various polymers, which are the items that are to be most strongly stressed during the seven-year plan. Most such industries are new to the Soviet scene, and the Soviets have not announced what kinds of new plants are to be located where. It has been stated that during the seven-year plan 140 large chemical enterprises are to be built or completed and more than 130 enterprises are to be modernized.

So far, most chemical industries have been connected with the coking and metallurgical industries in the Ukraine, the Urals, and the Kuznetsk Basin and in the manufacturing and marketing complexes of the Moscow and Leningrad areas. It can be assumed that construction of new plants will continue in these areas and also that new plants will be constructed in new areas, mainly those of gas production and of oil production and refining. This will allow for the use of the most valuable and cheapest raw materials; gases from oil extracting and refining, natural gas, and products of the coke-chemical industry. The largest quantity of these raw materials is in the eastern and western Ukraine, central European Russia, the Urals, the Kuznetsk Basin, the Caucasus, and in Middle Asia near Bukhara. A network of pipelines is being laid to facilitate the utilization of oil and gas products outside of the areas of their production, thus allowing for

new chemical complexes to be located in such places as Omsk and Krasnoyarsk in Siberia.

Besides the plants located near oil and gas, coal, or large industrial complexes, there are chemical enterprises located near special sources of raw materials. Several of these represent some of the oldest chemical combines in the country. Such are the Apatite Mining and Chemical Combine in the Kola Peninsula, the Berezniki and Solikamsk potassium combines, and nitrogen and superphosphate plants in the Urals, and the Artemovsk and Baskunchak sodium chloride works in the Donets Basin and the North Caspian Lowland.

Sulfuric acid is produced from sulfur, pyrite, gypsum, and from sulfur gases pro-

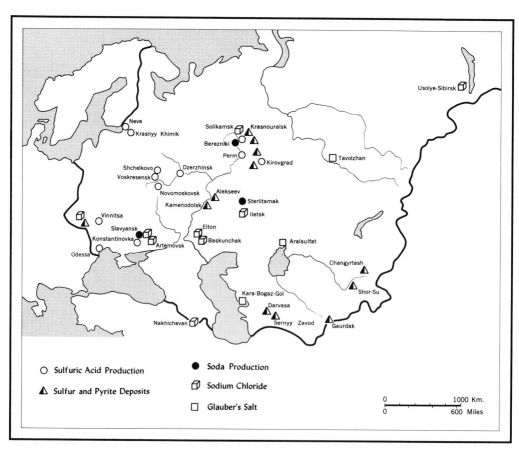

Figure 15-18   The production of sulfuric acid and soda.   After Shabad and Lydolph.

duced from coking and metallurgical plants. The three main plants producing sulfuric acid in the U.S.S.R. are at Konstantinovka in the Donets Basin, at Leningrad, and at Voskresensk south of Moscow, all of which produce it as a by-product from coking and metallurgical industries. But there are many other plants producing sulfuric acid from various sources. Many sulfur deposits occur in the republics of Middle Asia and along the foothills of the Carpathians, and pyrites are scattered abundantly through the Urals and, to some extent, along the middle Volga. Gypsum deposits are found primarily in the southern Urals, the Caucasus, and the Carpathians, with lesser deposits near Kuybyshev and Kerch and in the North Caspian Lowland. Ammonium sulfate production for the mineral fertilizer industries is concentrated in the heavy industry towns of the Donets-Dnieper Bend area, in all of the heavily industrialized cities of the middle and southern Urals, and at Novokuznetsk in the Kuznetsk Basin.

Soda is produced primarily from sodium chloride and Glauber's salt. The two main plants producing soda in the Soviet Union are at Slavyansk in the Donets Basin and at Berezniki on the Upper Kama River, which utilize the rich underground deposits of rock salt at Artemovsk and at Solikamsk respectively. A new soda works has been established at the city of Sterlitamak, south of Ufa, since World War II to utilize the salt deposits at Iletsk. Other soda works of lesser size utilize the surface deposits of sodium chloride and Glauber's salt at lakes Baskunchak and Elton in the North Caspian Lowland, of Kara-Bogaz-Gol, of Aralsulfat, and of the Kulunda Steppe in the vicinity of Tavolzhan, as well as underground deposits in the Carpathian foothills.

Mineral Fertilizers The mineral fertilizers —phosphates, potash, and nitrogen—are based on apatite and phosphorite deposits, potassium salts, sulfur and pyrites for the production of superphosphates, and coking and other gases for nitrogen synthesis. The

Soviet Union is well endowed with these necessary resources; the Soviets claim now to hold first place in the world in deposits of potassium salts and natural sulfur and to own one third of the phosphate reserves in the world. They intend to put these enormous resources to use immediately to offset the effects of a long history of notoriously poor use of mineral fertilizers. Thus far supplies have been so short that mineral fertilizers have been applied primarily only to cotton, sugar beets, tea, and some other industrial crops. The production of mineral fertilizers is concentrated in European Russia, the Ukraine, the Baltic Republics, the Urals, Transcaucasia, Middle Asia, and southwestern Siberia near sources of raw materials and in areas where the fertilizers are most needed.

Superphosphate plants treat phosphate with sulfuric acid, and thus are located near sources of both phosphate and the means of producing sulfuric acid. The principal source of phosphate is the apatite of the Kola Peninsula at Kirovsk, which supplies all superphosphate plants in European Russia. The second source of phosphate is the phosphorite mine at Chulak-Tau near Dzhambul in southern Kazakhstan.

Potash production is more limited in amount and in areal extent than is the production of phosphate. The principal source of potassium salt is at Solikamsk, with factories at Solikamsk and Berezniki. Potash is also mined at Stebnik and at Kalush in the western Ukraine. A new potash plant is being constructed in Belorussia near Starobin.

The location of nitrogen fertilizer plants is dictated by the source of hydrogen, which combines with nitrogen from the air to produce ammonia. Most of the hydrogen of the country is derived as a by product from coking and metallurgical industries or from the utilization of low-grade coals such as the Moscow lignite.

Synthetic Rubber The Soviet Union embarked on an all-out program of synthetic

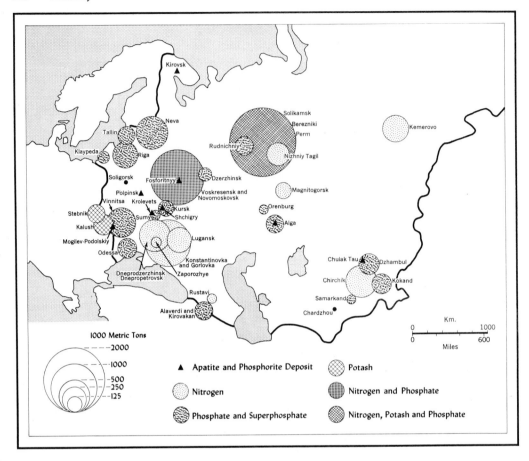

Figure 15-19   The production of mineral fertilizers.   After Shabad and Lydolph.

rubber production in 1932, considerably earlier than did either Germany or the United States. The Russians largely were responsible for the early advances in the technology of synthetic rubber production, but they have lost this lead to the United States. The Soviet Union now produces no more than 45 per cent of the amount of synthetic rubber that the United States does. Since the U.S.S.R. relies much more heavily on synthetic rubber than the United States, it can be deduced that the U.S.S.R. consumes much less total rubber than the United States. About two thirds of Soviet rubber is synthetic. The seven-year plan calls for a rapid expansion of synthetic rubber production with the goal that in 1965 Soviet production shall be slightly higher than the United States production was in 1960. This rapid increase is to be accomplished by an attendant shift in the basis for industrial alcohol from edible farm products to natural gas and by-product gases from oil refining.

The early Soviet synthetic rubber factories were located in or near the potato-growing zone in central European Russia. The first pilot plant was established in Leningrad in 1931, and the first industrial synthetic rubber plant was opened at Yaroslavl in 1932 to supply the local tire factory. A second rubber plant was completed the same year at Voronezh and a third in 1933 at Yefremov. A fourth was opened somewhat later at Kazan. All these factories were located close

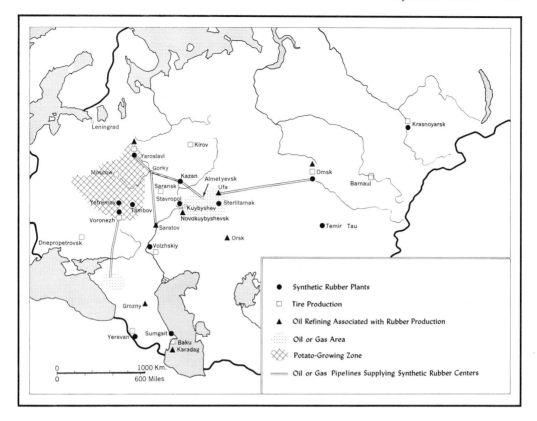

Figure 15-20   The production of synthetic rubber and tires.   After Shabad and Lydolph.

to principal rubber consumers—the tire plants of Moscow, Yaroslavl, and Voronezh—which in turn served the automotive factories at Moscow, Yaroslavl, and Gorky. The synthetic rubber factories were also situated favorably with respect to the rubber footwear industry which was concentrated in central European Russia and Leningrad.

In Armenia abundant limestone resources and cheap hydroelectric power were used to produce calcium carbide and acetylene, the raw materials for polychloroprene rubber at a plant established at Yerevan in 1940. This neoprene rubber was a special type with adhesive qualities and resistance to crude oil and refined products which was used widely in the petroleum industry at Baku and for conveyor belts and cable coverings.

During World War II many of the syn-

thetic rubber plants of European Russia were either damaged or evacuated, but after the war they were restored, and a new factory at Tambov appeared in operation. Since 1955 these rubber plants largely have been converted to the use of gas and oil by-products.

The first synthetic rubber plant to be situated near an oil-refining center opened in 1957 at Sumgait north of Baku. It supplies general purpose rubber to the Baku tire plant which opened in 1959 and to the Yerevan tire plant which opened in the early 1940's. Two more synthetic rubber plants based on oil refinery by-products opened in 1960 and 1961, one at Sterlitamak, near the oil fields of the Bashkir Republic on the western slopes of the Urals, and the other at Stavropol, on the Volga near the Kuybyshev oil-refining complex. The fourth synthetic rubber plant that will utilize products of the oil-refining industry is nearing completion at Omsk in western Siberia. A synthetic rubber plant that opened at Krasnoyarsk in 1956 is based on alcohol derived from the hydrolysis of wood, and a plant under construction at Temir-Tau near Karaganda will use the carbide-acetylene process. The workers' settlement at Volzhskiy at the eastern end of the Volgograd Dam is to become an important chemical center. A synthetic rubber and tire plant is under construction in Volzhskiy, and tire plants are under construction at Saransk in the Mordovian A.S.S.R. and at Barnaul in the Kulunda Steppe.

Machine-Building Industries

Machine building is the foundation of technical progress and development of a modern economy. The Soviets claim to have increased the machine-building and metal-fabricating industries since the Revolution by more than 240 times to make them the second largest industries in the world after the United States. One third of the industrial workers and one fourth of the industrial fixed capital of the U.S.S.R. are in these industries. During the seven-year plan it is intended that the output of these industries will double once more. Although the Soviet Union does not produce a great abundance of many of the consumer items, such as automobiles, that are so common to everyday living in the West, it cannot be disputed that the Soviets have worked wonders in their machine-building industries, bringing about a change from a backward economy that largely lacked a machine-building industry to one capable of producing earth satellites, atomic reactors, and some of the most modern jet airplanes in the world.

Machine building began in Tsarist Russia in the Central Industrial Region, in St. Petersburg, and in the Ukraine. Many of the machine-building industries are still con-

centrated in these regions, but a considerable dispersal of industry has taken place to outlying areas, either to utilize raw materials in those regions or to serve markets. Some of these newer areas are growing at much faster rates than the older areas. Between 1940 and 1955, western Siberia increased its machine-building production by nearly twenty times, Armenia by nineteen times, the Uzbek Republic by twelve times, and the Volga region by twelve times, whereas the Central Industrial Region increased approximately four times and the Leningrad area and the Ukraine approximately three times. It has been estimated that the eastern regions including the Urals now produce one third of Soviet machines.

Moscow and Leningrad largely have served

Table 15–21   Rate of Growth of the Production of All Industry and of Machine Building and Metal Fabrication in the U.S.S.R. (1940 = 100)[a]

	1955	
	All Industry	Machine Building and Metal Fabrication
U.S.S.R.	320	466
R.S.F.S.R.	314	472
Northwest	244	311
Center	281	413
Volga	523	1163
North Caucasus	213	351
Urals	515	640
Western Siberia	563	1993
Eastern Siberia	338	458
Far East	254	438
Ukrainian S.S.R.	220	331
Belorussian S.S.R.	237	851
Uzbek S.S.R.	294	1240
Georgian S.S.R.	265	555
Azerbaydzhan S.S.R.	202	444
Armenian S.S.R.	476	1876

[a] *Source: Soviet Geography: Review and Translation,* March 1960, p. 48.

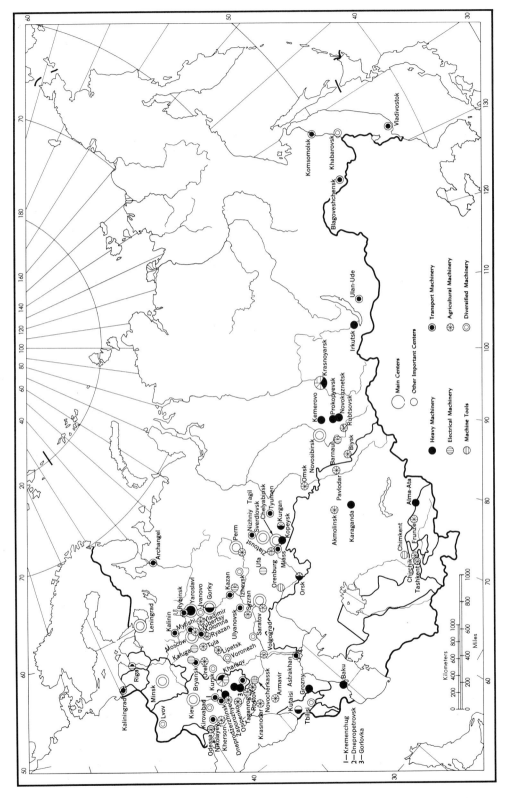

Figure 15-21   The machine-building industries.   After Cherdantsev.

as the proving grounds for prototypes of new industrial production, and thereby they have controlled the direction of many of the machine-building industries and have retained virtual monopolies on certain items. For instance, Leningrad produces almost all the large turbines for hydroelectric installations being constructed about the country. Power-generating equipment and the production of precision machines, equipment, and tools are the outstanding industries in Leningrad.

The Central Industrial Region contains large machine-building centers with a wide range of diversified machine building. It is difficult to name a branch of machine building and metal fabrication that has not been created in Moscow. The region contains 80 per cent of the automotive industry of the country, including the manufacture of cars, trucks, and buses, as well as all of their accessories, primarily in Gorky, Moscow, and Yaroslavl.

After the Central Industrial Region, the second largest machine-building complex has been created in the Ukraine. It specializes in machines requiring large amounts of steel, such as metallurgical, mining, and chemical equipment, Diesel locomotives, railroad cars and tank cars, tractors, agricultural machinery, metal-cutting machine tools, and building and road machines.

The Urals have become the third largest machine-building region in the country. They contain dozens of large machine-building plants manufacturing machinery and equipment for industry, agriculture, transportation, and construction. The "Uralmash" machine-building plant in Sverdlovsk is known throughout the country for its manufacture of metallurgical, petroleum-extracting, chemical, coal, and mining equipment. About 75 per cent of the pig iron produced in the U.S.S.R. is smelted in blast furnaces equipped by Uralmash. Rolling equipment bearing its trademark turn out one fourth of the rolled steel products in the country. Eighty per cent of all the ferrous and nonferrous ores are processed in crushers and grinders manufactured by this plant.

The Chelyabinsk tractor plant is one of the largest in the country, and one of the largest railroad car plants is in Nizhniy Tagil. In 1944 an automobile assembly plant was established at Miass in the Urals.

A new large region of machine manufacture has emerged in the cities along the Volga. The Volgograd tractor plant, the Syzran combine plant, the Kuybyshev electric milking machine plant, as well as petroleum equipment plants, ship yards, automobile assembly plants, and many plants concerned with the aircraft industry dominate this region. Some of the older machine industries in this area are turning out business machines, typewriters, watches, and the like.

Western Siberia is the most rapidly growing region for machine-building industries in the country. The cities of Novosibirsk, Omsk, Kemerovo, Barnaul, and others have grown rapidly, primarily under the impetus of the machine-building industries. These industries grew especially during World War II when many plants were relocated from European Russia. Novosibirsk turns out farm machinery, electric generators and motors, Diesel-electric equipment, electric saws, coal-mining equipment, structural steel for bridges and the mining industry, pumps, drilling equipment, river vessels, telephones, bearings, and various instruments. Tool making and machine tool plants turn out forge and press machine tools, and measuring and cutting tools. Omsk produces electrical goods, motors, machine tools, foundry equipment, farm machinery, equipment for transportation and the leather, wool, meat, and dairy industries, precision tools, and spare parts for tractors.

Distribution of Some Machine Industries Before the Revolution about 80 per cent of the machine tools were manufactured in the Center and the Northwest, but now only about 30 per cent are manufactured in the Center and 4.4 per cent in the Northwest. Machine tools are now manufactured in regions that formerly had no machine tool plants. Twelve per cent of the present production is in the Ukraine, about 10 per cent in Belorussia, more than 10 per cent in the Urals, about 9 per cent in the North Caucasus, and more than 7 per cent in the Volga region.

The railroad locomotive industry inherited old plants from Tsarist Russia in the cities of Kolomna, Gorky, Bryansk, and Kharkov. Since then locomotive works have been constructed in Krasnoyarsk, Ulan-Ude, Lugansk, and Novocherkassk, near the Donets Basin in Rostov Oblast. By the time of the Revolution there were fifteen railroad car building works in Russia, the largest of which were in Koloma, St. Petersburg, Sormovo (Gorky), Bryansk, and Revel (Tallin). Since then large plants turning out railroad rolling stock have been constructed at Tagil in the Urals, at Dneprodzerzhinsk and Kremenchug in the Ukraine, at Engels on the Volga, and at Barnaul in the Altay region. The largest railroad car works in the country at present is the Tagil works in the Urals.

The output of automobiles in the Soviet Union is much less than that in the United States, and the lack of highways will probably keep it that way for a long time to come. In 1960 the Soviet Union produced only 523,591 vehicles of which 384,769 were trucks and buses. Only 138,822 passenger cars were produced. By contrast, in 1960 the United States produced 7,869,271 motor vehicles of which 6,674,796 were passenger cars. The Soviet industry has shown very little increase since 1958. From the beginning, the main centers of the automobile industry have been Gorky, Moscow, and Yaroslavl. Gorky had the first large plant in the country and is the main manufacturer of automobiles to this day. Since World War II new plants have been established at Ulyanovsk on the Volga, at Miass in the Urals, at Kutaisi in Georgia, at Dnepropetrovsk, Zaporozhye, Kremenchug, Lvov, and Odessa in the Ukraine, and at Minsk in Belorussia.

The large Moscow ZIL factory turns out the well-known ZIL and Moskvich cars. The ZIL car used to be known as the ZIS car before the death of Stalin. The letters ZIS stood for Zavod Imenniy Stalin, which means "the plant named after Stalin." After his death the car was renamed ZIL in honor of an ex-manager of the plant. Gorky contains several automobile plants manufacturing the ZIM, a large limosine named after Molotov, as well as light passenger cars such as the Pobeda and the Volga. Most of the taxis in the Soviet Union are Volga cars. Gorky also manufactures trucks, and the Yaroslavl plant manufactures heavy trucks. The Minsk plant specializes in trucks and highway tractors, and the Kutaisi plant in trucks and dump trucks. The Miass plant in the Urals manufactures a 10-ton cargo truck called "the Ural" which can negotiate any road condition. The Lvov plant manufactures buses, and the Kremenchug plant is to start production of a powerful truck called "the Dnieper."

One of the latest light passenger cars, the Chaika, or Seagull, also is manufactured at Gorky. Mass production began in December 1958. A newer model passenger car, the Zaporozhets, was to go into production in 1960 at the Zaporozhye plant. It is a small four-passenger car with four cylinders having 20 to 25 horsepower and an air-cooled engine located in the back.

Shipbuilding during Tsarist days was located in St. Petersburg on the Baltic, and at Sevastopol and Nikolayev on the Black Sea. New shipyards have been built at Murmansk on the Kola Peninsula and at Komsomolsk in the Far East as well as at Kherson on the Black Sea. The river fleet is supplied by shipyards at Gorky, Rybinsk, Krasnoarmeysk, and Astrakhan on the Volga River, Perm on the Kama, Kiev on the Dnieper, Tyumen on the Tura River, and several small shipyards located on the Ob, the Yenisey, and the Amur Rivers. The Sormovo shipyards in Gorky have been experimenting with an ultramodern hydrofoil rocket-type ship, which is a cigar-shaped, jet-like ship capable of carrying 150 passengers at speeds of up to 100 kilometers per hour. These so-called "meteor ships" were to start regular runs between Gorky and Kuybyshev on the Volga River in 1960. In these boats the distance between the two cities can be covered in 14 hours, whereas a regular Diesel ship takes 3 days.

Very little information is available on the aircraft industry in the Soviet Union, although it is obvious that it has developed to a high degree. Apparently airplane factories are concentrated in the Central Industrial Region, the Ukraine, the Volga region, and the Urals. There is some evidence that the aircraft industry is dispersed throughout all industrial regions of the Soviet Union.

Agricultural machine building takes place primarily in the richest agricultural regions where the bulky machines can be delivered without too much transportation. The Ukraine is perhaps the region of the most concentrated agricultural machine building. Plants are located in Kirovograd, Kharkov, Zaporozhye, Kherson, Odessa, and other cities. The largest single agricultural machinery plant in the country, "Rosselmash," is in Rostov just east of the Ukraine. Similar plants exist in the North Caucasus and in the Central Black Earth Region. New plants have been established in western Siberia, particularly at Kurgan, Omsk, Rubtsovsk, and Tselinograd, to serve the agriculture in that area. A new plant is under construction at Pavlodar to help meet the needs of farm machinery in the newly plowed virgin lands.

Tractors are manufactured primarily at Volgograd, Chelyabinsk, Kharkov, and recently, at Rubtsovsk, Vladimir, and Lipetsk. Potato harvesters are built at Tula, flax harvesters at Bezhetsk in Kalinin Oblast, cotton pickers at Tashkent, and corn pickers at Zaporozhye.

Textile Industries

The textile industries are some of the oldest industries in Russia. They initiated the industrialization of the Center and still are one of the more important groups of industries in that area. Although their value of output in the Central Industrial Region has been surpassed by that of the machine-building industries, and in some cities by that of the chemical industries, a greater percentage of their value is represented by labor. Hence their importance to the region in terms of number of workers engaged is more important than the money value might indicate. All the textile industries are still heavily concentrated in the Central Industrial Region, although the concentration is not quite as great as it was before the Revolution. In 1960 the Center produced 77.5 per cent of the country's cotton cloth, 57 per cent of the wool, 70 per cent of the linen, and 71 per cent of the silk.

Many new plants have been constructed during the Soviet period both in areas where the raw materials are produced and in areas of growing markets. Thus in 1935 large cotton mills were built in Tashkent in the heart of the cotton-growing region of Middle Asia and at Barnaul in the Kulunda Steppe of southwestern Siberia. Barnaul receives raw cotton from Middle Asia over the Turk-Sib Railroad and produces cotton textiles for the growing markets in southwestern Siberia. During World War II new cotton mills were constructed at Dushanbe in the cotton-growing region of southwestern Tadzhikistan and at Chelyabinsk and Ufa in the Urals. Since the war new mills have been constructed at Kansk in eastern Siberia, at Chimkent in Middle Asia, at Gori in Transcaucasia, at Cheboksary and Kamyshin along the Volga, and at Kherson on the Black Sea coast of the Ukraine.

In the Central Industrial Region the cotton textile industry continues to be heavily concentrated in Ivanovo and surrounding cities along the Volga northeast of Moscow and in Moscow and its suburban cities. In 1913 the textile industry in this region depended for nearly 50 per cent of its raw cotton on areas outside of Russia, primarily Egypt. By 1933 the Soviet Union had ex-

Table 15–22 Textile Production by Regions, U.S.S.R., 1960 (in Millions of Running Meters)[a]

	Cotton	Wool	Linen	Silk (Including Artificial)
U.S.S.R.	6387.8	341.8	559.4	809.7
R.S.F.S.R.	5546.6	271.8	472.7	645.8
Northwest	239.6	16.2	29.7	47.7
Center	4945.8	194.3	391.1	575.0
Volga-Vyatka	93.7	1.6	20.0	—
Central Black Earth	4.3	12.1	—	—
Volga	46.6	26.2	26.6	—
Northern Caucasus	15.8	12.2	—	—
Urals	15.1	5.6	1.2	0.4
Western Siberia	97.7	2.2	4.2	—
Eastern Siberia	81.1	1.3	—	22.8
Far East	6.9	—	—	—
Ukraine	96.0	19.1	—	40.0
Donets-Dnieper	13.4	10.8		—
Southwest	37.6	4.9		27.1
South	45.0	3.4	55.3	12.9
Belorussia	4.7	15.2	55.3	1.0
Uzbekistan	234.7	—	—	24.1
Kazakhstan	20.3	4.1	—	—
Georgia	49.5	4.9	—	19.4
Azerbaydzhan	103.3	2.1	—	7.6
Lithuania	17.4	6.8	11.3	14.3
Moldavia	1.4	0.3	—	6.0
Latvia	49.8	8.7	11.2	10.3
Kirgiz S.S.R.	1.5	1.1	—	5.4
Tadzhik S.S.R.	51.5	—	—	25.7
Armenia	65.6	3.9	—	6.8
Turkmen S.S.R.	23.6	0.4	—	0.1
Estonia	121.9	3.4	8.4	3.1

[a] Source: Narodnoe khozyaystvo SSSR v 1960 godu, pp. 325–328.

panded cotton growing in Middle Asia and Transcaucasia to the point where it served 97 per cent of its own needs, and this has continued to the present.

Fine wool materials traditionally have been centered around Moscow and Leningrad, and coarse woolens have been manufactured in the Volga area. During and since World War II new factories have been built in Minsk and other cities in the west and in the sheep-producing areas in the mountains of Middle Asia, Siberia, and the Caucasus.

Chardzhou and Alma-Ata are important woolen centers in Middle Asia, Ulan-Ude is important in eastern Siberia, and Tbilisi is the most important center in the Transcaucasia.

Linen is produced primarily in the Center and the Northwest where the flax is grown. Kostroma traditionally has been the leader in linen production, and other cities in the Volga region northeast of Moscow are important.

The traditional centers of the silk industry

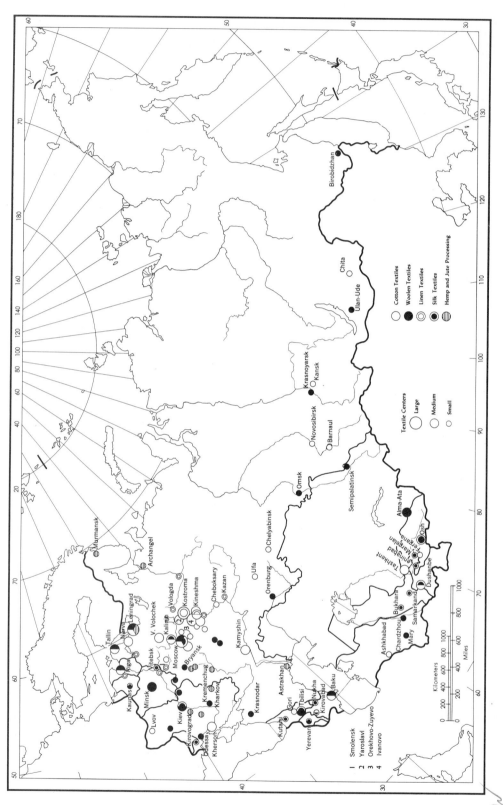

Figure 15-22   The textile industries.   After Cherdantsev.

are in Middle Asia and Transcaucasia where silk worms are grown utilizing mulberry trees that are planted along irrigation canals. According to the statistical handbooks for 1960, 71 per cent of the silk production of the Soviet Union was in the Central Industrial Region, but apparently the statistics on silk production include rayon and synthetic fibers. Apparently natural silk accounts for only about one sixteenth of what is reported as silk in the Soviet Union at present. The most important producers in the Central Industrial Region are Kalinin and Moscow, but what they produce is probably all rayon. Rayon factories also have been established in the Ukraine, in the Central Black Earth Region, and in Krasnoyarsk in eastern Siberia.

Hemp is an old crop in Russia, and jute is a newcomer. The largest hemp–jute industry originally was concentrated in port cities since it provided the shipping industries with rope. Smaller factories have been built in the hemp-growing regions of Belorussia, Smolensk, Orel, Bryansk, and Kirovograd Oblasts and the Mordovian A.S.S.R. Before the Revolution jute was imported, but now it is planted in Middle Asia, particularly around Tashkent. The first jute factory was constructed in Tashkent in 1952. Several jute factories are planned for the Tadzhik Republic.

Of the total fabric production in the U.S.S.R. in 1960 only about 7 per cent was artificial and synthetic. This compares with 25 per cent in the United States, and, of course, total production of fabrics in the United States is much higher than it is in the U.S.S.R. By 1965 the Soviets hope to produce 15 per cent of an expanded fabric output by artificial and synthetic means.

Food Industries

The main branches of the food industry are flour milling, sugar processing, meat processing, canning, vegetable-oil production, and fishing. Flour milling has grown with grain production in the regions of the Center, the South, the Volga, the southern Urals, southwestern Siberia, the Far East, and Middle Asia.

The sugar industry in the Soviet Union is based on the sugar beet crop which until recently was produced entirely in the Ukraine and the Central Black Earth Region. In 1955, 71 per cent of the sugar production in the U.S.S.R. was in the Ukraine, 17 per cent in the Central Black Earth Region, 2 per cent in the Kazakh Republic, 2 per cent in the Kirgiz Republic, and 4 per cent in the rest of the country. New regions of sugar production are the Kuban in the North Caucasus, the Kulunda Steppe in southwestern Siberia, and the Ussuri-Khanka Lowland in the Far East.

Meat processing is centered in the rich farming areas of the country. In 1955 the Ukraine processed 19 per cent of the country's meat, the central regions 19 per cent, the North Caucasus 9 per cent, western Siberia 8 per cent, the Urals 8 per cent, Kazakhstan 7 per cent, and the Volga region about 6 per cent. The largest meat combines are located in Moscow, Leningrad, Baku, and Semipalatinsk. In 1960 the Soviet Union processed 7,922,000 metric tons of meat; this compared to 12,391,000 in the United States.

Since there is so little refrigeration equipment in the Soviet Union, the canning industry has become the mainstay of the food industries. Much of the meat produced in slaughter houses is immediately canned, and the fresh meat supply depends primarily on the Kolkhoz markets where the farmers bring newly slaughtered meat each day. The canned goods industry has grown rapidly in the Soviet Union along with urbanization and public catering. Canned vegetables are mostly prepared in the steppe regions of the Ukraine and North Caucasus, canned meat in Kazakhstan, canned fruit in Transcaucasia, North Caucasus, Crimea, Moldavia, and other southern regions, and much fish canning is carried on in all regions of fishing.

In the Soviet Union vegetable oil is produced 44 per cent from sunflower seeds, 34 per cent from cotton seeds, 6.9 per cent from soy beans, and 5.7 per cent from arachis. Other oil sources are flax seed, hemp seed, castor seed, mustard seed, and tung nuts. In 1957 Middle Asia produced 27.4 per cent of the country's vegetable oil, the North Caucasus produced 21.8 per cent, the Ukraine 19.6 per cent, the Central Black Earth Region 8 per cent, and the Volga 4 per cent. Middle Asia produces mainly from cotton whereas the other regions produce mainly from sunflowers. The major portion of vegetable oils goes for the production of margarine. The main margarine, plants are located in Moscow, Leningrad, Kharkov, Rostov, Krasnodar, and Gomel.

Fish   In 1913 Russia caught about a million tons of fish of which two thirds came from the Caspian Sea, about 10 per cent from Far Eastern waters, 7 per cent from the Black and Azov Seas, and about 6 per cent from the European North. The 1960 catch was more than three times as large as the 1913 catch, and the geographical distribution of the catch had changed considerably. In 1960 the Soviet catch was 3,051,000 tons, which ranked it third in the world, after Japan and Peru, and slightly ahead of the United States.*   At present the Arctic and Atlantic Oceans produce about 30 per cent of the total catch, the Far East about 30 per cent, the Caspian about 17 per cent, the Baltic 10 per cent, the Black and Azov Seas 6 per cent, and Antarctica about 5.5 per cent. Siberian rivers and lakes add another 2.5 per cent, and the Aral Sea and Lake Balkhash add more than 2 per cent. The fishing in Antarctica is exclusively for whales. The Soviet Union ranks third in the world in whaling after Japan and Norway. The largest fish-processing plants are at Murmansk on the Barents Sea, Archangel

* 1961 data indicate that Communist China has surpassed the Soviet fish catch, which makes the Soviet Union fourth and the United States fifth in the world.

on the White Sea, Astrakhan and Guryev on the Caspian, Zhdanov on the Sea of Azov, and Vladivostok in the Far East.

Perhaps the best fishing grounds are in the Barents Sea and the White Sea. Herring, haddock, halibut, cod, sea perch, and salmon are the main fish caught in these waters. The Caspian is especially famous for its sturgeon from which is obtained the Russian black caviar. The sea of Azov also is a very rich fishing ground particularly around the estuaries of the Don and Kuban Rivers. Many fish migrate into the Sea of Azov through the narrow Kerch Straits in spring to spawn and in the fall they reverse their movements back to the Black Sea.

Table 15–23   Types of Fish Caught in Soviet Waters, 1957, in Per Cents of Total Weight[a]

Herring	25.3
Cod	15.7
Other sardine-like fish	11.0
Whales	7.8
Crabs	1.1
Walruses and seals	0.7
Flounder	5.4
Salmon	7.0
Sturgeon	0.5
Other fish and sea products	25.5

[a] *Source: Atlas selskogo khozyaystva SSSR, p. 206.*

The Far East is especially known for its salmon and crab. Sixty per cent of the salmon catch in the U.S.S.R. comes from the shores of Kamchatka. The eastern waters also are rich in flounder, smelt, herring, mackerel, cod, and sea animals—whales, walruses, and seals. Some of the new Soviet floating factories used for whaling in the Antarctic during the southern hemisphere summer return to Vladivostok and are used to catch white whales in the Sea of Okhotsk during the northern hemisphere summer. The fishing industry is very important to the food supply of the Soviet Union, regularly contributing from one third to one half of the meat supply of the country.

Lumbering and Woodworking

The Soviet Union traditionally has been a great lumbering country, and wood has been the primary construction material throughout the history of old Russia and the Soviet Union. Until recently the buildings of even the largest cities of the country were built primarily of wood. Fires were a constant hazard. The great Moscow fires that have occurred all through history are legendary. Now the building industry is switching heavily to reinforced concrete and other materials, but the uses for wood still continue to increase, and production is to approximately double during the seven-year plan.

1960. Except for some mountain areas in the south, forest growth is limited primarily to the area north of a line running through the northwestern Ukraine, the southern Urals, and southern Siberia. Thus large sections of the populous south must be served by long hauls of large quantities of wood from the north. Lumber makes up 14 per cent of all the cargo transported by railroads and 40 per cent of the cargo transported by water.

In 1955, 212 million cubic meters of saw timber were cut in the U.S.S.R. The Center produced the most with 44 million cubic meters, the Urals 37, the North 29, eastern Siberia 25, western Siberia 19, the Northwest 19, and the Far East 10.8. The heavy cutting in the Center reflects the great market demand, and it greatly exceeds the annual growth rate in that region. It has been estimated that if cutting continues at

Table 15–24   Production of Wood Products, U.S.S.R. and U.S.A., 1960[a]

Item	Unit	U.S.S.R.	U.S.A.
Lumber	1000 cubic meters		
From coniferous trees		90,100	67,038
From broadleaf trees		15,900	14,851
Wood pulp	1000 metric tons	850	4,054
Chemical pulp	1000 metric tons	2,282	18,765

[a] *Source: United Nations Statistical Yearbook, 1960.*

About 30 per cent of the territory of the U.S.S.R. is covered by forests; this represents about one fifth of the forested territory of the world. In 1960 the U.S.S.R. cut 369 million cubic meters of roundwood. This compared to 311 for its closest competitor, the United States, and 1732 for the entire world. The Karelian A.S.S.R. has 60 per cent of its territory covered by forests. Even in some of the heavily populated parts of European Russia a surprisingly high percentage of the area still is covered by forests; Moscow Oblast, for instance, is 35.6 per cent covered according to a survey taken in

the same rate in the Central region many of the oblasts will be exhausted of reserves of mature timber within about 6 years. At the same time hundreds of thousands of square miles of territory go nearly unexploited with overripe dying trees crowding out younger growth.

Forty-one per cent of the reserves of mature forests lie in the northern regions of Siberia and the Far East where only 1 per cent of the country's population live. The little forested or unforested regions in the Center, the South, the West, the Northwest, the Caucasus, and Soviet Middle Asia, where

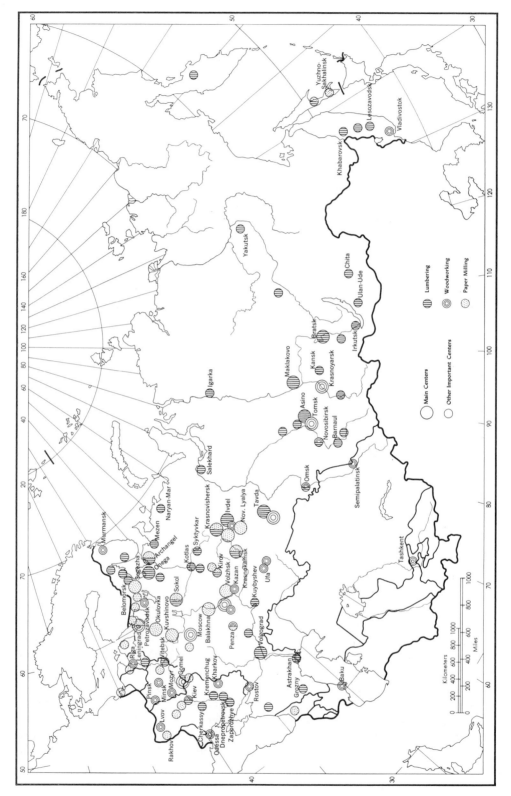

Figure 15-23   Lumbering, woodworking, and paper milling.   After Cherdantsev.

Table 15–25   Types of Production in Soviet Manufacturing Centers[a]

Center	Type of Manufacturing Activity
Alma-Ata	General food products, wool, woodworking, general fabricated metal products, general machinery, general chemicals and allied products, and fertilizers.
Archangel	Fish, lumber, shipbuilding, wood chemicals.
Ashkhabad	Food products, textile products and clothing, burlap, machinery, chemicals and allied products.
Astrakhan	Fish, fruit, shipbuilding.
Baku	Food products, textile products and clothing, petroleum, fabricated metal products, machinery, petroleum refining.
Barnaul	Grain milling, cotton, fabricated metal products, machinery.
Bryansk	Food products, meat, phosphate, machinery, farm machinery, transportation equipment, railroad equipment, cement.
Chelyabinsk	Iron and steel, fabricated metal products, machinery, tractors and farm machinery, metalworking machinery, aircraft and parts, industrial chemicals and allied products.
Chita	Meat, leather products, lumber and wood products, lignite, fabricated metal products, railroad equipment.
Dneprodzerzhinsk	Iron and steel, railroad equipment, industrial chemicals and allied products.
Dnepropetrovsk	Food products, textile products and clothing, iron and steel, fabricated metal products, machinery.
Donets	Coal mining, iron and steel, metalworking, machinery, chemicals.
Dushanbe	Meat, leather products, cotton, silk, general fabricated metal products, farm machinery.
Dzerzhinsk	Grain milling, peat, general chemicals and allied products.
Frunze	Grain milling, meat, fruit, wool, general fabricated metal products, farm machinery.
Gorky	Food products, general fabricated metal products, general machinery, metalworking machinery, electrical machinery and equipment, motor vehicles, aircraft and parts.
Gorlovka	Coal, general fabricated metal products, general machinery, ceramics.
Groznyy	Meat, fish, beverage, petroleum, metalworking machinery, petroleum refining.
Irkutsk	Food products, lumber, general fabricated metal products, general machinery, construction and mining machinery, motor vehicles, hydro generating electric power, oil refining, aluminum.
Ivanovo	Meat, cotton, general machinery.
Izhevsk	Meat, woodworking, iron and steel, farm machinery.
Kalinin	Food products, general textile products and clothing, general fabricated metal products, general transportation equipment, general chemicals and allied products.
Kaliningrad	General food products, woodworking, paper, general machinery, shipbuilding.
Karaganda	General food products, coal, general machinery, construction and mining machinery, iron and steel.
Kaunas	General food products, general textile products and clothing, peat, general fabricated metal products, general chemicals and allied products, rubber products.
Kazan	Leather products, textile products and clothing, general machinery, farm machinery, railroad equipment, aircraft and parts, general chemicals and allied products, vegetable and animal oils, general rubber products.
Kemerovo	Coal, general fabricated metal products, general machinery, industrial chemicals.

Table 15–25   Types of Production in Soviet Manufacturing Centers[a] *(Continued)*

Center	Type of Manufacturing Activity
Khabarovsk	General food products, lumber, general fabricated metal products, farm machinery, motor vehicles, shipbuilding, aircraft and parts, petroleum refining.
Kharkov	General fabricated metal products, engines and turbines, tractors and farm machinery, construction and mining machinery, metalworking machinery, electrical machinery and equipment, railroad equipment, motorcycles and bicycles.
Kiev	General food products, general textile products and clothing, general fabricated metal products, farm machinery, metalworking machinery, electrical machinery and equipment, railroad equipment, shipbuilding, aircraft and parts, motorcycles and bicycles, chemicals and allied products, rubber products.
Kirov	Meat, woodworking, general fabricated metal products, general machinery.
Kishinev	General food products, leather products, textile products and clothing, general fabricated metal products, cement.
Komsomolsk-on-Amur	General food products, lumber, steel, general fabricated metal products, general machinery, shipbuilding, aircraft and parts.
Kostroma	General food products, leather products, linen, lumber, general fabricated metal products, general machinery.
Krasnodar	General food products, wool, general machinery, electrical machinery and equipment, petroleum refining.
Krasnoyarsk	General food products, lumber, general fabricated metal products, farm machinery, construction and mining machinery, railroad equipment, stone, clay and glass products, oil refining, aluminum.
Krivoy Rog	Iron mining, iron and steel.
Kursk	General food products, woodworking, tractors and farm machinery, electrical machinery and equipment, chemicals and allied products.
Kuybyshev	General food products, general fabricated metal products, general machinery, farm machinery, petroleum refining.
Leningrad	General food products, textile products and clothing, iron and steel, general fabricated metal products, general machinery, engines and turbines, metalworking machinery, electrical machinery and equipment, general transportation equipment, general instruments, chemicals and allied products, printing and publishing.
Lipetsk	Iron mining, iron and steel, tractors and farm machinery.
Lugansk	General fabricated metal products, general machinery, construction and mining machinery, railroad equipment, ceramics.
Lvov	General food products, textile products and clothing, general fabricated metal products, electrical machinery and equipment, petroleum refining, glass products.
Magnitogorsk	Iron mining, iron and steel, general fabricated metal products, general machinery, industrial chemicals.
Makeyevka	Coal, iron and steel.
Minsk	General food products, textile products and clothing, general fabricated metal products, farm machinery, electrical machinery and equipment, motor vehicles.
Moscow	General food products, textile products and clothing, woodworking, general fabricated metal products, general machinery, motor vehicles, railroad equipment, aircraft and parts, chemicals and allied products, printing and publishing.

Table 15–25   Types of Production in Soviet Manufacturing Centers[a] *(Continued)*

Center	Type of Manufacturing Activity
Murmansk	Fish, burlap, woodworking, general machinery, shipbuilding.
Nikolayev	General food products, textile products and clothing, general machinery, shipbuilding.
Nizhniy Tagil	Meat, iron mining, iron and steel, general transportation equipment, industrial chemicals.
Novokuznetsk	Coal, iron and steel, aluminum, general fabricated metal products, general machinery, railroad equipment, industrial chemicals.
Novosibirsk	Grain milling, textile products and clothing, iron and steel, general fabricated metal products, farm machinery, motor vehicles, general chemicals and allied products, vegetable and animal oils, oil refining.
Odessa	General food products, grain milling, textile products and clothing, farm machinery, metalworking machinery, shipbuilding, chemicals and allied products, petroleum refining.
Omsk	Grain milling, meat, wool, general fabricated metal products, farm machinery, railroad equipment, chemicals and allied products, oil refining.
Ordzhonikhidze	Fruit, metal industries, general machinery, hydro generating electric power.
Orenburg	Grain milling, meat, leather products, general fabricated metal products, general machinery, engines and turbines.
Orsk	Meat, iron mining, nickel mining, metal industries, general machinery, railroad equipment, petroleum refining.
Penza	General food products, paper, general fabricated metal products, general transportation equipment.
Perm	General food products, copper, general fabricated metal products, general machinery, engines and turbines, general transportation equipment, aircraft and parts, industrial chemicals, hydro generating electric power.
Prokopyevsk	Grain milling, coal, general fabricated metal products.
Riga	General food products, general textile products and clothing, general fabricated metal products, general machinery, electrical machinery and equipment, railroad equipment, shipbuilding, general chemicals and allied products, stone, clay and glass products.
Rostov-on-Don	General food products, general tobacco products, leather products, tractors and farm machinery, metalworking machinery, shipbuilding, aircraft and parts.
Ryazan	Meat, fruit, general fabricated metal products, general transportation equipment, railroad equipment.
Rybinsk	Grain milling, lumber, general machinery, shipbuilding, hydro generating electric power.
Saratov	General food products, general machinery, petroleum refining.
Shakhty	Leather products, general textile products and clothing, coal, thermal generating electric power.
Simferopol	General food products, general tobacco products, general machinery.
Smolensk	Meat, dairy, linen, woodworking, general fabricated metal products, general machinery.
Sverdlovsk	General food products, iron and steel, copper, general fabricated metal products, engines and turbines, construction and mining machinery, metalworking machinery, electrical machinery and equipment, industrial chemicals.
Syzran	General food products, oil shale, tractors and farm machinery, railroad equipment, glass products, petroleum refining.

Table 15–25   Types of Production in Soviet Manufacturing Centers^a (Continued)

Center	Type of Manufacturing Activity
Taganrog	Iron and steel, general machinery, tractors and farm machinery.
Tallin	Grain milling, fish, general textile products and clothing, woodworking, electrical machinery and equipment, shipbuilding.
Tambov	General food products, general machinery, electrical machinery and equipment, railroad equipment, aircraft and parts, industrial chemicals, wood chemicals.
Tashkent	General food products, leather products, cotton, general fabricated metal products, general machinery, farm machinery.
Tbilisi	General food products, leather products, wool, silk, general machinery, general chemicals and allied products.
Tomsk	General food products, woodworking, general fabricated metal products, electrical machinery and equipment.
Tula	Lignite, iron and steel, general fabricated metal products, general machinery, farm machinery, general instruments.
Ufa	General food products, cotton, woodworking, general fabricated metal products, engines and turbines, farm machinery, electrical machinery and equipment, petroleum refining.
Ulan-Ude	Grain milling, meat, wool, general fabricated metal products, general transportation equipment, glass products.
Ulyanovsk	General food products, lumber, general machinery, motor vehicles.
Vilnyus	General food products, woodworking, general fabricating metal products, farm machinery, metalworking machinery, electrical machinery and equipment, fertilizers.
Vladimir	Cotton, general fabricated metal products, farm machinery, general instruments, general chemicals and allied products.
Vladivostok	Grain milling, fish, lumber, general fabricated metal products, construction and mining machinery, shipbuilding.
Volgograd	General food products, lumber, iron and steel, tractors and farm machinery, petroleum refining.
Voronezh	General food products, general machinery, railroad equipment, petroleum refining, general rubber products, ceramics.
Yerevan	General food products, general tobacco products, leather products, wool, general machinery, general chemicals and allied products.
Zaporozhye	Iron and steel, aluminum, general fabricated metal products, farm machinery, chemicals and allied products, hydro generating electric power, motor vehicles.
Zhdanov	Fish, graphite, iron and steel, general machinery, shipbuilding.

^a *Source:* Lonsdale, Richard E., and Thompson, John H., "A Map of the U.S.S.R.'s Manufacturing," *Economic Geography*, January 1960, pp. 44–50.

85 per cent of the population of the country lives, have only 4 per cent of the timber reserves. Thus much timber has to be shipped over long distances. Since 60 per cent of all sawn wood is produced in the consuming centers, much of the transport of forest products is constituted by raw timber. Twenty per cent of all wood sawing takes place in the cities of the European Center, and 45 per cent of the prefabricated houses are made in the Center, the Ukraine, Belorussia, and the Baltic Republic. In the better lumbering regions of northern European Russia, accessibility to markets is a

problem since transportation of most of the lumber is oriented toward the waterways, and all the waterways flow out to the north to the Arctic.

The uses of lumber in the Soviet Union so far have been rather wasteful. Less than 5 per cent of the total wood cut has been given any chemical processing. Whereas in the United States 2 cubic meters of plywood, 5.6 tons of paper, 4.4 tons of cardboard, and 0.5 tons of fiberboard are manufactured for every 100 cubic meters of lumber logged, in the U.S.S.R. the corresponding figures are 0.3 cubic meters of plywood, 0.6 tons of paper, 0.2 tons of cardboard and 0.05 tons of fiberboard. During the last 35 years lumbering in the United States has been reduced to less than half, whereas improved wood processing has increased the availability of most wood products. In the Soviet Union in order to maintain constant levels of consumption of wood products lumbering has had to increase at a rapid rate, and apparently it is to continue to do so in the future. Although firewood has been reduced in the fuel balance of the country from 58 per cent in 1913 to 10 per cent in 1958, it still consumes about 50 million cubic meters of wood per year, and unused waste makes up another 150 million cubic meters. The lumbering industry also is inefficient in terms of labor and capital outlay. About 15 per cent of the country's industrial workers and about 5 per cent of the capital funds are engaged in all branches of forestry, but their share in the total production of industry does not exceed 3 per cent.

According to the recent forestry survey, the river banks in most of the river basins of the European part of the Soviet Union have lighter forest covers than do the whole territories of the respective oblasts. This is a surprising reversal of what might be expected under natural growing conditions; one usually would expect the heaviest tree growth to be along streams where constant supplies of moisture are available. It reflects the heavy cutting of wood for all uses, including heavy use for firewood, along the more accessible portions of the landscape nearest the local villages, which in the main are located along stream valleys. Such practices have laid bare to erosion some of the hillier parts of the country.

Reading List

American Steel and Iron Ore Mining Delegation to the Soviet Union, *Steel in the Soviet Union,* American Iron and Steel Institute, 1959, 376 pp.

Bornstein, Morris, "A comparison of Soviet and United States National Product," *Comparisons of the United States and Soviet Economies,* Part II, 377–395.

Clark, Mills Gardner, *The Economics of Soviet Steel,* Harvard University Press, Cambridge, 1956, 400 pp.

Hassmann, Heinrich, *Oil in the Soviet Union,* translated by Alfred M. Leeston and published by Princeton University Press, Princeton, N.J., 1953, 173 pp.

Hodgkins, Jordan A., *Soviet Power: Energy Resources, Production and Potential,* Prentice-Hall, Englewood Cliffs, N.J., 1961, 190 pp.

Hodgman, Donald R., *Soviet Industrial Production, 1928–1951,* Harvard University Press, Cambridge, 1954, 241 pp.

Holloway, Robert J., *The Development of the Russian Iron and Steel Industry,* Stanford, 1952, 59 pp.

Hoyt, John Stanley, *An Investigation of the Economies of Soviet Locational Doctrine, Policy, and Practice, with Special Emphasis on Heavy Industry,* University Microfilms, Ann Arbor, 1959.

Krengel, Rolf, "Soviet, American, and West German Basic Industries: A Comparison," *Soviet Studies,* October 1960, 113–125.

Livshits, R. S., *Razmeshchenie chernoy metallurgii SSSR,* Moscow, 1958, 371 pp. (in Russian).

Lonsdale, Richard E., and Thompson, John H., "A Map of the U.S.S.R.'s Manufacturing," *Economic Geography,* January 1960, 36–52.

Lydolph, Paul E., and Shabad, Theodore, "The Oil and Gas Industries in the U.S.S.R.," *Annals of the Association of American Geographers,* December 1960, 461–486.

Nove, Alec, "The Industrial Planning System Reforms in Prospect," *Soviet Studies,* July 1962, 1–15.

Nutter, G. Warren, the *Growth of Industrial Production in the Soviet Union,* Princeton University Press, Princeton, N.J., 1962, 733 pp.

——, "The Structure and Growth of Soviet Industry: A Comparison with the United States," *Comparison of the United States and Soviet Economies,* Part I, 95–120.

Omarovskiy, A. G., "Changes in the Geography of Machine Building in the U.S.S.R.," *Soviet Geography: Review and Translation,* March 1960, 42–56.

Petrov, Victor P., *Geography of the Soviet Union, Part IV, Soviet Industry,* Washington, 1960, 90 pp.

——, *Geography of the Soviet Union, Part IV–B, Electric Power,* Victor P. Kamkin, Inc., Washington, 1959, 70 pp.

Pociuk, Stephan G., "The Territorial Pattern of Industrialization in the U.S.S.R.," *Soviet Studies,* July 1961, 69–95.

Promyshlennost SSSR, Moscow, 1957, 447 pp. (in Russian).

Rodgers, Allan, "Changing Locational Patterns in the Soviet Pulp and Paper Industry," *Annals of the Association of American Geographers,* March 1955, 85–104.

Shabad, Theodore, and Lydolph, Paul E., "The Chemical Industries in the U.S.S.R.," *Tijdschrift voor Economische en Sociale Geografie,* August/September 1962, 169–179.

Shabad, Theodore, *The Soviet Aluminum Industry,* American Metal Market, New York, 1958, 25 pp.

Shimkin, Demitri B., *Minerals: A Key to Soviet Power,* Harvard University Press, Cambridge, 1953.

Shimkin, Demitri B., *The Soviet Mineral Fuels Industries, 1928–1958: A Statistical Survey,* International Population Statistics Reports, Series P-90, No. 19, United States Bureau of the Census, 1962, 183 pp.

Soviet Handbook 1959–1965, London, November 1959, 70 pp.

Sudoplatov, A., *Coal Industry of the U.S.S.R.,* Foreign Languages Publishing House, Moscow, 1959, 155 pp.

Vasilyev, P. V., "Questions of the Geographic Study and Economic Use of Forests," *Soviet Geography: Review and Translation,* December 1960, 50–63.

16

Transportation and Domestic Trade

The transportation system is the lifeline to the economy of the Soviet Union, as it is in any country. It moves the traffic that is generated by the disparity between production and consumption in each locale, and is the critical factor in keeping materials supplied to industrial and agricultural concerns. At times its adequacy or inadequacy has had a governing effect on the further expansion of production. The transportation system not only has the function of providing services to the general economy, its operations constitute a significant portion of that economy. The transport system of the U.S.S.R. regularly consumes about one fourth the fuel and steel production of the country and employs about one tenth of the manpower.

Freight traffic in the Soviet Union has risen from 126 billion ton-kilometers in 1913 to 1886 billion ton-kilometers in 1960. In 1926 total freight traffic by all modes of transport in the Soviet Union was about 8 per cent of that in the United States. It rose to 37 per cent in 1940, but during World War II fell back to 20 per cent. Since then it has risen to approximately equal that of the United States. This great amount of traffic in the Soviet Union is carried by a transportation system that is considerably different from that of the United States or countries in western

Europe, and some understanding must be had of the underlying geographic factors and governmental policies controlling the system before it can be understood and appreciated.

Nature of the Soviet Transportation System

Vast distances, uneven distribution of population, physical environment, and party ideology concerning the development of the economy have imparted a somewhat special character and role to the transportation system of the Soviet Union. Special characteristics are: (1) an unusually close integration of the transportation system to overall resources of the economy and to the requirements of general developmental policy, (2) strict limitations on the volume and character of traffic in an effort to minimize transport, (3) limited investment in transport facilities, particularly in highways, which might provide a variety of transport operations, (4) especially heavy reliance on railroads for intercity movement of freight and passengers, and (5) an intensity of total railroad plant operation that is unheard of in the rest of the world.

Shortcomings of River Transport Soviet waterways suffer from several disabilities. First, most of the rivers, as well as many of the lakes and seas, freeze for long periods during the year and are not available for navigation. Even in the southern part of the country, the Volga and Don Rivers are frozen for approximately 5 months of the year (Table 16–1). Also, with few excep-

Table 16–1   Average Annual Length of Shipping Season, U.S.S.R., at Major Rivers and Ports[a]

Location	Length of Season (Days)	Percentage of Time Navigable
River		
Dnieper at Kiev	267	73.2
Lower Volga	264	72.3
Upper Volga	224	61.4
Western Dvina	236	64.7
Northern Dvina	177	48.5
Ob at Salekhard	152	41.6
Irtysh at Tobolsk	189	51.8
Yenisey at Krasnoyarsk	197	54.0
Southern (upper) Lena	145	39.7
Northern (lower) Lena	88	24.1
Seaport		
Odessa	328	89.9
Mariupol	288	79.8
Taganrog	252	69.0
Astrakhan	238	65.2
Tallin	283	77.5
Leningrad	200	54.8
Murmansk	365[b]	100.0
Archangel	175	47.9
Nizhne-Kolymsk	110	30.1
Vladivostok	255	69.9

[a] *Source:* Holland Hunter, *Soviet Transportation Policy*, 1957, p. 13.
[b] Kept open by icebreaker for 50 days.

tions, the major rivers of the country flow off to the edges of the land mass, and in so doing fail to join together the major concentrations of natural resources and economic activity. No river links are available between the iron ore and coal deposits of the Ukraine or between the coal and iron ore deposits of the Urals, Kazakhstan, and western Siberia. Neither of these basic industrial complexes is directly connected by river to Moscow or Leningrad.

The Volga River has been a great interregional connection in the past, and the new Volga-Don Canal has extended its sphere of activities toward the west, but even the Volga has not taken much part in the traffic between the Central Industrial Region and the eastern Ukraine. The Kama River brings timber into the Volga for the southern regions, and the Volga has been the main channel of petroleum traffic northward from the Caucasus to central European Russia. Both of these traffics on the river are diminishing, however, timber is more and more being transported entirely by rail, and the center of petroleum production has shifted away from the Caucasus to the Volga-Ural area whence oil is being carried by pipeline to the west and to the east. The growth of heavy industry in the cities along the Volga itself is enhancing the interregional transportation significance of this great river of Russian history, but the rail network that is gradually filling the territory all along the river is successively responsible for more and more of the traffic.

Rail shipment is much speedier, less seasonal, and in general more convenient than is water shipment, and so far in the Soviet Union the cost of rail shipment has not been appreciably higher than that of water. According to a Soviet report, in the two 5-year periods, 1946 to 1955, the relative capital investment per additional ton-kilometer of freight traffic was roughly two to two and one-half times as high for river carriers as for railroads, and in sea transport it was a little over three times as high.

Very little joint use of facilities involving transshipment from water to rail or vice versa seems to be practiced in the Soviet Union. Soviet economists ruefully joke that many shippers suffer from "hydrophobia." Transshipping points on the Volga are used very little. One transportation economist cited as an example the movement of wood southward from the Urals region. He said that the point had been reached where much of the timber was lifted out of the Kama River at Perm and then was railed all the way to the Donbas or the Caucasus. Since the opening of the Volga-Don Canal, of course, this timber could have gone all the way by water. In 1950 it was reported that only 0.5 per cent of timber consigned to the Donbas floated down the Volga River.

Use of canals has been rather disappointing. The Baltic–White Sea waterway in the first 5 years of operation, from August 1933 to August 1938, carried about 1.4 billion ton-kilometers of freight. In 1940 its traffic amounted to one-half billion ton-kilometers at a time when the traffic of the internal waterways as a whole amounted to 36 billions and that of all carriers amounted to 488 billions. Apparently the Volga-Don Canal is no more than one third utilized; bulky freight parallels it on railroads.

The huge river systems of Siberia unfortunately flow northward rather than in an east-west direction, and hence do not provide direct connections with European Russia. Connection of these streams, by way of the Northern Sea Route, from their mouths westward to Archangel and Murmansk is severely limited by the short shipping season and the high cost of navigating the northern seas. The Amur River in the Soviet Far East has proved to be of slight value in developing the territory around it.

In earlier days the Dnieper and the rivers of northwestern European Russia were the main traffic arteries of the territories through which they ran, but with the coming of the railroads the role of the rivers has steadily declined, and even the building of several canals during the interwar period has failed to reestablish their former positions.

All in all, the evidence indicates conclusively that the rivers of the U.S.S.R. do not mesh with the main traffic flows. This fact, combined with forced idleness in winter, largely explains their small and declining role.

Shortcomings of Maritime Shipping Geographic shortcomings also account to a large extent for the failure of maritime carriers to contribute on a major scale to domestic transportation in the U.S.S.R. The borders of the U.S.S.R. total approximately 37,000 miles, 70 per cent of which are bounded by water. Yet only a small fraction of the surrounding waters is suited to the carriage of freight between points of the U.S.S.R.

The Caspian Sea was landlocked until joined with the Black Sea by the Volga-Don Canal in 1952, and this canal is blocked by ice 5 months of the year. Canals now make water connections on Soviet territory between the Black and Baltic Seas possible during a few months each year. But year-round connections between the south and the north of European Russia by sea still require a trip around the whole circumference of western Europe. Sea passage from the Black Sea to the Soviet Far East entails a voyage almost half way around the world by way of the Suez Canal, skirting India and China. The Northern Sea Route has gradually been opened for traffic for approximately 3 months out of each year, but it does not seem likely to become a major artery for bulk freight in the foreseeable future.

The U.S.S.R. is a land power, and it must depend on land transportation to meet its domestic needs. In water transportation, it is probably less well endowed than any other major power on Earth.

Geographical Factors Favor Railroads On the other hand, the broad plains of the U.S.S.R. are unusually favorable for the construction and low-cost operation of railroads. According to 1933 data, only 4 per cent of the total main track operated had ruling gradients in excess of 1 per cent, whereas more than a quarter of the line was horizontal and more than 60 per cent had gradients below 0.5 of a per cent. Railroad operation is hampered to some extent by climate, extreme cold and snow in winter, and lack of water in the southern deserts, but the seasonality induced in railroad traffic by climatic factors is much less than that induced in the traffic of other carriers.

Lack of Highways and Pipelines The reluctance of the Soviet administration to divert capital from the industrialization effort to the transportation system, coupled with the lack of public demand for good automobile roads, has resulted in an almost complete neglect of the building of highways in the country. Compared to other modes of freight movement, motor transport is highly inefficient except on short hauls and requires inputs of fuel, labor, repair parts, and rates of vehicle replacement that are unacceptable to Soviet planners. Hence intercity truck traffic does not really exist; trucks are used almost exclusively for short-

haul distribution of materials from rail sidings in urban areas or for transport of farm produce from collective and state farms to rail heads in rural areas. The average length of truck haul in 1960 was only 11.6 kilometers. Concrete and black-top highways totaled only 77,100 kilometers. The United States in 1959 had 3,400,000 kilometers of hard-surfaced roads.

Until recently, the relatively small volume and geographical dispersion of oil movements did not seem to warrant the construction of many pipelines for the transport of petroleum and petroleum products. Thus the railroads in the Soviet Union typically have carried approximately 80 per cent of all freight and passenger traffic. The Soviets plan to reduce this percentage substantially

Table 16–2   Freight Traffic by Means of Transport (in Billion Ton-Kilometers and Per Cents of Total), U.S.S.R., Selected Years and U.S.A., 1960[a]

	U.S.S.R. (Within Present Boundaries)					U.S.A.
	1913	1928	1940	1960	(Plan) 1965	1960
Total, billion ton-kilometers	126.0	119.5	487.6	1885.7	2508–2558	1937
Railroad						
Billion ton-kilometers	76.4	93.4	415.0	1504.3	1800–1850	841
Per cent	60.6	78.2	85.1	79.8	71.7–72.3	43.5
Sea						
Billion ton-kilometers	20.3	9.3	23.8	131.5	235	—
Per cent	16.1	7.8	4.9	7.0	9.4–9.2	—
River						
Billion ton-kilometers	28.9	15.9	36.1	99.6	140	324[b]
Per cent	22.9	13.3	7.4	5.3	5.6–5.5	16.8
Pipeline						
Billion ton-kilometers	0.3	0.7	3.8	51.2	185	333
Per cent	0.3	0.5	0.8	2.7	7.4–7.2	17.2
Automobile						
Billion ton-kilometers	0.1	0.2	8.9	98.5[c]	146	435
Per cent	0.1	0.2	7.8	5.2	5.8–5.7	22.5
Airplane						
Billion ton-kilometers	0.0	0.0	0.02	0.56	—	1.2

[a] *Source: Narodnoe khozyaystvo SSSR v 1960 godu*, pp. 531 and 533, *75th Annual Report, I.C.C.*, Washington, 1961, and *Soviet Geography: Review and Translation*, April 1961, p. 71.

[b] Includes river, Great Lakes, and intracoastal shipping.

[c] Includes 70 billion ton-kilometers moved by trucks owned by industrial and agricultural enterprises. Only 28.5 billion ton-kilometers were transported by consolidated public trucking fleets.

Table 16–3 Movements of Main Commodities by Modes of Transport, 1960 (in Millions of Tons^a)^{b,c}

	Rail-roads	Petty Cabotage	River	Pipe-lines
Coal and coke	492	6	11	
Petroleum	151	not available	18	130
Ferrous metals	106	1	1	
Timber	141	2[d]	89[d]	
Grain	79	1	7	
Ores	127	6	2	
Firewood	20			
Mineral construction materials	430	9	70	
Other	338	0	12	0

[a] Rounded to nearest million.
[b] Commodity breakdown for freight hauled by trucks and airplanes is not available. These modes of transport are relatively insignificant in intercity freight transport.
[c] *Source: Narodnoe khozyaystvo v 1960 godu*, pp. 537, 543, 545, 552.
[d] Includes firewood.

Table 16–4 Modes of Soviet Oil Transport, in Per Cent of Total Oil Products Shipped, 1913 to 1955^a

Transport	1913	1940	1950	1955
By water	63.1	44.4	30.2	22.4
Sea movements	35.1	29.0	16.6	13.9
River and canal	28.0	15.4	13.6	8.5
By rail	34.5	44.4	50.8	46.5
By pipe	2.4	11.1	19.0	31.1
Crude	0.0	0.4	15.8	27.3
Refined products	2.4	1.7	3.2	3.8
Approximate total shipments (million metric tons)	17	67	85	165

[a] *Source:* Lydolph, Paul E., and Shabad, Theodore, "The Oil and Gas Industries in the U.S.S.R.," *Annals of the Association of American Geographers*, December 1960, p. 480.
Note: In 1960, oil pipelines in the U.S.S.R. totaled 18,700 kilometers. Traffic was 51 billion ton-kilometers in 1960 and 60 billion ton-kilometers in 1961. By comparison, in 1958 oil pipelines in U.S.A. totaled about 320,000 kilometers.

by 1965 by large-scale conversions to oil and gas as sources of fuel and to pipelines as the mode of transport for the bulk of these commodities. In 1960 oil pipelines in the U.S.S.R. totaled 18,700 kilometers and carried more than 40 per cent of the total crude and refined tonnage. This amounted to 2.4 per cent of total freight traffic in the country, whereas in 1950 pipelines accounted for only 0.7 per cent of freight turnover. By 1965 it is planned that pipelines will carry approximately 7.3 per cent of total freight traffic. At the same time the percentage accounted for by railroads is to drop to 72 per cent, automotive traffic is to increase slightly to 5.8 per cent, sea traffic is to increase significantly to 9.1 per cent, and river freight is to hold steady at about 5.5 per cent. By comparison, in the United States in 1960 railroads accounted for 43.5 per cent of the freight turnover, inland waterways for 16.8 per cent, motor trucks

Table 16–5 Motor Vehicles, U.S.S.R. and U.S.A., 1959^a

	U.S.S.R.	U.S.A.	U.S.S.R. as Per Cent of U.S.A.
Vehicle Registrations	3,760,000	71,531,153	5.3
Passenger cars	575,000	59,566,721	9.6
Trucks	3,145,000	11,699,318	27
Buses	40,000	265,114	15
Vehicles Produced	540,000	6,723,556	8.1
Passenger cars	124,500	5,599,492	2.2
Trucks	405,400	1,121,372	37
Buses	10,100	2,692	370

[a] *Source: Automobile Facts and Figures*, 1961, pp. 15 and 25.

for 22.5 per cent, and pipelines for 17.2 per cent. Pipelines in the United States totaled around 320,000 kilometers and moved 83 per cent of the petroleum and petroleum products.

The Railroads

Policies and Realities Determining the Development of the Rail Network Governmental policies and several economic counterpressures have controlled the development of the railroad system in the U.S.S.R. Rapid industrialization with the emphasis on heavy industry at the expense of services and conveniences has led to a stringent policy in the outlay of capital for railroad plants and equipment. This stringency has resulted in a railway system that at present carries almost twice the freight traffic and five times the passenger traffic that railroads in the United States do on little more than one third the trackage that exists in the United States. Whether considered in relation to land area, population, or traffic volume, the Soviet rail network is small. It is a planned system of main routes without competitive overlap and with feeder lines developed sufficiently to provide necessary minimum service to only the major sources of tonnage. Industrial plant location has often been determined by railway location, and farms have been forced to convey their produce to rail headings, usually by primitive means.

The rail net is the most adequate in the inherited systems of the Baltic Republics where rail density is 37.8 kilometers of line per 1000 square kilometers of territory. In the Ukraine the rail density is 34.4, in the Center 21.3, and in the Urals 12.1. However, freight movement in the Baltic Republics is hampered by the necessity to transship goods on about half the lines which are of narrower west European gauge, whereas lines in the rest of the Soviet Union are all wide gauge.

The benefits of economy of scale and the urgency for speed of industrialization, which

led to gigantomania in industrial plant construction, also led to supertrunklining of railroads between a few major producing areas at the expense of extending new lines into underdeveloped areas.

In the late 1920's the transportation system contained a good deal of slack, but by the middle 1930's this slack had been taken up and a transportation crisis impended unless preventative measures could be taken. Although it had been planned to locate industrial plants so that the average length of haul would decrease, actually the average length of haul consistently increased. In 1928 the average length of haul was 584 kilometers; by 1938 it had increased to 718 kilometers. In 1959 it reached an all-time high of 810 kilometers. The year 1960 showed the first reversal in this trend, with a slight decrease to an average length of haul of 798 kilometers.

A policy to adjust production and shipments to the present railroad plant rather than to expend capital on the railroads to make them more adequate for the needs of industry and agriculture has prompted the demand that more coal and other resources be found and mined in the European part of the country where three fourths of the industrial production is concentrated. This is an obvious reversal of the heralded eastward movement. In 1949 some 65 per cent of the country's freight traffic was still being generated by economic activity situated west of the Urals, and the eastern Ukraine still accounted for 25 per cent of the total traffic. Thus, although the Bolshevik regime has made substantial modifications in the regional pattern bequeathed to it, the present structure is a recognizable descendant of its prerevolutionary ancestor.

Freight Density and Efficiency Measures The rapid industrialization coupled with the rising average length of haul according to Soviet statistics has produced almost a twenty-fold increase in rail freight turnover and more than a five-fold increase in railroad passenger traffic since 1913. During this

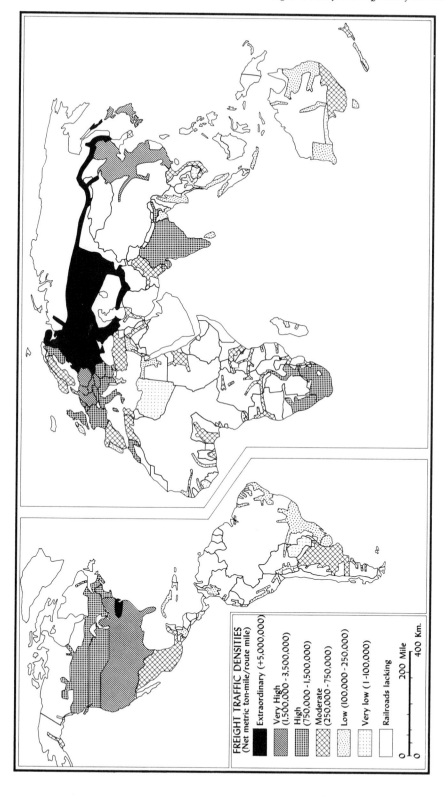

Figure 16-1 Freight traffic densities on the world's railroads.   From Wallace, William H., "Railroad Traffic Densities and Patterns," Annals of the Association of American Geographers, December 1958, p. 353.

Table 16–6   Freight Traffic Densities on Railroads of Selected Countries, 1955 (in Thousand Ton-Kilometers per Kilometer of Operated Line)[a]

U.S.S.R.	8050
United States	2561
Japan	2045
West Germany	1593
France	1173
Britain	1131

[a] *Sources: Soviet Geography: Review and Translation*, June 1961, p. 41, and *Narodnoe khozyaystvo v 1960 godu*, pp. 535–536.

time the length of line operated has less than doubled. Although Soviet bureaucrats tend to overstate traffic and understate equipment, it is obvious that the railroads have had to keep up with a tremendous task imposed on them by utilizing stringent measures of efficiency and greatly increasing density of traffic. Railroad freight traffic density per year increased from 1.1 million ton-kilometers per kilometer of line operated in 1913 to 10.7 in 1958.

It must be realized that in most countries the railway operation embodies a good deal of slack because of overlap between competing railroads and between the railroads and other forms of transport. In areas where traffic taxes existent transport facilities, this slack is taken up and much higher traffic densities are achieved. In small sections of eastern United States, just as high traffic densities exist on the railroads as exist in the Soviet Union. There, of course, is no competition between railroad lines in the Soviet Union, and there is little competition between railroads and other types of carriers. Unlike conditions in the United States where the railroads solicit business and provide all sorts of excessively luxurious services to gain it, the Soviet railroads urge shippers to use all other possible means of transport and to limit total shipments.

In the Soviet Union high efficiency is gained by a transport system that does not cater to its shippers but which sets standards for the shippers to live by. Consignments of freight from single points of origination are accumulated until an entire trainload is ready to be shipped, and similarly entire

Table 16–7   Railroads, U.S.S.R. and U.S.A., 1960[a]

	U.S.S.R.	U.S.A.	U.S.S.R. as Per Cent of U.S.A.
Length of line, in kilometers	228,200[b]	347,000	66
Number of locomotives	12,920[c]	29,513[c]	44
of which, Electric and Diesel-electric	1,890[c]	28,131[c]	7
Freight traffic, billion ton-kilometers	1,504.3	841	178
Freight, million metric tons	1,884.9	1,124	170
Average length of haul, kilometers	798	748	107
Billions of passenger-kilometers	170.8	34.6	490
Millions of passengers	1,950	326	595
Average length of trip, kilometers	88	106	77

[a] *Sources: Narodnoe khozyaystvo SSSR v 1960 godu*, pp. 535–541, *Comparisons of the United States and Soviet Economies*, Part I, p. 197, and *Yearbook of Railroad Information*, 1961, pp. 3 and 8.
[b] Includes 125,800 kilometers under the jurisdiction of the Ministry of Transport and 102,400 kilometers operated by industrial enterprises and organizations.
[c] Figures for 1958. It is not clear whether or not the Soviet figures include locomotives operated on lines under the control of organizations other than the Ministry of Transport.

trainloads are designated for single points of termination. Round-the-clock loading and unloading makes for a minimum of time lost by freight cars in railroad yards and at shipping enterprises and has cut the turn-around time for the average freight car in the Soviet Union to less than half that in the United States. Whereas in the United States box cars often are used as temporary warehouses on industrial plant rail sidings until the plant gets ready to use the ship-ment, in the Soviet Union enterprises are penalized for delaying a freight car more than 24 hours. Such measures lead to serv-ice conditions that would be intolerable in the United States or western Europe, but they certainly make for efficient use of rail-road equipment.

Greater frequency of trains in the Soviet Union counterbalances slower train speeds and lighter train weights than in the United States. During the years 1951–1955, aver-age net freight train weights in the U.S.S.R. were 83 per cent of those in the United States, net ton-miles per freight train-hour was 67 per cent that of the United States,

Table 16–8   Railroads by Type of Traction, U.S.S.R.; Selected Years[a]

	1950		1958		1965 Plan	
	Kilometers	Per Cent	Kilometers	Per Cent	Kilometers	Per Cent
Length of Line:[b]						
Total	116,900	100	125,000	100	134,000	100
Electric	3,000	2.6	9,500	7.6	30,000	22.4
Diesel-electric	3,100	2.6	11,100	8.9	70,000	52.2
Steam	110,800	94.8	104,400	83.5	34,000	25.4
	Number	Per Cent	Number	Per Cent	Number	Per Cent
Locomotives:						
Total:	10,490	100	12,920	100	9,930	100
Electric	240	0.02	1,020	7.8	3,075	31.0
Diesel-electric	250	0.02	870	6.7	3,510	35.4
Steam	10,000	99.96	11,030	85.5	3,345	33.6
	Billion-Ton Kilometers	Per Cent	Billion-Ton Kilometers	Per Cent	Billion-Ton Kilometers	Per Cent
Freight Traffic:						
Total	602.3	100	1504.3	100	1800	100
Electric	18.6	3.1	227.2	15.1	792	44
Diesel-electric	14.4	2.4	171.1	11.4	774	43
Steam	569.3	94.5	1106.0	73.5	234	13

[a] *Sources: Comparisons of the United States and Soviet Economies*, Part I, p. 197, *Narodnoe khozyaystvo SSSR v 1960 godu*, p. 531, and *Yearbook of Railroad Information*, 1961, pp. 3 and 8.
[b] Besides these railroads, which are under the jurisdiction of the Ministry of Transport, there are many lines operated by industrial enterprises and organizations. Such lines at the beginning of 1961 totaled 102,400 kilometers in length. In 1961 Diesel and electric engines handled 51.5 per cent of all freight traffic moved on railroads operated by the Ministry of Transport. Diesel and electric trackage amounted to 42,000 kilometers out of a total of 127,000 kilometers. By comparison, in 1960 railroad lines in the U.S.A. totaled 347,000 kilometers. Locomotives numbered 29,085 of which 465 were electric, 28,295 were Diesel-electric, 275 were steam, and 50 were listed as "other."

and freight train frequencies (train-miles per mile of road operated) were 3.3 times those of the United States. The resultant freight traffic density on all Soviet railroads was 2.8 times that on railroads on the United States.

Technological Advances With the present equipment and operating techniques it appears that the freight traffic on the railroads can hardly be pushed any higher, but there are two technological advances that can be and are being made that will allow for a considerably higher freight traffic on the existing lines. One innovation is the conversion from steam to electric and Diesel traction, and the other is the installation of a country-wide system of automatic block-signaling. As late as 1950, 110,800 kilometers of line out of a total of 116,900 kilometers were operated by steam locomotives which hauled almost 95 per cent of the total rail traffic. Since that time there has been a significant shift to electric and Diesel traction. In 1960, 9000 miles had been electrified out of a total of 80,000 miles operated by the Ministry of Transport. The Trans-Siberian Railroad has been electrified from Moscow to Irkutsk and the Moscow-Donets Line from Moscow to Slavyansk. During the seven-year plan the changeover is to be accelerated until in 1965 steam locomotives are supposed to haul no more than 13 per cent of total rail traffic. By 1970 all railroads are to be Diesel or electric. If these goals can be achieved, the movement of freight on railroads will be greatly improved; heavier trains can be pulled at greater speeds by more powerful engines. Also, the amount of coal hauled simply for consumption by the locomotives will be greatly reduced.

The Pattern of Commodity Movement

Around 1900 By the turn of the century three main flows of commodities had developed. Grain moved out of central European Russia and the Ukraine northwestward to markets around Moscow and St. Petersburg and to the ports of the Baltic for overseas shipment; it also moved southwestward to Black Sea ports for shipment to southern European markets. Coal, iron, and steel moved out of the eastern Ukraine in all directions, but particularly northward toward Moscow, and inflowing freight focused on the Moscow and St. Petersburg areas. The flow of timber and wood products southward to the industrialized and heavily populated areas of central European Russia and the Ukraine was significant, but it was in no way commensurate to the other three flows.

The river systems of the Volga, the Dnieper, and various smaller streams facilitated this movement of goods to a certain extent, but the railroad pattern had by this time developed to serve these routes of flow, and the railroads carried the bulk of the traffic. The Black and Baltic Seas handled much of the foreign trade, and the Caspian was becoming important for the shipment of oil from Baku northward into the Central Industrial Region.

In succeeding years, the grain traffic diminished somewhat, coal became the dominant commodity after 1907, the petroleum traffic on the Caspian and Volga system became very heavy, and some diversification in products and geographical distributions took place. Some grain now moved westward out of western Siberia into European Russia, and some cotton moved northwestward out of Middle Asia into the textile centers around Moscow.

From 1929 to 1939 With the advent of the five-year plans, and the industrialization of the Urals and western Siberia, a large flow of traffic developed eastward into those regions. The resulting pattern of traffic was a crossbar consisting of a broad north-south flow in European Russia and a long, slender flow perpendicular to it extending eastward into Siberia. Toward the end of the 1930's rapid development of industry in eastern Siberia and the Far East gave rise to increased freight traffic at this farthest end of the U.S.S.R. Traffic was overbalanced in the eastward direction, since the eastern regions were importing a greater volume than they were exporting. There was very little export abroad from this end of the country.

Industrial growth around Moscow and Leningrad intensified the net import balance of those regions and the northward flow of heavy freight to them. Industrial growth in the Urals and western Siberia stimulated a considerable two-way freight flow between this part of the U.S.S.R., Moscow and Leningrad, and the eastern Ukraine. Other elements of the pattern were less important, although the constant flow of timber and wood products was, of course, intensified by the industrialization, and the northward flow of petroleum from the Caucasus increased appreciably.

During and since World War II World War II brought on a trend for a significantly higher industrial growth in the eastern regions than in the south of European Russia. Also, the Volga Valley, which tended to lag behind some other regions during the 1930's, became the scene of exceptionally rapid growth during and after the war. Whereas there used to be primarily through traffic crossing the Volga region to and from Middle Asia, Kazakhstan, and the southern Urals, the through traffic is now combined with significant local originations and terminations of heavy freight. The crossbar of the interwar period has been modified by a diagonal connecting the Donbass with the "second iron and steel base," passing through the Volga Valley. Moreover, the concentrated shuttle of coal and iron ore between the two ends of the Ural-Kuznetsk combine has become somewhat diffused at both ends, and a larger north-south freight flow between this region and Middle Asia has developed. Consequently, the lateral east-west flow of the crossbar is broadening and the area between the two arms is filling in.

In the Far East there is now less evidence of rapid industrial development and increased freight generation than there was in the late 1930's, but since 1949 an increasing volume of freight traffic to and from China has moved over the Trans-Siberian Railroad and south through Manchuria, or, since 1955, through the Mongolian Peoples Republic.

In terms of total freight originated and terminated on all carriers, the Ukraine and the Center are the most important areas, but the Urals and western Siberia are a close third. All three regions, of course, are heavily industrialized. The Eastern Ukraine and the Urals concentrate on primary industries based on local raw materials and hence are primarily exporting regions. Coal and coke make up 39 per cent of the outgoing railroad freight of the Ukraine, iron and manganese ores make up 12 per cent, iron and steel 8 per cent, and grain 3 per cent. The Center, on the other hand, is a manufacturing area for finished products and depends on the import of great quantities of raw materials to sustain these industries. Therefore the Center is a region where tons terminated greatly exceed tons originated. To a lesser extent, this is also true of the West and the Northwest, particularly of the Leningrad area, where all sorts of raw materials are necessary for the population and industries of the city.

The highest railroad freight traffic densities occur between the Kuznetsk Basin and the Urals, the Donets Basin and the Central Industrial Region, and the Donets Basin and the Dnieper Bend. Three main rail lines connect the Donbass and the Central Industrial Region. North-bound freight predominates on all of them. Four main lines connect the Central Industrial Region with the Urals and western Siberia. Westbound traffic predominates on all of them. Farther east on the Trans-Siberian Railroad, eastbound traffic exceeds westbound.

The highest freight flow intensity in the Soviet Union is on the Omsk-Novosibirsk section of the Trans-Siberian Railroad. In 1955 it was 69 million ton-kilometers per

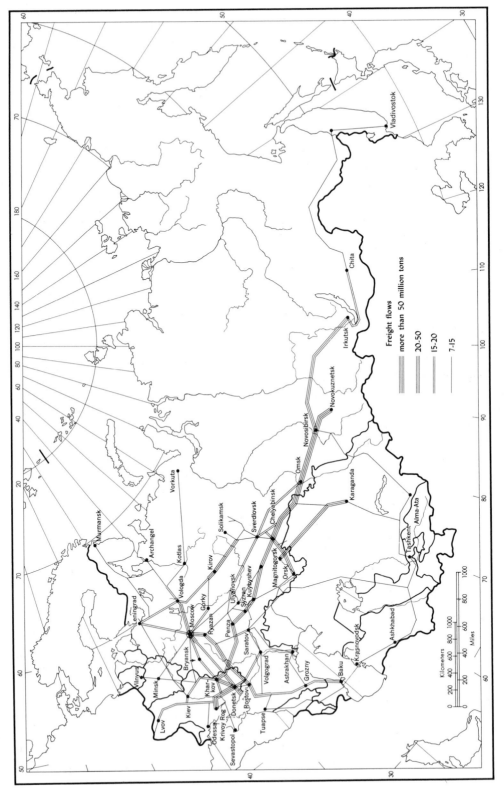

Figure 16-2   Annual freight flows on main railroads.   After Nikolskiy.

kilometer of route, 8.6 times greater than the national average. This traffic is dominated by coal, grain, and lumber, and is heavily imbalanced toward the west. In 1955 the Urals imported 19 million tons of coal from the Kuznetsk Basin; by 1960 this was to increase to at least 35 million tons. By contrast, Urals iron ore moving to the Kuznetsk Basin is unimportant. In 1955 it was estimated that 70 per cent of the freight handled on this section of the Trans-Siberian Railroad moved toward the west.

Commodity Structure by Modes of Transport

Railroads Coal and coke have dominated rail freight traffic since 1907 when they surpassed grain in tonnage transported. They reached a peak of 37 per cent of all rail traffic in 1947, and in 1960 they still accounted for 22 per cent of the traffic. Their role is to diminish as industries and power stations switch to oil and gas for fuels and as steam locomotives are replaced by electric and Diesel-electric. In the past the

railroads themselves have consumed as much as one third the coal production of the country, so it has been necessary to carry large amounts of coal on all trips just to feed the locomotives. Coal trains pulled by steam engines from the Kuznetsk Basin to the Urals consume about one fourth the coal they are hauling by the time they reach the Urals.

In rail traffic, coal and coke are followed in order by petroleum and petroleum products, timber and wood products, mineral building materials, ferrous metals, grain and milled products, and mineral ores. In tons originated, building construction materials are almost as important as coal and coke and much more important than petroleum or timber, but the distances that construction materials are hauled are short, so that in terms of traffic turnover their portion is much reduced.

In 1960 coal led railroad freight originated with 492.5 million tons out of a total of 1884.9 million tons, and mineral construction materials were a close second with 430.4 million tons. The average length of haul

Table 16–9   Railroad Freight Traffic Composition, U.S.S.R., Selected Years and U.S.A., 1958 (in Billion Ton-Kilometers and Per Cents of Total)[a]

	1913		1940		1960		
Commodity Group	Billion Ton-Kilometers	Per Cent	Billion Ton-Kilometers	Per Cent	Billion Ton-Kilometers	Per Cent	U.S.A. 1958 Per Cent
Total	65.7	100	415.0	100	1504.3	100	100
Coal and coke	12.8	19	106.9	26	333.8	22	29
Petroleum products	3.5	5.3	36.4	8.8	205.4	14	2.8
Ferrous metals	—		26.2	6.3	110.4	7.3	
Timber	5.1	7.8	43.6	11	213.6	14	6.1
Grain	9.9	15	32.8	7.9	90.7	6	8.0
Ores	—		21.5	5.2	71.6	4.8	7.9
Firewood	1.7	2.2	5.8	1.4	8.2	0.5	
Mineral construction materials	—		28.2	6.8	155.6	10	15.7
Other	—		113.6	27	315.0	21	30.6

[a] *Sources: Narodnoe khozyaystvo v 1960 godu, p. 536 and Williams, Ernest W., Jr., Freight Transportation in the Soviet Union, 1962, p. 82.*

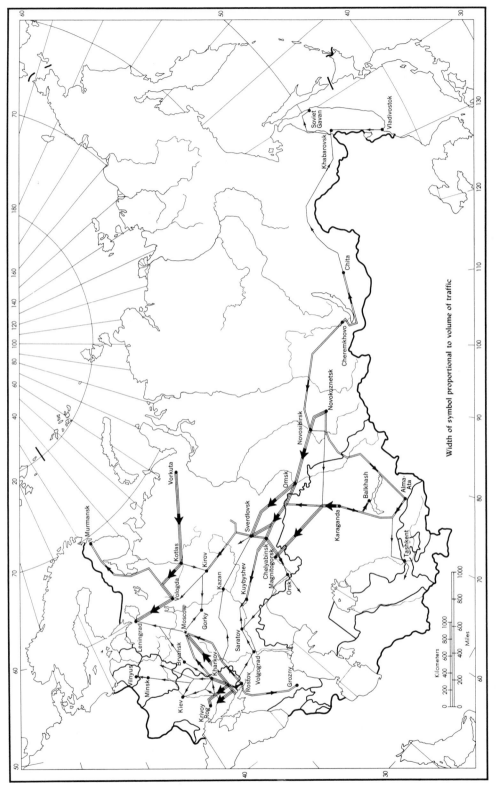

Figure 16-3   Coal traffic on railroads.   After Nikolskiy.

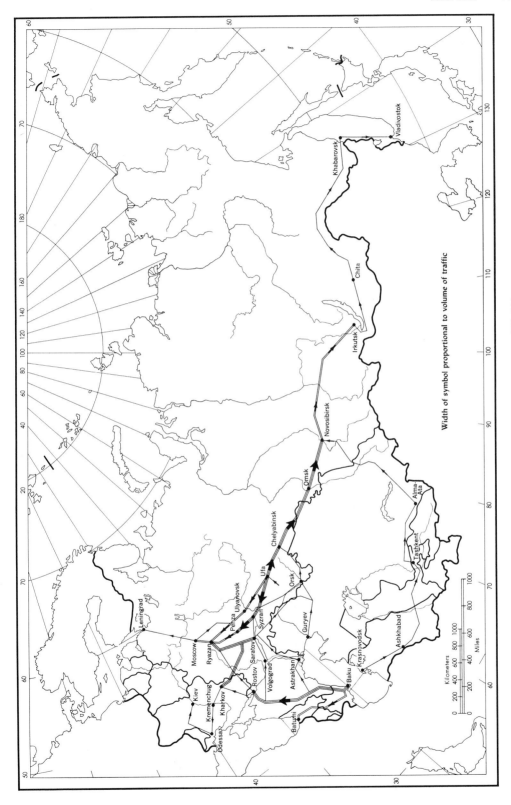

Width of symbol proportional to volume of traffic

Figure 16-4   Oil traffic on railroads.   After Nikolskiy.

for coal was 678 kilometers, whereas for mineral construction materials it was only 361 kilometers. Timber and oil moved farthest of all railroad freight, with average hauls of 1519 and 1360 kilometers respectively. Grain moved on the average 1152 kilometers, and ferrous metals moved 1037 kilometers.

By comparison, railroad traffic in the United States is more diversified, although it is also dominated by coal and coke. Mineral construction materials and ores make

of the Donets Basin in all directions to the Dnieper Bend, Moscow, the North Caucasus, and other destinations in European Russia; from the Kuznetsk Basin westward to the Urals and the Volga region, from Karaganda westward to the Urals and southward to Middle Asia; and from Pechora southwestward to Cherepovets and Leningrad. Oil on the railroads moves east and west from the Volga-Urals fields to Siberia, the Center, and the Ukraine and from Baku northwestward to the Ukraine.

Table 16–10   Railroad Freight Traffic, U.S.S.R., by Region, 1928 and 1949[a]

	1928		1949	
Region	Percentage of Tonnage Originated	Percentage of Tonnage Terminated	Percentage of Tonnage Originated	Percentage of Tonnage Terminated
Northwest	11.4	12.7	6.0	7.2
Baltic	—	—	2.6	3.1
North	4.7	3.9	4.5	3.0
Center	14.7	22.6	8.4	14.7
Caucasus	3.1	3.6	2.6	2.6
South	33.8	29.2	28.2	24.7
Southeast	14.7	11.7	12.5	10.6
Subtotal "West"	82.4	83.7	64.7	65.9
Urals	6.7	6.3	11.8	11.8
Kazakhstan and Middle Asia	2.8	3.3	6.1	5.7
West Siberia	3.5	2.3	8.3	7.5
East Siberia	1.5	1.2	4.7	4.2
Far East	1.8	2.7	4.3	4.9
Subtotal "East"	16.3	15.8	35.3	34.1

[a] *Source:* Holland Hunter, *Soviet Transportation Policy*, 1957, pp. 351–52.

up a larger percentage of the total, and petroleum products make up a very small percentage. Most of the fluid fuels in the United States are moved by pipeline.

Railroads in the Soviet Union in 1960 transported almost all the coal, coke, metals, and ores, 90 per cent of the grain, 85 per cent of the mineral construction materials, 60 per cent of the timber, and 50 per cent of the petroleum produced in the country. Main coal flows on the railroads move out

With the development of new lumbering areas in the European North, the Urals, and Siberia, the average rail haul of timber has increased from 415 kilometers in 1913 to 1469 kilometers in 1958. Sixty per cent of all sawn wood is produced in the wood-consuming areas, 20 per cent of which is in the Center; consequently 72 per cent of railroad traffic in forest products is raw timber. The heaviest flow moves southward from Archangel on the Northern Railroad.

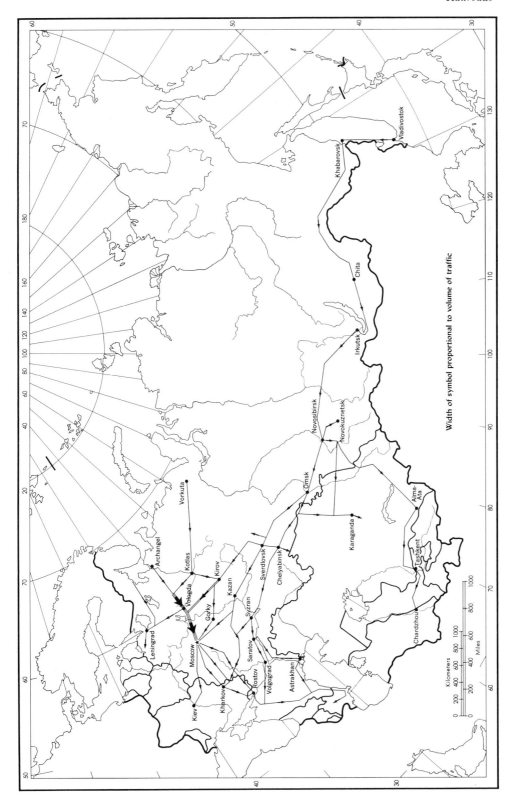

Figure 16-5 Lumber on railroads. After Nikolskiy.

It is joined at Konosha by wood coming in from the northeast on the Pechora Railroad and at Danilov by wood coming in from the east on the Kirov-Buy Line. From Danilov it flows to Moscow and fans out to the south beyond.

Large grain flows move out of the Ukraine, the North Caucasus, and the Volga region to the Center, the Northwest, and Belorussia. Since the opening of the virgin lands in 1953 there has been a sharp increase in grain flow from the southern Urals, western Siberia, and northern Kazakhstan to European Russia. In 1950 this traffic amounted to approximately 1 million tons.

Grain flow from the Northern Caucasus has largely shifted away from destinations in the Volga region and the Center to ports for foreign export and to Transcaucasia. There has been a reduction of grain sent from the Black Sea Steppes of the Ukraine to Transcaucasia and a cessation of grain shipments from the North Caucasus to Middle Asia. In fact, there has been a reversal of this flow. Grain now moves from Kazakhstan to Transcaucasia via Krasnovodsk and Baku.

River   River transport has long been dominated by timber and firewood, and this

Table 16–11   River Transport[a]

	1913 (Within Present Boundaries)	1940	1960
Length of navigable water-ways in thousand kilometers	64.6	107.3	137.9
Freight turnover in billion ton-kilometers	28.9	36.1	99.6
Freight originations, in millions of tons	35.1	73.1	210.3
Oil and oil products	5.4	9.7	18.5
Timber and firewood	11.0	40.2	89.4
Coal	0.9	2.2	11.0
Ore	—	0.1	2.0
Mineral construction materials	1.5	7.6	70.3
Metals and metal scrap	0.6[b]	0.5	1.0
Grain	6.1	5.2	6.8
Average length of haul in kilometers	823	494	474
Passenger turnover, in billion passenger kilometers	1.4	3.8	4.3
Number of passengers, in millions	11.5	73.0	118.6
Average length of trip, in kilometers	125	52	36

[a] *Source: Narodnoe khozyaystvo SSSR v 1960 godu*, p. 545.
[b] Without metal scrap.

In 1954 it was 6 million tons and in 1956 12 million tons. Grain loadings on the railroads of northern Kazakhstan and western Siberia increased twenty times between 1953 and 1956. Out of total loadings in 1956 grain accounted for 31.4 per cent on the Omsk Railroad, 28.8 per cent on the Orenburg Railroad, and 13.5 per cent on the South Urals Railroad. The heaviest flow moves from Novosibirsk to Chelyabinsk.

dominance has been increasing throughout the years at the expense of the second most important item, oil and oil products. In 1960, 89.4 million tons of timber were shipped on river transport facilities, but only 18.5 tons of oil and oil products were shipped. The average length of haul for timber is considerably shorter than that for oil, however, so that in total freight turnover the discrepancy is not so great. The

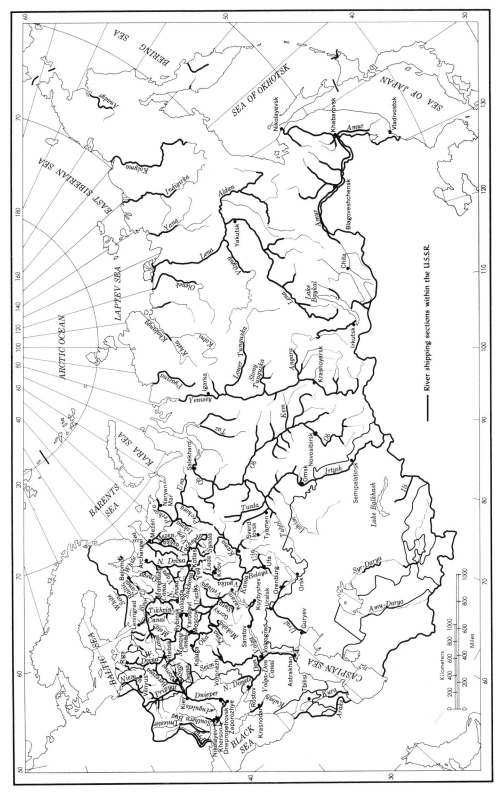

Figure 16-6 River routes. After Baransky.

hauling of mineral construction materials by river barge has increased rapidly since 1940 and now is the second most important commodity on the rivers. In 1960, 70.3 million tons of mineral construction materials were hauled by river. Coal and grain make up a minor portion.

Table 16–12   Freight and Passenger Traffic by River Basins and Areas, 1955 (in Per Cents of Total)[a]

	Freight Traffic	Passenger Traffic
Volga	29.6	33.6
Kama	12.1	12.5
European North	6.3	7.1
Dnieper	6.0	9.2
Irtysh	4.8	4.5
Moscow	3.9	8.5
Yenisey	3.8	4.9
European Northwest	3.5	3.4
Amur	2.1	2.7
Lena	2.1	2.4
Ob	2.0	4.0
Volga-Don Canal	2.0	3.4
Belomorsk-Onega Canal System	0.9	0.3
Pechora	0.8	0.5
Belaya	0.5	1.8
Eastern Siberia	0.5	0.8
Middle Asia	0.5	0.1
Neman	0.2	0.3
Other	19.4	0.0

[a] *Source: Transport i svyaz SSSR, 1957, p. 140.*

European rivers typically have carried most of the river traffic of Russia, the Volga alone accounting for about two thirds of total traffic. In 1955 the Volga and its tributaries still carried about 48 per cent of river freight traffic of the U.S.S.R. and 58 per cent of river passenger traffic. In terms of tonnage, the Northern Dvina is second only to the Volga, because of large-scale floating of timber, but since the distance is relatively short its freight turnover is not as large as some other streams.

Marine Petroleum has long dominated marine transport, particularly on the Caspian and Black Seas. But its relative role has been diminishing somewhat during the last few years with the development of the Volga-Urals oil fields. Besides petroleum, significant amounts of mineral construction materials, coal, ores, timber and firewood, and grain are shipped on the seas adjacent to the Soviet Union.

Table 16–13   Marine Transport of Main Commodities (Excluding Petroleum) in Petty Cabotage (in Millions of Tons)[a]

	1940	1960
Total	10.3	20.2
Coal	1.6	5.7
Timber and firewood	1.3	2.2
Ore	1.5	5.7
Mineral construction materials	0.7	9.3
Metals	0.1	0.59
Grain	1.5	1.4
Salt	0.29	0.22
Fish and fish products	0.08	0.09

[a] *Source: Narodnoe khozyaystvo SSSR v 1960 godu, p. 543.*

Oil shipments on the Caspian, primarily from Baku to Astrakhan, traditionally have comprised about one half the total sea freight turnover in the U.S.S.R. The Black Sea, exporting primarily oil, grain, and coal has handled more than 50 per cent of the foreign trade turnover. It also handles interregional trade between the Ukraine and Transcaucasia. The Ukraine ships coal and iron ore across the Black Sea to Transcaucasia, and Transcaucasia ships out petroleum, manganese ore, and cement. The Baltic and the Pacific have significantly increased their trade since 1917. The major export in the Baltic, Arctic, and Pacific is timber. Major ports on the Black and

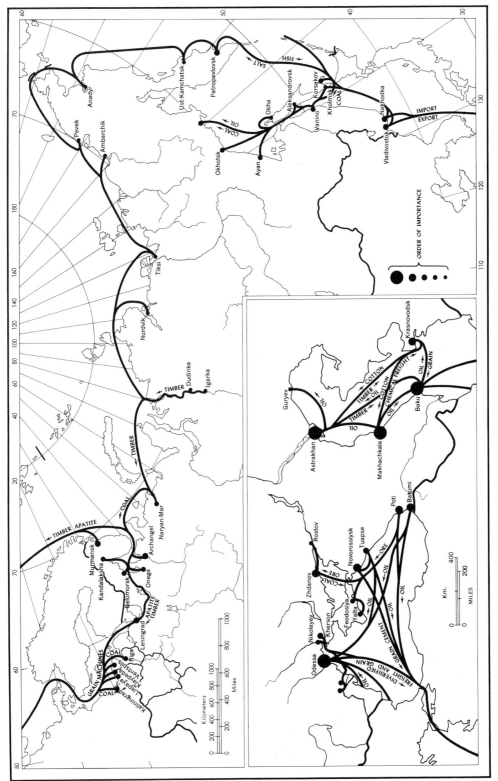

Figure 16-7   Ports and marine routes with commodity flows.   After Cherdantsev.

Azov Seas are Odessa, Rostov, Nikolayev, Zhdanov, Novorossiisk, and Batumi; on the Baltic are Leningrad, Riga, Tallin, Liepaya, Ventspils, and Kaliningrad; on the Arctic are Murmansk and Archangel, and on the Pacific is Vladivostok.

The Soviets have not published shipping statistics by seas, but it can be speculated that oil traffic on the Caspian has diminished with the development of the Volga-Urals oil fields and the construction of new pipe-

Passenger Traffic   The railroads tradi-tionally have also carried the bulk of passen-ger traffic in the U.S.S.R. Intercity bus traffic is beginning to develop, however, and it seems to be destined to grow rapidly. Also, air travel is now becoming a major form of passenger transport. In 1960 rail-roads accounted for 68 per cent of total passenger-kilometers traveled, buses ac-counted for 24 per cent, and airplanes for 5 per cent. It is planned that by 1965 buses

Table 16–14   Passenger Traffic by Form of Transport, in Billions of Passenger-Kilometers, U.S.S.R., Selected Years, and U.S.A., 1960[a]

Region	Year	Total	Railroad	Sea	River	Bus	Air	Private Car
U.S.S.R.	1913 (within present boundaries)	32.7	30.3	1.0	1.4	—	—	
U.S.S.R.	1928	26.9	24.5	0.3	2.1	—	—	
U.S.S.R.	1932	89.9	83.7	1.0	4.5	0.7	0.01	
U.S.S.R.	1950	98.3	88.0	1.2	2.7	5.2	1.2	
U.S.S.R.	1960	249.5	170.8[b]	1.3	4.3	61.0	12.1	
U.S.S.R.	1965 (Plan)	354.0	192.0	2.0	5.0	125.0	30.0	
U.S.A.[c]	1960	1210.0	34.6		3.4[d]	31.8	54.4	1085.0

[a] *Sources: Narodnoe khozyaystvo SSSR v 1960 godu*, p. 534, *Comparisons of the United States and Soviet Economies*, Part I, p. 196, *75th Annual Report I.C.C.*, Washington, 1961, and Williams, Ernest W., Jr., *Freight Trans-portation in the Soviet Union*, 1962, p. 174.
[b] Long distance passenger traffic involving 237,000,000 passengers averaging 549 kilometers per trip accounted for 130,100,000,000 passenger-kilometers, and commuting involving 1,713,000,000 passengers traveling an average of 23.8 kilometers accounted for 40,700,000,000 passenger-kilometers.
[c] Intercity only.
[d] Includes rivers, Great Lakes, and coast traffic.

lines, and that probably foreign trade has increased through Baltic and Far Eastern ports with the postwar establishment of more secure Russian footholds in those areas. It was reported in 1954 that 26 per cent of all maritime freight shipments took place in Far Eastern basins. Maritime shipping is the chief means of transportation in the Far East, and local shipping is much more im-portant than long-distance shipping, as is true on all the seas. Long-distance shipping along the coast between ports of different seas is insignificant.

will carry 35 per cent of the traffic and airplanes will carry 9 per cent. By com-parison, in the U.S.A. in 1960 private cars accounted for 90 per cent of total passenger traffic, airplanes for 4.5 per cent, and trains and buses each for less than 3 per cent.

More than 70 per cent of the total bus traffic in the U.S.S.R. is on city buses in spite of the short distances that most people ride in the cities. Buses and streetcars are the main means of city transport, private automobiles being almost negligible. In Moscow, Kiev, and Leningrad subways have

Table 16–15 Intracity Bus Passenger Transport[a]

	1950	1960
Number of cities having bus service	459	1,241
Passenger turnover, in millions of passenger-kilometers	3826	43,386
Number of passengers, in millions	1001.4	10,634.3
Average length of ride, in kilometers	3.8	4.1

[a] *Source: Narodnoe khozyaystvo SSSR v 1960 godu,* p. 565.

been constructed, which now compete with surface transportation. In 1939 passenger transportation in Moscow, excluding taxis and droshkis, was as follows: by subway, 11 per cent, by streetcars, 61 per cent, by suburban railroads, 15 per cent, and by buses, 13 per cent. Since World War II, it appears that subways and buses have increased at the expense of streetcars. It has been reported that in 1953 subways accounted for 29 per cent of the passenger traffic in Moscow. New subways have been constructed in Moscow until now the city is underlain by a crisscross of three major

systems, and new subways have been built in Leningrad and Kiev where subways did not exist before.

Subways seem to have captured the imagination of Russian planners, and no doubt they will be built in other cities in the near future. The subways of Moscow are world renowned not only for their good service but for their beauty and cleanliness. Built far underground, probably for protection during war, they are well lighted and ventilated and are lined with large murals and chandeliers. The escalators leading down into the subways themselves are something at which to marvel; they pitch at angles of 45 degrees and go so deeply into the earth that one cannot see the bottom when he enters the top.

Table 16–17 Intracity Passenger Traffic by Electric Transport, U.S.S.R., 1940 and 1960 (in Millions of Passengers)[a]

	1940	1960
Streetcar	7283	7827
Trolley bus	293	3041
Subway	377	1148

[a] *Source: Narodnoe khozyaystvo SSSR v 1960 godu,* p. 573.

Table 16–16 Intercity Bus Passenger Transport[a]

	1950	1960
Number of bus lines	1942	7505
Total length of bus lines, in thousands of kilometers	134.9	751.1
Passenger turnover, in millions of passenger-kilometers	1373	17,576
Number of passengers, in millions	51.9	681.3
Average length of trip, in kilometers	26.4	25.8

[a] *Source: Narodnoe khozyaystvo SSSR v 1960 godu,* p. 565.

All forms of public transportation in the major cities are overburdened by passengers. Great numbers of people must commute over rather long distances from apartment areas to factories and stores. At any time of day the subways and buses are jammed with crowding riders, and the sidewalks along the streets are jammed with pedestrians. It seems that much of the populace is constantly on the move from one place to another without a definite destination in mind. This probably stems from the crowded housing and the lack of private entertainment facilities. People simply wander along

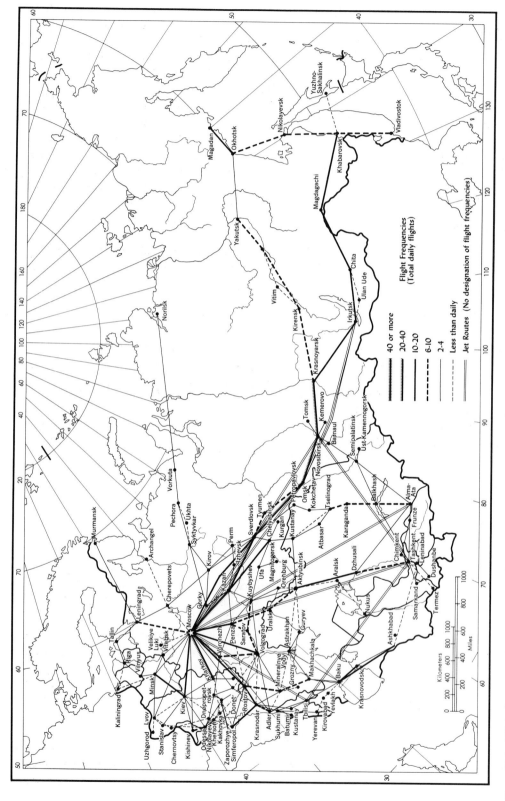

Figure 16-8   Flight frequencies on Aeroflot routes.   Adapted from Kish, George, "Soviet Air Transport," The Geographical Review, July 1958, p. 312.   Recently established jet routes have been added.

the streets and into the stores to kill time while they are off their jobs.

Since such long distances are involved in travel in the Soviet Union, and since the railroads run at agonizingly slow speeds (about 25 miles per hour on the average for passenger trains, as compared to 50 miles per hour in the United States), it appears that air travel may be the answer for fast passenger traffic in the future. Airlines have been established between all major points in the Soviet Union and jet airliners are as crowded with Russian workers and their families as are the surface means of transportation. Passenger rates on airlines have been set low arbitrarily to compete with those on railroads and buses. Hence, if one can get booking on an airplane it makes sense to travel by air over long distances rather than by rail or by bus. Although the line-haul cost of air travel is high compared to other modes of travel, the initial outlay for facilities is relatively small. The rapid development of airlines conforms to the general policy of the administration to neglect long-run costs in favor of the time element and the initial outlay of capital in the race to overtake the United States.

Reading List

Automotive Industries, January 1, 1958. (Entire issue devoted to Soviet transportation.)

Hunter, Holland, *Soviet Transportation Policy*, Harvard University Press, Cambridge, 1957, 416 pp.

——, "Soviet Transportation Policies—A Current View," in *Comparisons of the United States and Soviet Economies*, Part I, pp. 189–199.

Krypton, Constantine, *The Northern Sea Route and the Economy of the Soviet North*, Praeger, New York, 1956, 219 pp.

Nikolskiy, I. V., *Geografiya transporta SSSR*, Moscow, 1960. (Excerpted in English in *Soviet Geography: Review and Translation*, June 1961, pp. 39–92.)

Transport i svyaz SSSR, Moscow, 1957, 260 pp. (in Russian).

Williams, Ernest W., Jr., *Freight Transportation in the Soviet Union*, Princeton, 1962, 214 pp.

——, "Some Aspects of the Structure and Growth of Soviet Transportation," in *Comparisons of the United States and Soviet Economies*, Part I, pp. 177–187.

Zvonkov, V. V., *Principles of Integrated Transport Development in the U.S.S.R.*, University of Chicago Press, Chicago, 1957, 63 pp.

17

Foreign Trade and International Relations

For a country with the second largest economy in the world, Soviet foreign trade is strictly limited, in total value, in number of commodities exchanged, and in number of trading partners. Soviet trade makes up about 4 per cent of total world trade, and about three fourths of it is with other members of the Soviet Bloc. As a trader, the Soviet Union is sixth in the world, behind the United States, West Germany, the United Kingdom, France, and Canada. Prior to World War II Soviet trade amounted to very little. During the war the lend-lease program skyrocketed Soviet imports. This ceased with the war's end, but since then both imports and exports have been climbing steadily.

Table 17–1 Foreign Trade of Leading Countries, 1960 (in Millions of United States Dollars)[a]

	Exports	Imports
United States	20,325	14,709
West Germany	11,415	10,103
United Kingdom	9,955	12,368
France	6,862	6,276
Canada	5,563	5,665
U.S.S.R.	5,562	5,630

[a] *Source: U.N. Statistical Yearbook*, 1961, pp. 410–415.

The Soviets look upon trade as a last resort for procuring goods or gaining political advantages. State monopoly of foreign trade and a desire for national autarchy lead to extreme austerity in the planning of imports and exports. Imports are limited to those that will further Socialist development, and exports are planned only to pay for necessary imports. The Soviets have often voiced the intention to develop trade on the basis of comparative advantages and fiscal gains, which are the bases for free world trade, but so far there has been no real evidence of attempts to carry out these intentions. Soviet trade has expanded significantly during the last decade, but much of this expansion has been associated with political maneuvers to gain favor in the satellites and the less developed unaligned countries of the world.

During the 45 years of the Soviet regime Russian foreign trade has undergone major shifts both in commodities traded and in trading partners. Until World War II the U.S.S.R. was an exporter primarily of grain and lumber and an importer of machinery. Since the war the Soviet Union has become more and more an exporter of heavy equipment and mineral raw materials. The imports are chiefly machinery and other production goods from advanced countries of the free world and the more industrial satellites of

Table 17–2   World Exports by Origin and Destination, 1957 (Billions of Dollars)[a]

Area of Destination

Exporting Area	Total Free World	Soviet Union	Eastern Europe	China	Total Sino-Soviet Bloc	World
Free world industrialized	65.3	0.64	1.01	0.30	1.95	70.2
All primary exporting areas	28.1	0.35	0.34	0.23	0.92	29.7
Total free world trade	93.4	0.99	1.35	0.53	2.87	99.8
Soviet Union	0.96	—	2.55	0.54	3.23	4.4
Eastern Europe	1.19	1.98	1.41	0.30	3.83	5.5
China	0.60	0.74	0.26	—	1.53	2.1
Total Sino-Soviet bloc	2.75	2.94	4.21	1.34	8.49	11.5
World	96.2	3.9	5.5	1.9	11.4	111.3

[a] *Source: Comparisons of United States and Soviet Economies, p. 422.*

Table 17–3   Structure of Soviet Exports and Imports (Including Re-exports) in Per Cents[a]

	1913	1938	1956	1960
Exports U.S.S.R.	100	100	100	100
Finished products	36.0	40.8	62.5	60.1
Machinery and equipment	0.3	5.0	17.2	20.5
Liquid and solid fuels	3.4	8.3	9.5	11.2
Food items	18.9	8.0	4.1	4.0
Consumer goods	4.7	7.9	2.8	2.8
Raw materials	64.0	59.2	37.5	39.9
Crude oil	0.0	0.5	2.3	5.0
Ores and concentrates	1.3	2.3	3.6	4.4
Metals	1.1	0.7	7.6	6.4
Raw materials of plant and animal extraction	25.6	33.0	14.2	12.5
Raw materials for the production of food items	35.1	21.5	6.8	9.1
Imports, U.S.S.R.	100	100	100	100
Finished products	56.3	50.4	60.8	69.6
Machinery and equipment	15.9	34.5	24.8	29.8
Liquid and solid fuels	7.1	1.2	6.3	3.9
Food items	9.7	3.7	9.6	6.4
Consumer goods	11.1	1.0	9.5	17.2
Raw materials	43.7	49.6	39.2	30.4
Crude oil	0.0	—	0.8	0.4
Ores and concentrates	0.1	2.7	10.4	5.6
Metals	3.3	18.6	4.3	3.5
Rubber	2.9	3.5	3.4	3.2
Raw materials of plant and animal extraction	24.7	14.7	—	10.3
Raw materials for the production of food items	9.4	9.0	6.9	5.7

[a] *Sources: Narodnoe khozyaystvo SSSR v 1959 godu, p. 722 and v 1960 godu, p. 747.*

eastern Europe and food products and raw materials from selected less developed countries. Since the death of Stalin imports have included some consumers manufactured products, but this should not be viewed as a deviation from the basic policy to import only those goods that are necessary to the industrial development of the country. The import of limited quantities of consumers goods can be rationalized as necessary to provide needed incentives to further labor productivity. Monetary bonuses are largely ineffective without consumers items on which to spend them.

Before World War II much of the trade of the Soviet Union was carried on with the industrialized countries of western Europe and the United States—the traditional trading partners of Tsarist Russia—to gain necessary manufactured goods and equipment in

Table 17–4   Main Exports from the U.S.S.R.[a]

	1913	1938	1956	1960
Machinery and equipment (millions of dollars)	2	13	629	1,140
Included in which are:				
Equipment and materials for industrial enterprises (millions of dollars)	—	—	300	569
Automobiles (each)	—	7080	32,747	55,772
Trucks	—	6544	14,020	24,053
Cars	—	215	17,460	30,366
Tractors (each)	—	180	5,377	18,887
Combines (each)	—	—	1,448	5,526
Coal (1000 tons)	97	424	5,673	12,315
Crude oil (1000 tons)	—	168	3,897	17,825
Oil products (1000 tons)	952	1221	6,170	15,393
Iron ore (1000 tons)	470	7	9,124	15,182
Manganese ore (1000 tons)	1194	446	918	973
Pig iron (1000 tons)	—	6	1,359	1,801
Rolled ferrous metals (1000 tons)	28	53	1,830	2,728
Apatite concentrate (1000 tons)	—	528	1,124	1,806
Potash salts (1000 tons)	—	28	107	629
Ammonia sulfate (1000 tons)	—	57	56	170
Ammoniacal salt peter (1000 tons)	—	—	57	88
Timber (1000 cubic meters)	5066	1658	1,618	4,429
Sawed lumber (1000 cubic meters)	5924	3180	2,210	4,979
Plywood (1000 cubic meters)	—	120	47	129
Cellulose (1000 tons)	—	—	146	244
Paper (1000 tons)	2	3	76	122
For newspapers	—	—	61	94
Cotton fiber (1000 tons)	—	20	309	391
Linen fiber (1000 tons)	272	16	28	29
Furs (millions of dollars)	3	24	39	46
Oilcake	736	98	112	496
Grain (1000 tons)	9084	2054	3,215	6,818
Vegetable oil (1000 tons)	78	—	26	37
Canned crabs (1000 of standard cans)	—	8212	18,756	12,006
Sugar (1000 tons)	147	113	174	243
Cotton cloth (millions of meters)	172	157	115	195

[a] *Sources: Narodnoe khozyaystvo SSSR v 1959 godu*, p. 719, and *v 1960 godu*, p. 745.

Table 17–5 Main Imports into the U.S.S.R.[a]

	1913	1938	1956	1960
Machinery and equipment (millions of dollars)	112.89	94.15	895.25	1674
Coal (million tons)	8	—	6	5
Oil and oil products (1000 tons)	39	141	5308	4398
Rolled ferrous metals (1000 tons)	98	88	595	950
Zinc (1000 tons)	26	0.6	48	61
Lead (1000 tons)	58	42	27	40
Tin (1000 tons)	6	11	16	18
Cement (1000 tons)	188	0.1	1981	1693
Cellulose (1000 tons)	8	—	55	83
Paper (1000 tons)	126	1.4	79	70
Cartons (1000 tons)	16	1.0	43	43
Cotton fiber (1000 tons)	197	16	51	193
Wool (1000 tons)	55	23	48	62
Synthetic fibers (1000 tons)	—	—	51	56
Rayon yarn (1000 tons)	—	—	5	12
Raw tobacco (1000 tons)	0.4	0.1	73	74
Soy beans (1000 tons)	—	—	549	351
Cocoa beans (1000 tons)	5	15	16	58
Coffee (1000 tons)	13	1.2	3.3	19
Tea (1000 tons)	76	17	16	23
Meat and meat products (1000 tons)	15	3	207	67
Fish and fish products (1000 tons)	362	14	126	86
Edible vegetable oils (1000 tons)	13	6	96	59
Meal (1000 tons)	106	40	638	501
Sugar (1000 tons)	0.2	0.1	122	229
Raw sugar (1000 tons)	—	—	214	1468
Fresh fruits and berries (1000 tons)	133	34	157	335
Dried fruits and berries (1000 tons)	53	13	38	77
Cotton cloth (million meters)	37	11	21	143
Knitted wear (million dollars)	4.68	0.05	29.75	93
Furniture (million dollars)	3.09	0.0018	14.75	65

[a] *Sources: Narodnoe khozyaystvo SSSR v 1959 godu*, p. 721, and *v 1960 godu*, p. 746.

exchange for food stuffs and raw materials. Since World War II there has been a preponderant shift of trade to the other countries of the so-called "Soviet Bloc," the satellites of eastern Europe and Communist China.

Trade with the Satellite Countries

Immediately following World War II Russia filled a void in the foreign trade of Eastern Europe left by the collapse of Germany, and during 1945 accounted for all the imports and exports of the East European countries. During the next 2 years, however, as the East European countries established connections with Western Europe, the U.S.S.R. accounted for less and less of the East European trade. To counter balance this orientation of Eastern Europe toward Western Europe, the Soviet Union in June of 1947 refused to participate in the Marshall Plan program and evolved its own "Molotov Plan" with the East European countries. The Soviets utilized bilateral trade agree-

Table 17–6   U.S.S.R. Trade with Principal Countries, 1959 (Thousands of Dollars)[a]

	Imports	Exports
Total	5,073,250	5,440,825
Afghanistan	15,600	28,350
Albania	14,050	48,875
Argentina	27,900	16,800
Austria	81,725	39,825
Belgium-Luxembourg	9,700	27,250
Bulgaria	260,800	289,925
Canada	15,075	4,050
China (Communist)	1,100,275	954,575
Cuba	7,425	
Czechoslovakia	581,900	603,000
Denmark	13,225	26,625
Egypt	92,625	88,025
Finland	142,125	144,525
France	100,500	87,750
Germany, Federal Republic of	120,100	89,275
Germany, Soviet Zone of	889,475	1,030,100
Ghana	8,175	25
Greece	12,300	15,975
Hungary	206,550	259,825
Iceland	12,375	11,975
India	60,525	68,025
Indonesia	11,000	15,775
Iran	18,725	18,000
Iraq	2,325	23,300
Italy	52,775	77,975
Japan	23,400	33,350
Korea, North	51,600	74,125
Malaya, Federation of	126,700	900
Mongolia, Outer	49,525	78,725
Netherlands	13,100	66,700
Norway	17,225	17,700
Poland	316,575	486,375
Rumania	249,475	232,375
Sweden	41,625	44,350
Syria	6,150	15,150
Turkey	4,775	5,550
Union of South Africa	6,350	225
United Kingdom	90,850	165,675
United States	17,775	25,700
Uruguay	15,150	9,350
Viet-Nam, North	15,650	19,825
Yugoslavia	53,050	46,250
Other Countries	116,325	148,675

[a] *Source:* World Trade Information Service, Statistical Reports, Part 3, No. 61-9, *Foreign Trade of the U.S.S.R.*, 1958–1959.

ments, credit on favorable terms, scientific-technical collaboration commissions, and, from 1949, the Council for Economic Mutual Assistance to establish bases for long-term controls of foreign trade in Eastern Europe. Also established were Soviet-owned and mixed companies in the east European countries to administer financial arrangements and, in some cases, to manage enterprises that had been taken over from German companies after the war. The Russians took over German assets in Bulgaria, Hungary, and Rumania and set up their own company administrations which had the rights to conduct foreign trade operations with what amounted to extra-territorial privileges. The Russian-controlled companies naturally directed all their trade toward the Soviet Union.

Table 17–7   Growth of Soviet Trade with the Socialistic Countries after World War II (in Millions of 1961 Rubles)[a]

	1946	1956	1960
Total U.S.S.R. trade	1280	6502	10,073
U.S.S.R. trade with Socialist countries	698	4919	7,213
Total U.S.S.R. exports	588	3258	5,006
To Socialist countries	341	2456	3,725
Total U.S.S.R. imports	692	3254	5,067
From Socialist countries	357	2463	3,488

[a] *Sources: Narodnoe khozyaystvo SSSR v 1959 godu,* p. 718, and *v 1960 godu,* p. 748.
Note: In 1961 the ruble was worth $1.11.

In addition, the foreign trade of East Germany, Hungary, Rumania, and Poland was partially controlled by the fact that these countries had to pay reparations to Russia in terms of goods and labor over a specified period of years. Poland, in spite of the fact that it had not been an enemy nation to the Soviet Union, was required in 1947 to deliver 6.5 million tons of coal as "political export" at a very low price. On January 1, 1954 reparations ceased, and the Russian and mixed companies were turned over to the governments of the respective east European countries, but this type of control of the foreign trade of Eastern Europe was no longer necessary; other means of control had been established to assure that the orientation of trade toward the Soviet Union would continue.

Trade with the Soviet Union was a natural thing for the East European countries after World War II. Both prior to and during World War II the economies of these countries had been closely linked to, if not integrated with, the military program of Germany. As a result there was a trend toward greater industrialization, and in Czechoslovakia, Poland, and Hungary there was a definite shift toward the development of heavy industry. After the war, with the economy of Germany no longer able to absorb such products and the Soviet Union in need of capital goods, one could expect a marked reorientation of trade. The Czechoslovakian minister of foreign trade after the War stated, ". . . people in western countries often fail to understand why we are so interested that the U.S.S.R. should purchase the largest possible quantity of our heavy industrial product. The answer is simply that our best possibilities for the sale of these goods appear to be in the U.S.S.R. or in central Europe, and not in the western markets, owing to the high industrial capacities of the western countries."

The Soviet Union's largest traders within the bloc are Communist China, East Germany, Czechoslovakia, and Poland. Communist China is the leading exporter to the Soviet Union, and East Germany is the leading importer from the Soviet Union. Bulgaria has more of its trade with the Soviet Union than does any other country, about 53 per cent of its total trade. Rumania is not far behind, and such a heavily producing country as East Germany has more than 40 per cent of its trade with the Soviet Union.

Trade between the U.S.S.R. and mainland China has increased steadily since the Communist regime came into power in China. The U.S.S.R. regularly accounts for more

Table 17–8 Soviet Trade with Communist Countries, 1958 (in Millions of Rubles^a*)*^{b}

Country	Export	Import
Albania	177.2	56.2
Bulgaria	802.3	812.2
Czechoslovakia	1787.0	2048.4
East Germany	3199.0	3263.7
Hungary	802.2	647.7
Mongolia	259.4	188.7
North Korea	232.2	188.2
North Vietnam	32.6	39.7
Poland	1507.2	1060.6
Red China	2536.0	3525.0
Rumania	1005.6	934.0
Yugoslavia	204.3	203.5

^{a} The ruble in 1958 = $0.25.
^{b} *Source:* Katkoff, Vladimir, *Soviet Economy 1940–1965*, p. 451.

than 50 per cent of Red China's trade. In return Red China claims about 18 per cent of Russia's exports, with such items as metal-cutting lathes, drilling machines, tractors, and trucks. The China trade accounts for roughly 40 per cent of total Soviet machinery

Table 17–9 Percentage of Trade of Soviet Bloc Countries with All Other Soviet Bloc Countries, 1948 and Latest Reporting Year^a

Country	1948	Latest Reporting Year
Albania	100	99 (1955)
Bulgaria	78	95 (1955)
China	—	75 (1953)
Czechoslovakia	32	57 (1955)
East Germany	—	78 (1952)
Hungary	34	55 (1955)
Mongolia	—	100 (1953)
North Korea	—	100 (1953)
Poland	41	64 (1955)
Rumania	71	84 (1954)
U.S.S.R.	42	78 (1955)

^{a} *Source:* Smith, Glen A., *Soviet Foreign Trade: Organization and Operations*, p. 245.

and equipment exports. Russia imports from Red China such agricultural products as meat, rice, fresh fruits, and miscellaneous consumer goods, which amount to 40 per cent of total Soviet agricultural imports.

The Soviet Union's imports from the more industrialized satellites in Eastern Europe— East Germany, Czechoslovakia, Poland, and Hungary—are predominantly industrial machinery of all types. The Soviet Union supplies these countries primarily with mineral raw materials and some grain. East German exports of forge and press equipment, machinery for the food and chemical industries, railroad rolling stock, and ships regularly amount to about 40 per cent of Russia's total machinery imports.

The less developed satellites of Eastern Europe, such as Rumania and Bulgaria, import certain mineral raw materials and heavy industrial equipment from the Soviet Union in exchange for agricultural produce, certain mineral raw materials, and a limited quantity of consumer items.

Since 1954, with the expansion of imports, particularly of consumer goods, the Soviet Union has found it necessary to look more and more for products outside of the Soviet Bloc, and this has brought about a gradual reduction of the percentage of total Soviet trade carried on with the bloc countries. The trend for Soviet trade at present appears to be one of expansion in absolute amount, in variety of imports, and in number of trading countries.

Trade with the West

Outside the Soviet Bloc values of imports and exports drop sharply. In terms of trade turnover the main countries in the free world trading with the Soviet Union are Finland, West Germany, France, and the United Kingdom. For imports alone, Malaya is second in importance to Finland, because of the recent large buying of Malayan rubber by the Soviets; however, Soviet exports to Malaya are practically nil.

Trade between the two principal producing countries in the world, the United States and the U.S.S.R., is almost negligible, accounting for less than 0.2 per cent of total United States' trade and about 0.5 per cent of Soviet trade. This has not always been the case; in 1938 trade with the United States accounted for 18.5 per cent of total Soviet trade, and during World War II, with the lend-lease program, no doubt the figure was considerably higher. The cold war since World War II has artificially restricted trade between the two countries; the United States has placed trade embargoes on all sorts of strategic and semistrategic materials.

Table 17–10   Value of Soviet Trade, Total and with the United States, Selected Years (in Thousands of United States Dollars)[a]

	Total Trade		Trade with United States	
	Imports	Exports	Imports	Exports
1938	268,498	251,335	76,585	18,257
1955	3,060,550	3,468,575	550	23,800
1960	5,630,000	5,562,000	38,368	22,620

[a] *Source: World Trade Information Service Statistical Reports.*

As might be expected, the trade between the two countries consists of small quantities of a wide variety of relatively unessential items. Embargoes prohibit the shipment of items that might be vital to either country, and trade has had to develop around these embargoes. In terms of dollar value, sheet steel is the leading export from the United States to the Soviet Union, accounting for more than one fourth of the total. It is followed in order by carding, preparing, spinning, and twisting machinery for textiles. In 1960, cattle hides and helicopters made up a significant portion of exports to the Soviet Union, followed by dyeing and finishing machinery for textiles, synthetic fibers, and industrial articles.

The U.S.S.R. exports to the United States make up less than two thirds the value of imports from the United States. The most valuable single item is benzine, which in 1960 accounted for one third of the total value of United States' imports from the Soviet Union. Other chief Soviet exports to the United States are rare metals, such as platinum, paladium, and rhodium, and furs, particularly squirrel and sable. Persian lamb and karakul also are significant.

France it imports machinery for the chemical industry, railway rolling stock and streetcars, iron and steel rolling mill products, nonferrous metals and alloys, power cables and wire, wood, paper, rayon staple fiber, and various manufactured goods.

Punitive Restrictions of Soviet Trade
During the past 45 years the trade of the Soviet Union has almost always been subject to some form of restriction or discrimination by the nations of the West. For the first 20 years the discrimination was mainly in the form of higher interest rates because of distrust of the Soviets resulting from the

Table 17–11   Wartime Trade of the United States, United Kingdom, and Canada with the U.S.S.R. (in Thousands of Dollars)[a]

| | Exports | | | Imports | | |
Year	United States	United Kingdom	Canada	United States	United Kingdom	Canada
1941	107,524	118,025	5,331	30,095	4,450	78
1942	1,425,442	300,281	36,814	24,656	13,015	0.1
1943	2,994,828	237,543	57,916	29,850	7,156	2.5
1944	3,473,252	226,349	103,438	49,649	8,708	16
1945	1,838,282	118,976	58,906	53,793	15,354	1747

[a] *Source:* Huszar, George B., and Associates, *Soviet Power and Policy*, 1955, p. 352.

The chief Soviet imports from the United Kingdom are machinery and certain mineral ores, and the chief exports to the United Kingdom are lumber and some nonferrous metals. The Soviet Union exports Diesel oil, manganese ore, chromium ore, asbestos, pig iron, tin, benzine, chemicals, timber and lumber, cotton, barley, and corn to the Federal Republic of Germany and imports machinery for light industry, machinery for chemical industry, ships and other marine equipment, iron and steel pipes, tubes and fittings, cable and wire, and chemicals and pharmaceuticals. To France the Soviet Union exports anthracite coal, gasoline, manganese ore, asbestos, coal-tar products, chemical wood pulp, and newsprint, and from

annulment of all pre-Revolutionary debts. In addition to such discrimination by private individuals and firms, definite discrimination against trade with the Soviet Union has been applied by several Western governments on four specific occasions. These governmental actions were: (1) a blockade of the Soviet Union from 1918 to 1920 during the period of civil war and intervention, (2) embargoes in 1930 and 1931 to counteract dumping of grain and lumber, (3) failure to issue export licences for military goods in 1940 when the Soviets were fighting the Finns, and (4) the various restrictions on trade with the Soviet Union and other bloc countries dating from 1948.

Much of the difficulty that the Soviet

Union has with world trade organizations stems from the arbitrary limitations it has imposed on its trade by the institution of state monopoly and the policy of economic self-sufficiency. The practice of carrying on only absolutely necessary trade usually under bilateral agreements allows for very little flexibility in trade arrangements. When the Soviet Union finds that it must purchase certain raw materials, such as foodstuffs, from a country which is already an integral part of a well-established trade system or from an underdeveloped country, it must make some adjustments to gain the necessary imports.

In the case of importing goods from one of the primary producing countries, such as from one of the Commonwealth of Nations, the Soviet Union often finds that it cannot balance its imports because that country does not want to buy anything. Also, it finds it difficult to pay for imports in rubles since the foreign trade of the Soviet Union has been so limited that the ruble has no real world trade value. The ruble has led too sheltered a life to have acquired any value in the world monetary system; it simply has a value which the Soviets have arbitrarily fixed within their own sphere of influence. Hence, when dealing with a country that is a part of the sterling or dollar bloc, the Soviet Union must seek to balance imports from that country with exports to some other country of the same monetary system. It is forced to sell whatever commodity it has available whether the market for selling is favorable or not. In such cases, in order to make a market for itself, the Soviet Union has frequently found it necessary to offer certain items at prices considerably below those previously established by critically balanced supply and demand. Hence the accusations of "dumping" by the established traders of the western world.

In 1931, to pay for large imports of equipment to start the industrial machine rolling, the Soviets bent every effort to increase their exports of grain and lumber to pay for greatly expanded imports. Within a few months world grain prices dropped to less than half of what they had been, and other major grain exporting countries cried, "dumping." Again, in 1957, to acquire sterling credit to balance imports from Australia, New Zealand, and other members of the sterling bloc, the Soviet Union decided to sell aluminum to Britain at 2 cents per pound under the price charged by Britain's main supplier, Canada. Again the Soviet Union was accused of dumping with the object of upsetting the world market, which was at a critical stage anyway. Actually a price reduction was necessary in order for the Soviet Union to break into a long-established trade between sister members of the Commonwealth of Nations, but the effect on the world market was the same regardless of Soviet motives. Had the Soviet Union developed a broader base for its foreign trade, it would have been unnecessary to balance imports with exports over such a short-run period, and the Soviets could have held their commodities for export until the market was more favorable. It also would not have had to break into already well-established trade relations by cutting prices below prevailing levels.

When the Soviet Union wants to import raw materials or foodstuffs from an underdeveloped country it often finds that markets in this underdeveloped country for exports from the Soviet Union can be established only by extending long-term credit on such items as major construction projects, heavy machinery, and metallurgical items. The underdeveloped country simply does not have the market potential to buy the necessary heavy goods from the Soviet Union. Yet the Soviets wish to sell these goods to pay for imports. The only solution is for the Soviets to extend credit on large items of export which is to be paid off by the underdeveloped country in raw materials and foodstuffs over a period of years. This, of course, ties up the export trade of the underdeveloped country during the period and very often leads to other concessions, sometimes political, from the underdeveloped country to the Soviet Union. Thus the plan of long-term credit to underdeveloped countries initiated by the Soviets in 1951 has been branded by many members of the Western world as a device to control the international relations of underdeveloped countries. Again, as in the case of dumping, Soviet actions perhaps can be justified on economic grounds, but the associated results have occurred and have affected the rest of the world.

The Soviets might well solve many of their economic problems at home and keep themselves off the black list of world trading organizations while better achieving their political goals in underdeveloped countries if they would only expand and broaden their base of foreign trade. Importation of consumer items that can be more cheaply and better supplied by foreign areas than by the Soviets themselves would release their productive forces to concentrate even more intensely on the industrial buildup of their own country. At the same time a great expansion of trade would allow for much greater flexibility in dealing with individual countries and individual commodities.

The Western world is willing to trade with the Soviet Union as long as economic exchanges are reliable and political relations are stable. The Western powers reduced restrictions on the sale of goods to the Soviet Bloc in 1954 and again in 1958. But it is unlikely that further reductions will be made as long as the Berlin crisis exists and as long as Russia pursues a foreign policy of expansion of Soviet control and world Communism.

Trade with Southern Neighbors

It is only natural that through the years the Tsarist and Soviet regimes have carried on considerable trade with the countries immediately to the south. In most cases this trade has not been vital to the Soviet Union's economy, and considerable political overtones have been involved in the trade negotiations. Although great efforts have been made by the Soviets to establish extensive trade relations with Turkey, including an interest-free loan during the depression in 1934, Turkey has maintained complete economic and political independence from the U.S.S.R., and buys only when and what it wishes. A similar statement can be made with regard to the Arab countries; up until 1956 when Egypt entered into various trade agreements with the Soviet Union to begin industrialization. But even with the extensive trade negotiations and economic aid that has been extended to the United Arab Republic since Syria and Egypt joined, almost complete political independence from the U.S.S.R. has been maintained.

Iran, because of its geographical location and topographical division between north and south, has had a long and varied relation with the Russian Empire and the Soviet Union. At times northern Persia has been an almost exclusive market for Russia. In 1913 Russia controlled 55 per cent of Persia's imports and 65 per cent of the exports. Russia purchased almost 100 per cent of some Persian exports, particularly cotton and rice. Various trade agreements, as well as the establishment of Russian-Persian banks and trading companies, were made to continue control of Persian trade. During World War I the British occupied Persia and by various means quickly supplanted Russia as the chief supplier of goods to Persia. In 1919 the Soviet Union began an extensive propaganda campaign to win back the trade of Persia. The Soviet Union made a declaration of equality and noninterference in the affairs of Persia and included in it an annulment of all of Persia's debts to the Tsarist regime. These debts were not large, so the monetary loss to the Soviet Union was small and the propaganda gain was great. After the establishment of a new Persian government in 1921, the Soviet Union sent a trade delegation to Teheran to intensify the effort to increase Russian-Persian trade. By 1928 the Soviet Union had displaced Great Britain as Persia's primary trade partner. By 1933, however, trade with the Soviet

Union dwindled to about one fifth what it had been in 1930. Since then the Soviet Union has not been able to regain an eminent position in Iranian trade. Nevertheless the Soviets never desist from trying to dominate Iranian affairs and never fail to point out to the Iranians the inevitable consequences of juxtaposition of territories. The following statement is only one example of many well-calculated missiles of correspondence that have been exchanged between the two countries.

Soviet-Iranian Relations (Pravda, January 17, 1959)

On December 28, 1958, N. M. Pegov, U.S.S.R. Ambassador to Iran, visited Iranian Foreign Minister Hekmat, and, to supplement the Soviet government statement of October 31, 1958, handed the Minister a Soviet government memorandum on the proposed signing of an Iranian-American military agreement, which would result in a serious deterioration in Soviet-Iranian relations and increase tension in the Near and Middle East.

Excerpts from the text of the U.S.S.R. government memorandum to the government of Iran follows.

Memorandum.— . . . The Soviet government is disturbed by the fact that the Shah's government of Iran has for a certain period been taking foreign policy steps and military measures that can only be interpreted as a policy directed against the Soviet Union, which has a long common border with Iran. This is indicated by Iran's growing collaboration with aggressive forces of three countries which do not conceal their desire to use Iran and Iranian soil against the Soviet Union. In this connection the government of Iran is undertaking unfriendly actions against the Soviet Union, although the Soviet Union has not given the slightest pretext for such action, but, on the contrary, has been taking serious steps to strengthen friendly cooperation with Iran. In addition to the fact that Iran some time ago joined the Baghdad military bloc, which is directed against the U.S.S.R. (although the Iranian side has tried to assure of the reverse), the Shah's government of Iran is now taking steps to further strengthen the military and aggressive aspect of the Baghdad Pact. It is concluding new military agreements with states that are not in the least interested in maintaining peace and order in this region, states to which, as they have often shown, the genuine national interests of the countries in this area are alien. . . .

Unfortunately, the Iranian government is evidently inclined to believe that it can sacrifice good relations with the Soviet Union in the interests of strengthening military cooperation with the U.S.A., which, incidentally, makes Iran's chances for security highly doubtful. . . .

How can the government of Iran place its hope in a military pact with a state situated thousands of kilometers away, at the same time sacrificing Iran's friendly relations with neighboring states and the interests of peace and security in this area as well as the security interests of Iran itself?

Upon objective consideration of the situation one has to recognize that under present conditions and with modern weapons of mass destruction, plans of this type are profoundly erroneous and are based on outmoded views and conceptions. Moreover, the failures already suffered by the proponents of the notorious "brink of war" policy have clearly demonstrated the illusory nature of such plans. . . .

Who stands to gain from all this? There is no doubt that the gain will accrue only to foreign circles and the above power, which is very distant from Iran. The chief loser will be Iran, which because of such a policy would be threatened with annihilation should a military conflict break out. The Soviet government by no means intends this as a threat; these are merely the incontrovertible facts, facts which cannot be denied without contradicting reality. . . .

The U.S.S.R. government wishes to state with complete frankness that if the Soviet Union, whose might and capabilities are difficult to compare with the might and capabilities of Iran, feels uneasiness about the possible deterioration of Soviet-Iranian relations, then it would seem that Iran should feel much uneasier. This means that good and friendly relations between the two countries are just as necessary and useful for Iran as for the Soviet Union. Nevertheless, judging by everything, the Iranian side does not duly value the importance to Iran of good relations with the Soviet Union or the Soviet Union's friendly attitude toward Iran. . . .

The Soviet Union opposes the proposed military agreement between Iran and the U.S.A. not because it is afraid of an attack by Iran on the U.S.S.R. The Soviet Union certainly has no such fears. The U.S.S.R. believes, however, that this agreement would virtually transform Iran into a springboard for military actions against the U.S.S.R. and other peace-loving states by third powers. Moreover, it goes without saying that no arguments to the effect that American troops will be allowed on Iranian soil only in the event of "extraordinary circumstances" within or outside of Iran can change the Soviet Union's position on the impermissibility of having foreign troops in Iran. Speaking bluntly and reckoning with the actual state of affairs, one must recognize that in the event of a military conflict the territory in a state that has been made available to third countries can be used without the consent of this state for the simple reason that the circumstances will be beyond the control of its government. The fact that some persons may dispute this does not alter the situation. What is involved here is not the presence or absence of good intentions on the part of the government of this state but the very logic of the matter, which may turn out to be stronger than any other logic, even if it is backed up by the best intentions today. . . .

The official representatives of the Iranian government assure the Soviet representatives that the proposed military agreement between Iran and the U.S.A. is not directed against the Soviet Union, although they are not disclosing the actual content of the agreement. However, it is known, in particular, that the plans connected with this agreement call for stationing American naval forces in the Persian Gulf area, near the shores of Iran. It is perfectly understandable that the Soviet Union cannot but regard such an agreement between Iran and the U.S.A. as an act directed against the interests of peace in the Near and Middle East and against the security of the U.S.S.R., which is inviolably linked with the interests of assuring peace in this area. . . .

It is possible to cite "considerations of prestige" which allegedly make it difficult for Iran not to sign an agreement with the U.S.A. that has already been publicly announced. The Soviet government feels that steps which would help to maintain and strengthen a country's sovereignty, strengthen peace and forestall the possibility of military conflicts would correspond to the interests of the prestige of any state. . . .

Naturally, the Soviet government considers that if the agreement between Iran and the U.S.A. were not a military agreement and did not involve, as has been pointed out above, a threat to the security of the Soviet Union but provided for various measures of economic co-operation, then the question of a dangerous turn in Soviet-Iranian relations would not arise. It is self-evident that the Soviet Union has no intention of interfering in any way in Iran's domestic affairs and is solely interested in seeing its neighbor-state of Iran an independent and prosperous state. . . .

Afghanistan and China Afghanistan has never been forced into dependence on Russia as a result of topographical circumstances. Its location between Russian Middle Asia and British India, however, has made it a prime political target, and it has been the scene of numerous Russian-British clashes and intrigues, particularly during the nineteenth century. The British, by military force and political influence, maintained control of Afghanistan up until World War I, but when Afghanistan regained its political independence in 1919 the way was cleared for the Bolsheviks to spread their influence. Concessions were made by the Russians to the Afghans, and they have continued in various forms to the present time. Since the trade with Afghanistan is quite insignificant to the economy of the Soviet Union, its use to further political issues is apparent. Soviet trade delegations to Afghanistan have been instructed to organize Communist cells, to issue slogans, and to spread dissatisfaction among soldiers and workers. So far Afghanistan has done a good job of walking a tightrope between the great powers on either side to derive what she wants from Soviet trade while largely maintaining independence from Soviet influence.

Recently, the Soviets have made Afghanistan a principal target in the extension of economic and technical aid. A number of construction projects, including grain elevators and roads, have been completed in Afghanistan by these means, and more than 250 million dollars worth of credit has been extended. Soviet technicians are now in the process of completing a highway from Kushka on the Soviet border southward to southern Afghanistan to tie the economy of Afghanistan more closely to that of Soviet Middle Asia.

The relations of Sinkiang province in western China with the Soviet Union are similar to those of Tannu Tuva and Mongolia with the Soviet Union. The Russians have always been interested in establishing themselves in all three areas. In 1944 Tannu Tuva became an integral part of the Soviet Union, and the so-called "Mongolian Peoples Republic" is under very strong influence of the U.S.S.R. In 1959, 78 per cent of Mongolia's foreign trade was with the Soviet Union. But the Chinese, in spite of many internal disruptions, have been able to maintain nominal control over Sinkiang. The new rail link between the Soviet Union and China through Sinkiang should bring Sinkiang province closer to both countries. Which country will exert the greater influence in Sinkiang in the future remains to be seen. At present the Russians and Chinese, on the surface at least, are fraternal nations, and theoretically it makes little difference which one controls Sinkiang. Local trade, free of government channels has developed across the Soviet-Chinese border, not only between Sinkiang and the Kazakh and Kirgiz republics, but also between Heilunkiang Province and Amur Oblast in the Far East.

Soviet Economic Policy in the Less Developed Areas

Prior to 1954 the Soviet Union showed little interest in developing trade with the less developed countries. It viewed the less developed countries as merely occasional sources of various types of raw materials that were not available in the Soviet orbit, and for the most part the U.S.S.R. paid for such purchases with proceeds of sales to the industrialized nations of the free world. Since 1954 trade agreements for both export and import items have played a growing role in Soviet attempts to gain increased political influence among the uncommitted nations of the world. The Soviet Union has sent out large numbers of trade missions that have participated in trade fairs and exhibitions and have stressed the opportunities for expanded trade. Through the means of trade and aid the Soviet Union has now committed itself to convince the world of its power, to gain acceptance as the champion of peace, and to reduce the influence of the West in general and of the United States in particular among the uncommitted countries of the world.

Although the trade and aid offered to the less developed countries by the Soviet Bloc are considerably less than those offered by the free world, or even by the United States alone, the Soviets have wielded much influence through concentrated efforts in fewer countries and by calculated timing. Whereas the United States and other Western powers have given grants of aid to less developed countries to be thinly spread over broad areas, primarily to raise living standards and to improve social and cultural development, the Soviets have concentrated credits and grants on major construction projects in a few countries. Such projects have been much more conspicuous in many instances than the economic aid that has been given by the West.

The Soviet Bloc has on occasion been so presumptuous as to pretend that prior to its program of economic assistance there really had been no contributions. The facts are, however, that prior to 1953 the bloc had not contributed a single ruble of the 38.3 million dollars donated by United Nation member states to the United Nation's technical assistance program. Since it began to contribute, the bloc has extended 10.7 million dollars compared to 221.6 million contributed by other United Nation members. With regard to bilateral economic assistance, the United States alone obligated or otherwise committed 11.6 billion dollars through 1953 to the less developed areas. Between 1953 and 1959 the United States obligated

plied 56 while the entire Soviet Bloc contributed 23!

The Soviet Bloc often has psychological advantages over the West in less developed areas because its immediate interests coincide with many of the current objectives of less

Table 17–12   Soviet Trade with Selected Less Developed Countries, 1953 and 1959 (in Millions of United States Dollars)[a]

	1953		1959	
	Imports	Exports	Imports	Exports
Europe				
Iceland	5.5	1.6	12.4	12.0
Yugoslavia	0.0	0.0	53.1	46.2
Africa, Southwest Asia				
Egypt	11.9	14.1	92.6	88.0
Ethiopia	0.0	0.0	0.7	0.5
Ghana	10.1	0.0	8.2	0.0
Iran	8.9	9.2	18.7	18.0
Morocco	0.0	0.0	1.4	1.7
Sudan	0.0	0.0	5.0	4.0
Syria	0.0	0.1	6.2	15.2
Turkey	2.4	0.0	4.8	5.6
Southeast Asia				
Afghanistan	0.0	0.0	15.6	28.4
Burma	0.0	0.0	4.1	1.5
Ceylon	0.0	0.0	4.7	0.5
India	0.8	0.9	60.5	68.0
Indonesia	0.0	0.1	11.0	15.8
Malaya	0.0	0.0	126.7	0.1
Pakistan	7.4	8.0	3.7	1.0
South America				
Argentina	11.3	0.0	27.9	16.8
Brazil	0.0	0.0	4.8	0.9
Cuba	0.8	0.0	7.4	0.0
Uruguay	0.3	0.0	15.2	9.4

[a] *Sources: Vneshnyaya torgovlya, SSSR za 1959 god*, pp. 7–10, and Smith, Glen A., *Soviet Foreign Trade: Organization and Operations*, pp. 270–271, 286.

another 20.3 billion dollars, compared to 3.8 billion obligated by the Sino-Soviet Bloc as a whole. Some of the less developed countries themselves have contributed more to United Nation efforts than the Soviet Bloc has. In 1958 India supplied 146 technicians and the United Arab Republic sup-

developed countries that are striving to pull themselves up by their own bootstraps. Most important for the U.S.S.R. is the desire of all of the less developed countries and their leaders for status and prestige. Because the development of national consciousness by its nature reduces the role of outside forces, its growth is automatically associated with the lessening of influence of the West, the outside groups that in the past have been most consequential. Thus the U.S.S.R. sees in the supporting of nationalism in the less developed countries a method of serving its own interests.

Table 17–13   Percentage of Total Exports and Imports of Selected Countries Held by the Sino-Soviet Bloc, 1958[a]

	Exports	Imports
Iceland	35	32
Finland	25	26
Greece	16	7
Turkey	24	18
Yugoslavia	29	28
Egypt	44	29
Syria	31	12
Iran	26	9
Burma	3	12
Ceylon	6	9
Uruguay	21	5

[a] *Source: Comparisons of United States and Soviet Economies*, p. 460.

In most cases the Soviets have been content to offer economic assistance to newly independent states without forcing political showdowns with incumbent governments that might be indifferent or even antagonistic to Communism. Generally the bloc has been eager to discuss assistance and trade with new states as soon as they have become independent, so that maximum influence can be accomplished with least pressure during early periods of transition. The boldest gambit so far has been in the Congo where the U.S.S.R. made a rather brazen attempt to exploit an especially disturbed situation. Trucks and repair materials, planes and food, and medical and technical personnel were poured hurriedly into the Congo (Leopoldville) as the U.S.S.R. dramatically came to the aid of the faltering Lumumba government, which was ready to turn anywhere for

assistance. Although these efforts collapsed and the bloc personnel were ousted, the U.S.S.R. continued to seek a means of supporting a rump group in the Congo, and it used the Congo crisis to expand its influence in other countries of Africa, such as Ghana, Guinea, and Mali.

Whereas much of the aid extended by the West has been in the form of outright grants, the Soviet Bloc has primarily used the extension of credit, probably to give the impression that it is interested in business-like transactions and wishes to avoid the suspicion of political strings that may be aroused when gifts or interest-free loans are granted. Generally the Soviet Bloc has signed bilateral trade agreements with each trading country that begin with statements of willingness to trade and then proceed to the extension of credits to the underdeveloped country for the payment of construction projects or technical aid over long periods of time in products from the underdeveloped country. Ordinarily interest rates have been set at 2.5 per cent, considerably lower than those on loans from the World Bank or other sources in the West, which again serves Soviet propaganda that the capitalistic countries are charging exorbitant interest. The use of credit assures a prolonged association between the bloc and recipient country, a period during which the freedom of action by the latter may be limited because of the demands imposed by the payment conditions on its export capacity. Millions of rubles worth of credit extended for major construction projects may tie up exports of the recipient country for years while it is paying off the loan in produce. At the same time repayment will greatly reduce the real cost suffered by the bloc in the agreement.

One of the most important facets of the bloc economic offensive is the technical guidance that it provides in conjunction with construction projects that it finances. Soviet technicians, paid for by the recipient countries, are afforded valuable opportunities and means for ultimately influencing the nationals of less developed countries. Of equal importance is the training and study provided inside the bloc, particularly within the U.S.S.R., for students and technical personnel from less developed countries. Nearly 12,000 such nationals have received training of this character during the past 5 or 6 years. (By way of comparison, the United States alone has more technicians abroad and trains more foreign students than does the entire Soviet Bloc.)

The Communist orbit between June 1954 and June 1961 extended credits and grants to the amount of 5.2 billion dollars, 1.3 billion of which was extended for military purchases. India, Afghanistan, the United Arab Republic, Iraq, and Indonesia have received more than 80 per cent of the aid. Iran, Turkey, and Iceland are notable examples of countries allied with the free world which have been the targets of major bloc offers. The United Arab Republic, Indonesia, Iraq, and Cuba account for more than 90 per cent of all military aid extended. Afghanistan, Yemen, and Guinea account for the remainder. Bloc technicians are concentrated in some of the same countries. India,

Table 17–14   Communist-Bloc and United States Government Assistance to Selected Underdeveloped Countries, July 1, 1954, to June 30, 1959 (Millions of Dollars)[a]

	Communist-Bloc Total Assistance			U.S. Economic Assistance
	Total	Military	Economic	
Middle East and Africa	1427	580	849	1197
Egypt	658	315	343	140
Syria	304	128	177	2
Ethiopia	124	—	124	56
Guinea	1	—	1	2
Iran	6	—	6	353
Iraq	257	120	138	15
Turkey	17	—	17	623
Yemen	60	17	43	7
South and southeast Asia	1102	195	907	2495
Afghanistan	245	32	213	85
Burma	17	—	17	71
Cambodia	34	—	34	173
Ceylon	58	—	58	54
India	323	—	323	1166
Indonesia	402	163	239	189
Nepal	20	—	20	19
Pakistan	3	—	3	738
Europe	114	—	114	655
Iceland	5	—	5	25
Yugoslavia	110	—	110	630
Latin America	106	—	106	962
Argentina	104	—	104	345
Brazil	2	—	2	617
Total	2748	773	1975	5309

[a] *Source: Comparisons of United States and Soviet Economies, p. 447.*

Afghanistan, the United Arab Republic, and Yemen, with roughly equal shares, account for about 80 per cent of all economic technicians.

Table 17–15 Sino-Soviet Bloc Technicians in Less Developed Countries of the Free World, July 1 to December 31, 1959[a]

Country	Number of Technicians
Afghanistan	1025
Argentina	50
Brazil	20
Burma	65
Cambodia	175
Ceylon	45
Chile	5
Ethiopia	20
Ghana	30
Guinea	50
India	1170
Indonesia	75
Iran	20
Iraq	300
Nepal	25
Pakistan	5
Turkey	95
United Arab Republic	
Egypt	525
Syria	505
Yemen	810
Yugoslavia	10

[a] *Source: Communist Economic Policy in the Less Developed Areas*, Department of State Publication 7020, July 1960, p. 2.
Note: In the last half of 1960 nearly 7900 bloc technicians were occupied in twenty-three less developed countries for one month or longer.

The U.S.S.R. has provided the major portion of all bloc financial assistance, 3.8 billion dollars of the 5.2 billion total. The principal portion of U.S.S.R. funds has been extended for use on major development projects. Some of the projects getting worldwide attention are the Aswan Dam in Egypt and the million-ton capacity Bhilai steel mill in India, which went into full operation in 1961. Other major industrial installations have been built or contracted for in Cuba, Indonesia, Iraq, and Afghanistan.

Afghanistan was the initial target in the bloc's economic offensive in 1954, and it is believed that this country is intended to be a show piece of bloc economic assistance. In 1954 Czechoslovakia extended a 5 million dollar credit to Afghanistan for such projects as fruit-processing plants and cement plants. A Soviet credit of 100 million dollars was announced dramatically in 1955 during the visit of Khrushchev and Bulganin to Kabul. During 1959 the U.S.S.R. initiated new projects, increased its influence in the Afghan army, and placed experts in important Afghan ministeries. Under Soviet guidance and assistance the Afghan army is being modernized and expanded. A large number of Afghan officers have received military training in the U.S.S.R., and the program is to continue until all Afghan officers have had similar training.

Commodity Structure of Soviet Trade with Less Developed Countries Soviet exports to the less developed countries of the Middle East, southeast Asia, and south Asia, consist primarily of rolled steel, petroleum and petroleum products, manufactured goods, machinery and transport equipment, lumber, cement, cotton cloth, and wheat. Exports of machinery and manufactured goods account for about one third of total exports to these countries. In turn, the Soviet Union imports cotton, wool, rawhides, rubber, oil seeds, rice, tea, sugar, coffee, raisins, and spices. The U.S.S.R. claims to be the largest importer of Indian, Afghan, and Iranian raw hides, Egyptian cotton and rice, and Turkish cattle. It has purchased substantial amounts of Burmese rice, Moroccan citrus fruits, Indian spices, and Afghan and Iranian cotton, wool, dried fruits, and oil seeds.

In general it can be said that the Soviet Bloc has developed trade primarily to serve its import needs and has done little that was not economical from its own point of view, no matter how important the political element might have been. The Soviet Union has always been an importer of the primary raw materials listed earlier. In some of the items, the Soviet Union has been a heavier

autarchy, cotton growing in Soviet Middle Asia increased rapidly after 1929, and by 1937 the Soviet Union imported only 22 thousand tons of cotton, primarily from Iran. Immediately following World War II, Soviet

Table 17–16 Major Products Imported by the Soviet Union from Selected Underdeveloped Countries, 1957 (Millions of 1950 Rubles)[a]

Country	Total Imports	Products Imported and Value
Iceland	55.1	Fish (55.1)
Egypt	443.7	Cotton (404.0), rice (39.5)
Ethiopia	11.3	Coffee (8.3), hides (3.0)
Ghana	75.7	Cocoa (75.7)
Iran	74.1	Wool (27.4), fruit (13.9), cotton (9.8)
Lebanon	6.2	Oranges (3.6), hides (1.3), lemons (0.4)
Morocco	21.1	Oranges (21.0)
Sudan	11.6	Cotton (11.5)
Syria	21.7	Cotton (15.7), wool (5.6)
Turkey	21.9	Tobacco (7.3), cattle (6.9), fruit (7.6)
Union of So. Africa	106.8	Wool (105.4)
Afghanistan	82.7	Cotton (43.1), wool (27.8)
Burma	36.2	Rice (36.2)
Ceylon	1.1	Cocoa (1.1)
India	167.8	Tea (52.6), hides (24.6), wool (22.3)
Indonesia	79.1	Rubber (75.3), tea (1.2)
Malaya	195.2	Rubber (195.2)
Pakistan	20.5	Jute (12.3), cotton (6.1), hides (2.1)
Argentina	83.3	Wool (41.8), hides (33.6), meat (6.9)
Cuba	188.4	Sugar (188.4)
Uruguay	72.5	Wool (65.2), meat (5.8), hides (1.6)
Total	1776.0	Cotton (490.2), wool (295.5), rubber (270.5), hides (66.2), jute (12.3), cattle (6.9)—total industrial raw materials (1141.6)
		Sugar (188.4), cocoa (76.8), rice (75.7), tea (53.8), fruit (56.5), meat (12.7), coffee (17.2)—total food items (523.3)

[a] *Source:* Smith, Glen A., *Soviet Foreign Trade: Organization and Operations*, pp. 273–274.
Note: 1950 ruble = $0.25.

importer in the past than it is at present. For instance, cotton imports by the Soviet Union reached a peak of 145 thousand tons in 1927 and 1928. The major suppliers at this time were Egypt, Iran, and the United States. Following a policy of economic

cotton production dropped below previous levels, and Soviet demands for cotton exceeded the domestic supply. Cotton imports increased rapidly, primarily from Egypt, but also from Afghanistan, Iran, Pakistan, Syria, and the Sudan. Apparently, increased industrialization in the Soviet Union brought about an increased demand for cotton, and the Soviets chose to increase imports rather than to increase capital expenditures to grow cotton on marginal lands. But the present imports of cotton are still well below the peak of imports reached in 1928.

Wool has always been a major import in the Soviet Union. Prior to World War II, Mongolia, the Sinkiang Province of China, Iran, and Afghanistan were the primary suppliers. Australia was also a major supplier, but in the late 1930's it was replaced by Turkey. Imports of wool reached a peak of 39 thousand tons in 1929. Although imports declined in subsequent years, they could not be fully eliminated, and they remained at about 30 thousand tons per year. By 1957, imports of wool had risen to almost 60 thousand tons, and the Union of South Africa, Uruguay, Argentina, and India had become important suppliers. It is quite evident that the Soviet Union has utilized whatever foreign sources of wool are available whenever its controlled areas have been unable to supply the market.

Soviet trade in jute and rubber present an interesting picture. Prior to World War II, the Soviet Union imported somewhat more than 20,000 tons of jute per year mainly from what is now Pakistan. By 1955, the jute trade with Pakistan had become non-existent, and the Soviet Union reported an import of 20,000 tons from China. Since jute is not grown in China, the shipments obviously were re-exports of Pakistani jute. After the signing of a trade agreement with Pakistan in 1956, the China trade dropped to only 5000 tons, and the jute imported directly from Pakistan rose sharply to 11,400 tons.

In 1948 Soviet imports of rubber from Malaya amounted to about 70,000 tons. With the advent of the Korean War, however, rubber was declared a strategic commodity, and shipments by all rubber-producing countries to the Soviet Union and members of the Soviet Bloc were culminated. In 1952, Ceylon, which was not bound by the Battle Act nor the China Embargo, signed a 5-year agreement to supply China with rubber in exchange for needed rice. It appears that this rubber was subsequently delivered to the Soviet Union. In 1955, Malaya and Indonesia relaxed their bans on rubber shipments and in that year supplied the Soviet Union with 33,700 tons of rubber. In the same year, rubber imports from China dropped to 1000 tons. Since then, rubber imports from Malaya, Indonesia, and China have increased to a total of around 135,000 tons.

Remaining imports of the Soviet Union from the less developed countries are limited primarily to a few food items that are highly desired by the Soviet people; most important are sugar, cocoa, rice, fish, fruit, tea, and small quantities of meat and coffee. The primary purpose of these imports appears to be the need to match the monetary incentives paid to Soviet citizens by items that they can buy.

Sugar has long constituted the major food import of the Soviet Union. In the years following World War II, imports of refined sugar from the countries of Eastern Europe were begun. Because of political and economic instability in 1955 sugar imports from Czechoslovakia, Hungary, East Germany and Poland dropped to 351,000 tons. To meet the demand, the Soviets imported 235,600 tons of refined and 205,600 tons of raw sugar from Cuba. With continued political unrest in Eastern Europe in 1956, imports from Hungary, East Germany, and Poland were discontinued, and the importation of raw sugar from Cuba was sharply increased. In 1957 raw sugar from Cuba constituted roughly one third of all the food imports of the Soviet Union. Sugar imports from Cuba decreased in 1958 and 1959 as beet sugar imports from Eastern Europe were resumed, but in 1960, with a visit to Cuba of Soviet Deputy Premier Mikoyan and the extension of a long-term economic credit of 100 million dollars, imports of raw sugar from Cuba shot up to more than eleven times what they had been in 1959. In 1960 raw Cuban sugar made up almost 50 per cent of all food imports to the Soviet Union. Add to this the imports of refined sugar, primarily from Cuba, and sugar imports in 1960 made up 58 per cent of all food imports into the Soviet Union. Cane sugar production in the Soviet Union rose to 1.1 million tons in 1960 and 2.3 million tons in 1961.

Rice is considered a luxury by some Russians and a staple food by certain non-Russian nationality groups in the Soviet Union. Prior to World War II the importation of rice varied considerably from year to year but often exceeded 50,000 tons. At this time practically all rice was imported from Iran. Immediately following World War II it appears that China supplied the Soviet Union with all its needs, and in subsequent years it has remained the primary supplier, although other suppliers have entered the field. The Soviet Union in 1955 was quick to seize the opportunity to sign a 3-year rice purchase agreement with Burma when Burma was faced with a rice surplus that could not find world markets. Since 1955 Egypt has also become an important rice supplier to the Soviet Union.

In May 1946 the Soviet Union and Iceland signed a trade agreement by which the Soviets were to import considerable quantities of frozen fish and salted herring. The trade later dwindled and was finally severed, but in 1952 the Soviets again began buying fish from Iceland when Great Britain placed a boycott on Icelandic fish because of a British-Icelandic dispute in the intervening waters. By 1957 Iceland had become the major supplier of fish imports to the Soviet Union. Norway, The Netherlands, Great Britain, and Denmark also are important suppliers.

Chocolate and oranges are considered the ultimates in luxury among food items in the Soviet Union. In 1932 the imports of cocoa beans from the Gold Coast (Ghana) were begun. These grew quickly to about 11,000 tons per year at which level they remained until 1957, and when Ghana received its independence Soviet imports of cocoa tripled to 34,600 tons. This sudden increase was probably largely politically motivated. On the other hand, the great desire for chocolate in the Soviet Union may result in continuing imports at the higher level.

As part of the trade-expansion program in 1952, the importation of oranges from Israel was begun. Later Lebanon, Greece, Italy and Morocco were added as suppliers. With the Suez crisis in 1956, the Soviets cancelled all imports from Israel and greatly increased imports of oranges from Morocco. Later the Union of South Africa was added as a supplier. The sharp increase in orange imports has occurred in spite of high prices and indicates that there is an acute demand for oranges in the Soviet Union.

Reading List

Allen, Robert Loring, "A Note on Soviet Foreign Trade Statistics," *Soviet Studies,* April 1959, pp. 360–369.

——, "An Interpretation of East-West Trade," Holzman, Franklyn D., "Some Financial Aspects of Soviet Foreign Trade," and Aubrey, Henry G., "Sino-Soviet Economic Activities in Less Developed Countries," in *Comparisons of the United States and Soviet Economies,* Part II, 1959, pp. 403–466.

Baykov, Alexander, *Soviet Foreign Trade,* Princeton University Press, Princeton, N.J., 1946, 100 pp.

Berliner, Joseph, S., *Soviet Economic Aid,* Praeger, New York, 1958, 232 pp.

Communist Economic Policy in the Less Developed Areas, United States Department of State Publication 7020, July 1960, 38 pp.

Dillon, Douglas, *Economic Activities of the Soviet Bloc in Less Developed Countries,* United States Department of State Bulletin #8:469, March 24, 1958.

Pryor, Frederic L., "Foreign Trade Theory in the Communist Bloc," *Soviet Studies,* July 1962, pp. 41–61.

Smith, Glen A., *Soviet Foreign Trade: Organization and Operations,* PhD Dissertation, Stanford, 1959.

The Threat of Soviet Economic Policy, United

States Department of State Publication 7234, October 1961, 25 pp.

United Nations Yearbook of International Trade Statistics.

Vneshnyaya torgovlya SSSR za 1959 god, Moscow, 1960, 184 pp. (in Russian).

Rubinstein, Alvin Z., ed., *The Foreign Policy of the Soviet Union,* Random House, New York, 1960, 457 pp.

World Trade Information Service, Statistical Reports, Part 3, No. 61-9, *Foreign Trade of the U.S.S.R.,* 1958–1959 and No. 61-17, *Trade of the United States with the Soviet Bloc,* 1959–1960.

Equivalent Measures

Weight

1 kilogram	= 2.2 pounds
1 pood	= 36 pounds
1 centner	= 100 kilograms = 220 pounds
1 metric ton	= 1.1 short tons = 2200 pounds

Length

1 kilometer	= 0.625 miles
1 verst	= 1.067 kilometers = 0.6629 miles

Area

1 hectare	= 2.471 acres
1 dessiatine	= 2.7 acres
1 square kilometer	= 0.39 square miles

For the following crops one centner per hectare equals the corresponding figures in United States bushels per acre.

Wheat	1.48
Rye	1.59
Barley	1.85
Oats	2.78
Maize	1.59
Paddy rice	1.98
Potatoes	1.48

On the following dates the United States dollar equaled the corresponding numbers of rubles.

1913	1.94
1924	1.99
1925	1.94
1933	1.57
1934	1.16
1935	1.15
1936	5.03
1937	5.30
1950	4.00
1961	0.90

1 ruble = 100 kopeks

Index

DA